Praise for Michael Lynes

'Immensely gripping, great suspense, thoughtful and very satisfying'

— SOPHIE HANNAH, NEW YORK TIMES BESTSELLER, ON *BLOOD LIBEL*

'Lynes knows his history and tells the story with verve'

— HISTORICAL NOVEL SOCIETY

'I'm looking forward to reading the next Isaac Alvarez Mystery'

— VH MASTERS, AUTHOR OF *THE CASTILIANS*

'Written with cinematic flair. The terror, danger, and suspicious atmosphere prevalent at the time is palpable'

— 5* AMAZON READER REVIEW

First published by Romaunce Books in 2023
Suite 2, Top Floor, 7 Dyer Street, Cirencester, Gloucestershire, GL7 2PF

Copyright © Michael Lynes

A catalogue record for this book is available from the British Library

The Heretic's Daughter

Paperback ISBN 978-1-7391857-1-8

Printed and bound in Great Britain

Romaunce Books™ is a registered trademark

For my sons,
Adam and Danyal

THE HERETIC'S DAUGHTER

As the Inquisition's grip tightens Isaac and Isabel must choose between family and faith. Will they survive the consequences?

Isaac seeks revenge on Torquemada for murdering his wife and best friend. He's not the only one who wants The Grand Inquisitor dead. The King commands Isaac to investigate. Should he save the man he hates? Fail and he loses the King's protection — the only thing keeping him alive. Feeling abandoned by her father and conflicted by his heresy, Isabel sets out to discover the truth. The trail leads to the darkest places in Seville. She's unnerved by a shocking revelation and a surprising discovery about her real feelings. **Can Isabel use what she unearths to save her father and their family?**

THE HERETIC'S DAUGHTER

Michael Lynes

Vengeance is mine. I will repay.

— DEUTERONOMY 32:35

Iberian Peninsula at the end of the 15th Century

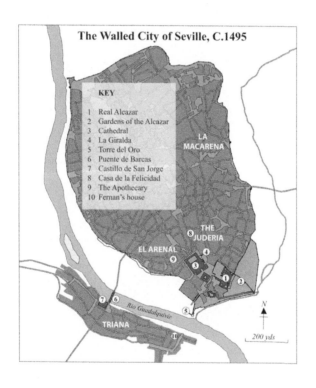

The Walled City of Seville, C.1495

KEY

1   Real Alcazar
2   Gardens of the Alcazar
3   Cathedral
4   La Giralda
5   Torre del Oro
6   Puente de Barcas
7   Castillo de San Jorge
8   Casa de la Felicidad
9   The Apothecary
10 Fernan's house

LA MACARENA

THE JUDERIA

EL ARENAL

Río Guadalquivir

TRIANA

N

200 yds

Andalusia,
April, 1498

PROLOGUE

Isaac yearns for a place that no longer exists — Seville before the Inquisition. A place where Torquemada did not call out the names of the heretics to be punished. Where Queen Isabella and King Ferdinand did not watch impassively as executioners smeared a blonde-haired girl's tunic with sulphur — to quicken the journey of the flames from the crackling pyre at her feet. A twisted mercy. Where Isaac did not see white tendrils of smoke, hear shrill screams or smell the bitter stink of charred flesh. Where he did not witness Juan's body melt into the inferno.

The Seville of his dreams is a blur of memory. Sunny afternoons with Juan swimming in the river, sword fighting, and wrestling. Sometimes Maria comes to him and those are the sweetest memories. Overwhelmed by the vision of his wife he pushes her away, returning to play with Juan.

Joy is fleeting and turns to guilt. Why should he be rewarded with visions of the good times? He had not saved his wife, had not defended his best friend. His penance is the sharp thrusts of pain in his chest as the horrors of Juan's execution and Maria's murder flash through his imagination. Each stab reminding him of his oath — *I will make you pay, Torquemada, no matter how long it takes.*

BOOK ONE

Seville

CHAPTER
ONE

Abu Ali Sina, the apothecary, began his morning ritual by kneeling to light the nuggets of oud on the incense burner. Crackling and sparking, they released their heavy, woody fragrance. Inhaling the smoke, he stood and stretched his tall, slender frame. The scent always brought Khadijah to mind, and he whispered a prayer for his wife's soul.

He kept the incense burner behind the counter; the Catholics did not appreciate the *Mudéjar's* perfume. He would have ten running all day, but that would be provocative. He could not afford to lose Catholic patrons; there were not enough *Mudéjars* left in Seville to keep his business alive. And there were no Jews left at all. He didn't want to run away to Granada, as so many of his friends had. It was easier to worship Allah there. But he would have to close the shop that had been in his family for five generations. He did not want that guilt.

Surveying the rows of orange and blue earthenware jars filling the tall mahogany shelves behind the counter, he took a mental stocktake. Enough cumin, anise and horehound, but mandrake root was very low. He normally prescribed it to ease stomach-ache, but perhaps its other use as an aphrodisiac was causing the high demand? The large glass jar on the counter was still full of slippery, copper-coloured leeches. Was blood-letting falling out of fashion?

The rasp of the shop door announced the day's first customer. A tall, cloaked figure moved through the deep shadows, disturbing motes of dust. Ali Sina had only lit a few candles; he had to save what little money remained. Besides, nobody usually came in this early.

'Good morning, apothecary,' came a deep growl from the half-light.

'Good morning. You're most welcome, señor.'

The man's wide-brimmed hat hid most of his face. Ali Sina could make out a beard and the glint of perhaps blue eyes. He looked familiar, but the apothecary didn't think he had visited the shop before.

The man wrinkled his nose. 'Couldn't you burn some orange or lavender? Can't stand that Moorish smell.'

'I'm sorry, señor. I rarely have customers this early.'

The man ignored the apology and looked up at the jars. Ali Sina followed his eyes, trying to guess what he was looking for. Perhaps some sage or chamomile to ease his digestion? The man coughed. Ah, a cold?

'I need something for my chest, it's very heavy.' He coughed again, louder this time, as if to emphasise the point.

The apothecary reached for an orange jar decorated with a complex geometric pattern. Setting it down next to the pestle and mortar, he measured a precise quantity of white powder on a brass weighing pan, tipped it into a square of cloth, twisting it closed with twine.

'Put a pinch of this hyssop into a glass of wine twice a day. You will feel better within two or three days.' The apothecary placed the small parcel on the counter.

The man rummaged in the leather pouch hanging from his belt, put twenty *maravedies* on the counter, pocketed the cure, but did not leave.

'Can I help the señor with another remedy?'

'Yes, I would like some arsenic.'

'Some arsenic?'

The man gave a curt nod.

The apothecary hesitated. 'Señor, I'm required by the authorities to enquire for what purpose?'

'Of course, it would be remiss of you not to ask. I need it for vermin.'

Ali Sina held the man's eyes for a few moments. The sun had crept into the shop and he could now definitely see glints of blue glimmer in the man's unblinking, pale eyes.

'We have a problem with rats. It's the only thing that keeps them at bay.' He moved his right hand to cover the grip of the rapier sheathed at his side.

The apothecary pushed a set of wooden steps that ran on wheels to the end of the counter. Climbing to the top, he reached for one of the highest jars. It was covered in a blue leaf design, a beautiful container for such a vile substance. Placing it on the counter, he cautiously removed the stopper. There was no scent – arsenic was both odourless and tasteless. The ideal poison. He tipped out a small pyramid of the shiny, silver-grey crystal into the weighing pan. He glanced at the man, who raised his index finger to signal a larger quantity. The apothecary doubled the amount; the man nodded. He poured the crystals into a glass vial and stoppered it with wax. The man reached into his leather pouch and placed one hundred *maravedies* on the counter, double what the apothecary would have charged. Ali Sina took half of the money and pushed the rest back. The man gave a sardonic grin as he scooped up the coins and returned them to his pouch.

Ali Sina kept hold of the vial.

The man stared at him.

'I will have to insist you sign the register for the arsenic, señor. It is a requirement of the authorities.'

'The authorities?' The man rolled his eyes.

He moved the vial down to his side. With his right hand he opened a large book, took a quill pen, and wrote the date and the amount of arsenic provided. He held out the pen. The man grabbed it, scrawled a signature, and slammed the register shut. Ali Sina placed the vial in the man's outstretched hand.

'Thank you, apothecary. If the rats prove stubborn, I trust you have plenty more?'

The apothecary narrowed his eyes. 'You already have enough arsenic to kill a hundred rats, señor.'

'Seville is teeming with vermin of all varieties. Some larger than others.' He arched an eyebrow and grinned.

'I have already given you the maximum quantity regulations allow. Señor.'

'Damn the regulations,' said the man as he again touched the grip of his rapier.

'As an apothecary, I have to abide by them. I'm sure you can understand.'

'How is business?' the man said, turning to survey the empty shop.

Ali Sina did not respond.

'You must be the last of your kind left in Seville?'

'If you mean the last apothecary, then yes, I am.'

'All the other Moors have run off to Granada.' He scowled. 'You're very brave to stay.'

'Thank you, señor.'

'Or perhaps, stupid.'

He forced himself to remain silent.

'That front door of yours is not secure. It would be a great shame were anyone to enter while you were asleep and vandalise your fine establishment. Or perhaps even harm your good self.'

Ali Sina tapped the stopper of the jar of arsenic and held the man's gaze. 'It's been a pleasure to help you this morning, señor. I look forward to your return.'

The man grunted in apparent satisfaction and turned to leave. He ducked under the lintel and left the door ajar behind him. Ali Sina opened the register of poisonous substances. The signature would have been difficult to decipher, even without the ink being smeared by the man closing the book so violently. Was that an A? But why write his real name? At least there was a record of the date and a description of the man in his mind. That might prove useful should a poisoning occur that the authorities investigated. He was sure it was not the last he would see of the stranger. He would need to be prepared. Perhaps Isaac knew the man and could advise the best way to handle the situation. He had many contacts in his position as adviser to King Ferdinand. His old friend would know what to do.

CHAPTER
TWO

Isaac's eyelids flickered as the early morning sun crept through the shutters of his bedchamber. Had he dreamt of Juan or Maria? Deciding he hadn't, he enjoyed the gentle warmth a few moments longer. Snapping his eyes open, he was dazzled by splinters of sunlight. He got up and relieved himself in the chamber pot. After scrupulously washing his hands in the earthenware bowl, he checked that his bedchamber door was locked.

He hauled a wooden chest from beneath the bed. Caressing the smooth mahogany, he felt the coolness of the inlaid ivory. The ordered geometric patterns of the design soothed him. Using the key he kept on a chain around his neck, he unlocked the chest and took out the Bible and set it aside. Removing the false panel from the base revealed two books lying side by side. The Torah required both hands to lift and held the secret of his true faith. Maria's Book of Hours could nestle in his palm. Possession of one would get him killed, possession of the other would earn Isabel's anger. One he would keep hidden in the chest, the other he would return to the prayer stand before his daughter noticed.

Isaac unwrapped the Torah from its linen shroud, enjoying its heft, and brought it to his lips. He read softly, so that no one could hear. He traced God's words to Moses in the wilderness with his right index finger:

> *I will espouse you forever*
> *With righteousness and justice,*
> *And with goodness and mercy,*
> *I will espouse you with faithfulness:*
> *Then you shall be devoted to the Lord.*

A reassuring balm to the beginning of every day. He kissed it once more and carefully returned it to the chest.

He cupped the Book of Hours in his palms, feeling the rough texture of the dark-blue leather binding. It had been his gift to Maria on their wedding day – he'd borrowed half the money from his father. He leafed through the delicate pages until he found her favourite image: etched in golden letters, the Archangel Gabriel announcing to Mary, 'Hail, full of grace, the Lord is with you.' Had Maria imagined the thrill of being the woman chosen above all others to conceive God's only son? He closed the book and brushed it with his lips.

Buttoning up his doublet, he secured a dagger at his waist. The household was stirring: creaking floorboards, coughing, the malty aroma of Catalina's rye bread, Isabel chivvying the children. Maria's voice a faint echo.

~

Isabel shivered as she clutched the iron balustrade of the roof terrace at Casa de la Felicidad. She looked across the Guadalquivir River towards Triana. Her stomach clenched at the memory of her flight from that damp, sun-starved den of thieves — feeling the darkness build inside her. The sun's ascent lifted her mood for a moment. Then it silhouetted the towers of the Castillo San Jorge. Her time there at the Inquisition's headquarters as Torquemada's 'guest' with Gabriel still burnt in her imagination. Her gaze settled on the Torre del Orro – the tower of gold – Torquemada's torture chamber. Where her mother died. She shook her head, trying to rid herself of these thoughts. The children must come first, not memory. There would be a time, in the dead of night, for that unforgiving scorpion to sting her.

The river was placid, the sunlight shimmering across its glassy surface. Soon it would rise, bringing the sea's salty scent. The smaller barques would arrive from Cadiz or Lisbon. As the Guadalquivir filled its banks, the tall-masted galleons would make their way to port and unload sugar, silver and gold from the Indies. She was troubled by all the money flowing into Seville and Papa's involvement in it. Wealth distracted people from their moral duty to study the Bible. Too many peasants came to the city, seeking the good life but ending up as vagrants. She would like to help them. But her time was full with her responsibilities at home. Perhaps she would go to the cathedral and ask Father Gutiérrez what she might do.

Isabel forced her mind to the day ahead. She felt the weight of her responsibility as governess for three children – her brother, Gabriel, and Juana and Martín — Juan and Ana de Mota's orphans. She was delighted when Papa became guardian to the ten-year-old twins after Juan's execution and their mother's apparent suicide. It was, she thought, the least he could do after their parents' passing. Papa harboured suspicions about Ana's death. She would not have deliberately orphaned her children. He held Torquemada accountable for her murder. Papa had no proof, but the belief fuelled his quest for revenge. Its intensity was frightening. Where would his burning need lead them all?

Papa was still in mourning for Mama – three years now – but she feared that what really kept her memory alive was his thirst for vengeance. The Inquisition claimed to have had evidence to arrest Mama as a crypto-Jew. Ironically, Papa was the guilty one, but her mother paid the price. He read the Torah in his bedchamber and in his heart was a Jew. What did that make her? The heretic's daughter? She'd come to terms with losing Mama, but couldn't quite forgive Papa.

She hoped Gabriel would pay more attention to his lessons. At fifteen, he was old enough to set a good example, especially to Martín. With his father dead and Papa often away at the palace, he needed a good male role model. She had no fears for his sister, Juana, so attentive, bright and quick-witted. Doors slammed from the bedchambers below, disturbing her train of thought. Martín and Gabriel. Why did boys have to be such louts? Papa would be getting dressed and on his way to the Real

Alcazar soon. She'd better go downstairs and ensure that Catalina had everything ready for breakfast.

The children were sitting around the trestle table as Isaac entered the dining room. Isabel sat at the head of the table, overseeing the children and supervising Catalina. He kissed the top of his daughter's head. He was proud of the way she had grown into her responsibilities. Catalina bustled. He was grateful the maidservant had stayed on after Maria's death. Gabriel and the twins smeared hunks of bread with butter and quince jam. Four children. It was still surprising to find himself responsible for so many. Juana and Martín returned his, 'Good morning,' enthusiastically. Gabriel sat opposite them – remote, stern and feigning maturity. He was a young man now. Where was the young boy who used to run into his arms?

He tore a hunk off the fresh loaf and put it in his pocket. He would eat it later at the Real Alcazar. Saying goodbye to his children, he kissed each of them on the forehead, Gabriel shifting uncomfortably in his seat. Hurrying through the courtyard – he was late – he brushed his fingers through the stems of the sky-blue agapanthus and smelt the woody musk of jasmine. The white flowers had been Maria's favourite. He hastened past the plashing fountain and the bench where they used to sit and headed into the *calles* of Seville.

After closing the heavy outer door behind him, he was affronted, yet again, by the derelict house opposite.

The shutters were off their hinges, the main door was cracked and pigeons flew in and out of the holes in the roof. The neglect was disgusting and made a poor start to his morning. He must inform the owner he was ruining the reputation of the barrio.

Turning right he walked quickly down Calle Abades, towards the Real Alcazar. When he'd first arrived in Seville, it had taken him a year or more to walk these streets with confidence. The narrow, winding *calles* confused you into following their gradual tangents, and before long, you were standing befuddled at the nexus of five streets, turning this way and that, searching for a way home. But now he paced the streets with assurance – he liked to think with authority. At least half the men he passed raised their hats to him – as senior adviser to the King he had dealings with many of them – but not one of them stopped to talk. They knew his nature.

Isaac turned into Calle Arfe and strode past the Apothecary. It was dark, the windows dirty. He should consult Ali Sina soon; there was no time now. The willow bark the apothecary prescribed for his backache seemed to have little effect. He should pay his friend a visit on his return from the Real Alcazar.

He weaved through the crowded, narrow lanes. He stepped around a gang of children – none more than six years old – splashing in the stream of piss wending through the cobbles. The streets were not normally so full this early in the morning. But then *Semana Santa* was only a week away. Why was so much effort put into celebrating the rebirth of Jesus Christ? As a *converso*, he could never utter such a thought out loud. It would be heresy to question his adopted faith.

The celebrations became increasingly lavish with every passing year, he thought. Families spent more and more on decorating their homes, buying new clothes and contributing to the ever more elaborate *pasos*. He was disturbed by the large wooden sculptures of a grieving Virgin Mary or a crucified Jesus Christ, carried on the shoulders of the *costaleros*. A shiver ran through him as he recalled what happened to Isabel during the procession three years ago. The family would do all that was expected of a good Catholic household – give up meat on Fridays for Lent, attend the required services at the cathedral and walk with the purple-hooded penitents as they accompanied the *pasos*. The children, at least, would do it with a good heart.

Approaching the royal palace, his thoughts turned to the day ahead. What mischief would Queen Isabella create? How would King Ferdinand involve him in it? But, most of all, would he have to be civil to Torquemada when all he really wanted to do was slit his throat? He saluted the soldiers at the Hunting Gateway and slipped into the palace of intrigue.

CHAPTER
THREE

After Papa left, Isabel decided it was warm enough to conduct the morning's lessons on the roof terrace. She sat at the head of a long wooden table, with Gabriel to her left and the twins to her right. They were waiting for her to begin. She'd become distracted by thoughts of Papa's deputy, Alejandro de Cervantes. She longed to see him again.

Gabriel thrummed his fingers insistently on the table. She resisted the urge to express her irritation. 'Children,' she glared at her brother, 'write two important things about Seville on your tablets.' The twins scratched with their styluses; Gabriel tapped his up and down on the table edge. She ignored him, even though she was conscious of the need to make good use of her time with the children. After lunch, Juana would sew and cook, whilst the boys learnt archery, sword fighting and riding. The afternoons were her sanctuary, to read and think.

Something in Juana's disposition, or her look, always

brought her mother, Ana de Palacios, to Isabel's mind. In his introversion Martín resembled his father, Juan de Mota. Juana was slender, like her mother, but more athletic and outgoing than her brother. Martín was larger-boned, clumsy, and shy. Juana's hair needed cutting, it was almost at her waist. If it was cut to the same length as her brother's it would be impossible to tell the ten-year-old twins apart. Both had bright blue eyes and blonde locks. The most obvious difference was the nearly invisible scar beneath Martín's right eye; residue from a bee sting when he was a baby.

She was glad she'd encouraged Papa to become the twins' guardian. It was the moral thing to do. It would help him bear the guilt of not doing more to prevent Juan's execution. She feared he would never forgive himself. The flashes of Papa's anger that still occurred even three years after his friend's death worried her. She drifted away to thoughts of Mama. Was this strange mixture of love, duty and wonder the same way Mama felt when she'd taught her and Gabriel? There was a twist in her gut as she remembered how badly she'd sometimes behaved towards Mama. Now, she was responsible for the moral instruction and education of three children. She felt the burden of it.

The children had finished the task and were looking at her. She shook herself free of her thoughts by sitting up straight. 'Gabriel, tell us something important about the history of Seville.'

Her brother looked at her from beneath a floppy fringe of brown hair and said, 'It's the most important city in Spain.'

'Would you provide some evidence, Gabriel?' she asked.

'I would have thought it was self-evident, sister.'

Glaring at him, she turned to Juana, who was tapping her chin with her stylus.

'Well,' she began, 'the Guadalquivir is the longest river in Andalusia and the surrounding valley is very fertile, providing a plentiful supply of rice, wheat and almonds.' She raised her pale blue eyes to the sky. 'And of course, Christofer Colombo discovered the Indies, and Seville now does much trade with them. And Uncle Isaac helps Their Majesties with the contracts.'

Martín looked at his sister with admiration.

Gabriel yawned, stretching his arms high, and leant back in his chair.

'That's excellent, Juana. Thank you.' She turned to her brother, but he was absorbed in flicking dust off his doublet. 'Can you think of anything that might be bad about the new wealth from the Indies?'

'Bad? About money?' Gabriel asked, his voice dripping with scorn.

'Don't you see all the peasants drawn to Seville chasing their dreams of finding gold?' She paused. 'Too many of them end up on the streets begging.'

'Perhaps they should work harder,' he replied.

She looked at Juana, hoping to get a more sympathetic response, but she was staring skywards. She'd try a different tack. 'Read Chapter 10, the gospel of St Matthew. You will find Jesus' instructions to his disciples.' She waited for all three of them to open their

Bibles. 'Martín, we'll read together. Then I will ask you what your favourite verse is and why.'

'That's easy. Mine's verse 36, "a man's enemies will be the members of his own household,"' Gabriel said, grinning.

She gave him a menacing stare, much as she remembered her mother giving. 'Thank you, brother.' She locked eyes with him for a long moment. 'I prefer, "The student is not above the teacher, nor a servant above his master. It is enough for students to be like their teachers, and servants like their masters."'

She waited for him to break eye contact with her.

He did not.

Juana suppressed a giggle.

'Please read the entire chapter,' Isabel said.

Half an hour later, she watched as Catalina laboured up the stairs. The housekeeper was becoming stouter by the day. She carried a tray with mugs of fresh orange juice – the daily delivery from the red-capped juice sellers. She hoped Catalina hadn't sweetened the bitter oranges with too much sugar. The apothecary had warned sugar was bad for the blood and made passing water painful. The only potential cure was oil of roses, but he didn't guarantee its efficacy. Gabriel gulped down his juice, banged the mug on the table, and ran off.

'The young master don't look too happy,' Catalina said as the twins followed him to play in the courtyard.

'Gabriel considers the twins too childish for him,' Isabel replied.

'He's getting too big for his boots, if you ask me.'

'Yes, you might be right. I'll discuss it with Papa.

Though he has a lot on his mind. And goodness knows what else His Majesty plans to burden him with.'

Catalina cocked her head, then seemed to think better of speaking her mind. She settled for, 'Well, that rabbit my good-for-nothing husband caught this morning won't roast itself.'

'Poor Rodrigo,' Isabel muttered to herself as Catalina trundled back down the stairs to the kitchen. The sun was at its zenith, making it too hot to stay on the terrace. The cathedral bells announcing the Sext prayers sent a shudder through her as the shadow of Friar Alonso flitted across her imagination.

Isaac shouldered his way past the noblemen waiting for an audience with His Majesty; all looking for their share of the Indies' treasure. He ignored those trying to catch his eye, hoping for the consolation of a meeting with the King's special adviser. Isaac and his deputy, Alejandro, occupied rooms adjacent to the Hunting Courtyard. Once the meeting point for noblemen to gather for the royal hunts, it was now the heart of the administration of trade with the Indies. Still a place for hunting – just gold, not animals. The rooms were also close to the Royal Chambers – Ferdinand liked to keep him near. The promotion was his reward for solving the murder of a child that could have had grave political consequences. If only Queen Isabella had been as pleased as her husband at the success of the investigation.

He stood in the doorway to take in his room – he was

still not used to its opulence. It was large and luxuriously furnished, a marked contrast to the small, stuffy rooms they used to occupy when their role was to review trade agreements. He was grateful not to have to spend his days wading through stultifying contracts. He enjoyed his strategic role in helping Their Majesties squeeze as much gold as possible from their burgeoning empire. But sometimes, when he became embroiled in palace intrigue, he longed for a little boredom.

Alejandro came in from a small ante-room where he had a desk.

'Ah, there you are, señor,' his deputy said with a quizzical look.

'Yes, yes, I'm a little late. What have I missed?' Isaac closed the main door, sat down behind his desk, took out the hunk of rye bread, tore and ate small pieces from it. It was too dry to swallow easily. He poured a mug of water from the earthenware carafe. He tipped the other mug towards his deputy, who shook his head.

Alejandro was in his middle-twenties and a graduate of Isaac's alma mater, the University of Salamanca. He reminded Isaac of himself at that age, fiercely intelligent, energetic, and passionate. Though he suspected Alejandro attracted far more female attention than he ever had. His fine skin was drawn taut across high cheek-bones. A straight Roman nose, thin lips and pale blue eyes gave him a delicate appearance. Always elegantly attired, he carried himself with an aristocratic, almost haughty bearing.

'His Majesty is vexed by the situation in Granada.'

'I don't see what we're supposed to do about his

disappointment with Archbishop Talavera when we're at least two days' ride away,' Isaac said, chewing furiously on a piece of bread.

'You know how worried he is about Ramadan. He thinks the *Mudéjars* will be disturbed by their fasting month coming so soon after *Semana Santa*. The timing could not be less providential. There might be riots and he doesn't want the trouble, not to say expense, of quelling any unrest.'

'It doesn't help when Torquemada pours poison in his ear. Promoting the use of the same brutal tactics on the *Mudéjars* that he employs here. His Majesty still hopes that talking will convert them to the True Faith.'

Alejandro arched an eyebrow.

This was only half the truth, as Isaac was well aware. Ferdinand was concerned about the impact on the treasury of a sustained battle in Granada. The Royal purse had not recovered from the siege. If he could just persuade the *Mudéjars* to cooperate they would remain a lasting source of revenue. Talavera's bishopric was the most lucrative in Castile.

'Well, at least His Majesty hasn't suggested sending Torquemada in yet. That would only add fuel to the fire.'

Isaac grunted. He'd bided his time for three years, waited for the perfect moment to avenge himself on Torquemada for Juan and Maria's murders. Was there an advantage in the situation in Granada he could exploit? It seemed too convoluted. He needed the impossible – something simple to execute that could not be traced back to him. An insistent tapping broke his concentration. He looked up and there was the devil himself. Did thinking conjure him?

'I'm sorry to interrupt your reverie, my son,' said Torquemada in honeyed tones that dripped insincerity. He leant on the wooden cane he had banged to get Isaac's attention. He did not have the same commanding presence of three years ago when he rode ramrod straight at the head of the procession for the *auto-da-fé*. The burnings. Though he did still possess a thuggish bearing reinforced by a broken nose and a vicious gleam in his obsidian eyes. Strip him of his friar's habit and he could have been an ageing street fighter.

'How can I be of assistance, Father?' Isaac replied with an equal lack of sincerity. He did not move or invite him to sit.

Torquemada's grip on the cane slipped. He stumbled, but Alejandro quickly stepped forward to support him.

'Bless you, my son,' Torquemada said with a smile.

Alejandro dipped his head in acknowledgement.

Isaac glared at his deputy.

Alejandro shrugged as if to say, 'What did you expect me to do?'

'Perhaps you would like to sit, Father Tomás?' Isaac pointed towards the two high-backed chairs in front of his desk.

As Torquemada settled himself, Alejandro made to leave, but Isaac stopped him with a shake of his head. I'll make you pay for helping that old bastard, he thought. Alejandro composed a fixed smile and sat down next to Torquemada. For the next half an hour, Isaac was kept amused by Alejandro's murmured vague assent to

Torquemada's thoughts on the situation in Granada – how Archbishop Talavera was just giving in to the *Mudéjars*. He was scathing about Talavera's opposition to Inquisitorial tribunals. 'He thinks we can correct heresies with Catholic reasoning,' he growled.

As he droned on, Isaac thought how satisfying it would be to draw the blade of a dagger across Torquemada's throat and watch as the crimson blood drained his life away.

FOUR

'The rabbit was delicious,' Isaac said.

Catalina smiled at the compliment as she cleared dishes from the table.

He was grateful Isabel instructed Catalina to serve lunch in the dining room abutting the kitchen and scullery. It was too warm to eat on the terrace – the early summer heat was becoming prohibitive. From his position at the head of the table he could see the long stems of the purple agapanthus fringing the fountain in the courtyard. Reaching out to hold Isabel's hand he turned to look at the three children on his left. A surge of warmth flowed through him. Well-fed and at home with those he loved, he was content.

'Rodrigo was out special early this morning to snare a couple in the fields just beyond the Alcazar,' Catalina said with evident pride in her husband.

Why did she have to mention the royal palace? He didn't want to be reminded of his place of work during lunch. Why had Torquemada suddenly appeared that morning? Ferdinand was determined to drag him into the mess in Granada. A yelp from Juana broke into his thoughts – Gabriel or Martín had evidently kicked or pinched her under the table. Isabel shepherded the children out for their siesta. No doubt they would roam the courtyard and the gardens instead of napping. He didn't begrudge them their freedom, and silently colluded with Isabel in pretending to be oblivious to their deception. He spied on them from his bedchamber; shouting, then whispering, running and hiding, fighting, then embracing. Was their behaviour so very different to that of adults? He enjoyed seeing Gabriel acting more like the boy he fondly remembered. His sullenness disappeared when no adults were present.

'Sherry, Papa?' Isabel suggested.

He was glad she'd read his mood and wanted to give him an opportunity to unburden himself. She'd always possessed this quality. When her mother was alive she sometimes used it for more selfish, even devious purposes. Perhaps the only solace to spring from Maria's death was the change in his daughter. She'd successfully taken on the burdens of governess and responsibility for domestic matters. He was keenly aware that some in the community considered it inappropriate for a widowed man to remain in the house alone with his children, especially an eighteen-year-old daughter. The situation could not last. Even if they continued to ignore the gossip, Isabel would soon want a husband and a family of her own. Then what would he do?

'So, Papa, tell me,' Isabel said, settling herself gracefully into one of the tall backed chairs in the parlour opposite her father.

He found her astonishing self-possession unsettling. Clearing his throat, he took a sip of sherry and began. 'Granada is becoming a big problem that His Majesty is determined to involve me in.' Employing a version of the truth to disguise his more pressing concerns about Torquemada. 'As if Alejandro and I don't have enough to contend with.' Was that a smile playing on her face at the mention of his deputy?

'Yes, Papa. I thought you were very busy organising the Indies trade.'

'Exactly, my dear. Since we took control of Granada after the siege and recaptured the Alhambra things have gone well. I thought the problems were behind us.'

'But that's because Their Majesties allowed the *Mudéjars* to follow their own law and worship in their mosques? They weren't persecuted in the same way as the Jewish people.'

He noted how she distanced herself from the Jews. He let it pass. 'At first, that was sufficient. However, the *Mudéjars* are chafing at their lack of power.'

'That's hardly your responsibility. Who's in charge in Granada?'

'Archbishop Talavera. He meets regularly with the *Mudéjar* leaders and has even even learnt some Arabic.'

'I still don't understand the problem.'

'Most human beings do not appreciate the status quo. The modern age breeds greed almost like a plague. The *Mudéjars* are not happy to settle for peaceful co-existence.' He continued talking until he noticed she seemed to be dozing off. 'Anyway my dear, there is no obvious solution.' He reflected for a moment. 'I'm feeling a little tired. I'll have a nap before returning to the Alcazar.'

Isabel retired to her bedchamber, intending to follow her father's example. But her mind was determined to wrestle with what he'd said. If His Majesty forced him to become involved in Granada he would face real danger. She'd heard all kinds of tales about what a savage city it was. Although she couldn't imagine how it could be any worse than Seville under the Inquisition. Interrupted by the children's shouts from the garden, she went to the window. She hid behind the curtain to observe them.

The twins were playing tag. Gabriel was sitting on the grass, resting his back against the trunk of the palm tree that swayed over the courtyard fountain. Isabel smiled at his enjoyment of the sunlight filtering through the palm fronds and playing across his face. He looked so innocent.

'Juana and Martín, sitting in a tree. Martín kissing Juana, hee, hee, hee.' Gabriel chanted the rhyme in a slow, menacing tone. Not so innocent then.

'Gabriel, you are *so* disgusting,' Juana said as she ran past him, blonde hair streaming behind her.

Martín stopped chasing his sister and smirked appreciatively at Gabriel.

'You should address me more formally. Uncle, or older brother,' Gabriel retorted. Isabel heard the familiar arrogant tone from her brother.

Juana stopped running, put her hands on her hips and laughed. 'You are not our uncle and our real Uncle Isaac says as long as we treat you with respect, we can call you Gabriel. So there.'

Good for you, Juana.

But then Gabriel's glare seemed to unnerve the girl, as she let her hands fall to her side and ran away from him.

'Tag, you're it,' Martín screamed as he rushed past her, slapping her upper arm.

'That hurt, you rat.' She scampered after him, head down, fists pumping.

Gabriel ripped a clump of earth from the base of the palm tree, took careful aim, and threw it. It exploded just in front of Juana, spraying dirt on her white dress. She turned and jutted her clenched jaw at him. Martín doubled up with laughter. Gabriel flashed her a sardonic smile. Howling with frustration, she stomped back to the house.

This was troubling. If she confronted Gabriel he would deny bullying Juana, he would say they were just playing. She did not want to burden Papa. He had enough to contend with. She would give it some thought. About to lie down she was momentarily dazzled by a bright light. Shading her eyes with a palm she saw it was coming from the second floor of the house opposite Casa de Felicidad. The derelict building Papa was always complaining about. Something metal was flashing from a window. She focused hard and thought she saw two figures and then a shimmer of red. Was someone else watching the children? It couldn't be. She was letting her anxiety over Papa and the children feed her imagination. The landlord had probably instructed workmen to repair the house.

'That's all it was,' she said to herself as she lay down to rest.

Thunderous banging jerked Isaac awake from his siesta. Realising groggily that not even the cathedral bells calling the Catholic faithful to None prayers had disturbed him. The assault on his ears had interrupted one of his bad dreams. The visitations were so real, so particular, so vivid. They had a strange, staccato quality as they flitted from horror to horror, like the swallows at sunset over the Guadalquivir. There were only so many times he could survive the reimagining of Juan's execution before his mind might crack in half. The visions always began with the yellow sulphur being smeared on the little girl and always finished with Juan's flesh being rendered into the flames. Why hadn't Maria come? She appeared less and less.

He tried to ignore the continued thumping which must be coming from the outer door. Why wasn't Rodrigo dealing with it? He was besieged by thoughts. It had been helpful to discuss his problems with Isabel. But there was still much he did not share with her, in particular, regarding the Grand Inquisitor. He would not utter his name in front of her. Torquemada's treatment of her after Maria's death had left a deep, lingering mark on both of them. Her pain was still obvious, even at three years' distance. Isaac understood. He still burnt with the pain of witnessing Juan's execution as Torquemada looked on. His hunger for vengeance had grown, fed by the forced co-existence with Torquemada commanded by the King.

The pit of his stomach ached with sorrow for those he had lost and for his failure to save them. Regret and grief crept up on him, assailed him, and left him hollowed out. Then the anger. Hadn't he been patient enough? Lulling Torquemada into a sense of comfort. There was little doubt his powers were in decline – both politically and physically. Why not wait for his inevitable death – surely it wouldn't be much longer? But that would repeat the mistake he had made over Juan. If he had taken matters into his own hands perhaps his best friend could have survived long enough to escape to Portugal with his family. Instead, he had remained in the shadows. The deep shame the memory induced was almost visceral. This was a matter of honour, of redemption. He wanted to witness Torquemada's burial and know he was responsible for putting him in the ground.

Sitting up, he heard a timid knock at his bedchamber door. 'What is it, Catalina?' he said, assuming it must be the housekeeper.

'No, it's me, Papa.' Isabel called out. 'His Majesty demands your immediate attendance at the Real Alcazar.'

'Send word I will be there directly.' He immediately regretted his impatient tone. She had enough to contend with. He recalled when he and Juan had been that age –

carefree, arrogant and, on at least one occasion, cruel. But he didn't want to open that box of memories.

A summons from Ferdinand was not an unusual occurrence. The timing of it was. A royal messenger during siesta was serious. It probably involved Queen Isabella – it almost always did. What was so important that couldn't wait an hour?

FIVE

Ferdinand was waiting for him in the throne room. He sat in one of a pair of golden thrones on a raised dais reached by five steps. Isaac was relieved that Her Majesty's throne, almost twice the size of her husband's, remained empty. On the wall behind the thrones were full-figure portraits of Their Majesties. To the right of the paintings stood a figure of Christ pinioned to a large wooden crucifix. His head hung to one side, blood dripping from the crown of thorns. The sculptor had given him an angry look. Isaac wondered whether that was appropriate.

Ferdinand was not an attractive man; bushy eyebrows and fashionably long sideburns framed a doughy face. But Isaac knew it was foolish to judge a person by his looks. Whilst his appearance might lead some to conclude otherwise, he was clever, usually honest, but ruthlessly pragmatic.

Torquemada stood beside the King, one hand hidden

beneath his white habit, the other resting on his cane. He towered over most people. Add an immaculately groomed tonsure and piercing eyes and he was, even at his advanced age, an imposing figure. But his recent physical deterioration was noticeable in his hunched posture and thin, reedy voice. Isaac had been glad when the King resisted Queen Isabella's demand for the Inquisition to operate in his beloved Seville. He did not have as much faith as his wife in the Inquisition's more brutal methods. But the slaughter of a child three years ago had changed things. The Jewish community was accused of murder, and of using blood in their rituals. This 'blood libel' became the pretext for Torquemada and the Holy Office to operate in the city.

The King looked down at Isaac and said, 'I'm glad you could find the time to join us.'

'I came immediately I received the summons, Your Majesty,' he replied, bowing deeply. He enjoyed as close a relationship with the King as was possible for an ordinary citizen; their families had a long-established connection.

'We've received disturbing news regarding Father Tomás.' Was that a smile on Ferdinand's face? 'The *inquisidores* have uncovered a plot to assassinate him.'

'I call that excellent news, Your Majesty,' Isaac would like to have replied. He settled for a raised brow and a thoughtful grunt.

Torquemada looked down at him with amusement. He must be aware of the antipathy his grunt had hidden. How could it be otherwise? Without the King's intervention, Isaac's family would have suffered even more.

'Your thoughts?' the King demanded.

He looked up at the monarch and then glanced at Torquemada. His mind was racing, calculating the least damaging way to proceed. How honest could he be?

'Well, Your Majesty, this is unsurprising news.'

The King's eyes widened.

'Unsurprising that a man of the great stature and weighty responsibilities of the Grand Inquisitor should inevitably make enemies in his quest to ferret out alleged heretics.'

'Alleged?' Torquemada snarled. 'There are no alleged heretics; only those who repent and those who do not.' He scowled. 'You should know that; from the unfortunate choices made by your friend. Juan de Mota.'

Isaac's jaw tightened.

Ferdinand stared at Torquemada, who gave him an almost imperceptible nod. 'There is no need to excavate old wounds. Isaac, we would both value your opinion.'

'It is unsurprising that there are rumours of an attempt to do harm to the Grand Inquisitor. Many families have suffered injury and loss –'

'Not without cause,' Torquemada said.

The King turned to him and held up a palm. 'Continue, Isaac.'

'Injury and loss foster enmity. It is only the veneration the masses have for the Church, and the deep loyalty to Your Majesties,' he bowed his head, 'that suppresses the hatred. That there is now a plot to assassinate the Grand Inquisitor shows your subjects are becoming actively intolerant of the Holy Office.'

'A few subjects,' Torquemada muttered.

'Some, yes,' Isaac replied with a nod. 'But enough to bring themselves to the attention of the *inquisidores* and, I suppose, the *familiares*?'

At the mention of his network of spies, Torquemada appeared surprised but remained silent.

'Your Majesty, I suggest you consider a review of the Holy Office's activities.'

Torquemada banged his cane on the floor repeatedly. 'This is *not* why you are here. The only authority who can suggest a review of The Holy Office is His Grace, Pope Sixtus.' He locked eyes with Isaac. 'Remember your position, my son.'

'You make a good point, Isaac, but Father Tomás is correct, that's not why you are here.'

'I have to admit I am at a loss how to proceed.' He bowed again. 'I apologise, Your Majesty.'

'You solved the mystery of the murder of that boy, Fernando? The 'blood libel' that the Jews liked to call it. Therefore, Her Majesty and I believe you should investigate this plot. Perhaps you can *prevent* a murder this time?'

He did not correct the King; the nine-year-old boy's name was Fernan. He had been the son of Rodrigo, now Catalina's husband. He should have known: Queen Isabella was behind this 'request' to investigate the plot to assassinate her confessor. Even in her absence she exercised power. No doubt this was a trap cooked up by the Queen and Torquemada. He assumed the Ferdinand was not in full agreement. But Ferdinand had little choice if both his wife – the reigning monarch – and the Grand Inquisitor demanded something. If he investigated and didn't find any evidence of a plot he would be diminished in the eyes of the King and might even lose his protection. If Torquemada was killed, then it would be his failure and he would pay with his life.

'I will, of course, do my best.' Isaac glanced at Torquemada. 'For Your Majesties.'

'Father Tomás will tell you all he knows,' the King said. 'You may leave us now.'

He bowed and turned to leave.

'Not you,' Ferdinand said. 'You may approach.'

He ascended the steps as Torquemada hobbled out of the doorway hidden behind the throne.

The King stared at him until they heard the door close. They were alone.

'Don't be fooled. He's not as infirm as he appears.'

'Your Majesty.'

'Isaac, I know you're clever, but are you clever enough to know exactly what game is being played here?'

'Whatever game is being played, I'm content to play along, Your Majesty.'

'For God's sake, we're alone. We can talk man to man.'

He reflected for a moment. There was no point lying. The King knew him too well. 'As a man, husband, and father, I expect you understand my feelings about the task you have assigned me, Your Majesty.'

'Yes. I do. But I'm speaking as your King.'

Dipping his head, he decided to ignore the contradiction between the monarch's last two statements.

'As a monarch, I must be more than just a man, a

husband, or a father. I'm sympathetic to your losses. But the plot to assassinate Torquemada is serious, the evidence credible. Whilst you, and others, may rejoice if it were to be successful, Her Majesty and I have to consider the political consequences.' He paused. 'The man will be a martyr for Catholics who will then blame the Jews or the Moors. The situation in Granada is combustible enough. With their fasting month coming so soon after *Semana Santa*, blood will boil anyway.' He waited for Isaac to nod his agreement before continuing. 'We cannot be seen to promote a full investigation into the plot; it will just increase tensions. I want no more riots or massacres. Act discreetly, indicate in the right quarters that now is not the time. Even if it only means delaying a few months so that we can resolve the situation in Granada. That is all that is required.'

He bowed his head. The King expected him to capitalise on his unique connection to the different communities across Andalusia. Isaac had grown up speaking Arabic to the Moorish servants his father kept. And, as a Jewish convert to Catholicism, he had associates in the *converso* community.

'You can see he's in decline. The natural order of events will take place soon enough.'

'Is Her Majesty in accord with this view?'

'Her Majesty does not want the death of her beloved confessor at any cost. That's all you need to appreciate.'

'Thank you for taking the time to apprise me of the full context, Your Majesty. I will do my best. With your permission, I will leave and discuss the matter with Father Tomás.'

The King dismissed him with the back of a hand.

He found himself once again caught in Ferdinand's tongs. It reminded him of an old Jewish verse:

> *With one hand, he brings you into the flames*
> *While protecting you from the fire,*
> *Which with both hands he sets against you.*

He would have to be very clever, very lucky – or both – to escape the flames this time.

Torquemada made slow progress hobbling along the long passageway leading to the Queen's quarters. Only a year ago he would have stridden along; now he had to use this damn cane. Isabella would be pleased, the meetings with His Majesty and Alvarez had been satisfactory. He'd been Isabella's confessor ever since she'd ascended to the throne, almost a quarter of a century ago. Time damages us all, he thought, but it also brings us closer to heaven.

The golden eagle emblazoned on the door of the Queen's chamber flickered in the crackling torchlight. Underneath was written, "Protect us in the shadow of your wings." It was a line from David's prayer in Psalms and he whispered the rest of the verse, "'from the wicked who assail me, from my mortal enemies who surround me.'"

He did not knock – he was expected. She lounged in a low armchair, her feet stretched out on a bench.

Dressed in an ankle-length white smock, her hair untied.

'Father Tomás, sit with me.' She gestured towards a high-backed chair at her side. He eased himself down and rested his hands on the knob of his cane.

'I assume Ferdinand was helpful?'

'Yes, Your Majesty.'

'I know he doesn't always approve of your more... robust methods.'

'No, Your Majesty.'

'But he values you just as highly as I do.'

'Thank you,' he dipped his head.

'Do you think Alvarez is up to the job?'

He hesitated. 'The connections his father established with both the Jews and the Moors are still strong.' Should he admit what he was thinking? 'He is perhaps the only man left in Seville with such standing.' The praise left a bitter taste.

She steepled her fingers.

'He will be able to discuss the plot to murder me in a more,' he paused, 'subtle way than my *familiares* would be able to.' He inhaled deeply. 'Performing The Almighty's work has not made me popular.'

'But you do not seek earthly approval, Father.'

'No, I don't.' His tone was emphatic. 'I hope and pray daily that The Almighty will assess my value by the number of souls I snatch from the fires of hell.' He stamped his cane repeatedly to emphasise the final words.

'I'm sure he will.' She smiled. 'You will send me reports?'

'Your Majesty?'

'I will be in Cadiz for some weeks. I want to be near the sea.'

'Of course, Your Majesty.'

'Perhaps it might do you some good to come and visit me.'

'As you wish. Though I've been thinking...'

'What?'

'Of moving to Avila, to the Monastario de Santo Tomás.'

'Your convent is built?'

'Very nearly, Your Majesty.'

'We'll discuss it on my return.'

'As you wish.'

'Father, will you hear my confession?'

'Yes, my child,' he said softly.

She took a cushion from the armchair, placed it at his feet, and knelt before him. Bowing her head she began, 'In the name of the Father, and of The Son, and of The Holy Spirit ...'

As she recounted her sins, his thoughts drifted away to heaven. Part of him welcomed death, even at the hands of an assassin. He would become a martyr, and then a saint. He was tired of his failing body. Soon he would be seventy-eight. If he survived until his next birthday. To take his rightful place with The Almighty would be a great relief. Peace at last. She'd stopped talking, and he hadn't heard a word. He said hastily, 'May Almighty God have mercy on you, and having forgiven your sins, lead you to eternal life. Amen.'

She gave him a quizzical look, returned to the

armchair, and closed her eyes. He pushed down on the cane to lever himself up and trudged wearily out of the chamber.

CHAPTER
SIX

Isaac propped his elbows on the desk, resting his chin on interlinked fingers, and closely surveyed Alejandro's reaction as he sat down. His deputy looked at him from beneath his brows, lips pursed. His pale blue eyes glinted in the late afternoon sunlight streaming through the leaded window set high in the wall of Isaac's chamber at the Royal Alcazar. The discussion with Torquemada after his audience with the King had revealed little of substance. Now he wanted to find out what Alejandro made of the problem.

'Let me get this straight, señor,' his deputy said, crossing his legs.

He mentally braced himself for Alejandro's forensic analysis of the situation he'd just outlined.

'You intend to respond to a direct instruction from His Majesty by *reluctantly* investigating a conspiracy to murder The Grand Inquisitor of All Spain?'

Isaac glared.

'Did I misunderstand anything, señor?'

'No, Alejandro, that about sums it up.'

'How, exactly, do you propose to accomplish that, and keep your flesh on your bones?'

'That's why we're talking. If you're just going to be satirical then a better use of your time would be to attend to the stack of contracts you've yet to review.'

Alejandro grinned.

He sighed and sat back. 'You're clever enough to summarise an impossible problem. Perhaps you'd like to use that rapier-like brain of yours to come up with a solution.'

His deputy looked up and let the fading sunlight play on his face. 'A half-hearted investigation is risky: firstly, His Majesty finds out, and secondly, you don't discover the truth.' He seemed to take a moment to reflect. 'If he realises your game not even he will be able to protect you from Her Majesty. But if you don't have the complete truth how can you confidently decide how to proceed?'

Isaac narrowed his eyes.

'If you ...'

He arched an eyebrow expectantly.

'If *we* investigate and discover who is behind the plot you at least have the choice to share the identity with His Majesty.'

'I'm not an investigator, Alejandro. I leave that to the *inquisidores* and *familiares.'*

'The *inquisidores* are brutal interrogators, señor, and the *familiares* are just neighbourhood spies, little better than vermin. We could do with leaving some arsenic out for *them,* not just the rats.'

He grunted appreciatively at the sentiment.

'There's something nobler about investigators. We seek the real truth.'

Isaac tilted his head and widened his eyes.

Alejandro screwed his eyes shut, realising his mistake. The 'Seeker of Truth' was the title given to the Inquisition's chief interrogator. 'My meaning is still clear.'

'Certainly.' It was Isaac's turn to grin. 'Where do we begin?'

'Let's start with what we know. What did Torquemada tell you?'

'Precious little. He's received some notes telling him he will burn in hell. His network of *familiares* assures him they've received evidence of a plot to murder him.'

'I'll wager the 'evidence' consists of nothing more than rumour, conjecture and anecdote designed to make the vermin look useful and important.'

Isaac nodded.

'He's not discovered anything more solid by employing the water cure, or stretching some poor wretch out on the *escalera*?'

'If he had I'm sure he would have delighted in entertaining me with every last detail.'

'Then we can only pursue one course of action. On the assumption that it is not a Catholic plot....'

Isaac shook his head, dismissing the idea.

'We start by speaking to our *converso* and *Mudéjar* associates immediately. Which would you like to pick?'

As he'd already intended to consult the apothecary about his aching back it was a simple choice.

Isaac stooped under the lintel and stumbled into the gloom of the Apothecary. It was just after Vespers and the sun was beating a retreat, leaving only shadows behind. Through the darkness he could make out the rows of earthenware jars filling the tall shelves behind the counter. He grimaced at the glass jar on the counter full of leeches.

'Who is it? I'm closed,' a voice called out from above.

'Not to me, I hope,' Isaac replied to his old friend's unusually tetchy tone.

'Come into the light. Let me see if you are indeed friend or foe.'

He went behind the counter, removed his hat and looked up the ladder leading to an opening in the ceiling. He was rewarded with a broad grin from the apothecary.

'Salaam Alaikum, Isaac.'

'And peace be upon you too, my old friend. Why so irritable, Ali?'

'I thought you were... never mind, I'll tell you later. It's high time you visited. Thought you might be dead. But I'm sure I would have heard the news of your demise,' he paused, 'especially now that you are so important.' The apothecary climbed down the ladder from his bedchamber and shook his outstretched hand.

'As you appreciate my importance you'll understand why I haven't got the time to be skulking in dingy shops.'

Ali Sina closed his eyes and sighed. 'Your wit is as razor-sharp as ever. Your father taught you well.'

He smiled at the memory of his father's various

minor ailments and the apothecary's many visits to prescribe cures.

'Do you mind?' Ali Sina gestured towards an incense burner on the floor in the middle of the shop. At a nod from Isaac, he knelt to light crystals of *oud*. He inhaled deeply. 'Ah, that's better.'

'It was a scent I grew up with.' He inhaled a lungful of the smoke.

'I've been wondering about selling up and moving to Granada. My brother's there. The two years since Khadijah's death have been ... difficult.' He trailed off, seemingly lost in memory.

'They'll be waiting for us in *jannah*, in heaven, my friend,' Isaac said.

Ali closed his eyes. 'Yes, I forgot for a moment that you understand only too well.' He clapped his hands lightly, as though dismissing his melancholy. 'Are you here on the King's business?'

He pursed his lips and tilted his head from side to side.

'It's like that? Let's go up to the roof garden and you can tell me all about it.'

The apothecary went behind the counter. He released the catch on a ceiling-high row of shelving that stood proud from its neighbour. Grunting as he pushed the shelves aside to reveal a cast iron, spiral staircase, he ascended and beckoned Isaac to follow.

It was almost sunset as Isaac looked out from the roof terrace, over the medicinal herb garden, towards La Giralda. He gently crushed some lilac stems between his fingers, releasing their sweet vanilla fragrance. Two centuries ago, the cathedral bell tower was home to the *muezzin* who, at this precise moment, would have been calling the Muslims to *Maghrib* prayers. Now the bells were tolling for Vespers, to summon the Catholic faithful. At least the apothecary has a visual reminder of his religion. We Jews have nothing, only memories. And it was not a sin for the *Mudéjar* to practise their faith in private. They were not accused of heresy as the Jews were. But that was a bitter, uncharitable train of thought.

Ali Sina busied himself pouring glasses of *nabidh*, indicating with his open palm that they should make themselves comfortable on the chairs placed in front of a delicately carved, octagonal wooden table.

'This was one of the Prophet Mohamed's favourite drink. Peace be upon him.'

Isaac's eyes widened.

'Do not concern yourself, my friend, it is not *haram*, it is permitted. It is indeed from the grape but is steeped for less than three days so it is not alcoholic.'

He took a sip of the red liquid. There was a taste of grape, but no hint of alcohol. They savoured the *nabidh*, as the sonorous chimes faded away and La Giralda was bathed by soft moonlight.

He responded politely to Ali Sina's enquires about the family. The apothecary knew the children well, as he often prescribed mandrake root for their stomach aches and other childhood ailments. He recalled the occasion – it must be almost three years ago – when Ali attended Catalina after she cut her hand deeply. A strange event that he'd never told the apothecary the absolute truth about. It was at the time the Jews had been accused of the blood libel. Strange days indeed. Though the present wasn't any less strange.

'So, my friend, how can I be of assistance?' Ali Sina eventually asked.

'It's highly confidential and extremely delicate.'

'Isn't everything in Seville nowadays?'

Isaac acknowledged this with a thin smile.

'Have you heard anything about a murder plot?'

Ali Sina scrunched up his eyes. 'A murder plot? To kill who?'

'Tomás de Torquemada.'

Ali Sina threw back his head and laughed. 'Where should I start? Half of Seville wishes him dead. There's not a good Catholic family without at least one casualty from this wretched Inquisition. That's before we even consider the *converso* community.' He looked pointedly at Isaac.

'I'm not talking about the general antipathy towards the Grand Inquisitor.' He was taken aback by his friend's response and couldn't disguise his impatience.

'Apologies, my friend.' Ali Sina said, touching him lightly on the knee. 'I did not mean to dismiss your question.'

He held his glass out and Ali Sina filled it. He drank and murmured his appreciation. 'This is a specific plot that has come to my attention.'

'And Their Majesties have asked you to investigate?'

'His Majesty.'

'And you think it involves us, the *Mudéjars*?'

'I'm exploring various areas. Your community is only one possibility.'

Ali Sina put his glass down on the table and looked up thoughtfully. 'No, I can't bring anything to mind. You must remember there are very few of us left in Seville. Most have gone to Granada. Archbishop Talavera is more hospitable towards Islam, and we still have some influence there.' He picked up his glass and took a sip. 'For the moment.'

Isaac said nothing.

'If there was a *Mudéjar* conspiracy I would have heard something.' He held Isaac's eyes. 'Isn't the threat more likely from a *converso*? You fellows have suffered at least as much, perhaps more, at the hands of those Inquisition fiends.'

He dipped his head in agreement.

'Something odd did happen yesterday.' He picked up his glass and savoured another mouthful of the *nabidh*.

Ali Sina loved stories and he sensed his friend was settling in to tell one.

'I was awoken as usual by the cathedral bells ringing for Prime. I completed my dawn prayers in my bedchamber. At least Their Majesties allow us to pray in private. I wonder how long that dispensation will last.'

Isaac cleared his throat noisily and raised an eyebrow. To his irritation, Ali Sina ignored the hint and continued the story at the same leisurely pace.

'It was early morning and I was doing my weekly stocktake, consulting my mental checklist of what was missing and what needed further preparation. I've got far too many leeches. Why do you think that might be?'

He responded to Ali Sina's invitation to discuss the details of his profession with a smile. Hoping that by remaining silent his friend would get on with his tale.

'Anyway, I was standing at the counter and the shop was still dark.'

'It would help if you lit more candles, my friend.'

'I need to save money. A tall man came in and growled a good morning. His hat disguised most of his face. He was about your height and I believe his eyes were pale blue. Definitely didn't look like a *Mudéjar*. A Catholic, a *converso,* perhaps. I couldn't say for sure. Seemed familiar but I don't think he's visited the shop before.'

Ali Sina refilled both of their glasses with *nabidh*.

'I saw him scanning the jars behind me and I tried to guess what he was looking for. He coughed rather loudly so I ground some hyssop for him and told him to take it twice a day. I expected him to leave.' Ali Sina drank and looked towards La Giralda.

After a few moments Isaac said impatiently, 'But he didn't?'

'No. This is where it gets worrying.'

Isaac waited patiently.

'He asked for arsenic.'

'Is that very unusual? Isn't it used as a rat poison?'

'Yes, and that's what he told me he wanted it for. But it was the way he asked and the quantity he purchased that made me concerned. I tipped out the usual small amount but he demanded much more. He then tried to pay me double the normal price. Which, of course, I did not accept.'

This was not surprising – his friend's integrity was unimpeachable.

'And then it got even stranger. I told him he would have to sign for the arsenic. It's a requirement of Their Majesties.'

Isaac nodded.

'I gave him the register. He took the quill, scrawled a signature and slammed the book shut. Then he told me he would probably require more on his return.'

Isaac raised his eyebrows.

'When I said I'd given him quite enough to cope with a large infestation he became threatening.'

'How?'

'He asked me how business was. And he said' – he closed his eyes as though concentrating on getting the words exactly right – '"That front door is not secure. It would be a great shame were anyone to enter while you were asleep and vandalise your fine establishment."'

'God's Blood.'

'And then,' Ali Sina paused as though to collect himself, 'he put his hand on his rapier and said, "Or perhaps even harm your good self."'

Isaac swallowed the rest of his drink.

'When I opened the register the signature was smeared. I suppose that was why he slammed it shut so quickly. But I thought I could make out an A.'

'Why would he write his real name?' he asked.

'That's what I wondered. But at least I have a record of the date and some idea of what he looks like. That might prove useful information.' He bit the inside of his cheek. 'In the event of a murder.'

'And you definitely didn't recognise him?'

Ali Sina was pensive. 'No... perhaps... no, definitely not. You will laugh, but when you arrived just now, I thought you were him. That's why I was irritable. The whole incident has quite unnerved me.'

'I don't blame you.'

'I'll show you the register when you leave. You might recognise the signature.'

CHAPTER
SEVEN

As he left the shop Isaac refused the apothecary's offer to relieve the pain in his lower back by applying leeches. The whole idea of bloodletting was insane. Instead, he promised his friend that he would steep willow bark in hot water and take it four times daily. The apothecary thought doubling the dose might help. He would try, though it wouldn't lessen the pain of losing Juan or Maria. It wouldn't reduce the tension he felt over the conflict in his religious identity. Perhaps the pain was connected? Was his body reacting to his emotional anguish? He dismissed the thought as farfetched.

He meandered home; needing time to think. A mysterious stranger had threatened to wreck Seville's remaining *Mudéjar* Apothecary if he was not provided with arsenic. Ali Sina believed the stranger might be a *converso*, but there was no evidence. The apothecary claimed he had heard nothing from the *Mudéjar* community about a plot to assassinate Torquemada. Isaac tended to believe his friend. Why would the *Mudéjar* want to kill the most powerful cleric in Andalusia? Torquemada's prime target were the *marrano*, the insincere converts from Judaism. Like Juan. Like him.

He was deeply troubled. Ramadan coinciding with *Semana Santa* this year would inevitably lead to a rise in religious tension. Add to this a plot to kill the Grand Inquisitor and Seville – perhaps even the whole of Andalusia – could descend into chaos and violence. Ferdinand was right. Torquemada's assassination would only make matters worse. Seville would become an even more dangerous place for his family. He had to stop the assassination and bide his time to avenge the deaths of Maria and Juan. Forced to protect the man he wanted dead. For the moment.

An unwanted thought circled in his mind like a fly. There was something familiar about the description of the arsenic buyer. And he signed his name with an A. But it was ridiculous. Why would Alejandro purchase large quantities of arsenic? He swatted the thought away.

The next morning, on his way into the cathedral, Isaac's attention was drawn by an unusually large crowd congregating in the plaza. They were loud and unruly. Was the trouble already starting? An orange seller trundled his cart through the mob. They ignored the merchant's warnings to 'move aside', forcing him to weave around them. Attempting a sharp turn, a wheel caught in the cobbles and the cart turned on its side, tumbling oranges across the plaza. A pair of youths scrambled for the fruit. The leaner one was stronger than he looked; fighting off the smaller boy, he scooped up an armful of fruit. An orange escaped and bounced towards Isaac. The smaller boy scuttled after it with impressive speed and agility. Isaac lifted his boot and trapped the golden treasure. The boy made a grab for it. He applied more pressure, threatening to burst the orange, but then relented. Oranges were a prized delicacy in Seville, even this late in the season. Besides, the boy reminded him of Gabriel. And he clearly needed sustenance. He grabbed the fruit, peeling and consuming it in almost one motion – juices smearing his face. Grinning, he offered the last segment to Isaac, who declined with a smile and a shake of his head.

Inside the cathedral, he lit a votive candle and watched the flame sputter and come to life. He quickly crossed himself, just in case anyone was watching – the *familiares* were everywhere. He bowed his head and tried to focus on Maria, but thoughts of the children intruded. On his way out of the house he'd noted a sour atmosphere between them. Gabriel and Martín looking at each other conspiratorially and giving Juana sly smiles. She appeared sullen and downcast. He would discuss it with Isabel later. Closing his eyes, he returned to the present and tried to conjure Maria. The cathedral was one of the few places he could still sense her.

Maria was buried, according to her wishes, at her family's estate in Valdezzoras, about an hour's ride away to the north of Seville. He'd wanted a Jewish burial for her, but that was impossible, even if it had been what she wanted. He didn't know, they hadn't discussed it. The family estate was a suitable compromise. He only visited the grave in March, on the anniversary of her death. Even then he didn't go alone, Isabel and Gabriel accompanied him – bulwarks against his sorrow. He told himself he didn't have the time to go more often — the pressure of work, his responsibility for the children. But he knew that he was too scared to face the grief. Coming to the cathedral, where Maria had felt at home, been part of the choir, brought him closer to her. He felt more able to control his emotions. It helped that it was a place of Christian worship, a place he was ambivalent about. Where would he be buried?

A sharp tap on his shoulder interrupted him. He wheeled around, right hand moving towards the rapier sheathed at his side.

Father Gutiérrez arched an eyebrow. 'I'm sorry I startled you, my son.'

Releasing the tension from his shoulders he gave a slight bow. 'My apologies, Father.' He took comfort from Gutiérrez' familiar, dishevelled appearance and long white beard. It had been too long since he'd spoken with the elderly cleric.

'My fault for disturbing you.' Gutiérrez studied him closely. 'Maria?' the priest said glancing at the votive candle.

He gave a thin smile of acknowledgement.

'Then I shall leave you in peace.'

'No, Father. I've finished.'

'Then walk with me.'

They turned and proceeded towards the door leading

out to the Patio de los Naranjos. He always found the courtyard of neat rows of orange trees soothing. Something in the predictable arrangement, the lack of confusion. He took a deep breath of the delicate floral scent.

'It's wonderful at this time of year isn't it?' Father Gutiérrez said, as they slowly paced between the rows.

He smiled as he remembered Maria loved to listen to the cleric's warm, honey-toned voice.

'The children are well? Isabel flourishes under her responsibilities?'

'Yes, I think so. The children are fine. Gabriel is half-man, half-boy.'

'Keep him close to you, Isaac. Even if he doesn't show it, he needs you, especially now.'

'I know, I know.' He looked up at the oranges glistening in the morning sun. 'I'm glad you disturbed me, Father. I was meaning to ask you something.' He looked behind to reassure himself they were not being overheard.

'You can ask me anything. I can't guarantee an answer.' Father Gutiérrez raised his eyebrows. 'Or not one that will satisfy you.'

He lowered his voice as he asked, 'Have you heard anything about a plot to kill Torquemada?'

Father Gutiérrez pursed his lips. 'Why would anyone bother? His powers are clearly waning. It can't be much longer before he's called to meet his maker.' He paused. 'I'd like to eavesdrop on that conversation,' he said with a wry smile.

He returned the smile.

'Why do you ask, my son?'

'It's been brought to my attention...'

'The King?' He studied Isaac's face again. 'Or more likely the Queen?'

He stopped walking and turned to face the cleric.

'It's hardly surprising that talk of conspiracies dominates Their Majesties' minds. Or that they would seek to use you.'

'Granted, Father. But this must remain between us.'

'Consider this conversation to be taking place in the confessional ... if you can still recall?'

He grimaced at the sardonic reminder of his failure to regularly conform to Catholic practice.

'I apologise – that's a different conversation for another time.' The priest took him by the arm and they walked. He leant across and whispered into Isaac's ear, 'But you really must be more careful.'

'Yes, Father. So, have you?'

'I hear all sorts of things in the confessional...'

The priest heard Ferdinand's confession. Torquemada heard Isabella's.

'Which remain sacrosanct. However, I hear all sorts of things outside of it. And, I'm sorry to disappoint you, but I've heard nothing of any plot to kill Torquemada.'

Neither the most important cleric nor one of the more prominent *Mudejár* remaining in Seville had heard anything about a plot to murder the Grand Inquisitor. He had absolute trust in both men. Even if they couldn't tell him the complete truth they would have hinted at something. If there had been anything. He must talk to Alejandro and find out if he'd extracted anything from his contacts in the *converso* community. If he hadn't, the investigation was over before it had even begun. He would incur the King's displeasure, and there was no way to know how that would turn out.

Was there something he'd overlooked? What of the visitor to the Apothecary? Should he confront Alejandro with his suspicions? But if it had been him, why would he have written any letters that were genuinely from his own name?

They continued their stroll until Father Gutiérrez left to perform his next service. He remained to absorb the peace and order of the courtyard before returning to the chaos and uncertainty that characterised so much of his life.

Later that evening Isabel sat in the parlour with the Book of Hours in her lap, the illuminated manuscript her father had given Mama on their wedding day. Cupping it in her palms she felt the leather binding's rough texture. Golden scrolls of leaves and flowers formed an ornate border around the cover. Engraved in the centre was the crest of the Camarino family – her grandfather. It must have cost Papa a fortune to commission such a fine book. She remembered how Mama loved to read verses from the book at the canonical hours, especially in the early evening at Vespers, or as night fell at Compline. They would sit together and read aloud. Then Mama would allow her to wrap the Book of Hours in its silk shroud and replace it in the walnut chest at the foot of her bed. It would remain there until the next morning when it would again take its place of honour on the prayer cradle. She recalled the time the manuscript was mislaid, her father investigating and questioning every member of the household. Catalina was particularly upset. And then, after all the fuss, Papa found it in his coat pocket. She never really believed that explanation.

Isabel used her finger to trace the raised words of the Archangel Gabriel to the Virgin Mary, 'Hail, full of grace, the Lord is with you.' What did it feel like to hear an angel say you've been chosen to conceive God's only son? She felt her skin prickle with the thrill of imagining the moment.

'So beautiful,' came a soft voice from behind her. She turned to see Alejandro standing in the doorway, peering over her shoulder. She loved his unusually pale blue eyes. Feeling herself redden, she quickly turned back to the book, and in her embarrassment slammed it shut.

'The Book of Hours – such a beautiful example. That's what I meant, señorita.' He emphasised his words by gesticulating with his long, elegant fingers.

'Yes, of course it is, Señor Alejandro. It always gives me great pleasure to read from it, and of course brings back many happy memories,' she said brightly, regaining her composure. 'I must return it to its proper place,' she said, standing. 'We wouldn't want it to be lost again, would we?'

She registered the confusion on his face. He remained in the doorway as she hadn't invited him in.

'Ah, perhaps you don't know that story. Another time,' she said.

He gave her a small bow. 'I'll look forward to it.'

'Was there something you wanted, señor?'

'Yes, I mean, no. I'm here to see your father.'

'Of course you are,' she said in a low tone, unable to disguise her disappointment. 'I'm sure you'll find him on the terrace. It's almost Vespers. You can find your way?'

Bowing again, he began to move away but then turned back and held her eyes.

'You're sure there's nothing else, señor?'

As he opened his mouth to reply, a cry of, 'You rat, I'm going to kill you,' came from outside.

She went to the window that looked onto the court-yard. 'I wonder which of the boys has upset Juana this time?' Recalling guiltily she had done nothing yet about the incident she witnessed from her bedchamber – Gabriel throwing dirt at Juana. She didn't want to trouble Papa. But she had to accept her brother was at an age where he would respond better to him than to her. She'd become distracted and had ignored Alejandro. She turned round to speak to him.

He gave her a rueful look, bowed, and left.

Isaac and Alejandro sat side by side on the roof terrace, the sun setting over the Guadalquivir in prospect. They had glasses of sherry in hand, and the bottle on the small wooden table between them. The last traces of azure in the sky were blending into the emerging blackness, and moonlight glistened over the river's surface. Swallows looped and chattered, making the most of the vanishing daylight.

'Nothing? Absolutely nothing?' Isaac said.

Alejandro shook his head. 'Correct. No one in the *converso* community has heard anything about an assassination plot.'

'And you're quite sure they were telling you the truth?' he said and took a sip of sherry.

'Absolutely certain? Of course not. But my ancestral *converso* connections and my link to you are well known. They would have been as helpful as they could, they would have indicated something.' He hesitated. 'If there was anything.' He put his glass down, walked over to the railing, turned and looked directly at him.

'So, all we have is Ali Sina's mysterious stranger.' Isaac said. 'I wonder who it could have been?' He looked pointedly at Alejandro, giving him an opportunity to confess.

'Arsenic is a powerful poison, especially as it is odourless and tasteless. Does Torquemada have any symptoms of poisoning? Vomiting? Diarrhoea?'

'Yes, yes, thank you, Alejandro,' he grimaced and held up his glass to show he was drinking. 'I'm acquainted with the symptoms.'

His deputy grinned and turned to look at the last remnants of sunlight.

It was quite ridiculous to accuse Alejandro of plotting a murder because of one letter. He decided to let the matter drop. He joined his deputy. 'I'm going to have to pay him a visit, aren't I?' he said, finishing his sherry.

'I don't see any other way. You can't go to His Majesty without some information. You'll need to interview Torquemada to establish whether there are any signs of arsenic poisoning. It's the only lead we have. The sooner the better.'

'And what will you do?'

'Review the sheaves of contracts scattered across my room like an autumnal leaf fall.'

He looked across at the Castillo de San Jorge and shivered.

'Feeling cold, señor?' Alejandro asked.

Turning, he gave him a wry smile. He would have to visit one of the two men the following morning. Either Ferdinand and admit he had almost nothing to report, or Torquemada at the Castillo. He'd learnt bitter lessons from his inaction three years ago, during the days of the blood libel. He'd faced down the regret caused by his passivity over Juan's capture by the Inquisition. He could summon the power, on most days, to fight his grief. Did he have the strength to conquer both regret and grief again? Regret could be vanquished by action. If grief still followed he would at least have the solace of believing that he could have done no more.

'Enough,' he said decisively. 'Let's go and enjoy the feast Catalina's prepared.'

CHAPTER
EIGHT

E arly the next morning, Catalina rubbed her wrist as she bustled down Calle Abades away from Casa de la Felicidad. It was sore from turning the key in the lock of the outer door. She'd mention it to the señor on her return from the butcher. Perhaps Rodrigo could fix it. No doubt a bit of oil would sort it out. Approaching the junction with Calle Avenida she realised two men were eyeing her, slyly, mind. The taller one was lean and had a stiff-necked air. The other was of a sturdy build and had a crop of unruly red hair. She stared at the large bald spot on the side of his head and wondered how that could've happened. They saw her looking and turned away, appearing to be greatly interested in the wall of the building they were leaning against. She hoisted her skirt, tilted her chin and hurried away. They couldn't fool her. She hadn't lost all of her good looks.

Her day had not started well. The señor had been in a terrible mood, complaining that her freshly baked rye bread was too dry. It had taken all her strength to keep her mouth shut. She'd given him a good hard look instead. To make sure he understood how unhappy she was, she'd kept her peace when he bade her farewell. She'd overheard the señor and Alejandro on the terrace last night and she could've sworn they were saying something about the Grand Inquisitor. It sounded like the señor was going to see him that very morning. That would explain his mood. Enough to put anyone in a foul temper, having to see that old bastard. She'd make it up to him with something nice for lunch. Perhaps the butcher would have lamb? He was favourable to a nice piece of pink lamb, though he claimed it gave him indigestion. More likely to be all that sherry he was so fond of.

The queue outside the butcher's was ridiculous. It was Lent – weren't they supposed to be fasting? Perhaps they were just stocking up to feast on Sunday. As Seville got richer people were eating more, even at Lent. She bought a good-sized leg of lamb that would roast well on the spit with some olive oil and herbs. She preferred the taste of lard, but the señor must have his olive oil. He reckoned the apothecary thought it was better for his digestion. She worried that some called olive oil, 'the smell of the Jews', but the señor would have his way.

She put the joint in her basket and decided to take a turn around the town. The streets were full of people buying provisions and clothes for *Semana Santa*. The Holy Week was supposed to be about thinking of the Holy Lord and his sacrifice for them all. How had it turned into this? But the ladies' dresses were so pretty. If only she still had the figure. Though those pair of scoundrels didn't think she looked so bad, did they? The thought put her in a better mood and she swung the basket gently at her side as she turned into Calle Arfe.

A few paces ahead, she saw a tall lady in a black dress emerge from a shop. The woman looked quickly to her left and right and then hastened away. Didn't she know her? It looked like Isabel. How could it be? Wasn't she at home, giving the children their lessons? She called out, 'Señorita,' but the figure was moving quickly. Walks just as fast as her father, she thought. Catalina ambled after her, pausing to look at the shop Isabel – she was sure it was her – had just come out of. Why in God's name was the señorita visiting the Apothecary?

Isaac picked his way around the beggars on the Puente de Barcas. There seemed to be more every day making their homes on the disused barges forming the pontoon bridge across the Guadalquivir. Disembarking from the last of the vessels he smelt a damp tang in the air, a lingering reminder of the last flood. He turned onto the wide *calle* of San Jacinto and made his way towards the Castillo de San Jorge, the Inquisition's headquarters and Torquemada's lair.

He was expected – Isaac had sent a boy with a message the day before – but Torquemada did not look up from his desk when he entered. He remained hunched over sheaves of papers, grunting as he studied each one before casting it carefully aside with one hand, whilst in the other he rotated a string of rosary beads through his fingers. Whilst waiting, Isaac admired the magnificent view. The room looked out across the river, and La Giralda was clearly visible in the near distance on the far bank. As was the Torre del Oro – the golden, twelve-sided tower originally constructed by the Moors, now the Inquisition's torture chamber.

Eventually, Torquemada leant back, looked up and raised his brows. He placed the rosary beads on the desk. How different his welcome had been the first time he'd entered this chamber. Greeted as a long-lost friend, and offered sherry from Torquemada's private collection in Jerez. In those days, just three years ago, the game had been more subtle, and he'd been more naive. Torquemada had then only recently established the 'Office for the Propagation of the Holy Faith' in Seville and did not appear entirely sure of how much influence Isaac had with the King. Now, after the torture and execution of thousands, he clearly felt secure enough to treat him with disdain.

'I need to ask you some more questions, Father Tomás.' His stomach mutinied at showing such deference. He would love to address him in the terms he had overheard Catalina use when she talked to Rodrigo; but calling him a 'devil' or an 'old bastard' would not elicit very much information.

Torquemada pointed towards the single chair in front of his desk.

'Who prepares your food?' Isaac said as he sat down, casually crossing one leg over the other.

Torquemada's expression made it clear he was not expecting that question. 'What do you mean?'

'Exactly what I say.' Isaac locked eyes with Torquemada. 'Who prepares your food?'

'How would I know? Some woman in the kitchen. Whoever it is could do with taking some lessons.' His words were harsh, but his voice was frail.

'Have you noticed any change in the food of late? Any effects on your digestion?'

'No.'

'Forgive me Father, but have you,' he said, savouring Torquemada's evident discomfort, 'noticed any particular physical symptoms lately?'

'What do you mean, man? I'm not answering any more of your foolish questions until you explain what this is about.' Standing up with difficulty, he placed the knuckles of both hands on the desk and loomed over Isaac.

He held Torquemada's stare until he relented and sat back down.

'Our enquiry into the assassination plot has thrown up one potential threat. The apothecary, Abu Ali Sina, reports that a man recently purchased a large quantity of arsenic. The stranger refused to give his name, and the apothecary could not identify him.'

'What would that have to do with me?'

'Arsenic is tasteless and odourless and could easily be used as a poison.'

Torquemada's eyes widened. He spread his palms on the desk as if to steady himself.

Isaac saw something he thought he would never witness: fear in the Grand Inquisitor's eyes. He enjoyed the moment.

'What are the symptoms?' Torquemada said, almost in a whisper.

'Diarrhoea, vomiting, and,' he said, looking pointedly at Torquemada's hands, 'red blotches on the skin.'

Torquemada hastily hid his hands underneath his habit. 'I'll get rid of all the kitchen staff immediately. I'll appoint an official taster. That should take care of it,' he murmured to himself. 'Are the effects permanent? Can they be reversed?' he asked, raising his voice.

He said nothing, allowing the moment to stretch itself out.

Torquemada's lower jaw shifted from side to side.

'I have no idea. Perhaps you should consult an apothecary.'

Withdrawing his hands from beneath his habit, he picked up the string of rosary beads and fingered them thoughtfully. Seeming to come to a decision he replaced the beads on the desk, leant his weight on his cane and came out from behind it.

'Thank you, my son, for bringing this to my attention.' He reached for Isaac's hand and pulled him to his feet. 'I don't know how I can repay you.' He grinned, revealing large brown incisors.

The smell of decay washed over him, and he involuntarily pulled his head away. He could not think of anything to say; his hand moving instinctively towards the rapier sheathed at his waist.

Torquemada's eyes followed the movement and he smiled. 'Shall we pray together before you go, my son?' He indicated the prayer desk with two kneelers placed in front of it.

Wrenching his hand from Torquemada's grip he said, 'Not this time, Father, thank you. I'm sure we will meet again.' He turned to leave.

'One more thing.'

He stood with his hand on the cool iron of the door handle.

'Do let your poor, motherless children know that I think of them often in my nightly prayers.' He sighed. 'Especially Isabel.'

He turned, fist clenching the handle to look at Torquemada coolly. It took all his restraint to say nothing and walk away, leaving the door ajar. He needed a drink.

Torquemada smiled to himself as he closed the door and sat down in the chair by the hearth. Alvarez didn't even have the courage to slam the door. What a pathetic man he was. But he supposed he should be thankful to him for uncovering the assassination plot. He'll choke on his supper tonight thinking that he helped to keep me alive.

It was at times like this that he missed Brother Alonso. It had been useful to have a spineless but committed deputy who he could rely upon to do his bidding without complaint. But also someone he could test his ideas on, and who showed some initiative. He didn't mind his subordinate taking action without informing him so long as it fitted with the mission to save souls. As long as it gave him plausible deniability with Their Majesties, particularly the King, who was no great supporter of what he considered the Inquisition's crueller methods.

Alonso had been particularly useful three years ago when that boy Fernan had been killed. Of course the Jews complained they'd been unfairly accused of killing him to use his blood in their rituals – what they had the temerity to call a 'blood libel'. A pity he'd had to agree to Their Majesties' decision to send Alonso to the Indies. At least he would be serving the Lord by saving the souls of those savages. Perhaps enough time had passed that he could be recalled. With everything that had happened since then, particularly taking back Andalusia from the Moors, surely Their Majesties would have forgotten an insignificant friar?

But what to do about Alvarez? There was no doubt he was a *marrano*. Why couldn't the man just be a normal *converso*, give up Judaism and embrace the True Faith? Hadn't he learnt from his friend's execution, or from Maria's death? Damn Ferdinand for protecting him. The degree of proof required to convict him of heresy was far greater than for any ordinary citizen. And he'd heard a rumour that the King's loyalty to Alvarez ran so deep because he was of *converso* stock himself.

His *familiares* had told him that Isaac was the last *marrano* of the group that he and Juan had been part of. The remainder had been executed or fled to Lisbon. Alvarez's heresy was an affront to the True Faith that had stood for too long. His duplicity placed the souls of his own children in jeopardy. The children's innocence – especially poor Isabel's – was tainted. But his family was also his greatest weakness. Perhaps it was time to act.

Even though the sun was at its peak, Bar Averno was shrouded in darkness as Isaac entered. A cauldron of noise greeted him, mainly from a volley of raucous male voices. A fire muttered and flickered in a stone hearth at the far end. Blackened wooden beams overhung the shadowy corners, tendrils of pipe smoke curling into the air. Rough-hewn trestle tables were placed around the perimeter of the room. Most of them occupied by drinkers, talking loudly and gesticulating wildly. He noticed the flaming red hair of a stout young man sitting at the table nearest the fire. His companion was a few years older, lean and with a predatory look about him. They were the only ones not talking.

He waited at the serving counter. He watched as a red-faced girl in an apron ferried wooden platters, jugs of beer, and glasses of sherry from the counter to the tables. She stopped occasionally to push a tress of hair from her eyes or wipe the sweat from her brow with the back of her hand. When she noticed him her expression transformed into one of delight.

'We've not seen you in here for a good long time, señor. Welcome back.'

'Yes, busy, you know.' He remembered she was the barkeep's daughter, but struggled to remember her name. It came to him, Luisa, that was it.

'On the King's business, no doubt?'

He gave her a thin smile. He was still disturbed by the meeting with Torquemada. But Luisa had been helpful to him once, she deserved his politeness at least. 'I'll have some of your finest *mojama* and a glass of sherry, please, Luisa.'

She quickly returned with a glass of sherry and a platter. He put a slab of the salty tuna atop a hunk of rye bread and washed it down with a large mouthful of sherry. He felt calm enough to consider the meeting with Torquemada. How dare he say he would keep Isabel in his prayers? He could have throttled him. Perhaps Torquemada had wanted him to be violent. He would have arrested him for assault. It would have been beyond even His Majesty's power to save him. Her Majesty would make certain of that. Glancing around, he noticed the red-haired youth and his companion staring at him. He held their gaze, but they did not look away.

He turned back and waggled his glass at Luisa, who responded, 'Immediately, señor.'

There was a loud thud, followed by a crack. He wheeled around as a hush descended over the room. A man was slumped over the trestle table nearest the fire. A pool of crimson encircling his head, staining the surface of the table. The red-haired youth and his friend were standing over him. Red hair raised a mug to his lips, took a long draught, and wiped the back of his hand over his mouth. He slammed the mug down onto the blood, splashing red flecks onto his companions' doublet. The predatory one looked down, unsheathed a dagger from his waist and used the tip of the blade to scrape the blood droplets off his doublet. He arched an eyebrow at Isaac, surveyed the room, threw some coins on the table and made to leave. Red hair followed close behind. A loud cough broke the silence. The chattering restarted to the background of clinking wine mugs.

Two men hauled up the battered youth and braced their shoulders under his arms.

'Best get him to the surgeon,' someone suggested.

'Throw him in the gutter, with the rest of the garbage,' another voice cried out to subdued laughter.

'Who were they?' Isaac asked Luisa as she passed by, cloth in hand, heading for the blood-stained table.

'I've not seen them in here very often,' she whispered out of the side of her mouth. 'But they're well-known *ladrones*. Ramos and Roja,' she said, hurrying away. Roja was obviously the red-haired one's nickname. He stayed to finish his drink, but was unnerved by the incident. Why had the thugs looked at him? He kept a nervous watch on his way home.

That afternoon Isabel shut herself in the parlour of Casa de la Felicidad. Away from the children's noise so she could browse through Mama's Book of Hours in peace. After about an hour there was a knock, and the door was flung open.

She swung around to face Alejandro.

His eyes widened in surprise. 'I'm so sorry to startle you, señorita, I thought your father was in here. He asked me to bring some papers to him on my way home. I thought he would have returned from his meeting with Torquemada by now.'

She hoped her expression did not reveal the hatred she felt at the mention of the Grand Inquisitor. The transition from the beauty of the Book of Hours to his evil disturbed her.

'No, no, that's quite alright, Señor Alejandro. I was just in another place really,' she said dreamily. 'Come in and sit down.' She gestured towards the chair opposite.

He sat down, tucking his long legs under the chair, his knees almost touching hers. She did not move.

'I see you're admiring your Mama's book again,' he said.

She looked down at the book cradled in her palms. 'I look at it every day. I like to remember when my mother let me read it with her.'

'You had to have permission?'

'Yes.'

'It must be a real treasure.'

'It's quite valuable. A gift from Papa on their wedding day.'

'It's a boon to have something so significant to remember your mother by.'

She arched an eyebrow.

'Of course, you would rather have her here with you,' he added hastily.

She rewarded his empathy with a smile. 'I promised I would tell you the story of when my mother lost it. Would you like to hear it?'

'Of course I would.'

She recounted the time her mother was half-crazed by the loss of the book. She looked everywhere and then, with some trepidation, told Papa, who interrogated the entire household. 'You can imagine how upset Catalina was.'

'Yes, I know your father's questioning style.' Alejandro grinned.

She loved his smile and felt her face become warm. She stared down at the book. 'Papa made us all meet where he went over his investigation and then produced the book, claiming he'd found it in his jacket pocket. I've never believed it.'

'What do you think really happened?'

'I'm not sure and I don't think the truth of it really matters. What's important is making sure we keep telling the story.' She paused. 'To keep her alive.' She broke his gaze. 'Papa loved her so much, he would do anything for her.'

'It must be wonderful to share such love,' he said.

She looked down at the book and then up into his pale blue eyes.

'What are you two talking about?' Isaac said from the doorway.

She jumped up, the book slipping to the floor. 'I

wasn't expecting you back so soon, Papa. We were just talking about Mama.'

Alejandro picked up the book and returned it to her, his fingers grazing hers. 'And a fascinating story about your first investigation, Señor Alvarez,' he said with a grin.

Isaac gave him a stern look. 'Can you bring those papers up to my study, Alejandro? I'll have a quick look at them.' He glanced at her. 'Before I speak to Gabriel.'

She was left alone, conscious of the quickened beating of her heart. Was this what love felt like?

～

'I don't know what you could possibly mean, Papa,' Gabriel said, slouching against the jamb of the door to Isaac's study.

It was shortly before dinner, the bells from the cathedral announcing Vesper prayers were dying away. Isaac sat in a large, low-backed wooden chair with his hands resting lightly on its arms.

He had waited two days to discuss Gabriel's behaviour towards the twins. Too long. He now regretted starting the conversation so soon after witnessing the *ladrones'* brutality. The casual nature of it still shocked him. There were regular scuffles and heated disagreements in Bar Averno. But he had never seen anything as violent as the incident that afternoon. The nonchalance with which the predatory one, Ramos, used his dagger to flick the specks of blood from his doublet was truly disturbing. He felt the anger simmering away inside him.

'I think you do, Gabriel. And for God's sake, stand up straight when I'm speaking to you!'

His son looked startled. He moved quickly into the room and stood on the blue Persian rug. Standing erect with his hands behind his back, he did not make eye contact, his gaze seemingly fixed on a spot behind Isaac's head.

Isaac exhaled a long breath. 'Gabriel. Look at me.' He waited for his son to obey. 'Do you remember the story I once told you of how I behaved towards Juan, Señor de Mota, at the river when we were a similar age as you are now?'

'How could I forget? You've told it to me more than once over the years,' Gabriel said softly.

He smiled wryly. 'Well, perhaps you can understand my feelings about how I behaved towards Juan that day. When I was cruel and embarrassed him for no good reason.' He waited. 'Can you?'

Gabriel looked at his father. 'Regretful? Guilty?'

'Both.'

'But didn't you seek absolution in the confessional?'

He gave his son a sharp look. Was he taunting him? But Gabriel's expression was open and apparently genuine.

'Of course I did, but the feelings don't go away, especially after what happened to Juan.'

Gabriel looked down at the floor and mumbled. 'Didn't Señor de Mota deserve his punishment?'

He fought to keep his anger under control. Gabriel might look like a young man, but he was still only a boy. He put his chin in his left hand and looked searchingly at his son, buying time to come up with an answer that would help Gabriel understand. Crossing his arms, Isaac eventually said, 'According to the Inquisition's rules, yes.' He held his son's eyes. 'But do you think The Almighty wanted to deprive two children of their father by burning him alive? Rendering his flesh into the flames whilst his wife looked on?'

Gabriel flinched and grimaced at the image.

He had his son's full attention now and pursued his advantage. 'And all because he chose to follow his father and worship The Almighty in a manner considered heresy by the Inquisition?' His voice rose with indignation. 'He did not venerate a different God, like those savages in the Indies. Catholics, Jews, *Mudéjar*, all the civilised peoples – we all pray to the same God.' He gave Gabriel a moment to consider this idea. 'We are all People of the Book.'

Gabriel looked down at the rug. 'I've never really thought about it that way, Papa.'

He reflected for a moment before continuing. 'Maybe it's my fault for not encouraging you to. It's a dangerous way to think in these times. I'm trusting you to keep this between us.' He paused to give weight to his next words. 'Man to man.'

'I think I understand.'

'Think hard on it, my son. Pray on it. Men, at least good ones, don't treat girls the way you treated Juana. And you know that Martín looks up to you, don't you?'

Gabriel nodded.

'Go on now. Be off with you and wash your hands for dinner.'

Gabriel shut the door softly behind him.

He rubbed his palms over his eyes. What he would give to ask Maria if he had handled the situation correctly, if he'd said the right things. He'd ask Isabel instead.

CHAPTER
TEN

Isaac awoke, realising he'd delayed the audience with His Majesty for long enough. It was three days since his visit to Torquemada. He had hoped that nature might take its course – the Grand Inquisitor had appeared much frailer of late – but he recalled the Ferdinand's words of caution. Torquemada was an excellent actor.

He proceeded directly to the Real Alcazar and the Stucco Patio adjacent to the Hall of Justice, where the King usually enjoyed a morning stroll. Ferdinand liked to spend time in the oldest area of the palace, the last intact vestige of the Almohad builders. Ferdinand stood alone at the far end of the Patio.

'Your Majesty,' Isaac said, bowing deeply.

The sunken pool in the centre of the courtyard babbled gently as it filled with water. He would normally have taken the time to admire the delicate filigree of the stuccowork honeycombing the brick pillars lining the Patio, but His Majesty's impatience was clear from the hardness in his eyes. He beckoned him with a forefinger.

'Well?' he said, with an arched eyebrow and slight grimace. He picked a leaf from the densely foliaged hedge surrounding the pool. Tearing it, he let the pieces fall into the gulley flowing into the pool.

'We've completed the first stage of the investigation.'

The King remained silent.

'We have it on good authority that there are no rumours of any conspiracy to assassinate the Grand Inquisitor. We've questioned those in the *converso* and *Mudéjar* community.'

'What about our people?'

Isaac raised a questioning brow.

'The Catholics,' the King snarled.

'Torquemada... Father Tomás reported to me when I first spoke with him that his *familiares* had only anecdote and no actual evidence of any murder plot. They are surely in the best position to know?'

The King grunted his agreement.

'But I also spoke with Father Gutiérrez.'

The King smiled at the mention of his confessor.

'He confirms he hasn't heard anything either.'

The King's brow tightened.

'But there is one avenue we're still exploring. I've discovered that a substantial amount of arsenic was recently purchased from the *Mudéjar* apothecary, Abu Ali Sina. He did not recognise the buyer, neither was the reason for such a large purchase – an infestation of rats – wholly convincing.'

'What would that have to do with Torquemada?'

'As Your Majesty is aware, arsenic is both tasteless and odourless, the perfect poison. A member of Father

Tomás' household could easily be suborned – either by money or doctrine.'

'Or both.'

'Quite so, Your Majesty.'

'Have you reported this to Torquemada?'

'I have, Your Majesty, and he's replaced all the members of his household and employed a food taster.'

A puzzled look crossed Ferdinand's face. Then he saw him looking past him, and his eyes widened. Isaac turned to see a courtier running towards them.

'Your Majesty, Your Majesty!'

'What's so important you have to disturb my peace?'

'Your Majesty,' the courtier said, bowing and then pausing to catch his breath. 'There's been a death.'

'I'm sure there are many deaths every day of the week in Seville. What's so odd about this one? What's it got to do with me?'

'It's the Grand Inquisitor, Your Majesty. At the Castillo de San Jorge.'

Isaac looked at the King, who nodded his assent. He bowed and followed the courtier out of the Stucco Patio.

It was a brisk ten-minute walk to the Castillo from the Real Alcazar. On his way out of the palace, Isaac collected Alejandro. As they strode down Calle Adriano towards the Puente de Barcas he let his deputy know what had happened – the Torquemada was reportedly dead. It came as something of a surprise then that when they were ushered into his chambers at the Inquisition's headquarters, Torquemada was standing behind his desk, very much still alive.

'Thought it was me, didn't you?' He interpreted their startled expressions with a delighted grin. 'No need to explain,' he cut them off with a wave of his cane. 'Seville is full of lies and half-truths. What's heresy after all? Just another kind of untruth.' He remained standing, leaning on his cane, and did not invite them to sit.

Isaac was about to respond when he was interrupted by a loud rap on the door.

Torquemada barked, 'Enter.'

They turned and Isaac had his third surprise of the morning. This one was far more welcome than the first two. Ali Sina advanced, shook his hand, and bowed as Alejandro introduced himself. Isaac studied Ali Sina's face intently for any sign of recognition when he met his deputy. He saw none. They stood in a line before Torquemada, the apothecary in the middle. Isaac noted that Ali Sina was sweating; he had never seen him so flustered and out of sorts. But then he doubted the apothecary had ever been so close to the Grand Inquisitor before. This was just how my father made Juan and me stand before him, he thought, when we were children and in for a lecture.

'Now that you've completed the social niceties perhaps you would like to share your findings with us, apothecary?' Torquemada boomed.

'My apologies, Father Tomás,' Ali Sina said with a low bow. 'May peace be upon you.'

Torquemada gave no greeting or benediction in return.

Ali Sina cleared his throat. 'I've examined the body of your food taster, may Allah bless his soul. The body was discovered early this morning in his bedchamber. It was still slightly warm so he must have died in his sleep.'

'Yes, man, this much I already know,' Torquemada said.

Ali Sina appeared to compose himself by clasping his hands in front of him and pushing his shoulders back. 'It has all the signs of a poisoning.'

Torquemada banged his cane on the floor and jutted his chin at Isaac.

'In all probability,' the apothecary continued, 'arsenic.'

Isaac and Alejandro simultaneously turned to glance down at the apothecary, who continued looking at Torquemada.

'How can you be so sure?' he bellowed.

'He has patches of red, swollen skin all over his body and warts around his fingernails.'

'Seems very sudden, he's only been with me a few days.'

'With the right dose ...' Ali Sina said with a shrug.

Torquemada crossed himself and brought the crucifix from his neck to his lips. He made his way stiffly from behind the desk to stand in front of Isaac. He stopped to regain his breath from the brief exertion. 'Bless you. It seems I have you to thank, my son,' he said to Isaac with a smile.

He clenched his jaw as he smelt Torquemada's garlic-laden breath.

'You appear to have saved my life.'

'Yes, indeed I do,' he replied softly. He allowed Torquemada to clasp his shoulder, all the while meeting his gaze.

Alejandro stared at the floor.

'I am in your debt, my son,' Torquemada said. 'I'd be grateful if you would pursue your investigations and discover the identity of the perpetrator.'

Isaac turned and made to leave.

Alejandro and Ali Sina followed.

None of them said a word.

CHAPTER
ELEVEN

'Did you know that alcohol was originally an Arabic word?' Ali Sina asked, pouring Isaac and Alejandro a glass of *nabidh*.

They shook their heads.

'It's from our holy book, The Qur'an. It refers to a demon that induces intoxication.'

They were sitting in the herb garden on the roof terrace of the Apothecary. The sun was high, but a pleasant breeze kept it from feeling too hot. They had come immediately after leaving the meeting with Torquemada. Isaac had decided that his preferred venue for the conversation – Bar Averno – was inappropriate. Ali Sina did not drink alcohol, but principally it was too public for the conversation the three of them needed to have after leaving the Inquisition's headquarters. Although the terrace was still not quite as private as he would've liked. On the roof of the adjacent building, less than twenty paces away, a stout man stood beside a large iron mews that caged a bird of prey. Isaac watched intently as the man sheathed his forearm in a thick leather glove, made a fist and tucked a small piece of raw meat into it. With his other hand, he opened the mews' door, put his arm inside and let the hooded falcon hop onto his glove.

'That's Pedro,' Ali Sina said, 'he trains falcons.' He waved a hand towards his friend, who put up a palm, then turned away and walked to the other side of his roof.

Isaac watched as the falconer offered the bird up to the sky. Pedro allowed the falcon to strain at its jesses, and then with a screech and a beating of wings it was airborne. It banked away towards La Giralda, climbing all the time, and for a moment was lost behind the bell tower. When it reappeared, Pedro gave a loud whistle and held his gloved hand high. The bird wheeled around, made a steep descent towards the falconer, its wings tucked away behind it, and the bells on its legs tinkling in the wind. As it neared the outstretched hand, the falcon extended its talons, clawed at the glove and nuzzled its beak into its master's fist to ferret out the tasty morsel concealed there.

Alejandro clapped loudly.

Pedro responded with a small bow.

Isaac dipped his head in appreciation of the falconer's skill. This distraction and the company of friends was welcome as he recovered from the shock of being Torquemada's saviour. He wanted the warm glow that a glass of wine would bring, but the *nabidh* was a reasonable substitute.

'You two have never met before?' he asked, studying

each of them in turn. He still couldn't rid himself of the suspicion Alejandro might be the arsenic buyer. But why?

'No, I don't think I've had the pleasure before, señor?' Ali Sina said, tilting his glass towards Alejandro.

'I'm certain we haven't met,' Alejandro said.

Ali Sina squinted and leaned closer to Alejandro. 'For a moment, I thought you reminded me of someone who'd recently visited the shop.'

'Who might that have been?' Isaac asked.

The apothecary looked up at the sky. 'No, it's gone,' he said, meeting Isaac's eyes, 'an illusion brought on by this morning's events and this strong drink,' he said with a smile.

'I don't suppose there will be a long list of people now willing to accept the position of Grand Inquisitor's Food Taster,' Isaac said with a sardonic grin.

His companions murmured thoughtfully. Ali Sina topped up their glasses, and said, 'I assume the King sent you to the *Castillo* this morning? In connection with our conversation about the plot to kill Torquemada?'

Isaac glanced at Alejandro, who nodded almost imperceptibly. 'Yes,' he replied, 'but I'm sure you appreciate this remains highly confidential.'

'Of course, but it won't take long for the murder of the food taster to become common knowledge,' Ali Sina said. 'Not that anyone will hear it from my lips,' he added quickly.

'How do I deal with Torquemada's request that I identify the perpetrator? He is now, apparently, in my debt?' Isaac placed his glass on the table, and it landed with more force than he had intended.

His friends glanced at him with concern. Before they could respond to his question he crinkled his nose and sniffed the air. 'What's that smell? Is that burning? Did you leave one of your incense burners alight?' he asked Ali Sina with a smile.

The apothecary shook his head, got to his feet and inhaled deeply. 'There's definitely something burning.' They heard a smash from the shop below and a loud 'whoosh', similar to the sound of a fire catching hold. Ali Sina quickly made for the spiral staircase, Isaac and Alejandro stayed close to him. He almost tripped on the narrow stairs but clutched on tightly to the handrail. He reached the bottom and stopped before the ceiling-high row of shelving that barred their way. 'I could have sworn I left this open,' he shouted over his shoulder. He pulled a wooden handle on the shelf, but it would not budge. He wrenched at it with both hands. 'It's been locked from the inside!'

Alejandro, who was on the bottom tread of the stair-case, pointed and called out, 'Fumes are coming from the shop.' White smoke curled from beneath the bottom of the shelving.

Ali Sina wrenched at the handle again. Isaac joined him and together they pulled as hard as they could, but still the shelving would not move. The smoke was becoming thicker and the crackle of flames louder.

Ali Sina turned away from the shelving, pushed past Alejandro and climbed the spiral staircase. The metal steps rocked under their weight as all three hastened upwards. Wisps of black smoke tracking them. Ali Sina looked over the parapet running along the side of the roof above the doorway of the Apothecary. 'There they are!' He pointed towards two figures running away from the shop down the *calle*. The taller one striding away, the shorter one shambling after. Isaac thought he saw red hair, but it was difficult to be sure at this distance.

'Never mind them. How in God's name are we getting off this rooftop?' Alejandro shouted, pulling Ali Sina round by the shoulder to face him.

'Have no fears, my friend.' He gestured towards Pedro's rooftop.

Isaac blurted out, 'Have you lost your mind?' His heart was racing as he wiped sweat away from his brow.

Ali Sina put a thumb and forefinger in his mouth and blew a sharp whistle. Pedro turned, shielding his eyes from the sun with one hand, the falcon pulling at his jesses in the other.

'My shop is on fire. We're trapped,' Ali Sina cried out through cupped hands.

Pedro walked quickly towards the mews, opened it and put the falcon inside. The bird spread its feathers, screeched, and then settled on its perch.

'This is no good, we can't wait,' said Alejandro. He strode towards the parapet facing Pedro's roof and looked across and then down. 'I think I can make it.'

'No,' said Isaac.

'Wait,' said the apothecary.

'Do you have a better plan?' asked Alejandro, looking back over his shoulder from the descent to the street below. Not waiting for a response he strode towards them. As he passed, Isaac put out a hand to restrain him but he shrugged it off. He reached the other side of the roof and turned.

'Alejandro, don't be so stupid,' Isaac shouted. 'You'll never make it.'

'Stop,' the apothecary cried, 'there's a better way.'

Alejandro lowered his head, his eyes fixed on Pedro's roof. Isaac saw a grim madness there. He gave a loud guttural cry and ran, pumping his fists.

Isaac covered his mouth with a palm and screamed, 'No!'

Alejandro reached the edge of the roof, braced a foot on it and launched himself. Cloak billowing out behind him, his hat sailing off into the sky, before pirouetting towards the ground. At one moment, his arms were wheeling through the air, the next they were clawing at the parapet on Pedro's roof. The falconer hauled Alejandro up and over to safety. He put his hands on his knees, panting for breath. He beckoned them to follow him.

'I think your friend may have acted a little precipitately,' Ali Sina said with a shrug. Pedro shook his head at Alejandro, strode past the shrieking falcon to the edge of his roof. He turned a metal crank beside an upright wooden ladder which creaked gradually downwards. Isaac noted the hand railings on each side. Landing with a gentle thud on Ali Sina's roof, it formed a bridge between the two buildings.

The apothecary strolled over to the now horizontal ladder and stepped up onto it. He turned and grinned at Isaac. 'Would you prefer to walk, or to fly?' he asked.

CHAPTER
TWELVE

I saac studied the apothecary from the doorway to the courtyard at Casa de la Felicidad. It was the evening after the fire at his shop. Ali Sina smoothed his palm along the surface of the marble bench. He tilted his head back to catch the last of the sun's warmth.

Isaac gently clasped Ali's shoulder. The apothecary opened his eyes, looked around and smiled up at him. 'This place is a balm for my soul,' he said, 'I'm very grateful to you. I have nowhere else to go in Seville. No family or close friends. All in Granada,' he said with great sadness.

'We couldn't let you sleep in your bedchamber above the shop, it still stinks of the bitter fumes from the fire.' He sat down next to his friend.

'I feel really afraid for the first time in Seville. Until yesterday I felt tolerated, not exactly welcomed, but not despised like the Jews or hunted for heresy like the *marranos*. Their Majesties had permitted,' he tilted his head from side to side, 'perhaps reluctantly, the private practice of Islam and *sharia* law.'

Isaac nodded.

'But lately I've noticed a shift in the attitudes of both the Catholics and, if you'll forgive me, the *conversos.*'

'There's no need to apologise, I'm aware of it too.'

'I assume the converts are becoming jealous of our freedoms – we're not forced to convert to "the True Faith". I wonder how long that exception will hold?'

Isaac had a suspicion not for very much longer, but chose not to share it.

'Anyway, I'm most grateful to you and your family.'

'There is no need, my friend. After all, you would do the same for me.'

'For you perhaps, but where would I put all the members of your household in my small shop?' he said with a wry grin. 'Let's walk.'

They strolled side by side in silence around the fountain and then wandered past the palm tree deeper into the garden that ran along the side of the house. At the far end, the three children were playing tag amongst the trees. Gabriel was sitting halfway up a palm tree and waving victoriously at the twins.

Juana stood at the base of the tree, fists on hips, repeating, 'Not fair, that's not fair.'

Martín looked up at Gabriel in admiration.

Isaac touched Ali Sina's elbow and they stopped to watch. He wanted to observe Gabriel. What was he going to do? Had his words had any effect on his son? He appeared to lose his grip on the trunk of the tree and fell to the ground. Juana immediately slapped him and yelled, 'Tag!'

He watched intently for his son's reaction. Gabriel got to his feet and said, 'Ahh, you got me! Well done.'

'They play very well together. You must be very proud,' Ali Sina said.

'Yes, he's a good son, they're good children.'

They ran past them, heading for the courtyard, Gabriel pausing briefly to bow toward Ali Sina, and mutter, 'Papa.' Isaac ruffled his hair, which he permitted, for just a moment.

'Alejandro and I have inspected the damage to the shop,' Isaac said as they continued their walk.

The apothecary took his time to respond. 'Completely destroyed?'

'Yes, the fire devastated the entire shop before your neighbours doused the flames. They formed a chain of buckets. They put it out before it reached upstairs.'

'No doubt concerned for their own properties.'

Isaac pursed his lips at this comment.

'Perhaps you're right, not everyone is completely selfish,' Ali Sina said.

'The people we spoke to expressed only regret and concern for your welfare. They want to know when you're opening up.'

'Hah. That's unlikely. And if they miss me so much it's a shame they didn't patronise the shop more often.'

Ignoring Ali's unusually bitter tone, he continued, 'The ladder on the rooftop was very fortunate.'

'I enjoy training the falcon with Pedro from time to time. My knees are not what they were. So, last year he manufactured the ladder to save me the journey up and down the stairs. He's a skilled carpenter, it was no trouble for him.'

'What will you do then, if you don't intend to open again?' He added hastily, 'You can stay here for as long as you care to, have no fears about that.'

'You're very kind. Your family has made me feel most welcome. But I think it might be time to visit my brother, Abdul Rahman. He has a thriving spice business in Granada.'

'You would be missed... I would miss you.'

Ali Sina laced his arm through Isaac's.

'Alejandro asked your neighbours if anyone recognised the perpetrators. No one was sure. But some of them confirmed that one of them had red hair.' Isaac paused. 'Perhaps it's just coincidence but I saw that red-haired *ladrone* last week in Bar Averno, behaving... monstrously.'

'It would be a very large coincidence, considering how few red-headed men there are in Seville.'

'The barkeep's daughter told me his nickname is Roja.'

'How inventive,' Ali Sina said sardonically. 'Why do you think they did it?'

'You're the last apothecary in Seville, one of the very few remaining *Mudéjars*. Perhaps that's reason enough,' Isaac said with sadness.

'Do you think it's got anything to do with the plot to kill Torquemada?'

'Why do you ask?'

'The timing seems very coincidental. I become

involved in the murder at Torquemada's headquarters and then my shop is destroyed.'

'I'm not sure I see the connection, old friend.'

'Perhaps a group of radical *conversos* have decided to improve their lot by wiping out both the last Muslim and their biggest threat.'

'I suppose it's possible,' Isaac replied.

Their stroll had brought them back to the courtyard. There was no sign of the children, but Isabel was sitting on the bench. 'There you both are,' she said, 'dinner is about to be served on the terrace.'

Before either of them could respond, Catalina appeared at the main doorway that led into the house, hands on hips. 'I was just about to say that, señorita. You've saved me the trouble.' She bobbed her head at the two men. 'Handy for you, señorita,' she said, eyeing Ali Sina.

'Why would that be, Catalina?' Isabel asked.

'Well, now you don't need to go out to visit the apothecary, he's right here.'

Isabel inhaled sharply and stared at the ground.

Ali Sina glanced up at the swallows that were congregating noisily on the fronds of the palm tree.

Isaac looked from the housekeeper to his daughter to the apothecary, trying to make sense of what had just occurred. 'Perhaps we should go inside and eat something,' he said, smiling at Catalina.

Isabel shook her head as she hurried past Catalina, who gave her mistress a perplexed look.

'I'm sure it will be delicious,' said Ali Sina as they went into the house.

~

'You wanted to see me, Papa?' Isabel asked, peeking cautiously around Isaac's study door. It was after dinner, the children were in their bedchambers and the apothecary had retired early, complaining of a headache.

'Yes, my dear, come in.'

He turned his chair away from his desk to face her as she sat down, smoothing her dress with both palms. She interlaced her fingers, rested them in her lap and arched an expectant eyebrow.

He coughed into his fist to clear his throat. 'Well, my dear, how are things?'

She creased her brow, giving him a questioning look.

'I mean with the children. I've been distracted with so many things these past few days. The King, the fire, the murder.'

'I think you can see for yourself, Papa. The children are fine. I'm fine. We're all fine. There's nothing out of the ordinary to concern you.'

'That's very reassuring.' He thrummed his fingers on the desk. 'Isabel. I sometimes wonder whether I'm asking too much of you, whether it's all too much responsibility.'

'We've discussed this before, Papa. If it becomes too onerous I will let you know.'

Nodding, he leant forward. 'Since I spoke to Gabriel have you noticed any change in his behaviour towards the twins?'

Cocking her head, she replied, 'He's been absolutely fine. I would have told you otherwise.' She studied him closely. 'Is that really what you wished to discuss with me, Papa?'

He coughed again. 'I was wondering what the exchange with Catalina before dinner was about?'

She looked down at her lap and inhaled deeply, her nostrils flaring.

'You've been consulting the apothecary? I hope there's nothing the matter?'

Her face reddened.

Rage or embarrassment? 'I didn't mean to cause you discomfort, my dear.'

'Damn that woman, she never knows when to keep her mouth closed.'

He sat back, studying his daughter, waiting. Would there be another eruption? Three years ago he would've been certain of it. But she'd matured since the death of her mother.

'I'm sorry, Papa. That should have remained inside my head and not passed my lips.' She gave him a very direct look.

'Very well.' Should he pursue the matter? 'But is there something you need to tell me?

'No, Papa. A woman has particular... needs at certain times and an apothecary can provide some relief. That is all you need to know. Papa.'

'Ah, that explains it. I'm glad that's all it is.' He cleared his throat again. 'There was another matter, my dear. I hesitate to mention it but I have need of a confidant with a fine mind.'

She smiled.

'His Majesty has become aware of a plot to kill the Grand Inquisitor.'

Her smile faded. 'You can give the devil his name. I'd rather you did.'

'There's a conspiracy to kill Torquemada and the King wants me to halt it.'

'Why you?'

'Because of my part in uncovering the truth behind the blood libel. He seems to think that I have investigative powers.'

'He knows he can trust you.'

'We've discovered an unknown man purchased a large quantity of arsenic from Ali Sina a few days before Torquemada's food taster was poisoned.'

'We?' Isabel asked.

'Alejandro and myself.'

He ignored Isabel's blush. He knew she was fond of him, but now was not the time to discuss that. The conversation had been delicate enough as it was.

'What else have you found out?' she asked.

'Very little. Ali Sina is certain it is not the *Mudéjar* community and Alejandro's *converso* contacts say it's not them.'

'So that just leaves the true Catholics.'

He chose to ignore her use of the word 'true' with its implication that as converts from Judaism they were not genuine. He'd still not summoned the courage to talk to her about his hypocrisy in continuing to practise his true faith. Yet another thing he didn't feel able to talk to her about at the moment.

'What do you intend to do next?' she asked.

'I'd rather hoped you might help, my dear.'

'If the plotters are Catholic, they're likely to be part of a radical, clandestine group. Difficult for you to penetrate.' Her eyes widened as though she had just had an idea. 'Could it all be just a hoax?'

'I suppose so. But that's not going to satisfy His Majesty.'

'Let me give it some thought,' she said, standing up. Kissing him on the forehead, she bid him goodnight.

Should he have told her what was really on his mind? He rubbed the bridge of his nose between his thumb and first finger. He should have asked her. Secrets and lies never get you anywhere. But how could he bring himself to ask her if she and Alejandro were involved in the plot to kill Torquemada? The signature in the apothecary's register had what looked to be an 'A', but surely his deputy was not stupid enough to sign his own name? But Ali Sina's description of the stranger matched Alejandro's in some respects: the height, the pale blue eyes. And when they'd been drinking *nabidh* together before the fire broke out the apothecary had been unsure whether he'd seen Alejandro before. Ali Sina had most definitely wavered when he'd asked him the question.

But why would he want to kill Torquemada? Had he become involved with a fanatical *converso* group, or he was doing the deed that he himself had taken too long over? Had Isabel asked Alejandro to help her take revenge for her mother's death by poisoning Torquemada? Were they doing it out of loyalty to him? Did they think they were protecting him? Why was Isabel so embarrassed and angry?

All he had were questions. Too many. Her story about her time of the month as an explanation for her visit to the Apothecary made sense, but he didn't entirely believe it. There was only one thing for it. He would have to get the truth from Ali Sina. In the morning, after a good night's rest. God willing.

THIRTEEN

'Come on, you two,' Catalina called to Juana and Martín over her shoulder the next morning as she locked the outside door of Casa de la Felicidad. The key turned easily now – Rodrigo had done a good job of oiling the lock. She looked around nervously to see if those *ladrones* were about. She'd overheard the señor mention a red-haired one running away from the fire when he was talking to that apothecary. When she'd first noticed the lock was stiff there had been a red-haired lout and his friend hanging around. She couldn't see them. She must remember to mention all this to the señor.

She put the key in her pocket. Perhaps she should compliment Rodrigo on fixing the lock? But she didn't want him getting too big for his boots. Maybe she'd just make him something special. But then again, when did she have the time? She had more work on now, what with the apothecary staying in the house. More cooking, more cleaning. That's why she had to do this extra shopping trip this morning. And the señorita had asked her to take the twins along with her. Had a headache, apparently, and couldn't manage their studies that morning. Must be catching. The apothecary complained of the very same thing last evening. More likely to be caused by the way the señorita excited herself by the way she'd spoken to her before breakfast. Questioning her in a loud voice why she'd talked about her visit to the apothecary in front of her Papa. How was she to know it was some sort of big secret? Little madam. Though she supposed she had to give her some credit, she'd grown up a lot recently. Had no choice.

She threaded her way through the crowded streets, wicker basket in one hand, Martín holding the other, and Juana skipping along behind. Throngs of shoppers were preparing for the big procession. The ladies were going to pick up their newly woven *mantillas*. The lace veils were beautiful, but she didn't have time – or the money – for such nonsense. As if she didn't have enough to do with it being *Semana Santa*, and now taking care of the twins as well. The Holy Week always meant more food preparation. This year Rodrigo was going to be one of the *costaleros* in the *paso*. She didn't envy him carrying that enormous wooden sculpture of the Virgin to the cathedral plaza on his shoulders. It was the *Juevos Santos* procession tomorrow night. The children enjoyed taking the ball of wax they'd carefully kept from the previous year and asking the *Nazarenos* to drip some of the hot liquid from their giant candles onto it. She was surprised they weren't more afraid of the white-robed figures with their tall, pointed purple hoods. Martín was so proud that his ball of wax was much bigger than his sister's. Juana was determined to catch up this year.

Reaching the end of Calle Abades they turned right, heading towards the butchers. Catalina felt Martín dragging his feet and pulling at her hand.

'Do keep up, young master. I've a lot to do today.'

She bustled onwards down the widening street, thinking of all the things she needed to buy. She really could have done without an additional mouth to feed, especially one that came with special requirements. No pork, no *jamón*, no lard. These *Mudéjars* were the same as the Jews when it came to their food. Why did they have to dislike each other so much?

'Juana,' the boy said.

'Oh, for goodness' sake,' Catalina said, turning around. Juana was not there. She called out her name, but she didn't appear. 'Stupid girl,' she muttered.

Martín looked up from under his brow and scowled at her.

'Your sister's probably just wandered off. There's nothing to worry about.'

Clutching his hand she began retracing their steps. She came to the crossing point of five *calles*. This was the problem in Seville, it was often difficult to get your bearings. Choose the wrong direction and you were hopelessly lost. Where was the little devil?

'Juana. Juana. Juana!' she called.

Martín joined in, shouting his sister's name through cupped hands. People stopped to look but soon moved on.

'This is what Seville is like now. No one trusts

anyone since that damn Inquisition came,' Catalina muttered. Then she had an awful thought. What if Juana's disappearance had something to do with those *ladrones* skulking around the house? And she hadn't told anyone. She would be in so much trouble.

There was nothing for it but to return home. Perhaps Juana would be there. Catalina tugged at Martín's hand, forcing him to keep up. He started crying more loudly and calling out his sister's name repeatedly. She shushed him, embarrassed by the stares he was attracting. Walking back down Calle Abades she heard loud wailing. Approaching Casa de la Felicidad Isabel was standing outside the main door clutching an inconsolable Juana to her.

'I... couldn't... find... them,' the girl said between jagged sobs.

As Catalina reached the house Isabel looked up, grimaced, clenched her jaw and pulled Juana into the courtyard. She slammed the door behind her.

Later that day Isabel peered through the door of Ali Sina's bedchamber, which was ajar. Kneeling on a prayer mat, he must have just completed the late afternoon prayers, the third of the five daily prayers for Muslims. He turned to his right and said, 'Assalamu alaikum wa Rahmatullah', then turned to his left and repeated the phrase.

She knocked.

Ali Sina opened the door and appeared delighted to see her.

'I'm not disturbing you?'

'Of course not, my dear,' he said, not moving from the doorway. 'How can I help you?'

Glancing backwards she asked, 'Would you mind if I came in? It's a private matter.' Catalina had tearfully admitted her fears about the *ladrones*, the red-haired one and the other one. She'd apologised for not speaking up sooner. It reminded Isabel of her suspicion about Casa de Felicidad being spied on from the house opposite. She needed to talk to someone apart from Papa about her growing fears. She didn't want to add to his burdens.

Ali removed his skullcap, rolled up his prayer mat, and stored them in a cupboard. They sat in front of a window overlooking the garden.

'It's very similar to the kippah,' she said.

Ali gave her a puzzled look.

'Your skullcap, it looks just like a Jewish kippah.'

'Ah, my *taqiyah*. It's not the only similarity between the faiths. How could it be otherwise when we have the same founder.'

Now she was puzzled.

'Abraham, of course, my dear. But I'm sure you didn't come to see me to indulge in religious conversation.' He raised his eyebrows, inviting her to proceed.

She was unsure where to begin. Could she completely trust him?

He filled the silence by asking, 'How is Juana? Has she recovered from losing her way this morning?'

'She seems to think it was all just a big adventure.

111

Catalina's lucky Juana had the good sense to remember her way home.' She shook her head. 'That woman.'

'She does her best and loves you all.'

She pursed her lips and looked out of the window. 'My father told me about the King's commission. To find Torquemada's assassin. He's asked me to help him. What do you think?'

Ali put his palms together, fingertips pointed at her. 'The suspects are legion.'

She frowned. 'Papa said that a man bought arsenic from you just before the food taster's murder.'

'That's correct.'

'And arsenic poisoning was definitely the cause of death?'

'All the signs point to it.'

'What do you know about the man?'

'He was tall, lean and I think had pale blue eyes. There was something familiar about him, but he kept his hat low and it was dark in my shop that morning.'

She remained silent.

'As per city regulations, I asked him to sign his name before he left.'

'And?'

'It was almost indecipherable, but I thought I could make out an, 'A'.'

She raised her eyebrows.

'Perhaps in his haste to disguise it he made a slip.'

'Yes, perhaps,' she said thoughtfully. 'Anything else?'

'No. Only that your Papa thinks he saw the ladrones who set fire to the shop beating up a boy in Bar Averno.'

'He didn't tell me.'

'One of them had red hair.'

'That can't be just coincidence.'

'No. It can't.' She took a deep breath. 'You've given me much to think about.'

'I'm glad to be of help,' Ali replied.

'We'll need to be very careful of the children tomorrow.'

Ali looked at her questioningly.

'*Juevos Santos*. The procession?'

'Ah, yes. Of course. The celebration of Jesus' last supper.'

She began to leave. 'There was one more thing.'

Ali gave her an encouraging smile and opened his palms.

'The day I came to your shop to buy,' she hesitated, 'the love potion. You will keep that between us? I told him I came to you for alleviation of my menses. It would be most embarrassing were Papa to find out the truth.'

'That was a confidential matter between apothecary and client. You are protected by my oath.'

'Thank you, that's a relief. If only Catalina had kept her mouth shut.' She smiled. 'I never used it though, the potion.' She looked out into the garden. 'And I don't think I'll need to, now.'

'Love will find a way.' He was silent for a moment. 'If you will pardon me, my dear, you remind me of my beloved wife.'

'How?' She was surprised and flattered.

'Khadijah was very kind and so intelligent. Perhaps that's why I find you easy to talk to.' He held her eyes. 'But headstrong too.'

She couldn't help smiling in recognition of this element of her character. 'You need have no fear. I'll not give you cause to regret your openness.'

Ali Sina gave a small bow. 'Yes, she was highly intuitive too.'

'I'll leave you in peace.' She gathered herself to go.

'Assalamu alaikum wa Rahmatullah.'

She looked at him.

'It means, 'May you be safe from evil and the mercy of Allah be upon you.'

'And I wish the same for you, Señor Ali.'

CHAPTER
FOURTEEN

The following day, Isaac was flanked by Alejandro and Gabriel as they took part in the *Juevos Santos* procession. They were staying close to Isabel and the twins. Catalina losing Juana had made Isaac even more cautious. He could see that Isabel was clutching Martín's and Juana's hands tightly. Perhaps too tightly. In their free hands the children held balls of wax. He was amused when Martín held up his white globe – as if feeling its great weight – and looked across at his sister. Juana glanced quickly at the ball of wax, shook her head and then stared fixedly ahead.

Gabriel muttered, 'Stupid kids' game.'

Isaac glanced down with disappointment at the sneer on his son's face. 'It was only last year that you were doing the same,' he reminded him.

Kicking at the cobbles, Gabriel did not reply.

About a hundred paces further down the *calle* Isaac could see that their progress would soon be blocked by one of the *pasos*. The elaborate floats moved agonisingly slowly as the forty or so *costaleros* shuffled along under the immense weight of the wooden figures. It looked to be the one that Rodrigo was helping to carry. He could make out the dying form of Jesus Christ, his prostrate body covered in scarlet blood. The *paso* was followed by *Nazarenos* dressed in white gowns and pointed, black satin hats. They held tall candles aloft and children lined up with their balls of wax to allow the penitents to drip more wax onto them. He didn't understand why the children weren't scared of these garish figures.

'The twins are enjoying themselves,' said Alejandro.

'I don't think Isabel is,' he replied.

'You can't really blame her for being tense after what happened with Catalina yesterday. She's become a proper mother to them.'

When Isabel informed him of Catalina's carelessness he had spoken firmly to her. She cried and begged forgiveness. He'd decided to leave it at that. No harm done. Lesson learnt. But Isabel had not spoken a word to Catalina since. The hostile mood infected the atmosphere of Casa de la Felicidad. Isaac was glad to be out of the house, even though *Juevos Santos* was not his favourite night. Too many terrible memories. Catalina had, wisely in his estimation, remained at home to await Rodrigo's return. Ali Sina's headache had apparently not receded, and he also elected to stay. Because of the commotion in the house he had still not asked the apothecary about Isabel's visit to his shop. Neither had he found an opportunity to ask Alejandro if he had visited the apothecary, let alone raise the idea of his involvement in the assassination attempt on Torquemada. Surely, it was too absurd to even contemplate? Perhaps it was for the best that he hadn't broached any of these matters.

A group of *Nazarenos* overtook them. One of the penitents fell in step with Juana and put his hand into the pocket of his gown.

Isaac and Alejandro instinctively reached for their rapiers.

Isabel glanced back at them, shaking her head.

The *Nazareno* took out a small rosary and handed it to Juana. She let go of Isabel's hand, took the string of beads and put them away in the pocket of her frock. She turned to grin triumphantly at Martín. Isabel dipped her head at the penitent and took hold of Juana's hand.

As they approached Rodrigo's *paso* Isaac became overwhelmed by the pulse of the drums, the sickly-sweet smell of incense, the chanting of prayers, and the proximity of so many people. The *calle* was bathed in shades of fiery orange from the blaze of the penitent's torches. The light distorted and elongated their hooded outlines onto the walls of the houses. It was a gruesome sight. A mournful *saeta* pierced the night. He looked up. A woman dressed entirely in black, her face covered by a finely filigreed mantilla, was singing from a balcony just above their heads. He stopped for a moment to listen. When he looked around to speak to Alejandro he wasn't there. He saw him up ahead, pushing his way through the crowd, past the *paso*, as the *calle* narrowed even further. He could not see the children, or Isabel. His stomach lurched. Not again, surely?

He tried to force his way through the crowd of

Nazarenos, but none would give way. They were too intent on reciting their prayers. The *calle* was now at its narrowest before it would open to allow the *paso* to burst into the cathedral plaza. There was no point in turning back, he would just have to endure the agonisingly slow shuffle of the *costaleros*. He glanced to his right and saw Rodrigo wincing under the weight, his face slick with sweat. The drumbeat swelled and the keening lament of the *saeta* grew louder.

Finally, they burst out into the plaza to join the *pasos* from the surrounding neighbourhood churches. He strode into the centre of the plaza, looking from left to right. The crowd swirled around him, blocking his view. He glimpsed them. On the far side, in front of the doorway to La Giralda. Isabel's head was on Alejandro's chest and he was stroking her hair. He knew they had feelings for one another, but why on earth were they doing that now?

Then he realised.

'Juana? Martín?' Isaac shouted as he ran.

Isabel turned towards him and collapsed onto her knees.

They were not there.

The beating of the drum subsided, and the plaintive sound of the *saetas* swelled to fill the plaza.

BOOK TWO

Seville and Granada

CHAPTER
FIFTEEN

The sun was dipping behind the Alpujarras, etching the outline of the mountains in an orange glow. Isaac, Gabriel, Ali Sina and Pedro rode in single file down the narrow track that they hoped led to the village of Palma del Río. Pedro, with the hooded falcon on his arm, was at the rear, alongside the pack mule carrying their clothes and food. They'd left Seville early on the morning after the twins' abduction. A letter had been delivered to Casa de Felicidad stating that the children were being held in Granada. It was signed, 'a friend and fellow traveller.' Isaac assumed it was from a fellow *converso*. Alejandro had counselled against the journey, believing the letter to be a hoax. Isabel argued strongly that they couldn't afford to ignore it and urged him to go. He had reluctantly sided with Isabel.

They'd made good time and were now more than halfway to Granada. The horses were tired and Isaac's black gelding could only amble. After a good night's sleep, and if they rode hard tomorrow, he reckoned they could reach the city by mid-afternoon. He was desperate to find Martín and Juana. Had he been alone he would have been tempted to ride through the night to arrive at first light. But they all needed to rest after a hot, dusty day in the saddle, particularly Gabriel. But where? The remnants of the *converso* community that fled Córdoba twenty years ago still lived in the village up ahead. Alejandro's contacts in Seville had suggested they try the Hostería del Infante, owned by Garcia Mora. It would be easy to find, according to Alejandro, as it was the only inn in the village square.

As they reached the outskirts of the village, a pair of yellow eyes emerged from the gloom. Pedro's falcon screeched as it sensed danger. A low growl was quickly followed by loud barking as a feral dog ran at them. Isaac struggled to stay in the saddle as his skittering horse threw up earth and pebbles towards the animal. The dog circled the group cautiously and then loped past them in the direction they had come. Back towards Seville. Isaac wondered whether he should follow it.

He was beginning to question his decisions to leave Alejandro in Seville to look after Isabel and to accede to Gabriel's plea to accompany them. Could he completely trust Alejandro? He had not discounted him as the arsenic buyer. And what exactly were his intentions towards Isabel? He chose to believe that Alejandro hadn't changed since he had helped to save the family three years ago. He was sure he was fundamentally loyal. What of Gabriel? Would he create more problems than he would solve? Isabel convinced him that Gabriel was sincere in wanting to help him find the twins. Perhaps his son sought penance for mistreating Juana. He understood that urge.

A few minutes later, they arrived at the outskirts of the village. His spirits were not improved as they rode past a few empty looking cottages; only the occasional glow of fire or lantern light piercing the near pitch black. He was about to suggest they lit a lantern when the horses began to clop across cobbles. They dismounted and led their mounts up a *calle* that emerged into a surprisingly large plaza. Across the square, he could just make out a pair of lanterns. He led them towards the solitary source of light. Alejandro's information had been correct. After tethering the horses, they entered the Hostería del Infante.

'Señor Mora?' Isaac asked the large man standing behind the counter of the dimly lit, empty inn.

'What if I am?' the man barked back.

He took off his hat, ran a forefinger around the inside rim and flicked the sweat away. 'We have travelled from Seville and were given to understand by our *fellow believers* that you would provide us with lodging for the night?' He hoped Mora was intelligent enough to understand why he had emphasised the two words.

The innkeeper looked at him and then at each of his four companions who flanked him – the five of them forming the shape of an arrowhead. His gaze lingered on the apothecary, then on the falcon.

'I thought you were all *fellow believers*,' he said, pointing his chin at Ali Sina.

'We are,' Isaac replied.

The innkeeper raised an eyebrow.

He approached the counter, took a small velvet sack of *maravedies* from his waistband and slammed it down on the counter.

Garcia Mora picked up the sack, weighed it in his palm. Loosening the cord around the pouch, he tipped the silver coins onto the counter. He picked one up and studied each side closely. He grunted as he put the *marevedies* back into the pouch. 'We are all believers in The Almighty, I suppose.'

Isaac splayed his palms on the counter and leaned towards the innkeeper. 'I can see you have your own strong beliefs,' he said, glancing at the money pouch.

'That bird will need to be caged outside.' The innkeeper put the coins away in his pocket and grunted again. 'The stable boy will tend to the horses. I'll show you to your rooms.'

After stowing away their few belongings in the two dingy rooms the innkeeper allocated, they went back to the bar. A young girl, who Isaac thought couldn't have been more than thirteen and assumed was the innkeeper's daughter, showed them to a rough-hewn table beside the empty fireplace. He sat down next to his son with Ali Sina opposite. Gabriel yawned and rubbed at his shoulders. He wasn't used to the exertion of a long day's ride over rough terrain.

Pedro came in through the inn's outer door and Ali Sina made space for him to sit down opposite Gabriel.

'The stables will do for the bird,' he said, by way of explanation.

Much to Isaac's surprise, the girl served them each a plate of hearty stew, a basket of rye bread, and a mug of beer. He saw Gabriel steal several glances at her as she wordlessly put their supper on the table. Was his son blushing? He shouldn't be surprised – Gabriel was almost fifteen. The girl took a cloth, wiped the bar counter down vigorously, and then perched on a stool. He watched as Ali Sina moved the beer away and pushed the stew around on his plate with a spoon.

'You're not hungry?' he asked his friend.

'I can't tell if the meat is pork,' he said in a low voice.

The girl looked up and said, 'It's not. It's rabbit that my Papa caught fresh just this morning.'

Ali Sina bowed his head and whispered, 'Bismillah ir rahman ir rahim,' and began eating enthusiastically.

Pedro wiped the last of the gravy from his plate with a hunk of bread, smacked his lips and held his plate up to the girl, who shook her head. 'There are limits to their generosity,' he said with a sigh.

Isaac smiled at the taciturn falconer. He was glad Ali Sina had persuaded him to bring him along. He was tall, young, and strong. They would have need of those qualities in the days ahead.

'If there are no more victuals,' Pedro said, glancing over at the girl who shook her head emphatically, 'I'll bid you all goodnight.' He headed upstairs to the room he was sharing with Ali Sina.

Gabriel yawned again, said goodnight and, with a final sly look at the innkeeper's daughter, followed

Pedro. Isaac watched with a mixture of amusement and pride as his son gingerly ascended the stairs, clearly feeling the effect of being in the saddle all day. He was young enough to recover quickly. He had better – they had another long ride ahead of them.

Glad to finally be alone with Ali, Isaac said, 'We haven't had a chance to talk about Isabel.' Was that surprise in his friend's eyes? 'She confided in me the reason she visited your shop.' Now it looked like genuine shock. 'Of course we don't need to discuss the details,' he continued hurriedly. 'I'm just glad she can seek advice from you on such things.'

'Yes, there are some matters that a daughter finds difficult to discuss with her father,' Ali said.

'Anyway...' He cleared his throat. 'Are you sure your brother will welcome all of us to stay with him? Without warning?'

'He'll be overjoyed. We haven't seen each other for over three years since Khadijah died.' He bowed his head and said, 'Inna Lillahi wa inna ilayhi raji'un.' He looked up at Isaac, 'We belong to Allah and to Him we will return.'

Isaac thought he caught the scent of jasmine, Maria's favourite flower, but it was just his mind playing tricks, triggered by Ali Sina's memory of his wife.

'What do you think our first move should be?'

The apothecary pushed his chair back, stretched his legs and crossed his ankles. 'We have the address Alejandro secured from his contacts. It's not far from my brother's house in the Albayzín area of the city. That's supposedly where the children are being held?'

'Supposedly?' He couldn't suppress his irritation.

'The location seems to have been discovered surprisingly quickly, and easily.'

'Your point?'

'It's either a trap or a red herring.'

Isaac leaned forward and rested his chin on interlaced fingers. 'Are you implying something about Alejandro's loyalty, because if you are...' his voice was rising, and his anger left him unsure how to complete the thought.

'Even if the information turns out to be false, I was not suggesting anything devious about Alejandro. He could easily have been misled. The question is whether the misdirection was deliberate.' The apothecary spoke in a low voice, nodding towards the barmaid.

'What do you mean?' Isaac whispered in response, understanding his friend's cues.

'It does seem coincidental that the man assigned to find out who is attempting to assassinate the Grand Inquisitor is dragged away from the task. Depending on your viewpoint, perhaps even fortunate.'

'You think whoever plans to kill Torquemada kidnapped the children as well?' he said, leaning back and crossing his arms. He glanced at the barmaid, jutting his chin at his beer mug. She got up from her stool, sauntered across and filled it from an earthenware jug.

Ali Sina waited until she'd returned to her station. 'It's possible. As is the likelihood that the two things are entirely unconnected.'

'So, it could mean one thing, two things or neither?' Isaac sneered and then took a large gulp of beer.

'Exactly, my friend. That's why, having decided to leave Seville, the only rational course of action is to carry on with the journey to discover the truth. Returning now would make no sense.'

'What do you make of Isabel's claim that one of the kidnappers had red hair?'

'Surely too many coincidences to overlook. You saw them in Bar Averno, and I'm sure they were responsible for the fire.'

'Exactly my thoughts. And the way those *ladrones* beat up that poor fellow...' a shiver passed through him. 'It was so casual. And the red-haired one just calmly drank his beer as he watched his friend beat that poor lad's brains out.'

'They won't do that to the children. They wouldn't be that monstrous.'

'Are you sure? They were callous enough to beat someone up for no good reason and burn down your shop.'

'But whoever is behind this needs the children to be alive. Otherwise, we would already know their fate.'

'I hope you're right.' He took another long draft of beer, then stood up. He clasped the apothecary's shoulder and made his way up to bed.

By the time Ali Sina followed him the barmaid was resting her head in her hands on the counter and snoring softly.

CHAPTER
SIXTEEN

I sabel paced the roof terrace at Casa de Felicidad. It was all she seemed to do since Papa and Gabriel had left three days ago to rescue the twins. In her room, in the courtyard, in the *calles*, she paced. She could not think of it as them going to find the children. They were not lost, as Juana had been the day Catalina couldn't locate her. Someone – who? – had kidnapped them. Evil people had ripped Juana and Martín away from the family. There was no other word to describe them. They were inhuman and deserved to burn in hell. Better yet, they deserved to burn where she could witness them suffer.

A series of high-pitched chirps interrupted her thoughts. She stood still, arms crossed, and leant over the iron balustrade that surrounded the terrace on three sides. A flock of swallows flitted through the trees below. The cathedral bells would toll for Vespers soon. The sun would go down on another day without the children and no word from Papa. Three days. He could have sent a rider by now to say they had safely arrived in Granada. Why hadn't he? Her imagination reeled with possibilities – none of them good.

She'd been trying to recall exactly the events of the night of *Juevos Santos*. Ever since then she'd felt dazed, shocked, unable — unwilling? — to recall exactly what had happened. Now she was determined to focus. With no news from Papa maybe if she could just remember the details she could help. Entering the plaza, she remembered having hold of each of the children's hands. They were excitedly pulling her ahead of Papa, Alejandro and Gabriel – eager to catch up with the *Nazarenos* to collect more wax. She smiled as she recalled how excited they'd been. But she cursed herself for allowing that excitement to get the better of her caution. As they moved into the centre of the plaza she'd become aware of two men approaching quickly, one from each side. Then the twins' hands were wrenched away and Juana was screaming and Martín was shouting.

She'd had an impression of red or orange. At the time she thought it was just the flames from the torches. But now she remembered what Ali had told her the night before the procession – that a *ladrone* with red hair was seen running away from his shop just after the fire. When she told Papa about her impression of a red colour he seemed to think it was very important. But he didn't tell her why. Recalling more of her conversation with Ali, her father's reaction now made sense. Papa had seen a youth in Bar Averno beaten by a red-haired thug. There had been something familiar about the kidnappers, in the roughness of their manner. She was sure she'd met them before.

She tried to locate the feeling sliding uncomfortably around inside her. Was it guilt, fear, frustration, anger? Yes, it was all of those, but what she felt most strongly was loss. She was lost without the children. What was her purpose? When the twins were there, she spent her time planning their lessons, resolving their squabbles, encouraging Gabriel to see himself as a brother to them. She immersed herself in the hubbub that children generate so naturally. She had often yearned for Casa de Felicidad to be still, longed to pray or study Mama's Book of Hours in peace, without having to secrete herself away. Now she did not need to hide. She had complete freedom to do what she wanted when she wanted. She could pray and study from Prime to Vespers and nobody could stop her, nobody would care. And that was her problem: nobody cared, nobody needed her. Except, perhaps, Catalina.

'Señorita.'

'What is it, Catalina?' she hissed, without turning round. Perhaps if she hadn't thought about her she wouldn't have appeared.

'I've brought a shawl. It's getting chilly,' Catalina said hesitantly.

Inhaling deeply she gripped the balustrade. She squeezed her eyes shut and her shoulders tightened.

'I've left it on the table for you, señorita, should you change your mind,' Catalina said. 'Oh, and by the way...'

She was clenching the railing so hard that she felt her knuckles might erupt through the skin.

'Señor Alejandro came just now. I didn't think you'd want to be disturbed, so I sent him away,' Catalina called out as she hurried back down the stairs.

She leant further over the balcony, hoping to catch sight of him. Damn that interfering woman. Why didn't she ask if I wanted to see him? Maybe she didn't, but she would have liked the chance to decide for herself. Should she tell Alejandro what the apothecary had told her? That a man who looked like him had bought a large quantity of arsenic and signed his name in the register with an 'A'?

She glimpsed him on the street below, carefully picking his way through the evening promenaders. Even though he had his back to her, she could tell it was Alejandro by his height and aristocratic bearing. She wanted to share her fears with him. Catalina probably thought it inappropriate for an evening visit from a man without Papa in the house. That she was right did not make Isabel feel any better. She took another deep breath and held it; waiting for Alejandro to disappear and for Catalina to have enough time to return to the scullery. Then she howled her frustration over the river, out into the night.

'And forgive us our sins, for we ourselves forgive everyone who has sinned against us, and do not bring us to the time of trial, but rescue us from the evil one, Amen.' Torquemada intoned the final word just as the Vesper bells faded away. He reached for his cane, rested both hands on its nobbled head, and levered himself up from the prayer stool. Wincing as his knees cracked, he shuffled across to the chair that provided a view from the Castillo over the Guadalquivir, towards the Barrio Santa Cruz. The old Jewish Quarter. Towards Casa de Felicidad. Where Isabel lived.

The maid had laid out some almond biscuits and a bottle of sherry, part of his private collection from Jerez. He broke the wax seal on the bottle and poured a glass. Since the death of his food taster, he'd insisted all bottles were resealed in his presence and that he alone reopened them. The nutty tang warming his throat, he sighed contentedly. He watched as the Puente de Barcas become a flaming path across the river as torches were lit to guide the townspeople crossing back and forth from Seville to Triana, from the Castillo towards Casa de Felicidad.

He had not seen Isabel for three years, not since she had been a guest here, along with her brother, whilst he had questioned their mother. What did she look like now? Had she grown into her body? Perhaps now that he and Isaac had established more cordial relations, he could visit her. Especially now that her Papa had left the city to search for those poor kidnapped orphans of his. She must be lonely. A pastoral visit to a member of his flock would be in order. It was a very long time since Isaac's invitation to dinner, which had never materialised as the events of that wretched boy's murder had overtaken them all. Yes, a visit to Casa de Felicidad seemed like a splendid idea. The right thing to do.

As he finished the last of the sherry, there was a

knock at the door. A maid entered, stood with her head bowed and told him that a friar was waiting outside.

'Send him in.'

A Dominican friar slipped into the room. Pulling back his cowl, he adjusted the rope girdle around his waist and clasped his hands in front of his body.

'Were you waiting outside, expecting to be summoned?' Torquemada said without turning around.

'Yes, Father Tomás.'

'I like a friar with a little initiative,' he said, craning his neck around.

The friar smiled.

'As long as that initiative is closely aligned with my intentions and desires.' Torquemada grinned and a twinkle played across his obsidian eyes.

'Yes, of course, Father, of course, of course.'

He beckoned the friar forward. He studied at him carefully. His habit swaddled his tall, wiry frame. The sleeves were too long, and the hem trailed on the floor. His eyes were deep-set and an unusual shade of green, suffused with glints of gold. He looked like an overgrown child.

'Do you know precisely why you are here?'

'Not really, Father.'

Torquemada arched an eyebrow.

'To do your bidding, Father.'

He raised the other brow.

'And the Lord's work, of course, Father.'

'Very good, you might just do very well.' He locked eyes with the friar. 'Aren't you wondering why I dragged you out of that shithole in Córdoba?'

The friar's shocked expression informed Torquemada that he would not have described the Monastery de San Jerónimo de Valparaiso in quite those terms. 'I'd rather hoped you'd heard of our good works in the community, Father.'

'Hah! I'm too busy dealing with the real work driving out heresy. I've got no time to listen to *good deeds*.' He hoped the friar was in no doubt as to his priorities. 'I've been keeping an eye on you for quite some time, ever since a close associate told me about you.'

The friar widened his eyes in surprise.

'In the confessional.'

'I... I... I... don't know what you mean, Father,' the friar said, blinking his eyes rapidly.

'Alonso used to stammer and blink like an idiot too, Brother Andreas.'

The friar compressed his lips tightly.

The idiot must be trying to prevent words escaping from his mouth. He wondered what Andreas would say about his friend – Torquemada's former deputy – if he gave him the licence to speak freely? But he would leave that delicious morsel for another occasion.

'Have you had any communication with Brother Alonso?'

'None, Father. I believe he was exiled to the Indies?'

He thumped his fist on the side table so hard that the sherry glass very nearly fell. 'Exiled! He was not exiled. I commissioned him to sail to the Indies to save the souls of our heathen brethren.'

'My apologies, Father Tomás. I misspoke,' Andreas said. Blinking again.

'Listening to gossip and lies. You concentrate on the Holy Book and my direction. Close those big ears and that tiny mind to all else. Do you hear?'

'Yes, Father,' he said meekly.

'Last I heard he was thriving and his mission successful.' He took three deep, calming breaths. 'Listen closely, the Lord and I have an important task for you.'

Andreas dropped his head and clasped his hands in supplication.

SEVENTEEN

J uana was jerked awake by the back of her head banging against the cell wall. She'd been disturbed by Martín's restlessness. He was lying with his head cradled in her lap, sleeping fitfully. She rubbed her head – no blood. She closed her eyes but after a few moments heard scratching. It – they? – were back. She peered into the blackness, straining to see where the scuttling came from. How far away were the rats? It was impossible to see. There was no light yet from the one small, barred window situated just out of their reach. It must still be the middle of the night. Their third night, the beginning of the fourth day in the cell.

The scratching was getting closer. She drew her knees towards her chest, forcing Martín to turn on his side. She wished they'd screamed and kicked when the kidnappers first pushed them into the cell. But she'd been too stunned by their sudden capture to react. One moment, they had been beside Isabel in the procession competing to accumulate the largest wax ball; the next, hands tied, they were being thrown around in the darkness of a wagon as it hurtled through the night.

During that first night in the cell they alternated between sobbing and half-sleep. She'd been woken by a rat chewing at the ends of her long hair. Why would it do that? Hair was not food. Maybe it was so hungry it would eat anything. She was getting to know how that felt. The one called Ramos and the other shorter one only appeared twice a day – in the morning, to give them bread and water, and in the evening to take away the bucket they were forced to use as a chamber pot.

The scuttling stopped. That frightened her even more. At least the sound gave her an idea of where the rat might be. It could be beside her, right now. She felt her thighs becoming wet and let out a muted cry.

Martín stirred, sniffed, sat up, and said, 'What's that smell?'

She turned away from him.

'Have you pissed yourself?' he asked, half asleep.

She sobbed.

He put an arm around her and said, 'I'm sorry.'

She continued crying softly. She patted his hand.

'Has Mr Rat come calling yet?' he asked.

'I heard it, but then it went quiet,' she said between sobs.

A single shaft of soft morning light broke the shadows and found the corner of the cell where the bucket was stowed.

'There you are, it's always darkest before the dawn,' he said. 'That's what Mama used to say.'

At the mention of her mother, she took a long, jagged

breath. Martín held her tightly. When he'd said 'Mama' her first thought had been of Isabel. And now she felt guilty. But it was such a long time ago. She couldn't even recall what Mama looked like. When she focused really hard she could hear Mama calling her name, but only in an angry tone. That made her feel even sadder and not want to try to remember.

'I'm so hungry,' she whispered.

'They'll be here soon.'

She got up and followed the beam of light to the corner where the bucket was. She sat down on it. Martín turned his face to the wall.

'I wish they would leave us a bowl to wash our hands. Mama would say "it's absolutely disgusting", in that posh voice of hers,' she said.

They laughed together at the memory.

'Do you think they're looking for us?' Martín asked.

'Of course they are. Uncle Isaac will turn Seville upside down to find us. Señor Ali, Señor Alejandro and Gabriel will all be searching for us.'

'That's if we're still even in Seville. It seemed to take a long time to get here.'

'I don't think it was that long.' She sat back down next to him and held his hand. 'It's going to be alright. Uncle Isaac will deal with those evil men and we'll be free soon.'

'I hope so,' he replied. 'Why do you think they took us?'

She didn't know what to say.

'I don't understand what they want with us,' he said, his voice rising.

'Maybe it's something to do with Uncle Isaac and the King.'

'Why the hell couldn't they leave us out of it?'

She tried to comfort him by stroking his hand. 'God always takes care of little children,' she said defiantly. She stood up, put her back to the wall beneath the window and put one foot precisely in front of the other and began to count.

'There's no time to play games,' he said.

Ignoring him, she continued to walk and count. When she reached the far side of the cell she announced, 'Twenty.' She went to the bucket in the corner next to the cell door and repeated the pacing and counting.

Martín shrugged.

'Twenty-five,' she said.

'What use is that?'

'In the middle of the night, if we need to use the bucket we can find our way to and from it if we sleep against the wall furthest from the cell door. It'll make us feel safer.'

He cocked his head to one side, thoughtfully. 'I suppose so, let me try.' He counted only seventeen by twenty. She began to explain that the difference was because his stride was longer than hers. She was interrupted by the sound of cartwheels on cobbles outside the window. He moved closer to her.

A voice called out, 'Whoa there,' and a horse whinnied.

She put an arm around him as they heard the distant clang of an iron door and the approach of heavy footfalls.

'It only sounds like one of them today,' he whispered.

'I hope it's the red-haired one. He seems nicer than Ramos.'

'Don't let them know we heard his name,' she hissed. 'I heard Ramos telling the shorter one off for saying it.'

He nodded.

Metal scratched against metal as the key turned in the lock. The cell door opened and a half-shadow materialised into human form.

'And how are you this fine morning, my pretties?'

CHAPTER
EIGHTEEN

Isaac roused the group early and a surly Garcia Moura watched them ride away. They rode the horses hard past gullies and hillsides covered with fig, quince and citrus orchards. They passed numerous smallholdings that Isaac knew were mainly inhabited by *Mudéjars* who bred sheep or cattle. Some tended the mulberry trees whose berries were turned into silk for the weavers and tailors of the Albayzín. But by nightfall they had only reached Alcaudete. He was irritated by their failure to reach Granada. An old peasant woman they passed on the trail told them it was another half day's ride to Granada. Recognising their exhaustion she took pity on them and gave them directions to the ruins of a Moorish castle they could sleep in. They arrived at sunset and had only stale bread and water for dinner. His stomach churned with hunger and anxiety.

They endured an uncomfortable night on the hard ground. Isaac's sleep was punctuated by strange visions and the intermittent screeching of Pedro's falcon. He dreamt he was chasing Juana and Martín through the *calles* of Seville. Every time he got close they sped away, turning to laugh at him. Suddenly they were in the cathedral plaza, confronted by a towering wooden crucifix. The twins held hands and danced around its base. Looking up at the bloodied figure nailed there he saw his own face smiling down at him. He awoke in the middle of the night gasping for air and clammy with sweat.

Lack of food and sleep did nothing to improve his or the group's mood the following morning. Gabriel was morose and Ali Sina taciturn. Only Pedro was in good spirits, appearing to relish the adventure. He was up first, before the sun was up, and had gathered a mound of plump berries. He made a fire and picked mint leaf to make tea. This foraged breakfast would have to suffice until they reached Granada.

They set off shortly after sunrise, Isaac leading the way. A few hours later, just as he thought he could ride no further, he was relieved as the track finally started to descend and they met more travellers. They were close. After trotting through a densely wooded copse they came to a halt at the edge of a steep drop. In the mid-distance, on the other side of a lush green valley, was the Alhambra Palace. The immense castle was framed against the backdrop of the Sierra Nevadas. The mountain tops were dusted with snow.

'I've never seen anything like it,' Gabriel said. Isaac noticed he was struggling to keep his mount still, his excitement communicating itself to the horse.

'You know why it's called the Alhambra?' Ali Sina asked Gabriel.

This was a good chance for his son to prove he had been paying attention when he had tried to teach him some Arabic.

'Hambra means red?' Gabriel replied.

'Mumtaz. Well done,' Ali Sina said.

Isaac smiled at Gabriel.

'Yes, it's red for the colour of the outer walls. It used to be very beautiful inside until...' Ali Sina tailed off.

He understood it was too painful for the apothecary to recall the destruction of the intricate interior of the palace by Their Majesties. They'd done a lot of damage since the capture of Granada had completed their *reconquista* of Andalusia. It must be difficult for Ali Sina to accept the end of the Moors' seven hundred year rule of the region.

Isaac coaxed his gelding forward and started the sharp descent. The river on the floor of the valley was shallow and they crossed it with ease. He led them up the narrow, steep track that emerged in Granada. Ali Sina pulled up alongside him and exhaled a long breath.

'Glad to be back?' he asked.

The apothecary's broad grin was answer enough.

They picked their way through the zigzagging streets that formed the labyrinth of the Albayzín. As the lanes narrowed they dismounted and led the horses in single file with Ali in front. Shouted greetings of, 'Salaam,' came from every side.

'It's noisier than Seville,' he said to Ali.

Ali turned, looked up at the sun, and tipped his head from side to side. 'Wait, It's about to get much noisier.'

Suddenly, the air was filled from all directions with

the cry of the *muezzin* calling the faithful to prayer at the mosque, a sound no longer heard in Seville. He envied Ali the opportunity for communal worship that he had been denied for so long. The scent of heavy, oaky, incense curled its way into his nostrils. He had only smelt it in church before. 'What's that?' he asked Ali, sniffing the air.

'Oud. Don't you recognise it from my shop?'

'Yes, I do now, but this is much... earthier.' Then he began to pick up the softer aroma of spices. He thought he recognised zafran. 'What are they using to cook with? It smells wonderful.'

'That's *ras-al-hanout*. It's a mixture of cumin, cinnamon, nutmeg, cardamom and ginger. If you're lucky we'll eat some dishes made with it at my brother's house.'

'What does he do? You told me, but I've forgotten.'

Ali did not answer, as he was busy pounding on a large horseshoe-shaped door flanked by tall cypress trees. The door was opened by a man wearing a long, white robe. He hugged Ali and they talked excitedly in Arabic. Ali turned and said to the group, 'This is Khaled, my brother's trusted retainer. He will see to the horses and will show you where to billet the falcon, Pedro. Come inside.'

They followed Ali through the arched doorway and entered a porticoed courtyard of three whitewashed bays with a pool and fountain at its centre. The central bay was double storey and had a balcony above it. A large man wearing a bright red silk robe leant over the railings and looked down with a broad grin. 'Brother, is that really you?' he cried out. That must be Abdul Rahman,

Isaac thought. Ali Sina looked up and began a rapid, high-pitched exchange with his brother. He could not follow their dialect, but he was absolutely sure of the emotions being conveyed.

~

'Welcome, most welcome to you all,' Abdul Rahman boomed from the head of a long trestle table situated beneath the balcony in front of the pool. Isaac thought his voice a good match for his personality and physique – loud and large. Ali sat to his brother's right, Isaac to his left. Gabriel was next to his father, opposite Pedro. The table was full and the air fragranced with spice. He marvelled that in the time they had been washing the dust off themselves the servants had prepared such a sumptuous feast. The babble from the fountain provided an accompaniment to their conversation that was sooth-ing, but he was still frustrated. Although the meal was very welcome, it felt like a waste of time. Juana and Martín would not be enjoying such warm hospitality.

'Eat, eat, my friends,' their host said, running his fingers through his long greying beard. His eyes shone as he took his brothers' slim fingers in his large paw and kissed them. Isaac was surprised by the intimacy of the gesture, but Ali just responded with a smile.

He saw Gabriel grimace as a servant filled their earthenware mugs with a sticky purple syrup. Ali had clearly noticed the expression too. 'It's pomegranate juice, perfect to quench our thirst after a long ride. It's the symbol of our city. Try it, my boy,' he said. 'The Holy

Prophet, peace be upon him, said, "There is not a pomegranate on earth that does not have a pip from one of the pomegranates in the Garden of Paradise."'

There was silence as everyone turned to watch Gabriel take a hesitant sip and then down the whole mug.

Their host thumped the table with joy. 'Now you are a real Granadino!'

Isaac ruffled his son's hair. Platters of roast lamb, chicken stew, and couscous were passed around. They all ate with their fingers, copying Ali and Abdul Rahman's example. The brothers took it in turns to tell them which dishes were flavoured with *ras-al-hanout* or how a particular dish was cooked.

Isaac had never seen Ali look so joyful. 'How do you come to know so much about spices and cooking?' he asked Abdul Rahman.

'Look around you, my friend, this place was built on meals like this. That's what I do, import and sell spices,' he said, laughing loudly. 'It was all I could find to do after we Moors lost the siege and your Catholic monarchs completed their so-called, "Reconquista".'

Isaac felt the intensity of Abdul Rahman's look but remained silent, refusing the chance to defend Their Majesties.

He smiled and continued, 'I fought for Baobadil's army, but I didn't want to die for the cause. I started the spice business in a small way, and with the help of Allah, I have a happy life. A wife, three children, a house. I'm truly blessed.' He'd clearly noticed Isaac's raised eyebrow at the mention of his family. 'She's taken the children to

Fez to visit her mother. You'll meet them on your next visit.'

Plates of sticky, sweet pistachio candy appeared on the table to complete the meal.

'These are delicious,' Gabriel said as he reached for his third piece.

'Have as many as you like my boy,' Abdul Rahman said, clearly relishing Gabriel's hearty appetite. 'My wife would be delighted. They're her speciality.'

He had been patient but could wait no longer. 'Thank you for one of the best meals I've ever had,' Isaac said. The others banged their mugs on the table in agreement. 'But as unforgettable as your hospitality is we have a more pressing purpose for being in Granada.'

'I understand. Ali has told me of your predicament,' Abdul Rahman said quietly. 'Do not worry, I have not been wasting your time. Whilst you enjoyed this fine meal my men have kept watch on the house where you believe those poor children are. They will report back to me the instant that anything significant occurs.'

'I am in your debt,' he replied quietly.

'No more than I am in yours. You have been a good friend to my brother.' He put an arm around Ali. 'You are all well fed, but you need to be well rested for tonight's adventure. Your rooms are ready. Sleep. Be assured I will wake you should my men alert me of anything. After Maghrib prayers, we strike.'

CHAPTER
NINETEEN

I sabel was startled by a loud rap at her bedchamber door.

Catalina called out, 'Señorita, there's a man here to see you.'

Alejandro?

'Tell the señor I will be a few minutes. Ask him to wait on the bench in the courtyard.' Finally he'd come. She jumped up from the bed, tingling with excitement.

'Are you sure, señorita, it's –'

'Yes, I'm *entirely* sure, Catalina,' she said curtly. Why didn't she just do as she was told? Why did they bother keeping Catalina on? She was getting older, grumpier, and slower. But getting rid of her meant losing Rodrigo, who she both adored and found useful around the house. And his loyalty to Papa was not in question, though why he seemed to love Catalina quite so much she could not fathom.

She sat at the dressing table and looked in the mirror. She breathed deeply, telling herself to stay calm.

Widening her eyes, she searched for lines and wrinkles. Pleased to find none, she arranged her hair using the tortoiseshell comb Papa gave her when she was a girl. How strange to think that she had actually once been a girl. She'd been forced to grow up and become a woman when Mama died – murdered by Torquemada. Had she missed out on an in-between stage? Was there such a thing? Could you be partly girl, partly woman? There was no one she could ask. She had no time for friendship, with her responsibilities to the children and Papa, and she was certainly not going to ask Catalina. Taking a final look in the mirror she left the bedchamber and took the stairs that led directly to the garden. To meet Alejandro.

Except he was not there. On the bench she saw the back of a domed head framed by a tonsure. Standing in the doorway, she put a hand on the frame for support, feeling faint. She could not see a friar without thinking of Alonso and feeling the accompanying tumble of horror, shame and guilt. Where was Catalina? But of course, the woman was never there when she needed her, and too often present when she did not. She was about to return to her chamber when the friar started to sing. He had a haunting voice and she thought she recognised the melody. She took a step forward. Was that the song Mama liked? The friar turned and gave her a broad grin that quite disarmed her. He had a round, almost cherubic face. This childish quality was reinforced when he stood up – his habit engulfing his lean frame, sleeves and hem too long.

'Good morning, my child,' he said looking at her

expectantly. His eyes were an unusual shade of deep green and twinkled with glints of gold.

'Good morning, Father.' It was strange to refer to him by this title, he was so young. His innocent appearance helped her to recover her composure. She was a woman, not a girl. Crossing her arms she raised an eyebrow.

The friar looked puzzled. He glanced around as though the answer might be found in the fountain, the palm trees, the very air itself.

'Who are you? Father.'

'Ah, yes, my apologies. I haven't introduced myself. I often forget to do that. It's been brought to my attention on many occasions but I –'

'Father?'

'I'm Father Andreas.' He said his name with finality, as though it were sufficient introduction.

She was growing impatient. 'I've never heard of you and I'd like to know what you are doing here, unannounced in my house.' Her disappointment at Alejandro not being there was manifesting itself as annoyance. But she didn't care.

'Perhaps if you would sit I could explain it,' he said, indicating the bench with an open palm.

They arranged themselves at opposite ends of the bench. Andreas turned towards her, ankles crossed. She folded her arms and looked straight ahead at the fountain. He told her he was from the Monastery de San Jerónimo de Valparaiso in Córdoba and proceeded to detail his routine there in exhaustive detail. Life at the monastery gave him great solace, he said. His soft voice and its slow cadence calmed her. She unfolded her arms and turned towards him.

'You can imagine what it feels like to be thrown into a big city like Seville after such a quiet existence. I'm still reeling from it all,' he concluded with a laugh.

'What was that hymn you were singing?' she asked.

'I didn't realise I was singing so loudly. It's Madre de Deus.'

'I thought so. Mama used to love it. She was in the cathedral choir.'

'Was?'

'She passed away. Three years ago.' She looked up at the sunlight playing on the palm fronds. She tried to push the pain away, but it took a grip, breaking her tranquility.

'May God have mercy on her soul,' Andreas intoned as he made the sign of the cross.

'What brings you here?'

'I was instructed to come. At very short notice, I might add.'

'Instructed? By who?' She had an idea, but wanted him to confirm it.

'By Father Tomás, of course.'

'Of course.' She turned away from him to look at the fountain.

'You've met him?'

How much did Andreas know about her history? He didn't seem to know about Mama. He was either a very convincing liar, or Torquemada had not fully apprised him. She was being manipulated by one of the friars, perhaps both. She could play games too. She was not the naive girl of three years ago. 'Yes, of course I've met him,' she said lightly. 'Papa works at the Real Alcazar so they're always running into each other.'

'Father Tomás mentioned your father.'

She widened her eyes at him.

'In the most glowing terms. He's a big admirer.'

She searched his face for signs of irony. But his countenance was so open, his golden flecked eyes so soft it was difficult to be sure. She was tempted to believe him. 'With all these stories you've quite forgotten to tell me exactly why you are here, Father.'

'Heavens above, do forgive me!' He uncrossed his ankles, sat up straight and placed his palms on his knees. 'Father Tomás would like to visit you. He's concerned for you now that your Papa has left to search for those villains who took the children.'

She hoped the churning cloud of black thunder filling her mind was not evident on her face. His startled expression told her that it was.

'I really didn't mean to upset you by mentioning the twins, my child.'

Looking down at her lap, she took a moment to change her expression from angry to sad. 'It's been a very testing time, as I'm sure you can imagine, Father Andreas.'

He smiled.

It was the first time she'd used his name. She'd done it deliberately, a mark of respect. She could play games too.

'I'm sure Papa would be delighted to invite Father

Tomás to dinner on his return from Granada with the children.'

He gave her a quizzical look.

'But I'm not up to receiving visitors by myself at the moment.' She took in a deliberately ragged breath. 'I'm sure Father Tomás will understand.'

'In the circumstances, I hope he will.'

She did nothing to break the silence that fell between them.

He looked around the garden, appearing to search for something. He got up and stared into the pool. 'If you change your mind, you can contact me at the Castillo – send a boy with a message. I'm the only Brother Andreas there.' Turning, he crossed himself and left the courtyard through the outer door.

She paced the garden. Torquemada surely knew she would never let him visit her alone, and certainly not whilst Papa was away. Why had he really sent Andreas? Was it just intimidation or was there a deeper game afoot? In Papa's absence, there was only one person she really trusted. She would send for him.

CHAPTER
TWENTY

Straining on tiptoes, Juana reached as high as she could. She jumped up and down until she was out of breath, bending at the knees to get extra spring. If she could just catch the stone ledge below the window. It was about the width of her hand, but if she could haul herself up on it she could look outside. To see where they were, to breathe fresh air, to feel sunlight on her face. She might even smell food, perhaps some freshly baked bread, not the stale crusts they'd had every morning. She was weak with hunger. On what seemed like the hundredth attempt, she finally braced her fingertips on the ledge, but they slipped and she fell onto her bottom with a loud squeal.

'I told you not to,' Martín said.

She stood up, folded her arms, and scowled at him. 'Mama said if you can't say anything helpful, then don't say anything at all.'

'Mama said, Mama said, *Mama said.*'

'Stop it Martín!'

'Shhh,' he said, emphasising the point by placing an index finger over his lips. Although the kidnappers were mostly regular in their daily visits – twice, at daybreak and sunset – Ramos had appeared at the hottest part of the day yesterday. He'd sauntered in, looked around the cell, sneered at them, spat on the floor and left.

'What about if we use the bucket?'

She regarded him thoughtfully. 'What would we do with what's inside it?' She grimaced.

'They already came this morning to empty it so there's not that much in there. If we turn it upside down carefully, the shit -'

'Martín!'

'OK, the solids will stay in one place and when we're finished we can scoop most of it up with the lip of the bucket. Then you can...'

She glared at him.

'Or I can fill it up again.'

With a shudder she went over to get the bucket. She retched as she picked it up. Turning away she beckoned him to come and help. They placed it beneath the window.

'Let me do it,' Martín said. He picked the bucket up by the bail and put his other hand underneath and spun it over onto the floor. It worked.

She returned his smile. 'Give me a hand to steady myself,' she said, stepping onto the bucket. Pulling herself up she braced her elbows on the ledge, legs dangling. She screwed her eyes shut at the brightness of the sun, having become accustomed to the darkness of the cell. She enjoyed the heat playing on her face for a few moments and then slowly half-opened her eyes. All she could see was a blur of colour. Immediately in front of her waves of green – was it grass? Then behind that a large block of red – the side of a building. She sniffed at the air – it was salty. Was that the sea?

'What can you see?' he asked.

'The sun is too strong, not a lot. Maybe some grass.' Her arms and shoulders suddenly began to tire. She dropped from the ledge, managing to place only one foot on the bucket, which toppled over. She landed on her back beside it.

Helping her up he said, 'Let me try.' He righted the bucket, hopped on, and braced his elbows on the ledge. 'You're right, there's definitely grass. I think I can see another house just beyond ...'

They heard the creaking hinges of the outer door.

'Quickly,' she hissed. 'Why are they back? They've already been.'

He shrugged.

The slap of footsteps on flagstones grew closer.

He jumped down. Using the lip of the bucket to scoop as much of the waste into it as he could he replaced it in the corner. They sat down opposite the cell door and held hands. She hoped their captors would not notice how hard they were both breathing. She prayed it would be the shorter one, the kinder one. The one with the red hair.

The cell door swung inwards. 'How are you, my pretties?'

Her prayers were answered. It was Red Hair.

'We're well, thank you,' she replied, squeezing her brother's hand.

'Yes, we're fine. I suppose,' he said.

'Brought you a treat.' His voice was gravelly, his words struggling to escape from his throat. He was stocky and muscular. Red Hair sat down cross-legged in front of them, an arm's length away. Reaching inside his jacket, he produced a stone jar and two wooden goblets with a flourish. He placed the goblets on the floor in front of them, uncorked the jar, and filled each to the brim.

Juana didn't know what to do. She looked at Martín.

'Go on,' the kidnapper said.

She leant forward and sniffed. It smelt like orange juice. Could it be? Were they trying to put them to sleep, or even poison them?

Martín reached for the goblet, but she knocked his hand away.

'You're a suspicious young filly,' Red Hair said, raising the jar to his lips and taking a swig. He wiped his mouth with the back of his hand and said, 'Delicious!'

Martín glanced at her, and she nodded. They grabbed the goblets, gulped down the juice, and held out the empty cups for more.

'Careful, my pretties, too much on an empty stomach will give you belly ache,' he said with a broad grin. 'Let's have a little talk first and then you can have some more.'

'What do you want?' Martín asked, unable to hide his eagerness for the juice.

'To be friends, that's all.'

'Why do you want to be friends with us? You stole us away,' Martín replied.

She elbowed him, warning him not to be too aggressive.

'You're just here for a little time. It's not really a kidnapping.'

'We can go?' she asked, glancing at the cell door, noticing Red Hair had forgotten to lock it.

'Soon, soon.'

'Why not now?' she pleaded.

'Because things need to happen, people need to do things, and the master has to tell us to let you go.'

'Can I ask you something?' she said.

'Go on.'

'How did you know about us?'

Red Hair laughed. 'We been watching you for quite some time.'

'Spying on us?'

'From that old house across the road. Watching you play your games.'

She set her jaw at him and remained silent.

'You oughtna let that Gabriel bully you. Need to stand up for yourself.' He sneered at Martín. 'Or your brother should anyways.'

Martín looked down at the cell floor.

Red Hair returned her glare with a smile that revealed a mouthful of rotten teeth. 'Your hair is lovely,' he said. 'Can I touch it?'

She shrank back against the cell wall.

'I just want to stroke it. I promise I won't hurt you. And then you can have some more juice.' He waggled the jar at her. 'Can you take the hair clip out?'

She used the silver barrette her mother had given her

to keep her hair tidy. It was a simple geometric design with a pin as a clasp. Taking a deep breath she stole a sidelong glance at her brother.

He nodded.

'I'll do it if you agree to tell me your name.'

He looked up at the window thoughtfully and said, 'I'm not allowed to ... I mean, my boss told me not to tell you.'

She gave him her sweetest smile and was surprised to see his face redden.

'If I do, you must swear not to use it in front of my boss.'

'We swear,' the children said in unison.

She unclipped the barrette and bent her head forward cautiously. She held her breath, bracing for him to touch her. Red Hair reached out and played his fingers through her hair. 'So soft. I've waited such a long time.'

'What do you mean?' she asked.

'Whilst we been watching you. I saw that older boy was mean to you. Give him a good whipping if you want me to.'

As he continued stroking, she felt the pressure increasing. She compressed her lips, willing herself to stay silent. But then he snagged a lock of hair.

'Owwww,' she screamed.

'I'm sorry, I'm sorry,' Red Hair said, snatching his hand away. 'Have the juice now. Make you feel better.'

The second cup tasted even sweeter than the first. She rubbed the back of her hand over her mouth and said, 'Delicious.'

Red Hair growled a deep laugh.

She was pleased her mimicry delighted him. It was important to keep him happy. 'Now you have to keep your promise.'

Red Hair scrunched up his face in confusion.

'Your name,' she said.

'See if you can guess,' he said, tilting his head up.

She was confused. Was he looking at the ceiling? Then she realised he wasn't, he was trying to indicate the top of his head. 'Roja!' she said.

'Clever girl!' He reached for her hair again, but she moved away. He stared at her until a shout from outside seemed to break his concentration. He shook his head as though trying to clear it. 'Been here too long, have to go. I'll come back.'

'Will you bring more juice?' Martín asked.

'Maybe.' The spell was broken. He was in a hurry.

'Goodbye, Roja,' she said.

'Goodbye, Juana,' he replied gruffly. Bobbing his head at them, he locked the cell door and was gone.

CHAPTER
TWENTY-ONE

Isaac's siesta had been disrupted by vague dreams and visions. Now he watched from the first-floor balcony as the brothers completed the evening Ishaq prayers. They sat back on their prayer mats for a long moment, then stood and embraced. He wished he'd had a brother, a sister even. Sometimes he'd felt very alone growing up as an only child. Perhaps that explained his solitary nature? It was strange he had never had a sibling. All the other families had at least five children, some as many as ten. Perhaps his mother or his father had some physical problem. Or was there another explanation? But there was no time for this. Actual children – *his* children – were in danger. This was not the moment to spend energy speculating about ones that had never existed.

'There you are my friend,' Abdul Rahman called up to him. 'Let's deal with these infidels.'

They gathered in the courtyard. There were nine, including Abdul Rahman's guards and his other two men watching the house. But Isaac had decided there would only be eight of them involved in the raid. He took Gabriel aside.

'You won't be coming with us.'

His son scowled.

'It's too dangerous.'

'Papa, please, I have my dagger,' Gabriel said.

'No, son. It was against my better judgment for you to come at all. We don't know what we'll find at the house. Besides, we need you to stay here to protect the servants, just in case something goes wrong.'

Gabriel's face brightened for a moment and then darkened again. 'What do you mean, if something goes wrong?'

'I'm not sure exactly, son. I just want you here. Do you understand?' He put his hand on Gabriel's shoulder and the boy briefly covered it with his own. A surge of warmth flooded his chest.

'If you'll permit me, Isaac?' Abdul Rahman said.

'Most welcome,' he replied, 'it's your city.'

Abdul Rahman bowed his head. 'Right, gentleman.' He circled a finger in the air. They gathered around him. 'We have a short time between Ishaq and Compline when the streets will be quiet. We need to move quickly.'

There were nods and murmurs of agreement.

'We'll divide into two units, one led by myself, the other by Ali.'

This made sense to Isaac as the brothers knew the city best. Abdul Rahman was clearly enjoying the opportunity to use his military experience. He was grateful for it.

'The disturbance will be too obvious if all of us approach at the same time,' Abdul Rahman continued. 'Isaac, and you' – he pointed at one of his men – 'you're with me. Pedro and you' – he pointed to the other man – 'you're with Ali. And Pedro, the falcon stays here.' Although the bird could be useful, there was a risk its screeching would alert the kidnappers.

'They're being held in a building behind the bath-house in Calle Banuelo, next to the river. We'll approach on foot, and each unit will wait at either end of the *calle*. When you hear the accursed bells ring for Compline we storm the house at the same time.'

More murmurs of agreement.

'Listen, this is of the utmost importance – protecting the children is our priority. If we have to let the dogs who kidnapped them go, so be it. But,' he said, raising his eyebrows, 'if we need to send them to hell, then it will be the will of Allah!' The words finished in a rallying crescendo.

'Allahu Akhbar,' the bodyguards chanted in unison and brandished their curved scimitars. Isaac noted that Ali did not join in. Perhaps he didn't agree with this bloodthirsty display? He recalled a time when he would have had the same reservations. Before Maria's death.

'Weapons?' Abdul Rahman asked. Isaac touched the rapier sheathed at his side. He also had a dagger secreted in his boot. Pedro wielded a large, bulbous cudgel. The brothers and the two guards raised their scimitars again before returning them to their scabbards.

'Yallah, gentleman. And may Allah,' he grinned mischievously, 'or whoever you pray to, be with you.'

Abdul Rahman held the lantern at arm's length, casting their distorted shadows onto the high walls on either side of the narrow lane. Isaac followed, keeping a close eye on the lantern – he wouldn't have a clue where he was should he lose sight of it. The very real bulk of the bodyguard at his shoulder provided some reassurance. The streets seemed even gloomier to him than those of Seville. Perhaps it was just a reflection of his mood? They were in the middle of the brief period between the Muslim Ishaq prayer and the Compline prayer for Catholics. A spiritual no-mans-land, a time when very few people were on the streets. The aroma of spice was fainter now, replaced by the rich, sweet smell of jasmine. The scent evoked a powerful sense of Maria's presence that he embraced for a moment.

He had not been forced to fight since Isabel's disappearance three years before. Then he had summoned the courage and determination to do what was needed to keep his daughter safe. Though, he recalled with a grin, she had made a pretty good fist of looking after herself. She would've probably been alright without his intervention. Hopefully, she was showing the same resolve and initiative now.

Turning a corner, Abdul Rahman brought them to an abrupt halt. 'We are in position at the river end of Calle Banuelo,' he whispered.

A soft breeze blew up the *calle* from the river. He was momentarily surprised. Where was the briny tang? Then he recalled that this was the Darro which flowed from the sierras not to and from the sea. 'How will we know if the others are ready?'

'Look,' Abdul Rahman said, lifting the lantern high.

And from the other end of the *calle,* a lantern swung in return.

'All will be well,' Abdul Rahman said, gripping Isaac's shoulder. 'Now we wait for the bells.'

'Why don't we attack now?' Isaac hissed.

'Sabr, my friend, patience. The bells will mask the noise we make as Pedro uses his cudgel to break down the door.'

'I understand.'

'We won't get very far with a polite knock,' Abdul Rahman said.

After what seemed to him an interminable wait, the church bells clanged through the air from all directions.

'Now!' Abdul Rahman called out as he ran surprisingly fast for a man of his size. He was closely followed by his bodyguard.

Isaac unsheathed his rapier and did his best to keep up. He focused on the lantern from the other unit as they rapidly drew nearer to it. It suddenly stopped moving. The others must already be at the door. He picked up his pace. Next came the sound of splintering wood. Pedro was making good use of the cudgel. As Isaac arrived he saw him shoulder aside the door's last resistance. Ali and the others, scimitars drawn, followed him through the gaping hole. Isaac, at the rear, was joined by two other men, who must be Abdul Rahman's watchers.

It was a two-storey building. The ground floor was a large open space with a steep staircase at its centre that led to a hole in the high ceiling. His first thought was that it must be some sort of warehouse. The floor was covered in earth and straw, and the smell of shit was overpowering. Was it used for storing animals? A slaughterhouse? His stomach roiled at the possibility.

He looked across at Ali, who was holding the corner of his robe to his nose as he swung the lantern from side to side. Shaking his head he repeatedly called out, 'Ya Allah, Ya Allah.'

Oh my God, indeed.

'Up here!' A cry rang out from above. Abdul Rahman and the other three were already on the second floor.

Isaac followed Ali as he clambered up the stairs. The wood was rough and as he reached the top he was sure he had splinters. He emerged into another large, open space. The air was less pungent up here. The roof space sloped on either side but was just tall enough for them to stand upright in the centre. Ali joined his brother in hunching over and walking the perimeter, swinging lanterns, searching every corner. Motes of dust danced in and out of the light.

Ali turned to him and held the lantern aloft. 'Nothing,' he said. 'No one.'

CHAPTER
TWENTY-TWO

'I came as soon as I could get away from the Alcazar, señorita,' Alejandro said.

Isabel stood between two chairs in front of the sitting-room hearth at Casa de Felicidad. She regarded him with a fixed expression and folded her arms. Her long brunette hair was drawn above her neck and kept in place by the tortoiseshell barrette Papa had given her. She'd deliberately made herself look austere. She wanted him to know that he should keep his distance.

'It's almost Vespers. My note said it was urgent.'

'The Queen,' he offered in explanation.

'Well, you're here now.' She did not ask him to sit.

He turned to shut the door.

'No, leave it open. Catalina,' she said, raising her voice, 'stay on that stool just outside the door and close your ears.'

'Yes, señorita,' Catalina replied.

'I'm sure you understand, señor?'

'Yes, of course, with your father not being here. Have you heard from him?'

She shook her head. 'Have you?'

'Not a word, either directly or indirectly.'

'Señor. I will come directly to the point.'

He took a step towards her, but she froze him in place by the coldness of her eyes.

'You know about the stranger who purchased a large quantity of arsenic from the apothecary a few days ago?'

'I'd heard.'

'Ali Sina told me before he left with Papa that the man was tall and had pale blue eyes.' She arched an eyebrow.

'And?'

'And that he signed his name in the register, beginning with an 'A'.' She cocked her chin at him.

'What *are* you saying, Isabel?'

She stared past him, eyes blazing, and jerked her head at the open door.

He glanced behind and smiled. 'Señorita.'

'I said I would be direct. You match the description and your name starts with an 'A'.'

Grinning broadly, he said, 'You're not serious?'

She pursed her lips.

'Why would I do such a thing? Buy arsenic to kill Torquemada?' His face contorted. 'Is that what you're accusing me of?' His voice rose with indignation.

Outside, the stool scraped on the floor and Catalina coughed.

'I think you might have done it with the best of

intentions, to protect Papa. To do what he hasn't been able to for the last three years.'

'That's absurd, Isabel.' He began pacing up and down in front of her. 'If I'd wanted to assassinate Torquemada there are far easier ways to do it. I could have hired a killer. I can easily find out his whereabouts and arrange access to him.'

She looked down and let her arms fall loose.

'And do you really think so little of my intelligence that I would sign my own name?' He held out his palms to her. His fingers were long and graceful.

'Perhaps it was a clever double bluff, so you could say exactly that.' Even as the words came out of her mouth she felt little conviction in them.

'So, now you're crediting me with enormous intelligence!' He laughed.

'It isn't amusing, Alejandro.'

Another scrape of the stool followed by another cough.

'I don't care anymore about propriety, Catalina. Go away!'

'As you like, señorita,' Catalina called out. Her heavy footsteps receded.

'It is though. Very,' he said.

'What?'

'Amusing.'

She wiped her face with her hands as though banishing her previous demeanour. 'Let's sit.'

They sat opposite each other on either side of the hearth. She relayed to him all the information she had about the red-haired *ladrone*. That Ali Sina had told her

169

one of the arsonists had red hair. How Papa had witnessed two thugs – one with red hair – beat up a youth in Bar Averno. That she had the impression of red hair when the twins were kidnapped. Her certainty she had come across him before.

'I've been so fearful and mistrustful since the twins were taken. It's all become so confusing, I don't know who to believe.'

'Haven't I proven my worth? I protected you during the blood libel. I hid your father from the Inquisition. I've remained loyal to him ever since.' He hesitated. 'I know things that would have him burnt as a heretic.'

She took his hand. 'I'm sorry,' she whispered. 'Can you forgive me?'

'Almost anything,' he said with tenderness.

Releasing his hand, she stood. 'We need to decide what to do. Papa is not here, and we don't know where he is. We can't sit idly by, but we can't go chasing after him. We need to find out as much as we can here in Seville. Will you help me?'

'Help you? Exactly what do you intend?'

'We need to find out more about those thugs.'

He looked at her quizzically. 'How will you do that?'

'The obvious thing.' She paused. 'A visit to Bar Averno.'

'That's far too dangerous. You can't go there.'

She reflected for a long moment. 'Well then, *I* won't go. But someone you know will accompany you.'

～

Shortly after daybreak, Torquemada ambled along the stretch of the Triana riverbank fronting the Castillo. He prodded his cane warily into the dewy grass to ensure it had sufficient purchase for him to confidently take his next step. Andreas walked alongside him, occasionally reaching out to offer support, but Torquemada batted his hand away. He might need the help, but he was certainly not going to look weak in public, even to the few who were about at this early hour.

A fine mist of vapour rose from the still river. The Guadalquivir was empty now, but, as the tide came in, it would soon fill with vessels, the smaller barques serving the needs of the larger galleons carrying treasure from the Indies, where Alonso still was. He missed him. Alonso had been an idiot, but a useful one. Perhaps he had been a little over-zealous, but his commitment to eradicating heresy had not been in doubt. Enough had happened for Their Majesties to forget about Alonso. He would see what he could do to get him recalled. And he was quite sure, from the servants' gossip he had overheard, that Brother Andreas would be thrilled to see Alonso again. That would be an amusing reunion to witness.

He stopped to watch a kingfisher swoop and glide over the water. Twisting left and right, it searched for breakfast. Then it was gone in a blur of iridescent sapphire blue.

'I expect you'd like yours,' he said in a frail voice, as he started to walk again.

'My what, Father?' Andreas asked.

'Your breakfast.'

'No, Father, I need some time after saying Lauds before I'm ready to eat. And even then just a morsel of bread and a small cup of wine suffices.'

'Does it now? I always need something far more substantial.'

'I'm sure you eat very well, Father.'

He stopped abruptly, stabbing his cane into the earth, and turned to look at Andreas. 'What do you mean?' he said, in a suddenly powerful voice.

'Nothing, Father. I assure you, I meant nothing, absolutely nothing.'

They all gossiped about his appetites, that he had gout from all the rich food he ate. So what if he did? He was entitled to some earthly comfort, for all the sacrifices he'd made to ensure the safety of the faithful in this world and to secure their place in the next. Saving souls was arduous. He grunted and walked on. 'Tell me again exactly what young Isabel said.' He noted the delayed reply and the thoughtful expression. He must be carefully composing his response. Perhaps this friar was smarter than he had given him credit for. Or more devious.

'That she appreciated your concern, but really didn't feel up to receiving guests at the moment. She was sure you would understand and that perhaps her father would invite you to dinner upon his return from Granada.'

Well done, nicely finessed. Torquemada was silent, concentrating on carefully placing his cane in the damp earth.

'I'm certain she was sincere,' Andreas added hastily.

He smirked and flapped the back of his hand at the friar. 'Yes, I'm sure *you* are,' he said.

Andreas folded his arms into the baggy sleeves of his habit and looked down. 'What would you have me do, Father?'

'I'm sure you agree that, with her Papa unavoidably absent, it is my duty to provide pastoral care for the poor child?'

'I do, Father.'

'Very well. If she won't allow us to carry out our duty then we must do so in secret. It would be remiss of me to bow to her immature wishes. She doesn't realise what's best for her.'

Andreas was silent.

'You're to keep watch and report her movements to me.'

'Alone, Father?'

'Yes. During daylight hours. You can start after Lauds and finish at Vespers. Take a break in the afternoon when she will no doubt be enjoying a siesta.'

Andreas did not reply.

'Too arduous for you, Brother? Should I get someone else to carry out my wishes?'

'Not at all, Father. It will be my pleasure. When should I begin?'

'Now. After you've had your morsel of bread and tiny cup of wine, of course,' he said, turning to grin at the friar.

Andreas was silent.

'And there's one more thing.'

'Anything, Father.'

He noted the enthusiasm of the response. Let's see how long that lasts. 'Father Alonso de Hojeda...' he glanced with satisfaction at the mixture of discomfort and joy that passed across Andreas' face at the mention of his friend's name. 'Find out exactly where he is, and when the next ship can take a letter to him.'

'What?'

He came to a halt and planted both hands on the head of his cane. 'Is something wrong, Brother?'

Andreas turned to face him. 'No, Father. No.'

'You seem to have lost some colour from your face.' He pinched each of Andreas' cheeks in turn. 'There, that's better,' he said with a broad smile. 'Rosier now.'

Andreas winced. Torquemada was not sure whether his distress arose from physical or spiritual pain. Either – or both – was equally pleasing.

TWENTY-THREE

Seven nights now. Juana could feel herself becoming weaker by the day. Her limbs felt heavy and it was increasingly difficult to breathe in the dank cell. It was a struggle to stand up, difficult to even crouch over the bucket. She was sitting in the corner farthest from the door. The corners were the most comfortable place to sit, as they provided some support. Martín lay on the floor under the window, knees curled into his chest. She was worried. He was so listless. When Ramos came the previous evening to empty their bucket, she'd asked him for more water. He'd sneered, spat on the floor, and told her to lick it up if she was thirsty. When he'd appeared that morning with bread and water, she remained silent, did not even look at him.

They'd used the upturned bucket to stand on and look out of the window a few more times. They confirmed that long grass was growing just outside and that it completely covered the opening. Martín thought the red bricks beyond the grass belonged to some kind of warehouse. They tried shouting for help, but there was no response. They saw no one pass by, heard no footsteps. The only voice they heard from outside was on the day Roja had given them the juice.

She enjoyed watching the grass sway in the cool breeze and the feeling of fresh air blowing the hair away from her face. It was tangled and dirty now. She tried to stop herself scratching at her scalp. She hoped the itch was from being unwashed and that it wasn't fleas. Oh, how she longed to wash her hair and to feel Catalina comb it one hundred times as she used to every night. She used the barrette to keep it as tidy as possible, but it was a losing battle.

Martín groaned, jarring her out of her thoughts.

'Are you alright?' she whispered.

'Why are you whispering? Nobody can hear us. *Nobody!*'

'It's okay,' she said, getting up stiffly and going across to comfort him. He pushed her away, but then relented and sat with his head on her shoulder. 'I was just thinking about Catalina brushing my hair. Look at it now,' she said, holding up a lank, filthy strand.

'Don't we have more important things to worry about?'

'I suppose you're right,' she said, pulling him closer.

'I thought you said everyone would look for us. It's been days now,' he whined.

'You're right. We need to do something.'

'What?'

She said nothing.

'*What?*'

'Shhh, let me think,' she said, stroking his hair.

She must have dozed off. She dreamt she was halfway up a tree in Casa de la Felicidad looking down at Gabriel and Martín fighting, with Isabel shouting, 'Stop, stop, stop.' The sound of wagon wheels woke her up. How long had she been asleep? Her shoulder ached from where Martín lolled his head. The room felt cooler. Evening must be close. Two sets of footsteps. A murmur of voices. They were coming. Her plan would not work if both their captors were there. She shifted her shoulder, encouraging her brother to wake up.

He shifted his head groggily. 'What is it?'

She whispered, 'They're here.'

He sat up straight.

Ramos ducked under the lintel and stood in the centre of the cell, looming over them. Roja was just behind him and gave her a small grin that she did not return. Ramos clicked his fingers and Roja put down a wooden tray with cups of water, some scraps of bread and bowls of grey sludge.

'You said you were hungry, so I've brought you some vegetable stew,' Ramos said, his voice high and strained. 'You'll need some energy for what's coming tomorrow.' He clicked his fingers again and Roja picked up the bucket and took it outside. Ramos looked down and smiled at her. It did not reach his eyes, which were beady, dark and dead, just like a falcon's. It reminded her of the afternoon she'd accompanied Gabriel and Martín to falconry training. She'd watched a bird swoop, sink its claws into a mouse, and devour it. She was repulsed and never went back. Ramos' eyes looked like the falcon's as he thrust his beak into the rodent flesh.

'Aren't you going to eat it?' he demanded.

They lunged at the food, stuffing it into their mouths with their hands, all pretence of manners gone. They washed it down with the water.

Ramos squatted on his haunches, pushed his face towards them and hissed, 'Get some good sleep tonight. You'll need it.'

Roja returned with the empty bucket and took his place behind Ramos.

'Why?' she asked.

'Never you mind,' Ramos said, quickly jutting his head at her.

She flinched and shrank back against the wall.

Martín whimpered.

'God's wounds, boy, be a man!' Ramos said. 'Your sister's braver than you'll ever be.'

Martín stood up unsteadily, fists clenched at his side.

'The worm turns.' Ramos shared a laugh with Roja. 'Go on then, boy, let's see what you've got,' he said.

She tugged at her brother's trouser leg, but it was too late. He launched himself at Ramos, head down. The kidnapper did not move as the boy's head cannoned into his stomach. Martín reeled back, took a boxer's stance and swung his right fist towards Ramos's jaw. The kidnapper deftly avoided the blow and as Martín staggered forward, Ramos planted a foot on his backside and pushed him to the ground.

She screamed.

'Not so much of a mummy's boy, after all,' Ramos said as Martín levered himself up. 'Stay down, boy, or I'll slice you open.' He produced a dagger from his waist with a flourish. He brushed the blade against Martín's cheek.

'Do as he says, *please*,' she cried. She saw Roja give Martín a pleading look.

Martín shuffled into the furthest corner of the cell, put his head in his hands, and sobbed.

'As I was saying before that bit of excitement,' Ramos said, studying his dagger before sheathing it, 'you should get some sleep. Big day tomorrow.'

Roja nodded his head vigorously.

'Lock up,' Ramos barked at Roja, 'I'll see you back at the house. Be quick about it – we've got things to do this evening.'

Roja fiddled with the keys until Ramos left. He knelt down next to Martín and said, 'You shouldnna done that, boy.' He looked up and scratched his chin. 'But you was looking after your sister. That's a good thing to do.' He patted Martín's head.

Roja came over to her, bent down and whispered, 'I'll try to come back with some juice tomorrow morning. You're not leaving till nightfall.' He stroked her hair.

She willed herself not to move away, to allow him to

caress her. 'That... would... be... very... kind... of you,' she said between sobs. 'Where are you taking us?'

He whispered, 'Sleep well, my pretty angel.'

As she heard the outer door slam her head slumped onto her knees, her body convulsed by weeping. *Tomorrow morning.*

CHAPTER
TWENTY-FOUR

Midnight. Isaac had been sitting with the two brothers in the courtyard since their return from the failed rescue. A nearly empty pitcher of *nabidh* was in the middle of the table. He tried another sip of the sweet, fermented drink. The intensity of the date flavour was too much. He craved red wine. Gabriel's tears on their arrival without the twins had been almost too much to bear. His son had gone to bed before they'd had a chance to talk properly.

Abdul Rahman slumped in his chair, even his natural ebullience flattened. Ali had said almost nothing, preferring to sip *nabidh* and keep his own counsel. Isaac found it too painful to make any direct mention of the twins. He focused on formulating a plan. But he had no idea of what to do. The pulsating buzz of cicadas filled the silences in their desultory conversation. The insects seemed to reach a much louder crescendo than in Seville. The full moon's reflection in the still surface of the pool at the centre of the courtyard sparked the memory of another full-mooned night. When he and Maria had taken a fateful decision. So long ago.

Ali got up and strolled around the pool, appearing to be deep in thought.

'Circles,' said Ali.

'What?' he said, pushing his mug of *nabidh* away.

'Circles. We're going round in them,' Ali replied.

He exchanged bemused glances with Abdul Rahman.

Ali stopped walking. 'Alejandro's contacts gave you the children's supposed location.'

There was that word again – 'supposed' – that irritated Isaac when Ali first used it back at Moura's tavern.

Abdul Rahman filled the silence. 'Go on.'

'Clearly, this was disinformation.'

Isaac thumped his fist on the table.

'My apologies, misinformation. Alejandro was misled.'

He grunted.

'The real question is who told the person who told Alejandro?'

'If we knew the answer then we'd know what to do!' Isaac said. 'But I'll wager the deeds to Casa de Felicidad that Torquemada's behind it.'

'Exactly, my friend, exactly. Circles within circles.'

'So, brother, how do we break this hellish circle?' Abdul Rahman asked.

'We need more information, but Alejandro is three days' ride away. We can either return to Seville as speedily as possible or make further enquiries here.'

'Who's able to help us in Granada?' Isaac asked.

Abdul Rahman stroked his beard thoughtfully.

'There's one prominent person who might be sympathetic to your plight.'

'Santo Alfaquí?' Isaac said.

'Well done, you know we *Mudéjars* call Archbishop Talavera the Holy Teacher,' he replied. 'Like yourself, he is of *converso* stock and we have a grudging respect for him. He's trying to learn our language – apparently, he can recite the Ten Commandments in Arabic.'

'Hasn't he got tougher recently? Didn't he prevent Catholics from renting houses to *Mudéjars* or buying meat from your butchers?' Isaac said.

'Yes, but these are minor matters. Circumstances forced him to do such things to prevent Torquemada from correcting our "heresy" with more extreme measures. Like fire and the lash.' He paused. 'Talavera took the necessary steps to prevent further evil.'

Isaac puffed out his cheeks. 'We have nothing to lose. Let's see him tomorrow. You can arrange a visit?'

'Of course. The Archbishop knows me well.'

Did Abdul Rahman really have such immediate access to the most powerful man in Granada? Isaac judged it would be pointless to express his uncertainty. 'And if the visit proves fruitless we head straight back to Seville,' he said to Ali.

The apothecary did not meet Isaac's eyes. His response, the merest nod. Ali shook his hand and embraced his brother. Watching him go up the stairs to bed he wondered about his friend's ambiguous response. It must be exhaustion.

~

His doubts were unfounded. At lunchtime on the following day, the three of them were waiting for Archbishop Talavera in his palace dining room. It was a rectangle of modest size, with doors at either end. There were four places set on each side of a square table. Two friars in the traditional habit of the order of St Jerome – white tunic with a brown scapular hanging from their shoulders – stood guard at each entrance. Dark wooden panels covered the walls but large, curved windows on the longer sides of the room filled it with sunlight. Isaac sat with his back to one set of windows and had a partial view, out of the other, of the formidable turreted outer wall of the Alhambra. To his left, behind the place reserved for Talavera, was a life-size wooden sculpture of Jesus on the cross, his forehead smeared with vivid blood dripping from the crown of thorns.

He looked across at Ali. Head bowed, palms cupped in his lap, muttering to himself in Arabic. He must be praying. Isaac's quizzical look to Ali's brother was returned with a shake of his head. Abdul Rahman leant forward and whispered, 'He feels uncomfortable, he's warding off evil spirits.' He grinned broadly, clearly not sharing Ali's misgivings.

The friar guarding the door to Isaac's right opened it and bowed as Archbishop Hernando de Talavera glided in. He wore the same white and brown habit as his brothers. He whispered something in the friar's ear, who lowered his head and left the room. Isaac noticed Talavera had a remarkably upright posture for a man who must be more than seventy years of age, a contrast to Torquemada's hunched, hobbled appearance. His grey beard and tonsure were perfectly groomed. His cheeks were deeply furrowed on either side of an aquiline nose. They stood as the archbishop took his place behind his chair. The brothers bowed their heads and said, 'Your Excellency.' He turned to Isaac and held out his hand, palm down.

Isaac looked into his soft brown eyes and saw a glint of steel. Taking the hand he lightly kissed it. 'Your Excellency,' he said. 'I am Isaac Alvarez, an adviser to King Ferdinand.'

'I know who you are.'

He wondered whether the note of disdain he thought he heard in the archbishop's voice was for him or His Majesty.

Talavera bowed his head, said grace, made the sign of the cross and sat down. Looking at the brothers, he intoned, 'Bismillah ir rahman ir rahim.'

'Your pronunciation is improving, Father,' Abdul Rahman said with evident delight.

'Slow progress is still progress,' Talavera replied. 'You must be Abdul Rahman's brother,' he said, turning to Ali. 'It's a great pleasure to meet you.'

Ali looked bewildered at the warmth of the greeting. He placed his right hand over his heart.

Two friars entered and set down bowls of soup in front of each of the men and left a platter of bread in the centre of the table. The friars filled their mugs with water from an earthenware pitcher and returned to their stations by the doors.

'Let us eat first. Then you can tell me why you had to see me at such short notice,' Talavera said.

Isaac was unsure of his tone. On the surface it seemed kindly. But was there just a hint of menace? They finished the watery mutton soup in silence. The archbishop held up his left palm and the friars cleared the table and left the room. They were alone. He looked at each of them, his gaze finally rested on Isaac. 'We have something in common, I believe.'

Was he referring to their shared *converso* origins? He was aghast that Talavera might begin their first meeting in this way.

'We are alumni of the University of Salamanca?'

'Ah, yes, of course, Your Excellency,' He said with relief.

'What else could I have possibly meant?' Talavera asked playfully. 'Perhaps you remembered I met your father once. It must be twenty years ago, when I was preaching in Seville. Is he still with us?'

'Yes, Your Excellency. In declining health but still with us, by the grace of God.'

'"Father" will do,' Talavera replied. He again looked at each of them. 'Whatever you tell me next I will deny hearing and whatever response I make I will also deny. This was simply a lunch between friends.' He paused. 'Do we have an understanding?'

Isaac joined in with the brothers' nods of assent.

'So, tell me how can I help. I have very little time.'

He rapidly explained why they had come to Granada and their failure to find the twins.

Talavera did not appear surprised by the story but clearly enjoyed Abdul Rahman's interjections to embellish the adventure. 'Those poor, poor children.

May The Almighty protect and preserve them.' He bowed his head in silent prayer. 'But what is it you think I can do for you?' He looked directly at Isaac.

'We thought you might have heard something, or perhaps be able to point us in the right direction.'

'Seems a little desperate.' Talavera hesitated. 'If you don't mind me saying so.'

'You're right, I am. In despair,' he replied. He saw Ali and Abdul Rahman exchange sympathetic glances.

'We are all tempted by despair, especially in times such as these. But it is a sin. It is a sign you have ceased to have hope of your salvation. It is contrary to God's goodness, to his justice and his mercy.' He took a sip of water. 'But I think you have suffered greatly at the hands of our Grand Inquisitor.' His tone was gentler. 'You've lost a friend, your wife, and now two children at the hands of that monster.'

Isaac grimaced. 'You believe Torquemada is behind this, Father?'

'Who else would be so cavalier as to sanction the kidnap of the children of one of King Ferdinand's most trusted advisers. The man who uncovered the truth of the so-called Seville blood libel.' He raised an eyebrow. 'Surely you are not surprised?'

'Are you certain of this, Father?' Abdul Rahman asked.

'Absolutely, my friend. If only you had come to me first I could have told you that the children were never in Granada.'

'God's blood!' Isaac cried out as he stood and paced up and down. 'Apologies, Father.'

'Under the circumstances...' Talavera said, waving away the oath. 'In fact, the children are still in Seville.'

'I'm sorry to ask, Your Excellency,' Ali said, 'but how can you be certain of this?'

The archbishop looked out of the window to his left, in the direction of the Alhambra. He put a hand beneath his habit and produced a string of rosary beads. He threaded them through his fingers. 'Torquemada is not the only one with a network of *familiares*. It is no secret he and I disagree profoundly on the way to convert our *Mudéjar* friends to the True Faith.' He dipped his head in the brothers' direction. 'But I believe reasonable persuasion rather than forced conversion will save their souls from eternal damnation. He thinks that burning and water torture will work. Carrot and stick. But human beings are not donkeys.'

Isaac sat down and asked, 'Do you know where Juana and Martín are?'

'No. Only that they are in Seville. They never left.'

Isaac thumped a fist into his palm.

'And Isaac, my son.' He waited until he had his full attention. 'They are not the only ones in danger. An order has been issued for your assassination.'

TWENTY-FIVE

'Why are you in that tattered thing, señorita?' Catalina asked her as Isabel descended the stairs that led to the courtyard. She was wearing an old, ill-fitting, full-length green gown.

'What business is it of yours?' she replied, coming to an abrupt halt halfway down and planting a fist on her waist.

'I'm sorry, señorita. Things come out my mouth that should stay in my head.' She laughed nervously.

Recognising that she was sometimes guilty of the same flaw, Isabel softened her tone. 'I have to make a visit somewhere that will help Papa and I need to be in disguise,' she said hurrying down the stairs.

'Nobody will ever know who you are in that bunch of rags.' Catalina covered her open mouth with a palm, realising she had repeated her mistake.

Staring at the maidservant she allowed an amused smile to play on her lips. Catalina had unwittingly paid her a compliment. 'Perhaps you can help. Give me that.'

The maidservant took off her apron and helped Isabel tie it around her waist. They went outside to the garden and Catalina tore holes in the dress and smeared dirt on it. Isabel was entertained by the enthusiasm at which she pulled away at the seams of the dress and rubbed earth on it.

'It wasn't so long ago that I was cleaning dirt off your face and now I'm putting it on you,' she said with a laugh. Isabel ignored her as she continued, 'I hope you know what you're doing. Your Papa wouldn't be happy if he heard what you was up to.'

Catalina took a step back and twirled a finger, and she obliged by turning in a circle. 'If you don't mind me saying, señorita, you look just like a slut from Triana.'

'Thank you. Then I've been successful.'

There was a loud knock from the exterior door.

'That will be Señor Alejandro,' Isabel said.

Catalina gave her a broad grin.

She had clearly failed to keep the excitement out of her voice.

'Señorita,' Catalina wavered, but then plunged on. 'Before you go, I need to tell you something about your talk with the señor, yesterday.'

'Go on,' she said, 'be quick.' Her eyes darting to the main door.

'You had me keeping guard outside so I couldn't help but hear you talking about the *ladrones*.'

She shook her head and exhaled loudly.

'It made me remember that day I saw you outside the Apothecary.'

'Really, Catalina, you want to drag that up, right now?'

'No, no, that's not it, it's not me seeing you that's the point. It's me seeing them.'

'Who on earth are you talking about?'

The knocking became louder.

'I saw them.'

'Who?'

'The *ladrones*. The one with the red hair. They were standing outside the house and they were staring at me and I thought...'

The maidservant was blushing and Isabel understood what she'd thought. 'It's alright, I understand.' She placed a hand on her shoulder.

'Yes, well what I thought then was foolish. At my age. Anyway, after listening to you and Señor Alejandro, I think they were spying on us. And...'

She waited patiently.

'Spying on the children. I think they been planning to take them for a while.'

'Why didn't you say something sooner?'

Catalina's face sagged, but she took pity on her. 'Anyway, you've told me now.'

Catalina gave her a weak smile.

She thought the kidnapping had been opportunist, that they would receive a ransom demand. Hoped for as much, because then there would be a solution. But there had only been the letter saying the children were in Granada - no payoff demanded. Now it looked as though the abduction had been planned. Her mind jumped to other possibilities. Were the fire at the Apothecary and the plot to kill Torquemada all part of the same plan? Was Papa the real target?

The knocking was now very loud and very persistent. 'Open the door for the señor.'

'What did you say?' Isabel asked Alejandro, raising her voice over the bells tolling for Sext, the midday prayer. They were in a narrow *calle* just behind La Giralda, the cathedral bell tower. She had her arm through his as they made their way to Bar Averno. They were avoiding the main streets. She did not want to have to explain what she was doing to any of Papa's friends.

Alejandro waited for the bells to finish. 'I said, she saw the kidnappers?'

'Yes, about a week before they took the children, on the same day that I...' She stopped, realising she was about to reveal her visit to the Apothecary. Alejandro was the last person she wanted to talk to about that. She couldn't reveal the truth, but she didn't want to lie. Not to him.

'You were what?'

'Never mind, it's not important.' She stumbled and looked up adoringly at him, playing the part of the drunken wench.

'Why didn't she say anything before?'

'She was embarrassed. She thought they'd been admiring her. Poor thing. She only remembered when she overheard us talking about Roja.'

'Is that what you've christened him?'

'Why not? It's probably his nickname anyway.'

'I suppose Catalina's prying has some advantages.' He puffed out his cheeks. 'But this is even more worrying. This means the kidnap was carefully planned. But by who?'

She followed Alejandro as took off his hat and lowered his head under the lintel of Bar Averno. It was her first time and she was taken aback by the intensity of everything. Her eyes took a moment to adjust from the midday sun to the darkness. The air was filled with loud, male laughter. Threads of acrid pipe smoke spiralled upwards to the ceiling to be absorbed into the heavy wooden beams. Alejandro tugged her hand roughly towards a trestle table situated under the only window and shoved her onto the long bench. He sat down next to her.

'You don't have to be quite so rough,' she whispered.

He mouthed, 'Sorry.'

'Do you remember the first time we did this?'

He shook his head.

'When we disguised ourselves to get out of Triana?'

'Yes, of course. Though I'd rather forget it.'

Then she had it. 'I know where I've seen Roja before.'

Before he could answer a slim, dark-haired girl sauntered over. 'Señor. Good to see you again,' she said, briefly resting her palm on Alejandro's shoulder. Isabel noted that she was pretty and looked, at first sight, to be in her early twenties. But taking a closer look she saw the wrinkles around her eyes and decided she must be in her thirties. The work she did, the hard life she must lead had put those lines there. She pulled Alejandro closer.

'And you, Luisa,' he replied. 'Mugs of your best red and some *mojama*.'

She watched as the serving girl rewarded Alejandro with a broad smile and a wink before she hurried off. She then lolled across him as though drunk, grinned up at him and hissed, 'Who's she?'

'Luisa is the barkeep's daughter and our best source of information. You understand?' he said, returning the grin. 'Before she comes back, tell me where you've seen Roja.'

'The escape from Triana. Three years ago. He was one of the thugs we fought with.'

He furrowed his eyebrows and then smiled. 'Yes, I remember the brute now. I thought I'd left him for dead.'

'Obviously not,' she said.

Before they could discuss it further the barkeep's daughter reappeared with the drinks, a platter of rye bread and sliced *mojama*, which she almost threw onto the table. Luisa gave her a withering look. Alejandro thanked her as she scooped up the generous pile of *maravedies* he'd left. Isabel gave him a sharp elbow to the ribs as she noticed him studying the girls' behind as she sashayed away. He winced and shook his head. Placing a morsel of the finely sliced tuna atop a hunk of bread he said, 'Delicious, why don't you try?'

'We're not here to eat and drink. Ask your friend some questions,' she muttered.

'Patience, we need to play our part. Drink your wine, enjoy the food.'

She took a sip from the goblet and grimaced. The wine was bitter and thin.

He picked up his mug, raised it, and said loudly, 'To you, my dear!' He looked at her pointedly.

She picked up her mug, clinked it against his and downed the wine in one long gulp. Banging it on the table she shouted, 'Another.'

He glanced across at her and murmured out of the side of his mouth, 'Don't go too far.'

Luisa appeared, carrying two more mugs of wine.

'We're looking for a friend,' Alejandro said.

'What sort of friend? Someone to join the pair of you?' she said, arching an eyebrow.

He was silent.

Isabel froze. Was the girl making a lewd suggestion?

'You should see the look on your face!' Luisa squealed, gently slapping his shoulder.

'Ha ha, yes,' he said.

Isabel was pleased he was blushing, grateful that he was uncomfortable consorting with tavern wenches. There was something sweet, something naive in his response that was endearing.

After clearing his throat he continued, 'We're supposed to meet two fellows. One of them has red hair.'

Luisa thought for a moment. 'You probably mean Roja?'

She nudged Alejandro in the ribs again, but restrained herself from saying, 'I told you so.'

'Yes, that's the fellow, and his companion... erm, what's his name...'

'Ramos?'

'Yes, yes, that's him.'

'You want to watch that one,' Luisa said. 'Nasty bits

of work, both of 'em, but Ramos especially.' She grimaced as she said the thug's name. 'Funny you should ask after 'em. Not been in this last week. Not since they beat up that boy. They done him good and proper. Goodness knows what for. Left him in a real bad way. Took me ages to clean the blood of this table.'

Isabel wrinkled her nose in disgust.

Luisa looked hard at Alejandro. 'Your boss was in that night. Wassisname? Don't tell me.' She tapped a finger on her chin thoughtfully. 'I got it. Señor Alvarez, him what works at the Alcazar with you. Didn't he tell you about it?'

'No, I don't think so,' he replied. 'Where might we find Roja and Ramos?'

'Good question, that is. Funny story. But all this talking is making me thirsty,' she said, widening her eyes at him. She shoved her bottom against his shoulder and he shuffled along the bench to make room for her to sit. Isabel gave a low grunt as she was forced to move. Luisa turned and signalled to one of the other serving women. A large pitcher and a third mug quickly appeared.

Filling their mugs he said, 'You were going to tell us a story?'

Luisa took a long draught of wine and wiped the back of her hand over her mouth. She lowered her voice and leant forward. 'It happened the same night as Ramos and Roja savaged that poor boy.' She shook her head at the memory. 'Anyway, I've got a friend over in Triana that I go to see every now and then.' She winked at Isabel. 'A *very* good lady friend.'

Isabel felt her face redden.

'Aren't you the coy one? You've got a fresh one there,' Luisa said, eyeing Alejandro, who glanced at Isabel. Luisa laughed and took another gulp of wine. 'After we closed up around midnight I set off.'

'Isn't your father concerned about you going around at night by yourself?' Isabel asked.

'Concerned?' Luisa said, her tone mocking the choice of words. 'Coy *and* posh. Good for you, señor,' she said, smiling at Alejandro. 'No, he don't give a shit what I'm up to, gives him more time to have his own fun.' She held out her mug to him. 'I've always got my little friend to keep me company.' She reached beneath her skirts to produce a slim dagger. 'Pity the man that gets to meet her.' She took another drink and replaced the weapon. 'Anyway, there was a full moon, so it was easy to see the way. As I made to go over the boat bridge I thought I saw those two *ladrones* at the other end. I pulled my cloak around me and decided to follow 'em.'

Alejandro shook his head. 'Wasn't that a little dangerous?'

'Stupid, more like. But I'd had a bit to drink and I was mad about what they done to that boy. Got it into my head that if I found out what they was up to I could get revenge for 'im. I kept my distance. They turned right after they got off the bridge.' Her voice dropped to a low whisper and they leant closer in. 'I kept behind 'em, minding to stay in the shadows of the Castillo walls. And *that's* where they went.'

'Where?' Isabel asked.

'They stopped beside a tree and looked around. I thought Ramos saw me – he was looking straight at me.

But they turned into a narrow tunnel that goes under the walls. That tree hides the entrance, it's damn hard to find if you don't know it. But me and my lady friend have used that tunnel sometimes, if you know what I mean.' She gave Isabel another wink. 'I waited a while at the entrance and then had a look-see. The tunnel was blacker than hell but I know there's a door at the end. Then there was a screech of metal and a bang.'

Isabel exchanged glances with Alejandro.

'They must've used their own key to get in,' Luisa said.

Isabel let out a long breath through pursed lips. Why were Roja and Ramos letting themselves into the head-quarters of the Inquisition? Into Torquemada's lair? She felt a scream swelling up inside her as her fear for the children grew.

CHAPTER
TWENTY-SIX

Juana was awoken by the trundle of cartwheels over cobbles and a shout of, 'Whoa, boy.'

Her sleep had been riddled with fear — pierced by visions of Martín fighting Ramos, and doubts about her plan. She gave him a shove to wake him up, pointed towards the window and then put a finger to her lips. 'Give me a lift up.'

He knelt down and she planted a foot in his cupped hands. Standing up, he gently lifted her. She reached for the ledge, grasped it and looked out. It was a quicker and less unpleasant method than the bucket, but he was so weak it only gave her a few seconds.

'There's a cart and horse. Looks like it's just Roja,' she hissed.

His arms began to wobble, so she let go of the ledge. Landing heavily, she suppressed an urge to scream.

'Remember the plan. Just do everything we talked about. OK?'

He nodded, but didn't seem very confident.

They heard the outer door being unlocked and listened intently for the footsteps.

'Only one of them!' she whispered. 'Get ready.'

He stood by the bucket, chewing nervously at his lip. She slumped down beneath the window and sobbed. Roja whistled as he approached the cell door. When she heard him turn the key, she wailed even louder. He walked swiftly towards her, leaving the keys in the lock.

'There, there my pretty, what's the matter?'

'I want to go home,' she said, jerking her shoulders dramatically.

'You might be in for a surprise,' he said, kneeling down and reaching out to caress her hair. She let him, even leaning her head into his hand, nuzzling like a dog with its master.

'Really?' she said, looking up at him. His stale breath made her want to gag.

'I've brought the wagon. You're going on a little trip,' Roja said in a cheery voice. The next moment he was sprawling on the floor, Martín standing over him. He raised the bucket to hit the kidnapper again but only landed a glancing blow on Roja's raised arm. She ran through the open cell door.

'You little bitch,' Roja screamed, 'you tricked me.'

Martín threw the rest of the bucket's contents in Roja's face. The kidnapper howled and clawed at his face to remove the excrement. Hauling himself to his feet he staggered towards Martín.

'Quickly,' she pleaded from the other side of the cell door.

Martín turned, but he was too late. Roja had him by

the arm. He backhanded the boy across the face and he fell heavily. Roja advanced on him. 'I'm going to make you eat this shit!'

She screamed, 'No! Roja. Please, leave him.' But he wasn't listening. He was completely enraged. She no longer had any influence over him.

Martín scuttled backwards. 'Just go,' he shouted.

She froze, not knowing what to do.

'Go!'

Why not lock the door and escape? She'd come back for Martín. Then Roja picked her brother up by the throat and shook him viciously. His face turned red. He tried to scream, but only a muted gargle escaped. Glancing back she saw that the outer door was open. Roja wouldn't kill him. She could run and bring help.

'You little bastard!' Roja shouted as he smashed Martín against the wall.

She wrenched the barrette from her hair and took out the long pin. Clenching it in her fist she ran into the cell and drove it as deeply as she could into the top of Roja's thigh. Screaming in pain, he let Martín drop. He looked down at the pool of crimson spreading across the top of his leg. He reached out to grab her, but she was too quick for him. Martín staggered to his feet, clutching his throat. He kicked Roja in the shin. The thug bent down to rub it and they dodged smartly through the door. She tried to turn the key. It was stiff in the lock. Roja hobbled towards them.

'Help me!' she screamed, furiously waggling the key.

Martín cupped his hands around hers and they forced the key to turn.

'Now *you* can eat the shit,' Martín said, his voice raspy.

They ran, accompanied by Roja's screams and the sound of his body smashing against the cell door. Martín pulled the heavy outer door shut and she locked it. Roja's cries of frustration were muffled. Blinking away shards of sunlight they looked around. A horse whinnied to their right.

'Can you manage the wagon?' she asked.

'Uncle Isaac lets me do it when we go to the estate in the summer,' he replied with pride.

She trailed her fingers through the long grass. If only they had time to stop and think. But Ramos could appear at any time. Or maybe Roja would have the strength to break through the cell door? But he couldn't possibly break through the outer door. He wasn't that strong. Surely?

Nearing the wagon, she caught the salty scent of what she thought must be the sea. They must still be in Seville! Martín climbed up on the wagon and patted the flanks of the large black cob that was waiting patiently. She was about to join him when she heard her name being shouted. She turned and saw a hand snaking towards her ankle.

'Not so fast,' Roja said as he stretched his arm to grab at her through the window bars.

'No,' she screamed.

Martín jumped down from the wagon and pulled her away. A red-faced Roja sneered at them from behind the bars, spittle forming at the sides of his mouth. His sneer turned into a broad grin. Putting an index finger and thumb into his mouth he gave a loud whistle and then a cry of, 'Away!'

The horse bolted, the wagon shuddering behind it.

Roja laughed, long and loud, his face turning even redder. 'That'll teach you, you little bastards.'

They ran.

Roja screamed after them, 'I'll get you, you've not seen the last of me.'

CHAPTER
TWENTY-SEVEN

'I suspected as much,' Isaac said to Ali, as they stood alone by the fountain in the courtyard. The late afternoon sun created diamonds of light in the pool.

Gabriel and Pedro were completing their packing. After the Talavera meeting Isaac was determined to return to Seville immediately. He'd dismissed Abdul Rahman's counsel to make an early start in the morning.

'Being back here, sharing food with my brother. It made me realise how much I miss Granada,' Ali said.

'I can't persuade you to change your mind?'

'What's left for me in Seville?'

His silence was recognition that the apothecary was right.

'My brother has a derelict shop in the Albayzín that I can turn into an Apothecary. And I can live here with him.' He smiled. 'I'll have a family again.'

He returned the smile. Ali's plan made sense. 'You'll be missed.' He clasped his friend's hand. 'I'll miss you.'

Ali pulled him into a brief hug.

'What will happen to your old shop?'

'Glad you asked. Here are the keys. Can you have the stock packed up and sent to me?'

'It would be no trouble at all.'

Gabriel appeared with a leather satchel slung over his shoulder. He shook hands awkwardly with the apothecary. They went out through the main door where Abdul Rahman and Pedro waited with the horses under the shade of the cypress trees. The falcon was on Pedro's forearm, nibbling at some meat between his fingers.

'Your stay has been far too short, my friends,' said Abdul Rahman as he pulled both Isaac and Gabriel into a hug. 'But you have my eternal gratitude for returning my brother to me, Alhmadulilah.'

Pedro shook hands with Ali, the falcon shrieking in apparent displeasure.

'Take these with you.' Abdul Rahman stuffed three small paper packages into their saddlebags. '*Ras-al-hanout*. You will cook with it and remember us.'

Isaac thanked him and thought, 'What on earth will Catalina do with the spices?'

They mounted their horses. He looked down from the saddle and said, 'Abdul Rahman, I can never thank you enough. We will never forget your kindness and your hospitality. Ma'aasalaama.'

'Rafaqatkal Salaama,' the brothers called out in unison as the group rode away.

I certainly hope we'll get home safely, Isaac thought.

❦

His frustration grew as they picked their way in single file through the congested lanes of the Albayzín in the early evening. He was eager to be galloping on the trail back to Seville. Perhaps they should have enjoyed one more night of Abdul Rahman's hospitality. They could have discussed at length what Talavera told them. And if they left early in the morning the way might have been clearer. But it was too late to change course now. He believed Talavera that Torquemada was behind the twins' kidnapping. It made sense that he wanted him out of Seville, it gave him an opportunity to shape the King's thinking. He'd prey on Ferdinand's constant financial worries, reminding him of all the revenue generated by the Inquisition's seizure of land and property. He'd argue that the same tactics should be employed in Granada, to make the *Mudéjar* pay. All under the guise of saving their souls. But what did Torquemada stand to gain by killing him? It must be pure vengeance, borne of frustration for having evaded his claws for so long.

He was embarrassed at being duped into leaving Seville on a fool's errand. He should have trusted his instinct, not Alejandro's information. His deputy had better not have been idle whilst he'd been away. Hopefully, he would have information on the twins' whereabouts. Perhaps they might even have been found? Was that too much to ask for? But what had Talavera said? You have to hope for salvation, to trust in God's essential goodness. Something like that. His faith in divine justice and mercy was certainly being tested now.

As the lanes widened Gabriel drew his horse alongside his father's. 'I think we're being followed.'

'By who? How do you know?'

'I keep seeing two riders in black cloaks riding white stallions every time I look around.'

Isaac twisted in his saddle to glance back.

Nobody.

'Are you sure?'

'Yes, Papa.'

He set his jaw. 'It could be nothing. It's busy. We're on the main thoroughfare out of Granada.' He thought for a moment. 'Don't look again. Wait until we get to the outskirts of the city, then just do as I do. Let Pedro know.'

Gabriel slowed his horse so he could rejoin Pedro and pass the message.

As the whitewashed buildings became sparser the road widened enough for the horses to trot. They passed a tavern and were about to leave the cobbles for the dusty trail, when he swerved his horse to enter a narrow lane on the left. Gabriel and Pedro followed. They dismounted and held the horses' reins.

Gabriel's steed whinnied; he patted its flanks to calm it.

Isaac placed a hand on the hilt of his rapier.

Pedro hooded the falcon to quieten it.

They waited in silence.

Two white stallions came to a halt at the entrance to the lane. Their black-cloaked riders seemed to be looking directly at them. Impossible to be certain, as their faces were lost in the shadows of their hoods. He began to unsheathe his rapier. The men flicked their reins and the horses cantered away.

They walked the horses around to the front of the

tavern, tied them up, and left them to drink from the water trough. He hoped this would give the cloaked riders time to get ahead of them. If they were ordinary travellers they would not come across them again. If they did, then there would be blood. He regretted his stupidity in bringing Gabriel along. He was still a boy who thought fencing lessons would enable him to prevail in a real sword fight. Hopefully, his son would not get the chance to prove him wrong.

Waiting until the sun was over the tip of the highest peak of the Sierra Nevada, he gave the order to proceed. Pedro gave him a hard look. He was a man of few words, but Isaac understood the message. Wouldn't it be safer to go back and spend the night at Abdul Rahman's house? He might be right, but Isaac was desperate to find out if the twins were safe. He couldn't bear to add their deaths to the responsibility he felt for the fate of their parents. Whatever choice he made he was putting his children in jeopardy. And by staying in Granada he might just be delaying the inevitable. Today was as good a day to be murdered as tomorrow.

He glanced up at the sky. They could probably ride for about another three hours before the light would fade. Then they would have to find somewhere secluded to sleep. Abdul Rahman had loaded their saddlebags with dates, bread and pomegranate juice. If they started at sunrise tomorrow and rode hard all day they could be home by the afternoon of the following day.

Pedro led the way as they left the cobbled streets behind, the hooded falcon in a wicker basket secured to the back of his saddle. As Isaac urged his horse forward from a canter to a gallop he was pleased that Gabriel kept pace with him. They followed a wide track at the base of a narrow, winding river gorge until the horses began to tire. There had been no sign of the cloaked riders. They dismounted in a clearing at the edge of a more densely forested area.

Isaac said, 'Give the horses water, time to cool a little, then we ride again.' The light was beginning to fade, but he hoped they would be able to make their way deep into a sheltered part of the forest before they slept.

Gabriel was the first to hear it. 'What's that?'

The faint, rhythmic noise sounded like a song to Isaac.

'Look,' Gabriel whispered, pointing to a line of three seemingly disembodied beacons of fire emerging from the forest. The light and the sound materialised out of the gloom to coalesce as three hooded friars attired in the brown habits of Franciscans.

Isaac recognised the words they were chanting, 'Pie Jesu Domine, dona eis requiem.'

The absolution of the dead.

The friars came to a halt and stood in a line about ten feet away from them, continuing to sing. It was an eerily disturbing sight, and he shivered as a chill ran through him. Pedro's falcon screamed in its cage and thrashed its wings.

The friar in the middle was a foot taller than his

companions. They stopped singing and the two shorter ones drew back their hoods in unison.

The tallest one – Isaac assumed he must be the leader – took a pace forward and said, 'Lost your way, gentlemen?' His voice was coarse, the manner gruff.

'Identify yourselves,' Isaac barked, placing a hand on the hilt of his rapier.

The leader threw back his head and laughed maniacally. The friars threw their torches at the horses who reared up, snorting and squealing. Pedro and Gabriel couldn't hold on as the reins slipped through their hands, and the horses bolted past the friars and into the forest.

'Come back,' Gabriel cried out.

The friars laughed and reached under their habits to pull out short swords. Isaac recognised them as falchions. Their sharp, single-edged blades were as adept at cutting down trees as slicing through flesh.

Flanked by Gabriel and Pedro, he unsheathed his rapier and saw his son do the same. But why did Pedro only have a dagger? His cudgel must be strapped to his horse. They were hopelessly outmatched. Their only chance was to kill the leader with one strike. Then it would be three against two.

The friars advanced, brandishing their falchions.

Isaac pointed his rapier at the tall friar, who had still not removed his cowl.

'Reveal yourself before you die, coward,' he snarled.

At a gesture from the leader, the friars stood still, with their weapons thrust forward. 'Kill the others first,' the leader said to his companions. 'I'll keep this one alive so he can watch them die,' he sneered, pointing his sword at Isaac.

The two friars moved forward again, sweeping their falchions through the air.

Pedro and Gabriel retreated.

Isaac stood his ground.

Then from behind them, out of the gloom, Isaac heard a thunder of hooves. He glanced back to see the two black-cloaked riders galloping their white stallions directly at them. They were wielding long, curved scimitars.

He raised his rapier.

So, today would be the day. His last on this earth.

Will Maria forgive me?

TWENTY-EIGHT

'Why, in the name of all that's holy, didn't you follow them into the tavern?' Torquemada bellowed at Andreas from behind his desk at the Castillo. He was angry that his siesta had been disturbed. But the servant with the unpleasant task of interrupting his slumber had told him that Brother Andreas insisted it was urgent.

'I... I... I didn't think it seemly of me to enter a tavern, Father. I've not been in one before. And this Bar Averno seemed rightly named. It looked hellish.' His neck sunk into his shoulders, his elbows tightening into his waist.

He enjoyed watching the friar shrivel. 'And she comported herself like a common slut?' A thin smile formed on his lips. 'Dressed like one as well?' The smile turned into a grin at the picture developing in his imagination.

'Yes, Father. The disguise was very good. I didn't know it was her at first when I saw her leave Casa de Felicidad with Señor Alejandro.'

'I suppose you think you deserve credit for not being fooled?'

Andreas bowed his head and remained silent.

He turned in his chair to look out over the Guadalquivir. The sun was past its zenith and making its descent. It would disappear behind the cathedral in a few hours. 'How long ago was this? What do you make of it? What do you think they were doing?' He fired the volley of questions as though he were a cannon.

'Not more than half an hour ago, I came straight here. I was nearby, as will become clear when I finish the whole story. I think they were looking for information about the children. That was uppermost in Isabel's mind when I first called on her, Father, if you recall.'

'Mmmmm. How did they seem to you when they left the tavern?

'I'm not sure what you mean, Father.'

'God's blood! Just tell me how they looked.' He turned and saw Andreas straighten and close his eyes, as though trying to recreate the memory.

'Isabel wasn't pretending to be drunk anymore. Her posture was that of a lady again. She was walking arm in arm with Alejandro.' Andreas took a deep breath. 'And she was talking very animatedly.'

'What did you overhear?' he asked in a low tone, not wishing to destroy the friar's concentration.

'Not much. I dared not get too close.'

He made a low, guttural sound.

'But I heard the word 'red.'

'Red? What's that got to do with anything?' Then he had an unpleasant thought. 'You heard nothing else?'

Andreas shook his head and opened his eyes.

'Then where did they go? Home, I suppose?'

'No.'

'Good God, man. Where?'

'Here.'

'Here?' he thundered.

'Yes, here.'

'Here? Where? How?'

'They crossed the Puente de Barcas, followed the Castillo walls and stopped beside a tree. They pulled aside some branches, peered through and then, I assumed, returned home. I didn't follow. I thought you would want to know immediately. That's why I disturbed you, Father.'

Torquemada pounded a fist on his desk. 'Get out! Get out!'

After confirming the existence of the tunnel Luisa had described Isabel and Alejandro quickly returned to Casa de Felicidad. They were sitting on either side of a table on the roof terrace. The moon was hidden by cloud, the cathedral bells had already announced Compline. Torches flickered from the other side of the now quiet, dark river — so dark that the Guadalquivir was almost lost from sight. And beyond the torch flames lay the Castillo, now invisible too, but looming over Isabel's mind.

'Now what do we do?' she said, breaking the silence that had seemed to last for hours, each of them absorbed by their thoughts, fears and imaginations. She could not allow the discovery of Torquemada's involvement to prevent them taking action. They must find a way forward, a way to rescue the children from his clutches.

Alejandro picked up his glass and took a sip of sherry. 'I wonder how your Papa would answer that question?'

'If only he was here to ask,' she said with some bitterness.

'I found it easy to give him advice when he had his difficulties.' He took another drink. 'But it's different when you're the one making the decisions. When *you're* responsible.'

She was about to tell him to toughen up when she had an idea. 'I'll pretend to be him and you can ask questions as though he were here. It seems to be my day for playing roles. I might as well continue.' She gave him a moment to consider. 'Ready?' She looked across at him and thought she could make out a faint smile. 'My dear Alejandro, what's to be done?' She continued in a gruff approximation of her father's voice. Now he was definitely smiling.

He sat up straight, getting into role. 'Señor.'

'Do you really still call him, "señor"?'

'Only in formal situations, which I thought this was. Alright, I'll start again.' He cleared his throat. 'Isaac, it appears Torquemada is behind the plot to abduct the children. What should we do?'

'How the hell should I know, Alejandro? You're the one who usually comes up with the bright ideas,' she replied, descending into a fit of giggles.

'Very amusing,' he said with irritation.

She gave him a broad grin. He relaxed and returned it. The role-playing had broken the silence and the tension, if nothing else. But then she felt guilty at finding enjoyment in a situation like this.

He inhaled deeply and sighed. 'We have to decide. What do we do with this information? We can't sit and do nothing.'

She murmured her agreement. 'To be clear, do we know that Ramos and Roja are the kidnappers?

'Yes. First,' he held up an index finger, 'you saw a blur of red when the children were taken. Second,' raising a middle finger, 'Catalina saw Ramos and Roja outside the house in the days before the kidnap. And, third,' adding a ring finger, 'Luisa saw them go into Torquemada's head-quarters via a secret entrance.'

'And don't forget they were seen running away from the fire at the Apothecary.' She reflected for a few moments. 'I think Papa's lawyerly response would be that the balance of evidence indicates they are almost certainly the kidnappers, but Torquemada's involvement is pure supposition.' She took Alejandro's silence as agreement. 'But it is highly likely. Who else would give them the power to enter the Castillo whenever they pleased?'

He jutted out his lower lip as he pondered his response.

She had never seen him make such an unguarded gesture.

'I tend to agree with your analysis, señor... I mean señorita,' he said with a smile. 'However, we are still left to ponder why Torquemada engineered the abduction and what to do about it. What we even *can* do about it.'

'Who knows why that devil does anything? He justifies everything from a warped sense of religious duty.'

'Indeed.'

'We do have one advantage though.'

'We do?'

'Yes. Torquemada doesn't know that we know. Unless Luisa has run to him or we were overheard.'

He shook his head, dismissing both possibilities.

'So, for once, we know more than the devil does.'

'Agreed. But how do we take advantage of our ... advantage?'

She thought for a moment and then said, 'I don't know.'

'If we don't act, he *will*.'

'Give me the night to think it over. Come back in the morning.' She reached across and gripped his forearm.

'My dear Isabel. There was one other matter.' He coughed. 'I hesitate to ask at a time like this, but who knows when I'll get another opportunity...'

Was he going to ask what she'd been hoping he would for weeks, months, even years? 'Just ask, Alejandro.'

'I should really wait for your Papa to return, but who knows ...' he trailed off.

'Just ask, Alejandro.'

'If I were to ask your Papa for your hand in marriage, would you accept?'

She jumped up and they embraced. They kissed clumsily at first, their lips touching lightly. Then he kissed her over and over, and she felt as though her body were ablaze. Her world seemed to go silent, as if it held its breath. She rested her head on his chest and felt his heart beating quickly. So, it *was* what love felt like.

Torquemada listened to the bells for Compline fade away. He knelt at his prayer desk. He couldn't focus – the correct words for the orison wouldn't come. Mumbling an 'Amen' and crossed himself. He stood up gingerly, clutching the side of the desk for support. He hobbled over to a chair by the hearth next to which a table was laid with a decanter of sherry and a pewter mug. After pouring a large measure, he took a long draught. It was bitter. He flung the mug across the room.

The clatter brought a knock at the door and a servant called out, 'Is there anything amiss, Father?'

'Go away!' he bellowed.

Damn these wretched people. Seville had been nothing but trouble since he and Alonso first came. Almost three years ago. His thoughts increasingly turned to Alonso. He had been one of the few who understood the mission at a primal level. He did what he was told but also took action on his own initiative. Action that, as Grand Inquisitor, it was better he didn't know about. It gave him plausible deniability. He could trust Alonso to follow instructions, but also to take other correct actions without being told to. If only he hadn't been found out. If only he'd been a better liar. He had a little too much conscience.

This fool Andreas was useful, but soft. He had a surfeit of empathy. You needed to see the bigger picture. It wasn't about this life. You had to consider your soul's destination. They had to save as many souls as they could. Sometimes that meant punishing earthly deeds. It was better to suffer in this life, as Jesus Christ had, to keep your place in the Kingdom of Heaven. Otherwise, the price was eternal damnation. Better a few moments of pain than to burn for all eternity. Alonso understood that. He needed him by his side again.

He would have talked to Alonso about what to do. Now Isabel was aware of those *ladrones*, would she connect them to the kidnapping? There was no reason for her to, and even if she did she had no evidence, not any that would stand scrutiny by Their Majesties. He could have her arrested as the heretic's daughter. It was accepted that her father was a crypto-Jew. They'd had sufficient evidence three years ago to detain Alvarez, before the King intervened. The rumours that Ferdinand's family was of *converso* stock must be true — it explained his sympathy and why he protected Alvarez. His Majesty disapproved of the Inquisition's more stringent methods. Ferdinand had once remarked that water torture proved nothing, except that you couldn't breathe with water in your lungs. Fool. He might be a King on earth but what did he know of heaven? The Inquisition's methods were sanctioned by Pope Alexander himself, and therefore approved by The Almighty.

He could easily send the *familiares* to watch Casa de Felicidad, talk to the neighbours and gather evidence of non-adherence to the True Faith – proof of heresy. Then he could arrest Isabel and have her executed before her father's return to Seville, if indeed he did come back. It would be a pity – he still harboured other plans for her. And Alvarez would be very upset, but what could he do? The Queen would protect the Holy Office. And Isabel's soul would be saved. But it was all too easy and she would never forgive him for the humiliation. And if he arrested her she would have to be questioned. Who knew where that might end up? He couldn't interrogate her himself. Didn't want to witness her pain. He wanted her love. And if he gave the responsibility to one of his inquisitors... they were sometimes a little over-enthusiastic. He couldn't bear it if she were to die at his hands.

He took out a string of rosary beads from the pocket in his habit and kissed the cross that hung at the base. He prayed The Almighty would help him to find a solution. If not custody, then what? He threaded the beads through his fingers and said the first of the Hail Marys. As he recited the fourth one, thank the Lord, it came to him. Why hadn't he thought of it before? It must be old age, not that he would admit it to anyone. He considered the plan from every angle, thinking through each outcome. It worked. Reciting the final Hail Mary, he kissed the cross and put the rosary away. Tomorrow morning. Early.

CHAPTER
TWENTY-NINE

The children ran towards the red-bricked warehouse. It was the only landmark they knew. Juana felt faint — she couldn't run much further. Perhaps some workers in there could help them? But as they got closer they saw the signs of neglect – doors off hinges, sagging roof. Abandoned. They turned in a circle. The way they had run from was just waste ground. The warehouse blocked their way forward. High stone walls loomed over them on either side.

'Look,' she said, pointing towards a narrow *calle* to one side of the warehouse. They had little choice. She reached for Martín's hand and pulled him forward. 'It'll be fine,' she said, hoping her voice suggested more confidence than she felt.

As they made their way deeper into the winding lane the walls sloped over them and cut out the daylight. It felt like night, even though it was still the middle of the morning.

'Where are we going?' Martín whispered.

'Away from them. We just need to keep moving.'

Eventually, they emerged into a small plaza. The houses on all four sides leant in towards each other. There was a deathly hush, broken by the clank of metal on metal. Peering into the gloom, she made out orange shards dancing in the air on the far side of the plaza. They walked towards the sparks and discovered they were being created by a blacksmith in a leather apron. He was hammering away at piece of red-hot metal on an anvil atop a large tree trunk.

'Please, señor, where are we?' she said.

The tall blacksmith stopped hammering and gave them a long look.

'Aren't you a strange pair? You look half-dead.'

At that, Martín fell to his knees and she started to cry. 'Help us,' she said.

The blacksmith picked him up with great ease and gently slung him over his shoulder. He took her by the hand and led her through a doorway behind the anvil. She was too weak and surprised to resist.

She cautiously placed a spoonful of the stew in her mouth. It tasted a lot better than the muck Ramos had given them the day before. The blacksmith's wife had ladled it out of a pot hanging from a wooden tripod that stood in the hearth. She was short, plump, and with kind eyes that reminded Juana of her mother. The children were sitting on either side of a wooden table set in the middle of the blacksmith's house. But it wasn't really a house, Juana thought. Just a room that contained everything they owned. There was a bed on the far side, the table they were sitting at, and a hearth for warmth and cooking. How different it was from their home, Casa de la Felicidad. She took a deep breath, suppressing the urge to bawl. Finishing her stew, she beamed as Martín asked for another bowl and demolished almost half a loaf of rye bread.

The blacksmith's wife looked on with pride. 'I make a wonderful stew, even if I say so myself,' she said.

'Yes, so I've heard you say many a time, my love,' her husband replied.

His wife gave him a playful slap across his back, and he grinned.

'Now that your bellies are full, I'd like to hear the story of how you came to be here, so far from home,' the blacksmith continued, settling himself on a stool next to the hearth. His wife stood beside him, placing her hand on his shoulder.

Juana glanced at Martín, who nodded his encouragement.

'Where are my manners? I'm Diego, the blacksmith, and Ynes is my missus.'

Ynes raised an eyebrow expectantly.

She stood up. 'I'm Juana and this is my brother, Martín.' At the mention of his name, her brother got to his feet and gave a deep bow.

Ynes gave a small, awkward curtsy. 'It's so lovely to

meet people with manners,' she said, clapping her hands with delight.

'We live in Casa de Felicidad in Seville with Señor Isaac Camarino Alvarez,' Juana continued.

Diego said, 'Him what works for the King?'

'Yes. You know him?' she asked with surprise.

'We know *of* him. Everyone around here does,' the blacksmith said. 'He's well respected for finding the real murderer of that boy, must've been three year ago. Not that Their Majesties ever admitted the truth, but we all know who did it. And why they killed Fernan. Beatriz and Rodrigo's boy, though she's passed on, God rest her soul.'

'Around here?' Martín asked.

'Triana,' Ynes said.

Juana squealed with joy. She remembered where Triana was from the lessons with Isabel. 'You mean we're near Seville?'

The blacksmith and his wife smiled.

'I knew I could smell the sea!' She recounted the story of their capture and imprisonment — omitting no detail.

When she'd finally finished, Ynes opened her arms wide and said, 'Come here my loves.' The emotion of the retelling swept the children into her warm embrace. She hugged them tightly to her. 'Now, you must have some more to eat.' She led them back to the table and produced fresh figs and almonds.

'We need to get you pair back to your family,' the blacksmith said. 'Right away.'

The children gave Ynes another hug, thanked her, and promised to return. Though Juana did not think Uncle Isaac would approve of them going to Triana. Isabel and Catalina might. Diego took each of them by the hand and led them quickly through the lanes. He didn't speak to them or to anyone that passed by.

She savoured the salty sea air in her nostrils as it became more pungent. 'Are we getting near the river?' she asked.

'Yes, only a few paces away. We'll get across the Puente de Barcas, then you can lead the way back to your house. You know where it is?'

She was silent, unsure.

Martín replied with a confident, 'Yes.'

They emerged from the gloom into the bright sunlight of mid-afternoon. They were standing atop a grassy mound. Ahead of them, the Guadalquivir river glistened as though covered with thousands of shards of tin. The pontoon bridge that led home was only a few yards ahead. Juana strained at Diego's hand, pulling him forward.

'Careful, young miss,' he said, 'let's just wait a few moments to see who might be about.'

The three of them sat down and surveyed the scene. To their left, the Castillo de San Jorge towered over them. To their right, on the further bank, the river flowed towards the Torre del Oro. She'd heard Isabel talk about it to Uncle Isaac. It was where his wife had been held when she'd been arrested. Where she'd died. But it was also the side of the river where Casa de Felicidad was. Home.

Diego looked from left to right every few minutes for what seemed like ages and ages to her. 'It's market day in Seville. Lots of people trying to cross the bridge. Might be good for us. Easier for you to go unnoticed.'

'What are we waiting for?' she whispered.

'As easy as it is for us to hide, others might be hiding too. Patience, young miss, I'll have you home soon enough.' He waited a few minutes more, then signalled for them to follow as he walked down the mound towards the bridge. They waited in line to cross. The queue moved steadily forward.

'Can't they go any faster?' she hissed.

They were about to set foot on the first vessel in the chain across the river when two men stood up from crouching positions on each side of the boat.

She screamed.

Martín cried out, 'No!'

The blacksmith stood still.

The crowd ahead appeared oblivious. Those waiting in line behind jostled and pushed ahead.

'We'll relieve you of your burden, blacksmith,' Ramos said, advancing from the left.

Diego took a step back, herding the children behind him.

Roja appeared from the right, grimacing at her. 'Told you I'd get you,' he snarled as he joined Ramos. She hid her face behind Diego. The horse must have bolted straight back to Ramos. He would have freed Roja. She remembered she'd stupidly left the keys in the lock. She should have thrown them away. They knew where Casa de Felicidad was from their spying, and that the only way for the children to return home was to cross the Puente de Barcas. All they had to do was wait.

The blacksmith reached into his apron and took out a large hammer. Turning his head, he whispered to the children, 'When I give the word, you run and you don't look back. You hear?'

They nodded their agreement.

'Your lives depend on it.'

He advanced towards the men, swinging his hammer in a wide arc in front of him. 'Let us cross and nobody gets hurt,' he said.

There were screams and shouts as those waiting in line dispersed.

'Don't be foolish, blacksmith. You're outnumbered,' Ramos said. He scowled at each of the children. 'And what are these brats to you?'

'Children, that's what they are. God's gift,' Diego snarled.

'Not got any of your own?' Ramos spat back.

The blacksmith stopped abruptly and stood very still.

'Bullseye!' Ramos cried out. 'You want to protect these *poor mites* because you never had your own,' he looked across at Roja, who laughed in a loud and forced way.

He didn't seem as kind now, Juana thought.

Diego raised the hammer above his head, hissing, 'Now!' at the children. He ran at Ramos and Roja. They each dodged to one side to evade the hammer, leaving a gap through which the children darted onto the bridge. They jostled and pushed their way through the crowd, never once looking back, doing exactly what Diego had said. Not even when they heard a piercing scream followed by a shout of, 'That'll teach you, you bastard.'

BOOK THREE

Seville

THIRTY

The ground shuddered as the white stallions thundered past Isaac. He watched in astonishment as their black-cloaked riders felled Pedro and Gabriel's attackers with one swing of their scimitars. The friars' torches fell from their hands. The riders brought their horses to a halt, jumped from their saddles and ran back to the fallen friars. Raising their swords high they thrust them down into their stomachs. The friars' screams pierced the night. He drew Gabriel to him, holding his head to his chest, grateful the encroaching darkness veiled the gruesome scene.

The leader held the circling riders at bay with his falchion. Pedro held his position, biding his time.

'Drop your sword, friar,' said one of the riders.

'You'll have to kill me,' the leader replied.

'Señor Alvarez. It's Khaled. You're safe,' called out the rider.

'Good God,' Isaac whispered to Gabriel, 'they're Abdul Rahman's men.'

His son hugged him with relief.

'Walk a few paces backwards and wait,' Isaac said to him.

He did as he was told.

Isaac breathed deeply and shook himself. 'Khaled, keep that one alive,' he said pointing his rapier at the leader. 'I want to know who sent them.'

'It's up to him, señor,' Khaled replied. 'He needs to put down his weapon.'

The horses continued circling the remaining friar. 'I'll die before I tell you anything,' he spat as he turned left and right to fend off the imminent attack.

As Isaac moved forward he caught sight of a blur of movement from his left. Then the friar was in the air, his falchion spinning. Pedro had timed his run so that the friar's back was to him as he shouldered him to the ground. Now Pedro sat astride him, repeatedly punching him in the face. Khaled and his companion stood by, watching in admiration.

'That's enough, Pedro,' Isaac shouted. 'We need him.'

Pedro turned with his fist raised, nodded, but slammed it down one last time. He stood up and said, 'Call yourself a man of God? You disgust me.' He kicked the friar in the ribs, panting with the effort of delivering the beating.

'Pedro,' Isaac said, 'stay with Gabriel and see if you can round up the horses. I want to ask our friend some questions. If he can still talk.'

The riders dragged the friar by his armpits and propped him up against a tree. After tying his hands behind his back, they picked up the dropped torches and thrust them into the ground at his feet. The torchlight sent flickering shadows across his battered, bloodied features. Khaled threw water in his face. His neck went limp and his head fell to his chest.

Khaled shook Isaac's hand and said, 'The master said you wouldn't accept our help. So he told us to follow you secretly and keep an eye on you until the morning.'

'I'm very grateful. You saved our lives.'

'Our great pleasure, señor,' he said with a bow.

'Start preparing a makeshift camp while I have a word with him.'

'Of course, señor.'

After the men left Isaac squatted beside the friar. 'You're lucky I didn't let him kill you.'

Struggling to lift his head the friar said through swollen lips, 'By Christ's fingernails, you'll get nothing from me.'

'Then I may as well let Pedro finish the job.'

He gave a weak nod.

'Who sent you?'

He saw a flash of defiance in the man's eyes as he said, 'It was God's will.'

'The Almighty sent you to kill a child?'

'A heretic and his child.'

'Thank you.'

'For what?'

'For confirming what I already suspected.'

He saw surprise and then fear in the friar's eyes.

'I could tie you to the tree and leave you out here for the boars and the bears to eat.' He paused. 'Or you might starve.'

'I was doing God's work and will receive my reward in heaven.' His head lolled forward and he mumbled what sounded like the Pater Noster.

He unsheathed his rapier and stuck the tip under the friar's chin, forcing him to lift his head. 'I may be a heretic, but I don't have the blood of innocent children on my hands,' he snarled into his face. 'I know who your master is and he will pay.' He withdrew the blade quickly, gashing the friar's chin and sending a stream of blood down his habit.

'Khaled, in the morning take this devil with you back to Granada,' Isaac called out. 'Deliver him to Talavera. Perhaps he can get the truth out of him.'

Pedro and Gabriel returned with the horses. They built a fire and the five of them finished making camp for the night. They unloaded the saddlebags and shared the dates, bread and pomegranate juice. At daybreak, they would ride as fast as possible back to Seville. To settle the score with Torquemada.

The children dodged through the market day crowd crossing the bridge. Their progress slowed by the women from Triana balancing large wicker baskets of fruit and vegetables on their heads. Goats and sheep were being taken from Seville to be slaughtered. Juana felt sick as they dodged the stinking clods of excrement. Were they shitting because they were being led to their death? She knew how they felt.

'I can see them!' Martín shouted.

She glanced back and saw a flash of red weaving towards them. Roja and Ramos were gaining. 'Help us!' she screamed. Nobody took any notice. They must look and smell like beggars. They hadn't washed properly for a week and their clothes were tattered. She remembered Isabel trying to teach them sympathy for the vagrants in Seville. She hadn't really understood then, but she was starting to.

They reached the end of the bridge.

'Which way?' she asked, glancing back over her shoulder.

Martín looked from left to right.

'You said you were sure!'

'Right, it's definitely right.' He pulled at her hand and ran.

She felt herself being tugged backwards. Someone had a hold of her dress. She tried to resist but fell heavily onto her bottom. She screamed out, 'Martín!' as he ran away from her. Powerful hands grasped her armpits and she was suddenly dangling in the air. 'Run!' she cried.

Her brother stopped and turned back.

'Don't move young man,' Ramos snarled. He put her down, crooked one arm around her neck and with the other took a dagger from his waist. He pointed the tip at Martín and then slowly placed it against her cheek. She tried to plead with her eyes for him to run, but he remained rooted. The cold metal of the blade scraped against her skin. She heard heavy footsteps from behind and started to cry.

'Don't cut her,' Roja said.

'Thought you wanted her dead after the way she tricked you,' Ramos said with steel in his voice.

'I did. I was angry. But she was kind to me,' Roja said softly. 'Besides, that's not what the master wants.'

'Tell that little runt to stay where he is and nobody gets hurt,' Ramos hissed in her ear.

She shook her head.

'By Christ, you're a foolish filly,' Ramos said.

'Make sure you get him and I'll spare her,' Ramos said to Roja.

'Just run!' she screamed.

As Roja advanced she saw tears welling in Martín's eyes. 'No, no,' he sobbed over and over. Roja led him gently back towards her. Ramos removed the dagger from her cheek but kept it in his hand.

'Thought you were braver than that,' Ramos said to Martín, who kept his eyes on the ground. 'But, on this occasion, you made the right choice.'

'I'm sorry,' Martín whispered to her

'It's ok, it's ok,' she replied between sobs.

'There's someone waiting for you,' Ramos said.

She felt her arm would come out of its socket as he yanked her forward.

'Come on boy,' Roja said softly as he put an arm around Martín's shoulder and coaxed him to follow.

'I like a family reunion. Makes me come over all sentimental,' Ramos said with a laugh.

Family? Mama and Papa? She became hopeful. Perhaps they'd been in hiding all these years. They planned the kidnap to keep them safe until they could all be reunited. But she soon found out how ridiculous that was. Ramos led them along the riverbank and away from the centre of Seville. Triana was to their right on the other side of the river. He was taking them to the Torre del Oro.

CHAPTER
THIRTY-ONE

Isabel spent a restless night, riven between the excitement of Alejandro's proposal, and the fate of the twins. She was to be married! She pictured the wedding day, the dress she would wear, and the house they would live in. And they would have children. She would become a real mother. Just like Mary, just like Mama. But wasn't she already a mother? She felt guilt burn through her for imagining so much happiness when the children were in mortal danger. With a shudder, she allowed herself to believe they really could be dead. In the early hours she resolved to put all thoughts of the wedding aside until the children were safe.

From her bedchamber window she watched the sun rise over the derelict house. Pigeons swooped in and out of the holes in the roof through shafts of golden sunlight. She remembered the time when she'd seen two men in the house. She'd thought they'd been spying, but dismissed it as paranoia. Now she was certain they'd been watching what the children did and when. So they could plan the best time to take them. They'd obviously decided it was too difficult to abduct them from Casa de Felicidad. So they took the opportunity afforded by *Juevos Santos*. They were in the open, the streets were crowded. It was perfect. It was all Torquemada's doing. But why would he kidnap them? He wanted something he couldn't be seen to take directly. Was it her? He had tried once, years ago. Or was it about Papa?

A knock at her bedchamber door was followed by Catalina calling, 'Señorita, señorita, you must come quickly. You have a visitor.'

Of course she did. It was all beginning to make sense. She dressed in a loose-fitting blue gown, cinched around the waist with a braided belt. She put a dagger in a leather scabbard and attached it to the belt, out of sight, at her back.

Torquemada was waiting for her in the parlour; sitting in one of the high-backed chairs positioned either side of the hearth. Leaning forward, he supported his chin atop hands cupping the bulbous end of his walking stick. He did not move, did not say anything as she walked towards him. He flicked his eyes at the other chair.

She shook her head. 'I'd prefer to stand. Father,' she said, adjusting her belt, reassuring herself that the dagger was still there, safely hidden. She clasped her hands loosely in front of her. Glancing through the window she saw three men standing by the fountain. Two red uniformed guards and a friar – Brother Andreas nervously pacing up and down.

Torquemada breathed heavily through his nose and cleared his throat. Was he considering how to proceed? It was most unlike him to be indecisive. He sat back, resting his cane against the arm of the chair. She held his gaze with what she hoped was a blank expression and remained silent. She would not give him anything to feed on.

'Do you know why I'm here?' he said in a low voice, each word carefully enunciated.

'Brother Andreas,' she inclined her head towards the friar, 'said that you were concerned about me, with Papa not being here.'

He curled his bottom lip out and tipped his head from side to side.

He was waiting for her to reveal something. She would answer his questions with as little information as possible.

'I had hoped you would have responded by coming to see me.' He looked sadly at her. 'I waited for you.'

'I thought it was my choice, Father.'

'Have you heard from your Papa?'

'No. Father.'

'Your brother's with him?'

'He is, as I'm sure you know.'

He smiled. 'And you assume they're safe? Even though you've heard nothing from them for... it must be a week now.'

'As you know only too well my Papa is a resourceful man. I'm sure he will return soon.'

'Will he now? Only The Almighty is entitled to such certainty.'

'Yes, Father, of course.'

'And he'll bring those poor orphans with him?'

'I've prayed very hard for their rescue, Father.'

'Whilst your Papa has been away I've been keeping a close watch on this house.'

Her eyes widened – she couldn't help betray her feelings.

'Why are you surprised? It's my duty to care for all my flock, especially the younger, vulnerable ones. And certain matters have again been brought to my attention regarding this household.'

She laced her hands behind her back, touching the hilt of the dagger.

'I've been informed that no smell of lard comes from the kitchen.' He wrinkled his nose. 'Only the aroma of olive oil.' Something dark passed across his face. 'The oil of the Jews.'

She opened her mouth to speak, but he cut her off with a sweep of his hand.

'No haunch of ham in the window. No smoke from your chimney on the Sabbath.' Father Alonso brought all this to my attention years ago. At that time was merciful.' He raised an eyebrow. 'But I cannot continue to ignore such obvious signs of heresy.'

'Father, all this is easy to explain. The apothecary tells us that olive oil is much healthier and –'

'Enough of your lies! I've known for a long time that your father is a heretic,' he said, his voice rising. 'He's been fortunate to have His Majesty on his side, but even his protection is no longer enough.' He thumped the arm of the chair to emphasise his words. 'If he returns he will be arrested, interrogated and,' he paused, breathless with outrage, 'purged in the fire.'

She looked down and placed a palm on the handle of the dagger.

He took several deep breaths. 'Of course, my child, all of this... unpleasantness is only necessary to save his soul. If I do nothing he will be damned to hell for all eternity.'

And he will never rejoin Mama, she thought. He will never honour her dying wish. She loosened her grip on the dagger.

'My child, you are innocent in all of this. You are just his daughter. Forced to go along with his wishes.' A look of sympathy crossed his face. 'Your poor Mama died for his heresy.'

'Under your interrogation,' she hissed, gripping the dagger tightly again. She was surprised by a gentleness that seemed to cross his face, and he looked away from her for the first time. Was he feeling guilty? But he was right, Mama died because of Papa's beliefs.

'I know your opinion of the Inquisition. I also know you are a pious believer in the True Faith. You must see this is the only way to save your father's soul.' He set his jaw and his eyes hardened. 'I just need one more piece of solid evidence to prove that I'm doing the right thing.'

'So you can protect yourself from His Majesty.'

He inclined his head. 'Yes, that as well. But, more importantly, so that The Almighty will be satisfied.' He inhaled deeply. 'And I know you can provide me with that proof.'

'Why don't you just ransack the house?'

'I could,' he said, tilting his head from side to side, 'but then I would have to arrest you. I would prefer it if you cooperated. And The Almighty would look more favourably upon you.'

She looked out of the window to give herself time to think. The guards were sitting on the bench. Brother Andreas was walking around the fountain, head bowed in prayer. The chest containing the Torah under Papa's bed was all the proof Torquemada would need.

'I would like to give you time to think, even to pray on your decision... but,' he waited until she held his eyes again, 'the twins' lives are at stake.'

'What do you mean?' She took a step towards him, still clenching the dagger.

'My spies have discovered where they're being kept. If *you* save your father's soul I will do *my* best to save them.' He paused. 'But I cannot release them into the care of a heretic. It would be a sin.'

'I know you had them kidnapped.'

'Yes, of course you do.' He gave her a wry smile. 'I know more about you and Señor Alejandro's 'investigation' than you think.'

'What do you think you know?' she sneered.

'I wonder what your father would think of you visiting a tavern, dressed as a slattern?'

She was stunned for a moment. How did he know? He must have had her followed. One of his *familiares*? Or someone she knew? She glanced into the courtyard at Andreas. Could the friar have been spying on her? It didn't really matter. Then she felt fury rising in her, took a step towards him and pulled the dagger halfway out of its sheath.

'What is it to be? Do your religious duty and save your father's eternal soul and the lives of those poor orphans?' He narrowed his eyes. 'Or damn him to hell and have their deaths on your conscience?'

She was clenching her jaw so tightly that she felt her teeth might crack. She withdrew the dagger and pointed it at arm's length into his face.

She was chilled by his lack of reaction. It was as if he'd expected it.

He grabbed her wrist and pulled the dagger towards his heart.

She grimaced as his foul breath filled her nostrils.

'If you murder me I will become a martyr and the Pope will make me a saint. Andreas has instructions to let the twins rot,' he snarled. 'You will be arrested and executed, as will your father, once we search the house and find the evidence of his heresy. And I will be looking down from heaven.'

His grip tightened on her wrist. She bit the inside of her cheek to distract herself from the pain. She would not give him the pleasure of hearing her cry out.

'I have no fear of death.'

Staring into his obsidian eyes, she pushed the dagger.

He did not resist. 'Whatever you decide, one of you is going to the Castillo.'

He released her and said, 'Take the righteous path, my child.'

CHAPTER
THIRTY-TWO

Isaac urged the gelding forward over the loose rock of the narrow track. The horse skittered and lost its footing. For a moment he thought he might fall, but the horse nimbly regained its balance. They had to get back home fast, to stop Torquemada. If he was behind the attempt on his life, then Isaac was certain he was also responsible for kidnapping the twins. He must have wanted to lure him out of Seville. And there was only one reason he could think of. Isabel.

'Be careful,' he cried out to Gabriel. Glancing back, he saw his son had navigated the treacherous section of scree with ease. He'd evidently learnt something from the long hours in the saddle over the past week. The sun was nearing its peak, arcing its way through an armada of grey clouds. They were near and should be home within the hour. A short time later, they were forced to slow down by the crowds of peasants heading towards the city gates. God's blood, it must be market day. No matter what else was going on in the world, trade continued, he thought.

Gabriel drew up alongside him and they ambled forward, picking their way past wagons full of almonds, barley, and wheat.

'Papa, are we going straight home?'

'Yes, but we have to make a stop first.'

'But we need to get home urgently?'

'We do. To ensure we succeed I need you to do just one thing.'

'What is it, Papa?'

'I need you to carry out an extremely important errand. It is of the utmost secrecy.'

Gabriel looked across at him questioningly.

'I need you to promise, on your Mama's soul, that you will not reveal this to anyone.' He paused. 'Not even your sister.'

'I promise, Papa,' he said solemnly.

'Listen carefully. I need to confess something to you.'

'Confess?'

'Yes, confess.'

A look of astonishment crossed his son's face.

'To prepare you for what might happen when we get home.'

Isabel paced the courtyard, waiting impatiently for Andreas' return. Torquemada had dispatched him to bring the twins home. She had insisted on their safe return before she would give him evidence of Papa's heresy. The bells had been ringing for the Terce midmorning prayers when Andreas left. The sun was now high in the sky. What was taking so long? The bodyguards lounged on the bench; Torquemada was still in the house. She saw him through the window on his knees with his back to her, praying. She could change her mind — he would be an easy target. If only she hadn't agreed to relinquish the dagger to him. There was sudden pounding from the external door. They were back!

Catalina heaved open the door to reveal Andreas with an arm around each of the twins. Isabel's joy quickly turned to shock at their appearance. Juana's hair was matted, her face smudged with dirt, dress torn. Martín's face was bruised and he rubbed at his left arm as though it was injured. She ran towards them calling their names and they tried to pull away from Andreas.

'Stop!' thundered Torquemada.

The guards blocked her and gripped the handles of their swords. Andreas gave her a mournful smile and lowered his eyes.

'Let. Them. Go. You *promised*,' she shouted at Torquemada.

'I did. I will. Once you keep your part of the bargain,' he replied, steadying himself on his cane.

She screamed in frustration. If only she had the dagger, she would have thrust it through his heart. 'Out of my way,' she snarled, pushing past him and running up the stairs to Papa's bedchamber. She pulled the wooden chest from under the bed. Locked. Picking it up she found it surprisingly light. She carried it easily down the stairs.

She hurled it at Torquemada's feet, where it landed with a heavy thud. 'Now give me the children.'

'Open it,' he said.

'I don't have the key.'

He jutted his chin toward a guard. He picked up the chest, raised it above his head and smashed it to the ground. Shards of wood flew across the courtyard. The children sobbed. A guard restrained Catalina as she moved towards them. A book tumbled towards Torquemada. With a hand on his cane he eased himself down to pick it up. He turned it back and forth.

'What's the meaning of this?' he yelled at her, thrusting the book in her face. She took the Book of Hours and clutched it to her chest.

'It was Mama's. She loved it.'

'I know what it is!' He pounded his cane on the ground. 'It's not proof of anything except your mother's piety. I'm not interested in that. Where's the evidence of your father's heresy?'

Catalina gasped.

'I thought it was there. I did my best. Now release the children.' She looked across at them. 'Please, Father Tomás, please.'

'Do you really think begging me after reneging on our agreement will save them?' He motioned with his head to the guards and said, 'Return them to the Torre. I will question them later.' The guards each took a child by the neck.

'No, no, no,' Isabel sobbed. 'I will give you proof.'

'Wait,' Torquemada said to the guards.

Catalina was shaking her head, her cheeks wet with tears.

Isabel drew herself to her full height and inhaled deeply. 'I have seen my father, Isaac Camarino Alvarez –'

'Wait,' he commanded. Reaching into his habit he produced a small Bible. 'Let's do things properly.'

She put a palm on the Bible and held his eyes with cold fury.

'Start again,' he said with a smile. 'Please.'

'I know that my father, Isaac Camarino Alvarez, reads the Torah.'

Catalina gave an anguished cry as she crossed herself.

'I know he says the prayers of the Jews.'

Juana's sobs grew louder.

'You swear this by Almighty God?' he said.

'I do.'

'And you will sign a written affirmation of your father's heresy?'

She nodded.

He replaced the Bible in his pocket. 'Say it.'

'I will sign a written affirmation attesting to my father's heresy.'

'Brother Andreas, do you confirm that you have witnessed Isabel state that His Majesty's adviser, Isaac Camarino Alvarez, is a heretic?'

She looked at Andreas. He held her eyes and she sensed his struggle. He had no choice.

'I do so confirm.'

'Release the children.'

She knelt and opened her arms as Juana and Martín ran into them. Hugging the children tightly, she kissed their cheeks. The Book of Hours dropped to the ground, its spine split.

'We have done God's work,' Torquemada intoned as he crossed himself.

Catalina was wailing.

'What a strange God you worship, one who endorses inflicting pain on women and children.' The voice came from behind Andreas, who remained in the doorway. Isabel was wracked by shock, hope, and fear as the voice manifested itself into a physical presence.

'What an opportune moment for you to join us,' Torquemada said. His tone was light and welcoming. 'I hope you heard your daughter's testimony?'

She covered her open mouth with her hands. Staring at Papa for a long moment, Isabel tried to find the words to explain her actions. She couldn't, and she dropped her eyes.

'You did well, my child, you did very well. You spoke the truth.' Isaac smiled at her sadly. 'I'm truly sorry you had to.'

Torquemada grimaced. 'Enough of the family reunion. Guards, arrest this heretic and take him to the Torre.'

She drew the twins to her. They were silent. Numbed by the same shock she felt. She held Papa's eyes as the guards grabbed him under his arms. He held her eyes as they dragged him backwards through the door into the street. She brushed tears away. Torquemada hobbled past her without a word or a glance. Andreas looked at her for a moment, made the sign of the cross, and turned to follow his master.

She picked up the damaged Book of Hours and shepherded the children into the house.

CHAPTER
THIRTY-THREE

He'd expected to share a damp, crowded cell with other heretics. Instead, the surly gaoler showed him into a small, clean, windowless room. Isaac sat on the bed and was surprised by how comfortable the straw mattress was. There was a chamber pot under the bed, an earthenware bowl to wash in, and a stock of candles. He was even more astonished when the gaoler returned with a fresh white smock, a jug of drinking water, a basket of bread and a plate of thinly sliced ham.

After changing out of his dirty clothes into the smock he sat down to eat. The forbidden meat must be Torquemada's idea of a jest. On reflection, he decided the bastard was incapable of humour. It must be meant as a temptation. If he ate the ham it was a sign he was willing to recant and seek mercy. He was hungry and finished all the bread, leaving the meat untouched. He'd just finished when the viewing hatch in the cell door slid open.

The gaoler growled through broken teeth, 'Lights

out. Time to get some sleep, señor. You'll need it.' He cackled as he slammed the hatch shut.

He snuffed out the candle, lay down, and pulled the thin cover over him. What did this special treatment mean? What message was Torquemada trying to send? That he didn't need to imprison him with other heretics who would inform on him in order to secure their own release? He'd already confessed, Torquemada didn't need to hear him confess again. But he was sure there was more to it. Then he had it. When His Majesty found out about his incarceration Torquemada could claim that he'd treated him in a manner befitting a special adviser. And the evidence for his heresy was cast iron– out of his own daughter's mouth, witnessed in public by a friar.

They would come for him in the morning and take him for interrogation. Just as Maria and Juan had been. To recant his apostasy. To express contrition for being a crypto-Jew. Would they stretch his limbs to breaking point on the rack? Or pinion him to an *escalera* and pour water down his throat until he believed he was drowning? He did not know – and did not want to know – what they'd done to Maria and Juan. Whatever torture they'd suffered had not broken them. Juan had not given the names of the others in their secret prayer group; Maria had not betrayed him. But Isabel had. Just as he had expected her to. Torquemada had found a unique way to torture her. Threatening her with imprisonment and the killing of the twins if she did not give him up. Convincing her that if he confessed his sins and recanted he would still go to heaven. To be with Maria. She had not had a choice. He was not angry. She had done the righteous thing. Just as Torquemada expected her to.

Physical escape from the Torre was impossible. Another form of freedom was possible. He could break the earthenware jug and use the shards to cut his wrists. If he did it without screaming he would bleed slowly to death before they came for him. He was going to die anyway, why not do it at a time of his choosing? Without the public humiliation, without the pain of torture. He wouldn't put it past Torquemada to have put the jug there deliberately. A further temptation. He would then claim suicide as proof of guilt.

He punched himself on the chest, punctuating each blow by muttering, 'Coward, coward, coward.' If Juan and Maria could face torture, so could he. And suicide was a mortal sin, whether you were Jewish or Catholic. It would ensure he would never see his dearest Maria again. He turned over and tried to sleep, hoping she would come to him.

Isabel waited outside Gabriel's bedchamber and listened. He'd returned home shortly after Papa's arrest. She told him briefly what had happened. He said nothing and went upstairs. She hadn't seen or heard from him since. It was late afternoon now. She tapped on his door with a knuckle.

'Gabriel. I'm coming in to light some candles.'

Nothing.

She tried the handle, expecting the door to be locked,

but it opened. Her brother lay face down on the bed, snoring. She lit several candles and drew the curtains. Sitting on the edge of the bed, she gently shook his shoulder.

He grunted and turned over. 'I've hardly slept for the past week,' he said with a yawn. He rubbed at his eyes, which were red.

'Have you been crying?'

He gave her a small smile. 'Just the dust from all the riding.'

He sat up and hugged her. At first she didn't know how to respond, it had been so long since he'd held her. Then she returned his embrace and kissed the top of his head.

'I'm sorry, Gabriel. I didn't know what to do.' She felt her eyes brim with tears.

'It's alright, sister. Papa explained it all to me.'

'What?' She pushed him away from her, holding his face in her hands. 'When?'

'On the way back, after the friars tried to assassinate us.'

'What are you talking about?'

He told her about the murderous attempt on their lives and how Abdul Rahman's men saved them. How Papa warned him what Torquemada might try to do next.

'You mean he predicted that he would blackmail me into telling lies about Papa.' She thought for a moment. 'To admit he was really a Jew,' she whispered.

His smile surprised her. 'It's alright, you don't have

to keep the secret any longer. Papa told me. He confessed it all to me.'

She walked over to the window. The outline of the deserted house where Roja and Ramos had spied on them was dimly visible. She didn't know whether to laugh or scream or cry. Perhaps all three?

'It will all work out, sister. We just have to stay brave and patient.'

She'd thought her brother would be angry with her, shout at her. She hadn't expected this calmness, this maturity, this... acceptance. Papa had been so wise, so thoughtful.

'Papa thought it all through. He has his plans, he knows what he's doing. I've done what he asked me to.'

She spun around to face him. 'What exactly did he ask you to do?' Now she doubted Papa's wisdom. Why would she ask Gabriel to do something that was undoubtedly dangerous?

'It's all over the city,' came a deep voice from the doorway. 'Your father's been arrested?'

Alejandro was scowling, his eyes hooded and dark.

Not now, she thought. She couldn't cope with him as well as Papa and Gabriel.

Catalina bobbed her head from behind Alejandro and said, 'I did ask the señor to wait downstairs, but he wouldn't have it, señorita.'

'For goodness' sake Catalina, it hardly matters,' she said sharply. Go and finish preparing dinner. Set an extra place for the señor.'

Her irritation with Catalina snapped her out of her mood and she regained her self-possession. She walked towards the door. Alejandro did not move, his jaw tight. She held his eyes, hoping he would understand that now was not the right time. His expression softened, and he moved aside with a small bow. Going down the stairs, Catalina bustling ahead of her, she heard him questioning Gabriel. He was responding excitedly. Did he really believe that everything was going to turn out well? What exactly had Papa asked him to do? Perhaps Alejandro would get it out of him.

Isabel and Alejandro sat silently in the gloom of the roof terrace. She'd told Catalina not to bother lighting any lanterns. She wanted to be enclosed by the night. On the small table between them was a full carafe of sherry and two empty mugs. She was grateful dinner was over. She'd eaten so little of the mutton stew that Catalina had arched an eyebrow and sighed. Gabriel was ravenous and finished two plates. Catalina beamed at him. She didn't care. The twins ate well and behaved as though nothing serious had happened. Juana breathlessly told the story of their kidnapping as though it was just a big adventure. Martín expressed concern for their saviour, the blacksmith – Diego? – Isabel wasn't listening properly. She vaguely promised to send Rodrigo to Triana to enquire after him in the morning.

'Did Gabriel tell you anything?' she asked.

'He described the attempted assassination and their escape. He told me about Isaac's confession. Isn't that enough?' he said curtly. 'Was there something else?' His tone was cold.

'He didn't say anything about what Papa asked him to do?'

'Nothing.'

'There's something very important that he won't tell me.'

Alejandro sighed deeply. 'Can you explain to me why you did it?' he asked, staring straight ahead into the night.

'Why I killed my father?'

'Isabel –'

'No,' she cut him off, 'that's what you mean, isn't it?'

He said nothing.

She sensed his seething frustration. 'Torquemada promised to spare the twins. I couldn't let them die.'

'I understand that, but...'

'But what?'

'They're not your blood.'

His callousness was shocking. 'Torquemada said that if Papa recanted he would go to heaven, to be with Mama.'

'Whilst Gabriel grows up without a father, as an orphan?' He paused. 'Haven't you both suffered enough?' he said gently.

'Would you prefer he grow up without his sister?'

He opened his mouth to reply but she interrupted him again. 'If I hadn't given him the evidence he would have arrested me as a heretic on some charges cooked up by his spies.'

'We would have had you released. Torquemada's power is waning, especially with Ferdinand.'

'You can't be sure of that.'

'No, not entirely, but I'm confident we would have had a good chance. Ferdinand could have overturned the gossip of spies. It's more difficult to ignore the testimony of a heretic's daughter.'

She gripped the arms of the chair. 'I know what I've done, and I know it can't be undone. I don't need you to lecture me. Besides...'

He was silent, apparently waiting for her to complete the thought. When she didn't he asked, ' "Besides," what?'

'It's the truth.' She sighed. 'And I know you must know that.'

He was silent again for a long moment. 'What's the truth got to do with anything? Your father's a good man. He doesn't deserve this.' The anger was clear in his tone.

'And I do?'

He went to the balustrade and looked out over the river.

'I think you should go,' she said.

'We could still try,' he said into the night.

'To talk to His Majesty?'

'Yes. It couldn't do any more harm.'

Did she have the strength to plead for her father's life? She was confused. Hadn't she already done the right thing? Then she felt a surge of fury. Why didn't Alejandro understand that there had been no good choices? Why did he think it would have been better for the twins to die and for her life to be in danger?

'I will talk to His Majesty. On one condition.'

'Anything,' he said, turning to face her.

'Whatever the outcome, you leave me alone.' She hesitated. 'You accept that I release you from your proposal of marriagte.' She searched his face, trying to judge his response, but there was not enough light to be certain. There was definitely anger and sadness. But was there also relief?

He stood very still for a few moments. Giving her a deep bow he said, 'As you wish, señorita.'

THIRTY-FOUR

The grinding of a key in the lock woke Isaac up. He had no idea of the time; it was pitch black in the windowless cell.

'Wakey, wakey,' said the gaoler as he entered carrying a tray. 'Some fine victuals, señor, for you to break your fast on,' he said mockingly. 'Got to keep up your strength.'

He sat up in bed but said nothing. The gaoler set the tray down on the bedside table with a small bow. He lit two candles. 'I'd be quick about it if I was you, the Grand Inquisitor requests your presence.'

He continued to ignore him.

The gaoler bent, put his face close and whispered, 'I'd enjoy a good long shit. Probably your last.' Clapping him on the shoulder, he laughed and left.

He ignored the food but took a long draught of water. He washed his hands, knelt at the bed, clasped his hands and recited the Kaddish prayer. It should only be said with a quorum of ten Jews, but he didn't think The

Almighty would mind, under the circumstances. It might be his last opportunity. He said the final 'Amen' and started to rise to his feet.

'Amen,' came a sonorous echo from behind him.

He turned to see Torquemada leaning on his cane in the doorway. He hadn't heard him come in, he must have been lost in prayer. Isaac held his gaze.

'I was curious to see how you people prayed, so I had the Kaddish translated.'

He did not reply.

'The sentiment is very similar to the Pater Noster. I was quite surprised. If only you people would follow the ways of the True Faith we might all get along.'

He folded his arms and remained silent.

Torquemada banged his cane on the flagstone. 'Quite right, no time for religious disquisition. Let's get on with it.' Walking out of the cell he called out, 'Come with me.'

Isaac followed him through a maze of narrow, stone corridors. Their shadows flickered in and out of the light thrown from torches crackling in sconces. They passed cells filled with prisoners reaching out through bars begging for their help. A tiny blonde-haired girl with large eyes pulled at Isaac's smock. He stopped and smiled at her.

She whispered, 'Help us, señor, please.'

He didn't know how to tell her that he was just like her. Powerless and doomed.

He tried to memorise each of the turns, but after about the tenth he gave up. Torquemada never faltered; he obviously knew this place very well. They eventually reached the end of a particularly long corridor to be confronted by a large, arched wooden door. On it was emblazoned the royal insignia urging the faithful to, 'prove their true loyalty to Isabella the Catholic.' A short gaoler stood guard. The sound of a woman's scream came faintly from behind the door. The gaoler took a large key from his waist, reached up, and inserted it into the lock. As the door opened the screams grew louder. Isaac wanted to run. He peered back. There were no guards. How far would he get? He turned back to see that Torquemada had already entered. The gaoler raised an eyebrow and held the door open expectantly. He walked through and the door clanged shut behind him.

Isaac stood alone on a small square of flagstones. Ahead of him a steep flight of stone stairs dropped into semi-darkness. He heard Torquemada's cane catching on each step. As Isaac descended the smell of sweat and excrement grew in his nostrils. The temperature fell and the screams suddenly stopped. By the time he reached the bottom he was shivering. He wasn't sure whether it was from cold or fear.

'Yes, it's much colder than it used to be when it was the Moors' bathhouse,' Torquemada said.

He looked around and as his eyes got used to the half-light he understood why he was here. They were in a large circular room, about fifty paces across. At the far end, he could make out a clerk and a physician sitting at a large, rectangular table. The clerk would record the details of the interrogation and the physician was there to monitor the health of the accused. The inquisitors didn't want the heretics to die too soon, not before they could confess and recant. At one end of the table were ten earthenware jugs. For the water cure.

In the centre of the room stood a tall, muscular man in a black cloak. His face was covered by a black hood with eyeholes. The Seeker of Truth. He stood next to an *escalara*. A woman was tied to it, extended to her full length, arms and legs bound to the ladder. She was tipped so that her head was lower than her feet. Iron prongs held her jaws open, her nostrils were stopped with muslin rags so she could only breathe through her mouth. As Torquemada walked towards her she thrashed her head from side to side.

'As you can see, we're well organised. I've implemented strict rules to ensure consistency and fairness. Due process must be followed. This is, after all, God's work. Come and stand next to me,' he said, beckoning Isaac with an index finger. He walked forward, clenching his jaw tightly, restraining himself from saying anything.

Torquemada raised an eyebrow and The Seeker picked up a jug. The clerk read out the charges, 'Your neighbours have told us that you wear luxurious garments on Saturdays and that smoke is never seen coming from your chimney on a Saturday. These are the habits of Jews on the "Sabbath". ' He said the final word with a sneer. 'You are a heretic and not a true Catholic. You are a Jewess pretending to share our faith. How do you plead?'

Is this what had happened to Maria? He felt sick at the thought.

The woman shook her head, her screams muffled by the gag. The clerk read out her statement, 'I have one silk shawl that my husband – he's a sailor – brought back for me from his voyages. I wear it to feel something soft. We don't always have enough money to buy kindling so can't make a fire. I'm not a *marrano*, I'm a faithful believer. These are wicked lies from my neighbours. I am innocent.'

Torquemada wiped the sweat away from her brow. The woman writhed under his touch. 'Do not worry, sister, we have taken every precaution to ensure natural justice and that God's mercy will prevail.'

He looked at the physician, who opened his palm to The Seeker. Water slopped from the jug as he walked towards the woman. He draped a linen cloth over her gaping mouth and poured. The water washed the cloth to the back of her throat, stopping her from spitting it out. Her gasps only pulled the cloth further back. She arched her back, eyes bulging. The Seeker continued pouring.

Isaac could not contain himself any longer. Lunging forward, he knocked the jug out of The Seeker's hands. The smashed pieces scattered across the floor, but only a thin dribble of liquid remained. The Seeker looked down at him impassively. Isaac saw a twinkle in his eyes. Was he smiling under that hood?

'Guards!' Torquemada called out.

He felt a sharp pain as his arms were pinioned and he was dragged away.

'Continue,' Torquemada said to The Seeker.

∾

'Your Majesty,' Isabel said, bending a knee and bowing. Alejandro repeated the greeting, bowing deeply from the waist.

They had gained admission to the Stucco Patio of the Real Alcazar by insisting to the courtier that it was a matter of life or death. Alejandro had merely nodded when the courtier asked, 'Do you mean His Majesty's?'

'Good morning, Isabel,' the King said, nodding at her from the far end of the rectangular courtyard. A babbling pool separated them. Her face must have betrayed her surprise at his remembering her name. 'You look very much like your mother,' he said, in explanation.

She smiled but couldn't hold his searching look and turned away as if to admire the stucco work honey-combing the pillars around the Patio.

The King turned to Alejandro and said, 'Why have you disturbed me?' It was well known that he prized the solitary hour he spent every morning in the oldest part of the palace.

He opened his mouth to reply, but the King cut him off with, 'No, don't tell me. It's Isaac. Again.'

At the mention of Papa's name, she drew herself to her full height and said, 'If I may approach, Your Majesty?'

She took his extended arm and they walked around the colonnade enclosing the pool. Alejandro followed a few steps behind. She told him everything she knew about Papa and Torquemada. When she'd finished the King sat on a stone bench and stared into the pool. They stood before him. Alejandro made to speak, but the King silenced him with a raised index finger. He sat silently for a long while. Finally, he asked, 'What's your actual evidence for accusing the Grand Inquisitor of plotting to assassinate Isaac?'

'The word of the friar who tried to murder him,' said Alejandro.

'Where is he?'

'In Granada, being questioned by Talavera.'

She studied the King's face. She watched his eyes flicker, his head tilt as he thought through his choices. Papa had told her how he disapproved of Torquemada's more brutal tactics, partly on religious principle but mainly for financial reasons. Hunting heretics fomented discontent and bred rebellion. That cost money to quell and took citizens' time away from working and generating taxes for his coffers. But Queen Isabella was far more in favour of the Inquisition. He must be considering how to meet the contradictory demands of his beliefs, his financial interests and his marriage.

'So it would take at least five days to get him here?'

'Give or take a day, Your Majesty,' Alejandro said.

'If he's alive. Are you prepared to repeat everything you've just told me?' The King asked her.

'Yes,' she replied.

'Everything?' He fixed her with a hard look. 'In front of Her Majesty?'

'She's returned from Cadiz?' Alejandro blurted out.

The King ignored him, and continued, 'And swear it on your mother's soul?'

Saying nothing, she glanced to one side. She had to swear on her mother's soul to save her father's soul.

Inhaling deeply she looked into the King's eyes. 'Yes, I will.'

He stood up. 'Very well, leave it with me.'

'But, Your Majesty, there's no time to waste. Señor Alvarez is being tortured at this very moment,' Alejandro said.

The King looked at him coolly and walked away.

CHAPTER
THIRTY-FIVE

Isaac was bound to a chair, positioned about twenty paces away from the *escalera*. The Seeker continued to pour water down the woman's throat. He shut his eyes but that didn't block out the sounds of her thrashing body or of her choking as the liquid flooded her lungs. Finally, there was silence.

'Physician,' Torquemada called out.

Isaac opened his eyes and watched as the physician examined the woman. After a few moments he shook his head.

'May The Almighty give rest to her soul,' Torquemada intoned. 'Untie him,' he said to the guards, pointing his chin at Isaac.

They shoved him into a chair at one side of the long rectangular table. Jugs and muslin rags lay in the middle. Torquemada sat opposite and picked up one of the jugs. He lifted it towards him and raised an eyebrow. Isaac shook his head. Torquemada filled a mug with water and took a sip.

'Leave us,' he said.

The clerk, The Seeker, the physician and the two guards filed up the stone stairs. The door banged shut.

'We are alone,' Torquemada said.

Isaac looked across at the woman, still bound to the *escalera*.

'She can't hear us. Her soul has already departed.' He made the sign of the cross. 'I believe she tried to confess. She will take her place in heaven.'

Isaac stared at him and set his jaw.

'You may hate me, but I am here to save you.'

He said nothing.

'We have incontrovertible testimony of your heresy. From your own daughter.' He paused. '"A man's enemies will be the members of his own household."'

He saw the glint in Torquemada's eyes and wanted to jump across and smash his skull into the table.

'St Matthew never said a truer word. Your fate is sealed. Your position in His Majesty's employ will save you from the *escalara*, but only...'

'If I admit my apostasy and recant.'

'Exactly, my son. Ask The Almighty's forgiveness and you may yet be reunited with Maria.' He crossed himself. 'God rest her soul.'

He held the Grand Inquisitor's eyes with a defiant glare. How dare he utter her name?

Torquemada pinched his chin between thumb and forefinger. 'Let me confess something to you, my son,' he said with a small smile. 'I admire you.'

Isaac's brow tightened.

'It surprises you?' He waited for a reply that didn't

come. 'Your dedication to your faith rivals my own. The lengths you are prepared to go to, the sacrifices you are willing to make are... impressive.'

'How does it feel?'

Torquemada looked puzzled.

'To be a murderer.'

'I wouldn't know. I carry out God's will in a manner sanctioned by His Holiness the Pope.' He grimaced. 'But you would. You've murdered a few men in your time.'

'Men, yes, women and children, never. And always in defence.'

'Those who've died under our questioning or who've burnt at the stake have had their souls saved. We've spared them the eternal fire prepared for the devil and his angels.'

Isaac stood up and leant across the table. 'If I put my hands around your throat I could squeeze the life out of you before they could get down those stairs to save you,' he snarled.

Torquemada did not flinch. 'And if you did so, my son, you would be condemned to eternal damnation. You know that.'

He glared, fists clenched.

'It's why you hesitate.'

He realised now why Torquemada sent the men away. To demonstrate the futility of his situation.

'And you could never be reunited with her.'

He slumped back into his chair, defeated.

'But there is a way forward. You recant, and it will be just a whipping and imprisonment.' He tapped a fore-finger on the table. 'I expect we can forego the whip and keep you in your current cell. I'll have to seize Casa de Felicidad of course, and your country homes. But I'll make sure the children are well provided for. And if you behave you will be allowed to see them. Occasionally.'

He looked at the floor.

'And in good time you will pass away naturally to be welcomed into heaven by The Almighty.' He paused. 'And Maria.'

'And will you join me? In good time.' He smiled.

Torquemada was silent. He tilted his head, as though considering this for the first time. 'Yes, of course. In good time.'

Isaac continued to smile.

'So, what's your answer?' Torquemada said, his tone betraying a hint of frustration.

'Tell me something first.'

Torquemada nodded.

'I know you kidnapped the twins to lure me on a wild goose chase and have me murdered away from Seville. To evade suspicion.'

Now it was Torquemada's turn to be silent.

'But why did you get your thugs to set fire to the Apothecary?'

Torquemada looked thoughtful. 'Why is this so important to you?'

'Indulge me,' he replied.

Torquemada sighed. 'He's one of the few Moors left in Seville. His Majesty allows them to practise their religion. I knew you were close friends. If I got rid of him he would have to go to Granada, to be with others of his kind.'

'Why not just kill him?'

'It would not have mattered to me had he died in the fire. An accident.' He shrugged.

'His soul is not important?'

'Enough.' Torquemada banged his cane on the stone floor. 'Give me your answer. What is it to be? Heaven or hell?'

'That is not *your* decision to make.'

Torquemada opened his mouth to reply but was cut off by Isaac's fist smashing down on the table.

'I will never recant, never apologise for following the faith my heart tells me to.' He was shaking with rage. 'There is only one God and he will condemn you to hell for your evil.'

Torquemada levered himself slowly up on his cane, turning his head towards the cell door. Before he could open his mouth Isaac threw himself across the table. He grabbed Torquemada from behind, stopped his mouth with a muslin rag, and kicked his cane away. Torquemada breathed raggedly through his nose as he pushed him across to the *escalera*. He shoved Torquemada's head down so that it was almost touching the woman's lifeless face.

'This will be your legacy,' he hissed, pushing Torquemada's forehead against the woman's. 'I will not recant. I will not betray Juan and Maria.' He began to weep and his body sagged onto Torquemada's back. 'If that's the wrong choice we'll endure hell together,' Isaac whispered into his ear. 'If I'm right I'll be with everyone I love forever.'

Slumping to the cold, stone floor he dragged Torquemada down heavily with him. Torquemada removed the cloth from his mouth and gagged. For a long moment, they sat side by side, breathing heavily. His head dropped onto Torquemada's shoulder, his tears flowing freely. Torquemada reached across and clasped his shoulder for a moment.

Isaac did not react.

Then he crossed himself. Using the edge of the *escalara* Torquemada hauled himself to his feet and bellowed, 'Guards.'

CHAPTER
THIRTY-SIX

The courtier hissed into his ear, 'His Majesty is talking to you.'

Isaac parted his lips to speak but his throat was too dry and all that emerged was a dry rasp. The courtier set a mug of water in front of him and he emptied it in one long draught.

'Your Majesty,' he whispered. The courtier refilled his mug.

He sat at the end of a long table in the King's chambers at the Real Alcazar. Astonished to still be alive. After taking his written confession, Torquemada had left him to languish in his cell for five days. The surly gaoler's attitude changed and he provided little food or water. Earlier that morning two guards had stormed into his cell, shackled him, and thrown him into a wagon. He assumed to be executed, but they'd delivered him to the palace. Ferdinand, whose eyes were locked on him from the other end of the table, must have intervened.

The Grand Inquisitor sat to the King's right. A guard

stood by the door and the courtier had a scroll of paper in his hand. The instruction for his execution? It was the middle of the day and sweat soaked his smock. His hands and ankles remained manacled at Torquemada's insistence. The King had at first protested, but relented once Torquemada recounted how Isaac had assaulted him at the Torre.

He was thirsty and hungry. His head lolled down to his chest. He ran his tongue over cracked lips.

'You are here so that I can be assured of the truth. Do you understand?' the King said.

'Yes, Your Majesty,' he said taking a sip of water.

'I will ask the questions.' He said, looking pointedly at Torquemada. 'I don't have time for long answers, religious disquisition or philosophical argument. Is that clear?'

Isaac bowed his head in agreement.

'To both of you?' The King turned to Torquemada and raised an eyebrow.

He returned the smallest of nods.

The King's eyes were like stones. 'You confessed to heresy?'

He nodded.

'You *admitted* you are a practising Jew?'

'Yes, Your Majesty.'

The King thrummed the fingers of his right hand on the table.

'I understand this confession was obtained under severe duress?' He looked sidelong at Torquemada, who grunted.

'It was, Your Majesty,' Isaac replied with difficulty.

'The Grand Inquisitor threatened to torture Isabel and remove my children.' He hesitated. 'But, my confession was truthful.'

Torquemada tilted his head and looked at the King enquiringly.

The door was suddenly flung open and the Queen strode in. Torquemada got to his feet. Isaac was too surprised to move. The courtier grabbed him under the armpits and hauled him up. Bowing his head he mumbled, 'Your Majesty.'

'What is the meaning of this?' The Queen thundered.

Ferdinand rose and kissed her outstretched palm. 'I'm glad you made it back in time from Cadiz, my dear.'

She gave him a tight smile.

'Please, join us,' he gestured towards his place, which she took. He sat down to her left, facing Torquemada.

'What is going on?' she asked.

'All will become clear, my dear,' The King said. 'If you will permit me?'

She gave him a curt nod.

'Senór Alvarez has just admitted heresy,' Torquemada said.

She raised an eyebrow and shrugged. 'So, why is he still here? Why is he not being prepared to meet his maker?'

'Just a few more questions, my dear,' the King replied.

She narrowed her eyes at him.

'I have received a letter,' he continued, glancing at the courtier who unfurled the parchment and began to read. 'From the office of Archbishop Talavera ...'

As the courtier continued, Isaac saw the Queen glance nervously at Torquemada, whose face was reddening.

'Let me summarise,' said the King. 'Archbishop Talavera confirms the friar who attempted to assassinate Isaac admits he was acting under instructions from the Grand Inquisitor.'

'Lies,' Torquemada muttered. 'Even if this were accurate I have the authority to wipe out heresy. And that man,' he pointed at Isaac, 'is a confirmed heretic.'

'Neither The Almighty nor His Holiness gives you licence to assassinate anyone, not even heretics,' the King said. 'We've already established that the confession was made after threats were made to Isaac's children.'

The Queen flashed Torquemada a nervous look. Then she turned to stare, unblinking, at Isaac.

'Bring in his daughter.' The King waved a hand at the courtier who left and returned with Isabel. She bent a knee and bowed her head. Isaac studied Torquemada's face. Horror, surprise and then softness seemed to flow across it as Isabel took the seat beside Isaac. She placed a hand over his and raised the cup to his lips.

He took a few sips. 'Thank you, my dear.' He felt suddenly weak, as though he might cry. He must be strong and face whatever was about to happen.

The King looked at the Queen, who nodded. 'Isabel, is your father a heretic?'

She looked down at her lap.

Isaac squeezed her hand and said, 'You must tell the truth. Again.'

'Yes, he is, Your Majesty.'

Torquemada thumped the table. 'There you have it from his own child's lips.'

'If...' Isabel began.

After a few seconds The King gently said, 'Your father advised you to tell the truth, whatever it may be.'

'If,' she cleared her throat, 'heresy means worshipping The Almighty with different rituals to our own, then yes, he is a heretic.'

'Blasphemy!' Torquemada shouted as he stood up. 'Guard take –'

'Sit down, Grand Inquisitor,' the King said.

Torquemada did not move.

'Or I will have you removed.' The King held Torquemada's eyes.

The Queen whispered, 'Father, please,' and he sat down.

'Tell us about the circumstances of the confession, child,' the King said.

She recounted Torquemada's threats to her at Casa de Felicidad: to imprison her and allow the twins to die.

'Was that the first time the Grand Inquisitor threatened you?' The King asked.

Lowering her eyes she took a sip from her father's mug. Wiping tears away with the back of her hand she replied, 'No.' She inhaled deeply and entwined her fingers tightly in front of her.

Isaac could see her fingertips turning red from the tension. He would give anything for her not to be put through this. But there was no other way now.

'Three years ago he held us prisoner in the Castillo whilst my Mama was tortured.' She took in several jagged breaths. 'He told me things would go easier for her if...' She looked down at her fingers which were writhing against each other. 'If I was kind to him, if I allowed him to...' She started to cry.

'Are you accusing Father Tomás of attempting to seduce you?' The Queen snarled in an incredulous tone.

She looked up and held the Queen's eyes. 'Yes, Your Majesty, I am.'

He thought he saw sympathy pass across the Queen's face, just for an instant.

'This is an outrage,' Torquemada bellowed, banging the table repeatedly.

'Enough!' The King shouted.

There was silence.

'There is one other matter to discuss. Juan de Mota's orphans were abducted?'

'Yes.'

'What do you know of this?'

'The children have described the two men. One had red hair and was called Roja.'

'What of it?' The Queen barked.

She took a deep breath. 'I saw them gain access to the Grand Inquisitor's quarters in the Castillo via a secret entrance.' She paused. 'I believe they are his men.' She pointed at Torquemada. 'And he ordered Juana and Martín's kidnapping.'

'An outrageous accusation!' Torquemada roared.

The Queen leant across to her husband and Isaac heard her mutter, 'It's time for this to finish, Ferdinand.'

'I only have a few more questions, my dear. Then I promise it will be over.'

'Quickly,' she replied.

'Father Tomás, you don't deny the circumstances in which the confession was obtained?' The King continued.

'No, why should I? It is perfectly natural to try to save souls by any means. His Holiness supports my methods.'

'So, the girl is telling the truth about how you extracted the confession?'

'Yes. Your Majesty.'

'And you have no reason to doubt her word about her own father's heresy?'

'Absolutely not.'

The Queen looked back and forth between her husband and Torquemada during this exchange. Isaac wondered whether it was nerves? Perhaps she knew as well as he did what the next question would be.

'So, can you explain one thing?' He paused. 'If the girl is telling the truth on all other matters, why would she lie about your attempt to seduce her, and your abduction of the children?'

Silence.

For once, Isaac thought, Torquemada didn't have a riposte. The Queen studied her confessor's face. Her expression was one Isaac had never seen before: a mixture of sadness and pleading.

She stood and said, 'Father Tomás, come with me.'

Isaac and Isabel got to their feet.

As Torquemada preceded the Queen out of the chamber, he seemed to stoop more than ever. He didn't look at them or say a word.

As the Queen left she turned, pointed at Isaac and said to The King, 'Deal with him.'

'I will, my dear.' He jerked his head at the courtier who immediately left.

Isaac struggled to make sense of what was happening. He'd expected the whirl of accusation, anger and confrontation to result in his execution. But Isabel's head was on his shoulder and she was stroking his hand. Was everything going to work out? He remembered Talavera's counsel against despair. Hope for salvation, trust in God's essential goodness.

The King sat next to Isaac. 'You're lucky to have her,' he said, looking at Isabel.

'I know.' He took hold of her hands and kissed them.

'You're very brave,' The King said to her.

'Thank you, Your Majesty.'

'But,' he exhaled noisily, 'you are still a heretic, Isaac.' He put a hand on his shoulder.

Isaac nodded.

'That cannot go unpunished.'

'I know.'

CHAPTER
THIRTY-SEVEN

Isaac imagined the flicker of sunlight across his eyelids. He was determined to embrace the warmth of the moment to recall his dreams – whatever they'd been – before he was forced to open his eyes. For the last time. Much of the previous night had been spent with Isabel. Reassuring her she'd acted the only way possible and that it had turned out to be the right thing for the family. She'd saved the children and protected her soul. That was all that mattered. She told him what had happened to the twins, and how brave they'd been. He held her as she cried over Alejandro, recounting how she'd turned down his proposal. There were tears, smiles, and goodbyes.

When he eventually fell asleep in the early hours, he searched for Maria and Juan. He dreamt of running along the dusty track from the family estate at Pozzoblanco to the river. He was young again and felt the ease of his limbs as he ran swiftly and gracefully. At the riverbank, he called out for Juan, but there was no reply. He broke the calm, glistening surface of the river and dived deep into the cold water. Suddenly, he felt the heat of the sun and was on dry land. An angel manifested above him and said, 'Hail, full of grace, the Lord is with you,' to a woman kneeling on the ground. The words materialised as golden letters in the sky. It was the Archangel Gabriel telling Mary that she would give birth to the son of God. He'd been in a scene from Maria's Book of Hours.

A knock at the door broke the daydream. For a moment he wondered whether the gaoler would feed him today. Then he remembered. He was at home. In his own bedchamber for the last time.

'Papa.'

'Yes, Gabriel, I'll come down soon.'

'Can I come in?'

A most unusual request. He sat up and rubbed his hands over his face. He couldn't recall his son ever asking to see him before breakfast. But this was far from a usual day. 'A moment,' he called out. After relieving himself, he washed his hands and opened the door. Gabriel lunged at him, head down and hugged him tightly for a long moment. He luxuriated in it; when would he get the next opportunity? Putting his arm around his son he kissed the top of his head. He walked him over to the chairs in front of the window that gave a view of the garden. Gabriel hunched over with his head in his hands.

'This is not the end,' Isaac said softly.

'It is,' Gabriel replied with anger.

'We discussed this on the road back from Granada. I told you what would happen.'

'It doesn't make it easier.'

'I know. But it could have been much worse.'

'How?'

'Come on my boy, instead of being burnt alive I'm being banished to Granada. It's hardly the same thing.' He tried to infuse his tone with a lightness that he didn't feel.

'It is. Either way, it feels like I'll never see you again.'

He took hold of Gabriel's hands and said, 'Look at me.' His son slowly raised his head and Isaac looked into his eyes. 'I make you a solemn promise that we will, in –'

'I know, I know, "in this life or the next," ' he said in a lightly mocking tone.

He cupped his son's cheek. 'Come on, let's eat.'

The family was waiting downstairs. Isabel sat broodingly at the head of the table. Isaac rested a hand on her shoulder. She put a palm over it. No words were needed, they'd said all they needed to the previous night. Juana and Martín were chasing each other around the room.

'Children,' Isabel called out, 'I have some good news for you.'

The twins stood still.

'Rodrigo visited Diego the blacksmith in Triana last night.'

They looked at her expectantly.

'He is well and looking forward to your visit.'

They cheered and ran to Isaac. He knelt down and embraced them.

'Will we see you again?' Juana asked.

'Definitely,' he said, glancing up at Gabriel. One way or the other, he thought.

'What's "banished"?' Martín asked.

'It's when you've got to go away and,' he paused, 'not return.'

'Not fair,' Martín said.

'His Majesty thinks it is, and we must respect that.' He stood up and looked down at the twins. 'But things change. Just remember what you felt like when you were in that filthy cell. I'm proud of how brave you both were.'

They smiled up at him.

'Keep on behaving like that and all will be well.' He returned their smiles, ruffled their hair and said, 'Let's eat.'

He thought the table would buckle under the weight of food Catalina had prepared. There was a saffron loaf fried in butter, pancakes soaked in honey, stuffed eggs, a roasted rabbit, rice and plates of sweet pastries. He sniffed the air and thought he could detect the scent of *ras-al-hanout*.

Catalina was watching him and said, 'Yes, I used some of those spices you bought back from Granada.'

'My goodness, you've outdone yourself this time. This feast is enough for breakfast and lunch.'

Catalina beamed.

They sat down together around the table. For the last time. That phrase just wouldn't leave him.

When Catalina saw he was struggling to eat everything, she bustled up behind him and whispered in his ear, 'Don't you worry, Master Isaac, I'll pack you up a basket for the journey.'

He looked up at her. 'You haven't called me that for thirty years.'

Her eyes moved from side to side until he saw in them that she understood. 'Oh my goodness, I'm so sorry, señor.' Covering her face with her apron she hurried off to the kitchen.

The rest of the meal passed by too quickly for his liking. The King had given him until noon to pass through the city gates, never to return. They gathered in the courtyard, stiff and awkward with one another. Catalina was silent when he clasped her hand and said, 'Thank you.' She wiped at her eyes with the corner of her apron.

He shook hands with Gabriel, Martín, and Juana. He took Isabel's hands and locked eyes with her for a long moment and then released her.

There was a knock from the exterior door and Catalina opened it.

Alejandro entered the courtyard. He bowed deeply to Isabel, who gave Isaac a questioning look.

'Apologies, my dear. I forgot to tell you, Alejandro will be accompanying me.'

'To the city gates?'

He gave his deputy a questioning look.

'No, señora.' Alejandro said. 'To Granada.'

'Will you come back?' Isabel asked.

'Not in the short term. Seville has become... a difficult place for me.' He looked away from her. 'Too many memories.'

Isaac studied each of them and sensed sadness and regret emanating from both.

'And besides, your Papa needs someone to look after him. Right, children?'

Juana and Martín shouted their agreement. Gabriel shook Alejandro's hand.

'Are you ready, señor?' he asked. 'The horses are waiting.'

Isaac strode through the door without looking back.

Isabel felt the slamming of the door in the pit of her stomach. It was the end of everything. She stood in the centre of the courtyard, willing the door to open and for them both to walk back through. She was aware of Catalina shepherding the twins into the house. Gabriel approached, but she shook her head. Thankfully, he understood her mood and he followed the children.

She sat down on the bench, closed her eyes and listened to the babble of the fountain. Her father gone forever. Alejandro with him. Why had she been so stupid? And why hadn't he made any attempt to change her mind? Hadn't he known she'd been upset, that she wasn't thinking straight? Perhaps he didn't really love her. Mama, Papa and now her love all dead, or as good as. Her only hope was to meet her parents in heaven, but she couldn't find much solace in that at the moment. Was it all her fault? If she'd given in to Torquemada three years ago would Mama have been safe? Did she have to betray Papa? Hadn't there been another way? No, she'd taken not just the righteous course but the right one, as painful as it was. But Alejandro was a different matter. She'd been foolish. There must be a way to get him back.

There was an insistent tapping at the door. He *had* returned! She ran to the door and hauled it open. 'Oh. It's you.'

Andreas made the sign of the cross and said, 'May I?'

She wanted to slam the door in his face. She still suspected he might have been spying on her, under instructions from Torquemada. But the sadness in his eyes and the softness of his voice made her relent. She left the door ajar and returned to her place on the bench, folded her arms and stared at the fountain. He sat beside her, saying nothing for a long moment. She was drawn into his stillness and noticed that her breathing began to match his. He started singing in a mournful, high-pitched tone.

She turned to look at him, intending to ask him to stop. But he had such a blissful expression, so she closed her eyes and listened.

'Mother of God pray for us,' he sang.

It was Madre de Deus, Mama's favourite song, the one he'd sung on his first visit to her. It was piercingly beautiful.

'And hell takes those who have done wrong,' he finished.

She opened her eyes.

He crossed himself and smiled at her.

'Is that where I'm going?' she asked.

Puzzlement crossed his face.

'To hell. Have you come here to lecture me, to hear my confession?'

His look of hurt seemed so sincere that she instantly regretted her words.

'I'm sorry, Father. It's been a tough day.'

He looked searchingly at her. 'I know what it's like to lose someone you love deeply.' He smiled. 'When I was young I once loved a fellow friar...'

She raised her eyebrows and sneered.

'No, my child, I know the reputation some of us have for inappropriate, sinful, carnal activity. But this was not like that. It was genuinely fraternal.' He sighed. 'We just saw something in each other, a spark, a connection outside of our religious duties.'

She was touched by the gentleness in his voice as he made this revelation.

'What happened?'

'We allowed our relationship to become too... frivolous. The Master and the Abbot decided we were disrespectful and sent him away.' He sighed. 'I haven't seen Alonso for almost twenty years.'

'Alonso? Friar Alonso de Hojeda?'

'Yes. Do you know him?' His voice betrayed a tinge of excitement.

'I did.' She considered telling him how she knew Alonso. But then recalled exactly what had happened. She felt the same confusion of fear, guilt and sympathy that always washed over when she brought him to mind.

'He's in the Indies. I don't expect to hear from him again.'

'What did you come to see me about? Father.' The spell cast by his singing was broken.

'I came to see how you were. You've endured a great

ordeal. If you feel the need to talk I would be happy to listen. Even to hear your confession.'

She was repulsed. Why would she confide in Torquemada's assistant? The man who might have spied on her. Let alone someone who professed love for Alonso. And yet. There was an innocence in him that was hard to ignore. 'Thank you, Father. Let me think on it.'

He grinned in a way that reminded her of Martín.

'Before you leave, what can you tell me about the men who kidnapped the children? Did you know them?'

He looked down at his hands, the fingers writhing against each other.

'I understand that one had a shock of red hair.'

'You deserve the truth. Roja and Ramos, they were Father Tomás's men.'

It fell into place for her. They were the ones who'd been watching the house. The same men who attacked her and Alejandro three years ago in Triana. Had they been Torquemada's men even then? No, that didn't make any sense.

'Where are they now?'

He pursed his lips. 'They can't be found. They seem to have left the city.'

She snorted. 'That's convenient. They won't face the consequences of their actions.'

'They will, my child. In heaven, or in hell.'

'"Hell takes those who've done wrong,"' she replied.

He smiled at the hymnal lyric. He stood up to leave.

'And what of Torquemada?' She felt no need to use his title. He didn't deserve to be called Father.

'The Queen suggested he might like to retire to Avila,

to complete the building of his convent.' He paused. 'He's become very unwell in the past two days.'

She gave him a sardonic sneer. 'And what will become of you? Without your master?'

He flinched. 'I'm not sure. Perhaps I'll be sent back to Cordoba.'

He looked so distraught that she took pity on him and decided not to confront him with her suspicions.

He left without saying another word.

Isabel heard the door slam shut for the second time that morning.

CHAPTER
THIRTY-EIGHT

Once they were through the city gates, and clear of the wagons loaded high with goods, Isaac urged his black gelding into a gallop. He wanted to stay ahead of Alejandro, he was in no mood to talk. So far, his plan had gone better than expected. He was still alive, wasn't he? But was a life in exile from the city he loved and his family worth living?

Riding hard through the long, hot afternoon they reached Palma del Río just before sunset. The patron at the Hostería del Infante, Garcia Mora, was far more hospitable this time, now that he did not have to welcome a Moor. He joined them after their dinner of rabbit stew and talked into the night with Alejandro about the changes in Andalusia. Isaac hardly spoke, he was lost in thought.

The next morning, they set out before sunrise, hopeful of reaching Granada before the end of the day. As the sun rose high, they were forced to slow the horses to an amble as they entered a dense forest. Isaac recognised the area. It was where he'd been attacked by Torquemada's friars.

Alejandro drew alongside. 'Are you ready to talk now?'

'What good will it do?'

'You haven't asked me whether I was successful.'

'I assumed you would've told me if you weren't.'

'The bottle of arsenic was delivered to the Castillo.'

'Then Torquemada's not long for this world.'

'My contact will make sure it does its work.'

'How did you find him?'

'You remember Luisa?'

'I think so.'

'The pretty barmaid at Bar Averno?'

He thought for a moment and then nodded. She'd taken a fancy to Alejandro.

'She put me in contact with him. Torquemada wiped out his entire family. He's only alive because he agreed to work in the kitchen at the Castillo.'

'So, he's motivated.'

'You took quite a risk going to the Apothecary to get the arsenic and asking Gabriel to deliver it to me.'

'The only other choice was not to return to Seville. I couldn't do that. I had to try.'

They continued riding through the forest.

'You know I thought it was you?' Isaac said.

'Who?'

'The stranger who bought arsenic from Ali Sina.'

Alejandro laughed. 'Isabel said the same thing. Why on earth would I do that?'

'I thought you and Isabel might be plotting to kill Torquemada.' He paused. 'To save me the trouble.'

'Why didn't you just ask?'

'I should have. There just never seemed to be the time. Or I didn't dare to. I'm sorry.'

'All water under the bridge. Did you ever find out who it was?'

'No, that remains a mystery. Though I still wonder about the death of the food taster. Was someone really plotting to poison Torquemada? Perhaps there was some truth in the rumour about a group of radical *conversos*.'

'Well, it's of no consequence now. Though, in an odd way, I might as well have been the mysterious arsenic buyer. I've ended up doing the deed you suspected me of anyway.'

They both laughed.

'Tell me something,' Isaac asked. He hesitated, unsure whether to raise the subject. 'Why did you agree to break off the engagement?'

Alejandro was silent for a few moments. 'I was angry. At the time I thought Isabel should have made another choice, she shouldn't have betrayed you. She could have waited for you to return.' Sadness clouded his face. 'And then I was too proud to beg her to change her mind.'

'And what do you think now?'

'She had no choice. I realise how brave she was.'

'So, why didn't you stay?' He couldn't hide his exasperation. 'You could have asked her again. I would have given you my blessing,'

'I wonder that myself.'

They rode in silence, accompanied only by the sound of the wind through the leaves.

'I thought,' Alejandro said, 'that I didn't deserve her after what I did.'

'You probably don't.' He glanced across to enjoy Alejandro's discomfit, for just a moment. 'And perhaps I don't deserve her as a daughter.'

They made good time through the heat of the afternoon, galloping through gullies and past hillsides scattered with fruit orchards. They trotted through a thickly wooded copse and came to a halt at the top of a steep-sided valley. In the middle distance was the Alhambra Palace, and beyond the snow-capped Sierra Nevadas.

'I've never seen it before.' Alejandro shook his head. 'It's magnificent.'

'Come on,' Isaac said, whipping his horse. 'I can't wait to see the look on Ali and Abdul Rahman's faces.'

The horses skittered down the scree slope and then galloped up the other side of the valley and on through the city gates of Granada.

EPILOGUE

It's much too cold to be outside, thought Master Bartolome as he started his second round of the cloisters. Still, it was a little warmer than his cell. At least he could breathe some fresh air and enjoy what was left of the gardens at this time of year. It would soon be Terce, and afterwards the Abbot wanted to discuss some matters. No doubt he was concerned about the monastery's shaky finances. He was feeling rather out of breath as he passed the door to the library and then entered the church.

He was accompanied up the nave by the echo of his sandals slapping on the stone floor. He was headed for his cell, looking forward to a nap before prayers. He crossed himself as he passed the tomb of Father Tomás de Torquemada. He'd almost reached the dormitory when a figure appeared that he could not immediately place. Living with the other friars for so long he didn't need to see their faces to recognise them – their gait, body shape or gestures revealed their identity. But he was sure he'd never seen this cowled friar. There was something about his posture that triggered a dim memory followed by a sense of unease.

'Good morning to you, Brother,' Bartolome said.

All he received in return was a curt nod as the friar strode on by. He watched as he walked up the nave. Reaching the tomb, he bowed his head. Bartolome considered leaving him in peace, but he was a stranger. After giving him a few moments of contemplation he went and stood behind him. He waited until he'd finished the Pater Noster prayer.

'Good morning, Brother,' he said, more briskly this time.

The stranger turned, looked up, and crossed himself again. Then, as if coming to a decision, pulled back his cowl and said, 'Good morning to you, Master Bartolome.'

'How do you know me?' He folded his arms across his chest. 'Who are you and what is your business here?

'Do you not recognise me, Master Bartolome?' the stranger said in a wheedling tone.

'Should I?'

The stranger smiled.

'You are *not* a member of this order and I did *not* authorise access to any visitors.'

'Have I changed that much? Perhaps three years on foreign soil and sea voyages have altered my appearance more than I'd appreciated.'

Bartolome saw something dark pass across his eyes.

There was a familiar quality to the timbre of his voice, but he still couldn't quite place him. He studied the friar's face: a predatory look emphasised by the curved, hawk-like nose that separated his deep brown eyes.

'I'm afraid you will have to help me. I do not recognise you.'

'Let us talk and perhaps it will come to you.'

Bartolome did not reply.

'There was some confusion over the cause of death?' He gestured towards the tomb. 'Murder was suspected?'

'He was seventy-eight,' Bartolome said, as though that should explain everything.

'But there was a plot to murder him? The King's adviser was involved? A Señor Alvarez?'

'You're very well informed.'

'You learn a lot if you listen carefully to sailors' stories and tavern gossip.'

'Alvarez investigated and a plot was never proven. But he was convicted of heresy and exiled to Granada. Had to leave his children behind.'

'Thank you, I wasn't sure that part of the story was accurate. I was surprised Alvarez wasn't burnt at the stake.' He grunted. 'The King saved him again, no doubt.'

Bartolome felt skewered by the sudden hard look in the stranger's eyes.

'I'm disappointed,' he said.

'What do you –'

'I thought you would remember someone to whom you once caused so much pain.'

Bartolome felt a chill run through him as the friar's eyes deadened even further.

His head jerked back involuntarily – the change in the tone of the conversation had surprised him. He scrunched up his eyes, trying again to place the friar's face. A memory filtered through from the recesses of his mind – something unpleasant. 'I have Terce prayers and then a meeting with the Abbot. Please reveal your identity and why you are here, or leave.'

'I've arrived too late.'

Bartolome shook his head. 'What do you mean? I don't have time for riddles.'

The stranger smiled again, closed his eyes, and inhaled deeply.

He's really enjoying this moment, Bartolome thought.

'I was summoned to return.' He reached beneath his habit and held out a scroll of paper. 'From the Indies.'

Bartolome unrolled it and read aloud, 'April 1498, from the office of The Grand Inquisitor of All Spain, Tomás de Torquemada. To whom it may concern. The holder of this order, Brother...' he trailed off as he saw the name.

'Yes, Master, it's me, Alonso.' He clasped Bartolome's shoulder.

He shuddered as Alonso's bony fingers dug into his flesh. 'I didn't recognise you.'

'Long voyages and foreign climes have their effect. But I'm still the same inside.' He grinned. 'You'll be pleased to hear.'

Removing Alonso's hand Bartolome said, 'I didn't expect you to return after the Queen sent you away after that business with the boy's murder in Seville. There were all kinds of rumours…'

'I was happy in the Indies. There was a great purity in saving the souls of savages. We brought so many to Christ… one way or the other. I had time to reflect on my previous actions and,' he paused, 'to forgive.'

Bartolome began to recall. It must have been twenty years ago, at least. Alonso had been a young friar in his care when he and that other one, what was his name? They dared to challenge his authority as Master and he made sure the other one was sent away.

'I can see the clouds parting, Master. Do you remember his name?'

It suddenly came to him. 'Brother Andreas.'

'Yes. You mistook our foolishness for disrespect.' Alonso's tone grew harder. 'And you thought our deep friendship was somehow… inappropriate?'

'You were disrespectful. The Prior did the right thing sending him away from the monastery.' My opinion of Andreas has been vindicated with everything that's come to light recently, Bartolome thought, but didn't dare say.

Alonso's jaw tightened.

Bartolome took a step back. Why was he really here? Had he come for revenge? Was he going to kill him?

A smile suddenly transformed Alonso's face. 'But, as I said, Master, I've had time to think, and to forgive. You did what you thought was righteous.'

Bartolome exhaled with relief and made the sign of the cross. 'Thank you. If that is all?' he said, making to leave.

'Where is Brother Andreas?' Alonso demanded, his tone harder again.

Bartolome raised his brow in surprise. 'I thought you knew.' His turn to smile. 'Seville. In the Torre.' He let the moment stretch out, allowing Alonso to dangle. 'Awaiting trial for the poisoning of Father Tomás.'

Alonso's face sagged, and his mouth contorted. This is what despair looks like, Bartolome thought. Then he remembered how disrespectful the two friars had been to him.

Alonso was pacing up and down beside the tomb, muttering to himself.

What was he saying? Bartolome listened closely.

'Isaac is in Granada, Isabel and Andreas are in Seville,' he seemed to be saying, over and over.

Bartolome looked around for help. Was despair turning into some sort of madness?

Alonso came to a sudden halt in front of Bartolome. 'Thank you, Master,' he said loudly. Crossing himself, he pulled up his cowl, turned, and hurried away.

'Where are you going?'

STAY IN TOUCH ...

I hope you enjoyed reading *The Heretic's Daughter* and I'd be delighted if you left an honest review on Amazon and Goodreads.

Sign up to my newsletter and receive a free short story: https://www.michaellynes.com/newsletter/

I'd love to hear from you:
michael@michaellynes.com

Also by Michael Lynes

If you want to join Isaac on his first investigation read:

Blood Libel

Historical Note

In late medieval Andalusia oppressive policies and attitudes forced many Jews to embrace Christianity. These *conversos* were suspected of continuing to practice Judaism in secret. They were labelled 'crypto-Jews', or even worse *marranos*, meaning swine. The religious establishment sought to save the souls of these heretics by persuading them to return to the right path.

Friar Alonso de Hojeda, a Dominican Friar from Seville, convinced Ferdinand II of Aragon and Isabella I of Castile Queen Isabella of the existence of crypto-Judaism in 1478. As a direct consequence the Spanish Inquisition was instituted in 1481 and a royal decree in 1483 expelled the Jews from Spain. Tomás de Torquemada, Queen Isabella's confessor, was appointed, 'Grand Inquisitor of All Spain'. Pope Sixtus agreed to the formation of 'The Holy Office of the Propagation of the Faith' in return for continued Spanish military support to defeat the Ottoman Empire.

The Inquisition used torture to elicit confessions and

delivered judgment at public ceremonies known as *autos-da-fe*, 'acts of faith', before they gave their victims over to the secular authorities for punishment. The first *auto-da-fe* was held in 1481, and in total some thirty-thousand men, women, and children, were condemned to death and burnt alive. Their gruesome fate was intended to set an example to others.

After fifteen years as Spain's Grand Inquisitor, Torquemada died at the monastery of St. Thomas Aquinas in Ávila in 1498. His tomb was allegedly ransacked in 1832, his bones stolen and ritually incinerated in the same manner as at an *auto-da-fé*.[1] The Spanish Inquisition was not finally abolished until 1834. The decree expelling the Jews from Spain was only formally rescinded by the Spanish government in 1968.

This is a work of fiction. Although the narrative has an historical foundation some dates and events have been conflated or amended to fit the dictates of the story. If the book inspires you to research the period, I found the following texts to be useful starting points:

- Carr, Matthew. Blood & Faith, *The Purging of Muslim Spain 1492 - 1614*, Hurst & Co, 2017.
- Fletcher, Richard. *Moorish Spain*, Phoenix, 2001
- Green, Toby. *Inquisition: The Reign of Fear*, Pan Books, 2008.
- Karabell, Zachary. *People of the Book*, John Murray, 2007.
- Lowney, Chris. *A Vanished World*, OUP, 2005.

- Mount, Toni. *Medical Medicine*, Amberley, 2015.
- Menocal, Maria Rosa. *Ornament of the World*, Little Brown and Company, 2002
- Rubin, Nancy. *Isabella of Castile*, St Martins, 1991.
- Ruiz, Teofilo Z. *Spanish Society 1400-1600*, Routledge, 2001.
- Schama, Simon. *Belonging: The Story of the Jews, 1492 – 1900*, Bodley Head, 2017.
- Thompson, Augustine, O.P. *Dominican Brothers, Conversi, Lay and Cooperator Friars*, New Priory Press, 2017

1.Murphy, Cullen (17 January 2012). *God's Jury: The Inquisition and the Making of the Modern World*. Houghton Mifflin Harcourt. p. 352

INTERMARRIAGE

INTERMARRIAGE

INTERFAITH   INTERRACIAL   INTERETHNIC

By Albert I. Gordon

BEACON PRESS   BOSTON

To the memory of
my father
Hyman Samuel Gordon

ACKNOWLEDGMENTS

I am deeply grateful to well over fifty men and women, from professors to instructors, whose active co-operation made it possible for me to secure statements of student opinions and attitudes toward intermarriage in the forty colleges and universities which I have included in this study. I regret that, because some of these expressed the desire for anonymity, it has been necessary to exclude a listing of those who were of such great assistance to me in offering to administer the questionnaires, and in returning the completed questionnaires so promptly.

I wish, also, to extend my thanks to the Harvard-M.I.T. Computation Center for allowing me to use their equipment, and to the Laboratory of Social Relations at Harvard University and particularly to Dr. Arthur Couch, its Associate-director, whose assistance and counsel were of such direct benefit to me. Messrs. Allan L. Tritter and Dr. Paul Abrahams, who programmed my questionnaire for the I.B.M. 7090 Computers at Harvard University and the M.I.T. Computation Center, aided me with their extraordinary skills and patience as did my dear son-in-law, Dr. Lennard Wharton, presently Assistant Professor of Chemistry at the University of Chicago. The devotion of these three men and that of Mr. Beba Varadarchar who, at the outset, served as my research assistant, will not soon be forgotten.

I wish to acknowledge with gratitude the material assistance provided through the grants from the Harris Trust Fund, the Phillips Trust Fund and the Irving Maidman Trust Fund to carry out this project. I am grateful, too, to Mr. Kivie Kaplan of Boston for his financial and moral support.

I acknowledge, with sincere thanks, the advice and assistance I received from Dr. William M. Genné, Director of the Department of Family Life, of the National Council of Churches in the United States, and Dr. Benson Landis, of the same organization; and also from Professors Louis Guttman of the Hebrew University in Jerusalem and Roberto Bachi, Chief Statistician of the Israeli Government, as well as Dr. Kalman J. Mann, Director of the Hadassah Hospital in Jerusalem. Others whose assistance I wish to acknowledge are: Dr. Jacob R. Marcus, Director of "Jewish Archives"; Dr. Kurt Wilhelm, Chief Rabbi of Sweden; Dr. Marcus Melchior, Chief Rabbi of Denmark; Rabbi Mika Weiss, formerly the Chief Rabbi of Finland; Rabbi Isadore S. Meyer, Librarian of the American Jewish Historical Society; his Excellency, Bishop Eric F. MacKenzie of the Archdiocese of Boston, head of the

Tribunal, whom I regard as a dear friend; Dr. Benjamin Kahn, Director of the Hillel Foundations of B'nai B'rith; Dr. Myron Fowell, Director of the United Church of Christ in the Boston area; and Drs. Joseph Weinreb and Maxwell J. Schleifer, whose counsel in the area of the psychological problems of the children of mixed marriages proved so helpful. My thanks are extended, too, to Dr. Morton Rubin and Dean Charles Havice of Northeastern University and to my dear friends and teachers, Dr. and Mrs. Wilson D. Wallis, formerly at the University of Minnesota and now at Annhurst College in Connecticut.

The inspiration, guidance and counsel of Professor Gordon W. Allport, Professor of Social Psychology at Harvard University, has been a source of strength to me. Words can hardly suffice to thank him for his many kindnesses.

The typing and retyping of this manuscript was left to the competent hands of Mrs. Jack (Nellie Rae) Burman whose devotion to and concentration upon her task will always remain a source of thanksgiving to me. The tables were ever so carefully prepared by Mrs. Henry Lever.

My great debt to my dear wife, Dorothy, and to my children, Judith and David, who encouraged me to continue with this work after a long and trying illness, is difficult to speak or write about. My indebtedness to my wife goes far beyond the limits of this book. Her encouragement and her inspiration have helped to make so much possible.

ALBERT I. GORDON

PREFACE

Over three years of study, time and effort have gone into this study of "Intermarriage." I suspect that I could spend the rest of my days in further study of this intricate, often vexing subject, and still not produce the answers to the many questions which I, as a rabbi for three and one-half decades and a student of the social sciences for over two decades, would like to know.

There are three basic objectives evident in this study. First, I felt that, in the requests that come to me, almost daily, for more specific information about intermarriage—interfaith, interethnic and interracial —it was important to gather all the major available resources and bits of information on this subject and to make it readily available to both the young people and their parents.

Second, the rapid social and political developments of our day may have resulted in a change or series of changes in the attitudes of contemporary college and university students. What some of them (notably students of the social sciences) are thinking today about intermarriage seems highly important inasmuch as it may well indicate what society may expect in the years ahead. Finally, I felt that the thirty-five years spent as a teacher of religion and my interest in and concern with the social sciences made it possible for me to offer my own views on this subject in a manner that would, perhaps, be of special benefit and assistance to parents and young people alike.

It is my hope that the factual information contained herein, coupled with the personal opinions which I have expressed as the result of that information, will serve to remove intermarriage from the highly emotional plane upon which it is often discussed and place it on a more rational basis. I readily acknowledge that I have a point of view. I believe it to be the result of the knowledge and experience I have acquired over the years. I offer no apologies for including in this volume my conclusions on this theme because I believe that the reader is entitled to know the views of the writer. Let the reader beware of that book whose author insists that it is completely "objective." All that I can say is that I have attempted to present my views as honestly and as objectively as possible. The reader must ultimately be the judge of whether or not this goal has been attained.

A NOTE CONCERNING THE INTERVIEWS

Interviews-in-depth with the intermarried were secured in an effort to obtain what statistical information and observation alone might not make sufficiently clear—the successes and failures, the challenges and the problems that are so often directly and indirectly associated with intermarriages. These personal and family histories make it obvious that even though not all intermarriages need be regarded as clear-cut instances of success or failure, the partners to such marriages believe that they need to "work much harder" to achieve happiness than do those who marry within their own religious, ethnic or racial group.

Suggestions for potential interviewees were made to the author by ministers, priests, rabbis, marriage counselors, university professors, students and others who expressed interest in the subject. In most instances, these interviewees were not known to the writer prior to his first meeting with them.

After a careful study of the various types of intermarriage among those suggested, a group of likely candidates was chosen. Each received a letter explaining the nature of the research. In most cases, it was necessary to follow up on the letter with one or two phone calls. Of the "cases" originally chosen, all but two agreed to an interview. One flatly refused and gave no reason, while the other stated that he and his wife were now living in a far-off section of the country, making the interview impossible.

It is fortunate that the confidence of the candidates was gained and that, fully aware as they were of the ultimate purpose of the interviews, these families proved willing to make themselves available for the meetings that followed.

The same series of questions, prepared in advance, was asked each of the persons interviewed, with such modifications as the special circumstances required. These interviews were semistructured in that they allowed those questioned full freedom to formulate their answers within the framework of the outline used by the author. The interviews required from one and one-half to two hours each and took place in the majority of instances, in the home of the intermarrieds. Their manner of life thus became evident. Photographs of children, of parents, and family, books on the shelves, all tended to suggest the familial and cultural milieu in which they lived. These informal meetings, usually arranged around the coffee table, were, in each instance, tape-recorded, thereby retaining the actual phraseology and detailed statements of those whose stories and comments were recorded. They were, of necessity, rearranged and edited to eliminate personal elements that might identify

specifically those persons who so generously shared their experiences with me. In some cases, the desire to avoid repetitive statements and other extraneous material required that entire portions be rewritten. Yet the heart, the essence and, in most instances, the exact manner of speech was captured and retained.

Most of these intermarrieds now live in the East, although originally they may have come out of the Middle or Far West. Included herein are the stories of professors at some of America's leading universities and their wives; businessmen, civil-service employees, doctors, lawyers, administrators, typists, housewives and mothers. These are the confidential stories of Negroes who are married to whites, Jews who have married Catholics or Protestants, Protestants and Catholics, Japanese and white. Interethnic marriages as well as marriages in which one partner has converted to the faith of husband or wife and those in which partners have refused formal conversion are also included. These stories do not presume to cover every possible type of intermarriage that could come to mind, but they do serve to highlight different kinds of intermarriages not only on religious, ethnic and racial lines, but on class and status lines as well.

In no instance were either successful marriages or those that were failing deliberately sought out. Often, intermarriages generally regarded as highly successful appeared to be far less so when the interviewees revealed their true sentiments. And the reverse is, of course, also true. Failures were sometimes actually better, happier marriages than friends suspected. That success or failure in marriage, including intermarriage, is most often directly associated with the courage, strength and faith of the individuals and families involved, coupled with "a little bit of wisdom" as one interviewee has suggested, becomes quite clear through these interviews-in-depth.

A careful reading of these stories should prove enlightening and, therefore, profitable. Knowledge of the intermarrieds, their joys and their sorrows, their successes as well as their failures, *as recounted by them,* will, it is hoped, develop further understanding of a significant and ever-increasing minority in America.

In a sense no personal history can be "typical." There are always some circumstances and facts that are different. R. E. Park's observation on the nature of experience deserves our consideration:

> Experience is concrete, personal and unique. It does not repeat itself exactly. We never have the same experience twice in exactly the same way. Any experience in life is an historical fact; it always has a date and a location and it happens only once.

Although personal histories cannot tell us all there is to know about the persons who intermarry, they serve to remind us of the varieties of experiences encountered by the intermarried and, in that relationship, they prove especially valuable. They help also to explain the attitudes and opinions of the intermarried. The social situations in which these people find themselves help us to understand them even when they do not understand themselves.

ALBERT I. GORDON

The Interviews

CONTENTS

INTERMARRIAGE: WHAT IT IS

This is a book about intermarriage—what it is, and what it does, both to the persons who intermarry and to their children as well. The term "intermarriage" is generally applied to those married persons whose religious, racial or ethnic background is or was different from each other's, either prior to or after their marriage. Even if the marriage partners differ from each other in only one of these three categories, they may be said to be intermarried. For example, a Catholic married to a Jew is intermarried. This is true, also, of a Protestant married to a Catholic or of a Negro married to a white person. Interethnic marriages involving persons of the same religion and color but differing with respect to national and cultural backgrounds are also said to be inter-marriages. An Irish-Catholic married to an Italian-Catholic is a party to an interethnic marriage. Although we are less inclined to regard the marriage of an Episcopalian to a Baptist as an intermarriage, it may technically be described in these same terms. If one of the parties to the marriage has not formally converted to the faith of the other, such a marriage is more properly termed a "mixed marriage." We shall use the term "mixed marriage" to describe only those marriages in which separate religious ideologies are maintained by the parties subsequent to their marriage.

To be more specific, an interfaith marriage is one in which the parties to the marriage were born or reared in families, each of which has identified with a different religion. If, prior to or following the marriage, the parties continue to identify with their separate religions, they are not only intermarried but are parties to a "mixed marriage" as well. If both parties formally accept the same religion even though they are intermarried, they are nevertheless of the same religious persuasion and hence no longer "mixed."

We shall refer to an "interethnic" marriage as one in which each of the parties to the marriage was reared in a cultural and national environment which differs from that of the other. Thus, an Irish Catholic differs in many ethnic characteristics from an Italian Catholic; a German Jew differs in the same respects from a Russian or Polish Jew. It should be noted that in both cases the religion of the parties is the same. However, in other characteristics and values, including that of nationality, they differ markedly from each other. These differences are cultural and national.

1

Interracial marriages are those in which the parties to the marriage belong to different races. Their skin colors are different and will, of course, always remain different. Hence, even though a Negro Protestant may marry a white Protestant, their marriage will correctly be regarded as "interracial." Persons of different color, no matter what their religion or national origin are and will remain members of different races. Such marriages will always be termed "interracial."

Interfaith marriages are said to occur rather frequently in the United States, but interethnic marriages are, by far, the most common. Racial intermarriages occur least frequently of any of these three types. Jacobson[1] has pointed out that "in 1939, the only year for which data are available . . . interracial marriages [between Negroes and whites] account for only 8 out of every 10,000 marriages in the country." The highest rate of interracial marriage in this country was recorded in Los Angeles during the 1924-33 period when 1.2 per 100 marriages was reported.[2] Yet, it must be pointed out that this record is very low as compared with the incidence of other forms of intermarriage. There are indications that the rate of increase in the three major forms of inter-marriage will grow in the years ahead. The reasons, therefore, may be outlined as follows:

In 1961, for example, there were 2,040 colleges in the United States. Where, in 1900 only 4 per cent of the college-age group attended colleges or universities, the college attendance in 1956 was 35 per cent of this age group. It is estimated that, by 1966, the college population will increase to 45 per cent of this age group. Eighty to 90 per cent of high-school graduates in some areas of this country now go to our colleges and universities. The total college-grade enrollment for the academic years 1960-61 was 3,610,000 for continental United States.

Since the school year 1929-30 the college population of males has tripled. In that year 619,935 men were enrolled. By 1955-56, there were 1,748,198 males in our college population. The number of college women has doubled in the same period (from 480,802 to 889,047).[3]

One out of every three high-school graduates in 1961 was enrolled in an institution of higher learning. There has been an increase of 61.2 per cent in college, university and professional school attendance since 1950. It is estimated that, by 1970, the number of Jewish students attending colleges and universities will grow from the present figure of 300,000 to 400,000. One-third of the students graduating from high schools are Jewish; two-thirds of them enroll in some school of higher education.[4]

The number is increasing annually. Seven million college and uni-

versity students are projected by 1970. The high birth rate of the 1940's is thus reflected as is the tendency to regard a college or university degree as indispensable in contemporary American society.

The number of Jewish youth who continue with college and university education is, according to a survey released by the B'nai B'rith Hillel Foundation, "much higher" than that of any other youth in the country, pointing up their traditional urge for learning and their belief in the status-giving qualities of education as well. The movement of Jews in large numbers from the lower-income class to a middle-class position has made higher education economically possible for more of them.

The attitudes of American young people, particularly those who are college and university students, has markedly changed with respect to intermarriage. The social controls of parents, family and organized religion that exerted influence upon our youth prior to World War II have lessened in influence and importance. The reduction of religious denominationalism, so good from one point of view, is nevertheless deleterious and damaging to the survival of Church and Synagogue. The lowering of barriers of race and religion in most fraternities and sororities has increased the opportunities for social intercourse among our college youth. These changes in attitude do not necessarily mean that these young people will, in all certainty, intermarry. There is a vast difference between a person's *attitude* and his ultimate *action*. He may be influenced by many factors that presently fail to impress him. His early religious training; the response to parents, to priest, rabbi or minister in the moment of decision; his knowledge of his own cultural tradition—among other factors—may, as he gets older, tend to sway him from an earlier attitude. The liberalism of an earlier age may give way to a greater conservatism at a later age. Hence, it is hardly likely that every liberal attitude of our college youth will later be translated into a liberal action such as intermarriage is supposed by some to be.

The number of females who attend colleges and universities today continues to increase also and there are more coeducational institutions than ever. All tend to increase the opportunities for social intercourse and the opportunity for intermarriage among American university students is thereby increased.

Our own evidence, gathered by sampling university-student opinion in forty universities throughout the country, located in the nine census areas and representing all kinds and types of schools and schooling, supports this thesis, as we shall see. The study makes clear, too, that the more "liberal" attitudes held by these young people today is not noticeably regional in character with but one exception; nor is it directly asso-

ciated with the youth of one kind of Church or Synagogue as compared with another. The nondenominational character of America's college youth is becoming increasingly clear.

Bossard [5] has stated that "currently, the annual toll of divorces and annulments approaches 400,000. The annual number of reported divorces has ranged between one-fourth and one-third of the total number of marriages consummated in the corresponding year." He points out further that, in selected cities, the number of divorces equaled or exceeded one-half of the total marriages. In 1959 there was 1 divorce for every 3.6 marriages in the United States. This constituted an increase of 7.5 per cent in the number of divorces that took place in that year as compared with the year 1958. These figures do not tell us the whole story in that we have yet to know the actual number of separations that occurred or the number of persons who, although not divorced or separated, believe that theirs is an unhappy marriage and speak of it as a "failure."

Many students have attempted to discover the specific causes that ultimately lead to divorce, separation or annulment. They generally conclude that (1) these causes actually run into the hundreds, (2) they do not follow the same sequence in all cases, (3) they are not necessarily the same for all people, (4) the incompatibilities that may lead to divorce appear to be related to the cultural, religious and psychological differences that exist between people.

The likelihood that religious, ethnic or racial differences will exist between people who come into contact with each other within the next generation means, too, the further likelihood that more marriages will end in divorce, annulment or separation.

For reasons which to date have not been fully explained, the number of divorces and separations between intermarried couples in the past decade has been two to three times as high (some authorities say that it is four times as high) as those divorces and separations involving marriages of persons of the same religion.

In the year 1959, in the United States 1,494,000 [6] marriages took place. In the same year 395,000 divorces, or 26 per cent of all marriages, are recorded. The statistics for 1960 are not yet available. In 1946, immediately following World War II, the number of marriages in the United States reached an all-time high (2,291,045). However, in that same year there were 610,000 divorces or approximately 37 per cent of the total number of marriages.

The divorce rate is obviously high. It is my conviction that the rates of divorce, annulment or separation will continue to increase with the increase in the number of persons whose religious, ethnic or racial backgrounds differ from that of their marriage partner.

It is my hypothesis, supported particularly by a study of attitudes of college and university students in forty schools throughout the nation, in addition to a review of the literature on the subject, that

(1) There will be an increase in all forms of intermarriage—interfaith, interethnic, interracial—with the greatest increase occurring in the area of interethnic marriages, the next greatest in that of different religions and the lowest among different racial and color groups.

(2) This increase will take place because, in addition to the general factors making for intermarriage, changes have occurred and are occurring within four special areas: (a) The number and per cent of young people attending colleges and universities are rapidly increasing. The propinquity resulting therefrom; the increasing similarity of backgrounds, with the consequent reduction in differences along ethnic, educational, economic and national lines; the elimination of sectarianism and denominationalism, in state-operated colleges and universities, and in private, church-founded schools tends to make cultural homogeneity more likely. (b) The elimination of religious differences and distinctions, in schools and out, the ecumenical trends in our society and the indifference to religion generally, tend to minimize the importance of those distinctions that in former years played a major role in separating and dividing men into distinctive groups. (c) The official change in status of colored nations, their recognition by the United Nations and the greater number of their citizens traveling throughout the world (including the United States) and attending our universities and colleges; the lowering of color bars that formerly separated men and women of different races; the increasing number of Negroes who are attending institutions of higher learning; the Supreme Court's decision of 1954, officially outlawing segregation in the schools—all these seem to assure a slow, but definite, increase in racial mixtures. (d) The general decrease in parental authority, and the weakening of family ties which is apparent in our day, as well as the attitude of an increasing number of parents who are less militant and more permissive than formerly with respect to intermarriage in any of its forms (with the possible exception of the Jewish people). Aware of this and other changes, young people of college and university age are more likely to intermarry in the decade ahead.

WHAT SOME COLLEGE STUDENTS THINK ABOUT INTERMARRIAGE

What do college and university students think about interfaith, interethnic and interracial marriages? Do they generally approve of such marriages? Are they unconcerned? Do they disapprove?

Aware as I am that vast numbers of our young people are either at college or headed for a college education, I sought to discover the attitudes and opinions of a selected group of students, 5,407 to be exact, in some forty colleges and universities throughout the nine census areas of this nation. One-third of all the students in my sample "majored" in the social sciences. The others were scattered in many different fields of endeavor. Because so many of these students were obviously interested in the social sciences, it is clear that my results may not necessarily represent the attitudes and opinion of *all* American college and university students. (No sample is likely to include everyone.) However, inasmuch as so many (34 per cent) of college students major in this and allied fields, this study may well represent what your son or daughter may be thinking on this important subject. An examination of Table 22 (*see* Appendix) will provide an exact list of the "majors" of all the students sampled.[1]

Forty-four per cent of our respondents were male and 55 per cent were female (1 per cent provided "no information"). Assuming that the liberal tendencies of social-science majors are generally more pronounced than those of students majoring in other fields, we must note, too, that our sample included students in colleges and universities that were state controlled, as well as those that were privately sponsored. It included also schools that have student bodies that are all-male as well as all-female. It included students in schools that, to this point, are segregated (all-white) Southern schools and schools of higher education that are almost entirely all-Negro. The schools of higher education included in this sample are located in all of the nine census areas of the country.

There are young people hidden behind these figures. They may very well represent the views of the youth in your own immediate family or of the community in which you live.

Inasmuch as the professors to whom I turned for assistance in administering the questionnaires were primarily social scientists, it was to be expected that the replies would come from students who were "exposed" to one or more courses in the social sciences. This sample, then,

is specialized. It may be more representative of liberal opinion on American college campuses than is general. On the other hand, it may be fairly representative of the opinion of college young people, who are usually more liberal than their elders. It may represent a point of view unlike those of the students who "major" in physics, chemistry, engineering, law, medicine or business. But it must be remembered that 66 per cent of our sample were *not* social science majors and students who are "exposed" to any course in the social sciences (even the most elementary) are not, by that fact alone, likely to become more "liberal" in their views.

The attitudes and opinions of these students were compared with the attitudes and opinions of students who had not taken any course in the social sciences, as a means of determining whether the attitudes of social science "majors" were more "liberal" than that of other students. Social-science students in one of the schools were compared with those who had never taken a course in the social sciences. The information obtained makes it clear that there is, in fact, no evidence of any radical difference in points of view between the two groups at this point in their studies.

Sixty-seven per cent of the students at Northeastern University who were part of the "control" group were "majors" in engineering while 11 per cent "majored" in business. Only 2 per cent of this group majored in the social sciences with the remainder majoring in other fields. However, the differences may be much more marked by the senior year when the major courses have already been completed. Inasmuch as the majority of our young people were young in years (1 per cent was seventeen years old; 14 per cent were eighteen years of age; 24 per cent were nineteen years old; 24 per cent were twenty years old, with 19 per cent indicating that they were twenty-one years old). Twenty per cent of our 5,407 students were freshmen; 30 per cent, sophomores; 26 per cent, juniors; and 20 per cent, seniors. In addition, 13 per cent of our total sample were known to be graduate students. However, 1 per cent of our sample gave us no information on this score. Of the total 96 per cent of our students consists of undergraduates.

Whether students enrolled in sociology courses or other courses in the social sciences are really more liberal than others, is, I believe, debatable.

The attitude of college students with respect to all forms of intermarriage is important because the number of young people who receive a college training is rapidly increasing. They represent, and will in the decade ahead, represent, a large proportion of the young people of college age in this country. What they think and how they react to such matters as intermarriage is of considerable importance to us.

It is estimated that by 1966 (only two years hence) 45 per cent of college-age youth will be attending schools of higher education. Parenthetically, it may be pointed out that in many middle- or upper-class suburban communities throughout the country the number of college students has already increased to 80 per cent or more. It is worthy of note that the number of coeducational colleges and universities has increased markedly. At present there are 1,549 coeducational schools with but 232 colleges and universities that are all male and 259 schools that are all female. An estimated enrollment of 400,000 Jewish undergraduates by 1970 is also envisaged. Since 1955, the number of Jewish students in our colleges has virtually doubled. The quota systems of former years are today virtually dead.

We attempted, too, to compare both of these groups with a sampling of students from the University of Hawaii. There were many reasons for such a comparison. First, the number of students in our sample at the University of Hawaii who are the products of interracial marriage is large (72 per cent). Second, we have many Buddhists in our sample. Third, 35 per cent of these students (almost the same for all other members of our sample) majored in the social sciences and fourth, very little is known about these students. About one-third (202,230) of the total population of the State of Hawaii are whites, another third are Japanese, and the remainder consists of 114,405 native or part native Hawaiian, 69,070 Filipinos, 38,197 Chinese, with but 4,943 Negroes and 472 Indians. The number of students at the University of Hawaii who are of mixed racial stock is marked. They therefore constitute a fascinating subject of study in their own right. They become especially important when we are able to compare the attitudes of students who are racially and often religiously "different" with those on the mainland.

A comparison of the attitudes of students, 34 per cent of whom major in the social sciences, with the students of varied racial and religious background, such as we find at the University of Hawaii—and both of these compared and contrasted with the views of students who, in 67 per cent of the cases, are engineering majors in the "control" group—offers, I believe, certain significant information concerning all three groups.

I offer a special word of caution: the present attitudes of students may not necessarily remain their attitudes five years or a decade hence. This is, of course, characteristic of all young people whatever their race, religion or ethnic background. Their views may change as the views of their elders, too, have changed over the years.

The questionnaire used in this study is included in Appendix A. It will be noted that not all the information obtained from the students

has been used for this volume. The reason therefor is that, in certain cases, the replies to particular questions did not provide information that added to our knowledge of the attitudes of the students. Had I asked question #39 "Were you ever in the Armed Services? Yes —— No ——" immediately after World War II, I suspect that the replies would have indicated that many students had been in the Armed Services. I would, then, have sought to correlate the replies to this question to those concerning their attitudes toward persons of other races, colors, nationalities and religions. But there were, in fact, very few students who had (1) been in the armed services, or (2) traveled abroad (see question #38). Hence, nothing was to be gained by including the results in this study.

I attempted, also, to gain some insight into the degree of personal security or insecurity that characterized students of different religious faiths (and of no faith, as well). The results did not appear to be conclusive and were, therefore, not used. In certain other cases the knowledge obtained through replies to questions #16 and #17 as well as #23 and #24, although interesting, appeared to prove nothing of any significance. The answers were, therefore, not used in this study.

In three instances I have maintained the anonymity of the schools involved (in all cases, all-female schools) because it was specifically requested. In each instance, however, a member of the teaching staff in each school actively co-operated with me in administering the questionnaires in their classes.

An effort was made to discover what differences in attitudes (if any) existed between college students in various areas of the country. I sought, too, to uncover differences in attitudes that might exist between students in state-controlled vs. private colleges and universities. Coeducational schools were grouped separately from all-male and all-female schools as were colleges that were predominately Negro as well as those Southern schools that were known to have all-white student bodies.

I sought, also, to discover if the attitudes of college students in the Mountain States were very much different from those of students in the Pacific States. Inasmuch as it is often said that people in the East have their roots most deeply implanted while the roots (and traditional attitudes) are less firmly implanted in the Western areas of this nation, Western schools were singled out for comparison with all the other groupings.

Who were these students whose attitudes and opinions I report? Forty-seven per cent call themselves Protestants, 31 per cent are Catholics, and 12 per cent are Jewish. Five per cent have no religious affiliation, one-half of 1 per cent are members of the Eastern Orthodox

Church while three-tenths of 1 per cent are Buddhists. The remainder, about 4 per cent of the total of 5,407 students, provided no information as to their religion.

Further, 86 per cent of all the students listed themselves as "white" while 12 per cent recorded themselves as "Negroes" and 2 per cent simply stated that they were "other" than Negro or white. In our sample of the students at the University of Hawaii, 72 per cent recorded themselves as non-white but not Negro, while 28 per cent of this total sample consisted of white students.

Eighty-nine per cent of our sample are unmarried students. Of these, 9 per cent are engaged to be married, while 6 per cent of those who replied are married. In this case 5 per cent of the students offered no information concerning their status.

We know also that 71 per cent of our respondents attended a public high school before going on to college or university. We know further that 12 per cent attended a Catholic high school and another 13 per cent attended a private non-church-supported school. It has been suggested that those who attended a private school might be more conservative than those who are graduates of public high schools inasmuch as they are generally members of a higher income group. It might even counteract the liberality that is said to be associated with students of the social sciences. Only 1 per cent of the students attended a Catholic private school. Three per cent of the students provided us with no information on this point.

Information about the parents of these students and the homes from which they come was also obtained.

As for the fathers of these students, 86 per cent are native-born, while 12 per cent are foreign-born. Two per cent failed to provide us with information. These college youth said of their fathers that 16 per cent had advanced college degrees, while 19 per cent are college graduates. In all, 35 per cent of the fathers, according to their sons and daughters, have received college degrees. Of the remainder, 22 per cent are high-school graduates while 18 per cent received only an elementary-school education. However, 25 per cent of our respondents failed to provide us with information.

Fifty-one per cent of the fathers, according to their sons and daughters, are Protestants (while 47 per cent of the students themselves claim to be Protestants), 25 per cent of the fathers are Catholics (while 31 per cent of the students are Catholics). There are then 6 per cent more Catholic students than there are Catholic fathers. This appears to be due to the fact that these youth follow the religion of the mother more frequently than that of the father. It is interesting to note that 12 per cent of the fathers are Jewish (exactly the same percentage as that of

the Jewish college youth). While 4 per cent of the fathers are, according to their sons and daughters, not affiliated with any religion, 5 per cent of their sons and daughters declare themselves to be nonaffiliated. Whereas, 1 per cent of the fathers were Buddhists, three-tenths of 1 per cent of the students are Buddhists. There is, too, a slight difference between the percentage of fathers who belong to the Eastern Orthodox Church and their college sons and daughters (.7 per cent vs. .5 per cent).

Unitarians will be disappointed to discover that while 4 per cent of the fathers identified themselves as Unitarians, only 1 per cent of their sons and daughters identified themselves in this way. Only 1 per cent of the students failed to provide information concerning the religion of their father while 3 per cent of the students gave us no information about their own affiliation.

We also obtained this kind of information about the mothers of our student sample. Fifty-four per cent of the mothers, according to their sons and daughters, are affiliated with the Protestant Church (as compared with 47 per cent of the fathers). Of the Catholic mothers there are 30 per cent whereas but 25 per cent of the fathers are Catholic. Interestingly, exactly the same per cent of mothers and fathers and children are Jewish (12 per cent). Only 1 per cent of the mothers is a Unitarian (as compared with 4 per cent of the fathers).

The formal education of the mothers appears not to be as high as that of the fathers. Twenty-five per cent are college graduates and 10 per cent have advanced college degrees (beyond Bachelor's degree). Twenty-five per cent have graduated from high school, but have had no college training in any degree, while 33 per cent of the mothers have not gone beyond elementary school.

However, 89 per cent of the mothers are native-born (as compared with 86 per cent of the fathers), while 10 per cent are foreign-born (as compared with 12 per cent of the fathers). In only 1 per cent of the cases were we not provided with information concerning the mother's country of birth.

The nature of the students and their background is further established when we consider the nature of the work or the professions engaged in by both fathers and mothers.

Twenty-one per cent of the fathers of our students are professional men (doctors, lawyers, teachers, etc.) while 16 per cent are business executives, estimated by their children to have an income of over $20,-000 annually. Another 15 per cent are executives, said to be earning less money. Twelve per cent are office workers while 13 per cent are foremen or blue-collar workers. Nine per cent are, according to their sons and daughters, janitors. The size of the latter category may be

due to the fact that our total sample contained many Negro students whose parents may not have been able to advance to any other status. Three per cent of the fathers are recorded as farmers. Eleven per cent were listed as having either some "other" trade or profession or were not recorded at all.

In the case of the mothers, 58 per cent are listed as housewives, while 10 per cent are recorded as office workers. Another 9 per cent are identified by their sons and daughters as janitors. Here again we call attention to the fact that many Negroes and other non-whites seem to be recorded in this category.

As for the economic income of these families, by far the largest number appear to belong to the middle class ("upper" as well as "lower"). Thirty-seven per cent of the parents, according to their children, have an annual income of from $5,000 to $10,000; 24 per cent earn from $10,000 to $15,000 annually. Twelve per cent claim that the family income is in the $15,000 to $20,000 category, while 11 per cent earn more than $20,000 annually. Nine per cent of these parents, according to their children, receive an income of less than $5,000 annually.

We must remember, of course, that these estimates are made by college youth (not their parents). There has been no opportunity to verify these responses. These figures must then be regarded as estimates of income. There is, however, no reason to believe that youth of college age are not generally aware of the economic status of their parents.

Because we are so often told that the attitude of the child depends in large degree upon the marital happiness of parents, we sought to discover what we could about the marital status of these parents. Our sample informed us that 83 per cent of the parents are living together, that 4 per cent are divorced; about 1.5 per cent are separated and 9 per cent are widowed. There is no way of discovering whether those parents who are living together are happy in their relationship. We can, however, be very certain that divorce and separation indicate that such a family has been unhappy. Unless each of these families "living together" were interviewed, we would have no way of knowing the status of its marital happiness. (It might be pointed out that even were such interviews to take place, we could still not be absolutely certain about it.) It is, I think, not improper to assume that the majority of these families regard their marriages as successful and that the children are not generally the products of unhappy homes.

Intermarriage has already occurred in 40 per cent of the families of our students. Of these, 28 per cent have occurred between uncles and aunts, while in 9 per cent of the intermarriages, brothers or sisters were involved. Two per cent of the respondents indicated that they

themselves are intermarried while 1 per cent declared that a niece or nephew was a party to an intermarriage. We may then point out that interfaith marriage is not an utterly new experience to our college youth. The opinions and attitudes are, in some degree, the result of their awareness of intermarriage as a reality rather than as a theory.

Fifty-two per cent of these young people state that they have, at some time or other, reacted against religion, while 47 per cent declare that they have not so reacted. Of those who have reacted adversely, 56 per cent were teen-agers (thirteen to nineteen years old) when they so reacted. It is natural to expect reaction against authority in any form at this age. Religion, parents, authority, in all manifestations, both in school and out, must bear the brunt of such overt or covert reaction by young people. A psychiatrist with whom I discussed this response stated, "My only surprise is that the percentage of those who rebel is not greater. It is during the teen years particularly that young people give full expression to their rebellion in one form or another, to their parents, their ideas and the institutions which they support."

A remark attributed to Mark Twain comes to mind in this connection. He is said to have commented: "When I was 14 years of age I was surprised at how ignorant my father was. When I became 21 years old, I was surprised to discover how much my father had learned in seven years!"

Twenty-seven per cent of our sample state that the religious influence of their home is "strong" while 57 per cent declared that it is "moderate." Yet, 14 per cent believe that the religious influence of their home is "weak." In 2 per cent of the cases, we were provided with no information.

There is every likelihood that, in each instance, these youth gave themselves the benefit of every doubt and declared, for example, that the religious influence was "strong" when it was perhaps "moderate." The same may very well be true for those who declared the religious influence of their home to be "moderate" when it may have been in fact "weak" or at least, bordering on the weak side. Those who declared that the religious influence of their home was weak may have been talking about homes where religious influence was actually nonexistent. Even if we accept the expressed view of these students, we will note that almost 60 per cent believe that the religious influence was "moderate." Clearly the influence is generally not strong. The conclusion at which we arrive is that the religious influence in the homes of these students is not especially marked. Parents either do not have or do not wish to have much of a religious influence upon the young people in this sample.

Another interesting bit of information ascertained through this study is that 44 per cent of these young people declare their mother to be the

"dominant parent" in the home. It must be pointed out, however, that 37 per cent of these college youth state that their father is the "dominant parent." Another 8 per cent of the students state that both parents are "dominant." Whether the latter reply indicates that we are dealing with potential diplomats or statesmen whose replies indicate a desire to please both parents and the interviewer cannot definitely be ascertained. That the latter may be the case can be suspected from the result. Eleven per cent of the respondents provided us with no information. Inasmuch as it is generally assumed that the mother is the dominant parent in the home in that her opportunities to mold the ideas and values of her children appear to be greatest, I would suggest that the information which our respondents have provided offers no evidence to the contrary.

In a series of questions designed to discover the attitudes of these college youth to intermarriage itself, much interesting and even valuable information was gleaned, as we shall see. But of particular importance at this point is the belief that these youth have about how their parents would respond to intermarriage. Sixty-nine per cent of these youth, almost 7 out of every 10 young people, in reply to the question, "Do your parents object to your dating a person of another religion?" replied in the negative. Only 28 per cent of these youth answered "Yes." What is clear then, is that these young people, mistakenly or otherwise, believe that their parents are not opposed to interdating with a person of another religion. This is important because the belief (not the fact) that parents are permissive in this respect certainly plays a significant role in the ultimate response of their children. Of course, we must distinguish between permissiveness with respect to "interdating" and "intermarriage." Whereas parents may have no serious objections to the former, they may indeed oppose the latter.

Table 1

Attitude of college youth
toward a sibling if "married out of the faith."

Response	Per cent
Would approve	25
Mildly disapprove	28
Uncertain	26
Strongly disapprove	14
No information	7
Total	100

Table 1 records the response of these college youth to the question, "If your sister or brother married outside of your own religion would you: Approve?—Mildly disapprove?—Be uncertain?—or Strongly disapprove?"

What is of special interest to us is that only 14 per cent of the students would "strongly disapprove" whereas 79 per cent would either approve, mildly disapprove or remain uncertain as to their reaction. There appears, then, to be no strong opposition to the interfaith marriage of a sibling.

The personal attitude of each respondent to his or her own interfaith marriage was also questioned. The response is given in Table 2.

Table 2

Attitude of college youth
if they loved boy (or girl) of a different faith

Response	Per cent
Would continue to date	45
Would break off at once	8
Be undecided	21
Ask other person to convert	14
Offer to convert to other religion	2
No information	10
Total	100

It will be noted that only 8 per cent of the students would "break off at once," while 45 per cent would continue to date, and 21 per cent would be undecided. The receptivity of these youth to interfaith marriage is thus clearly established. Even those who "hedge" on this score believe that by asking the loved one to convert, they have fully resolved the problem. Such responses make it even clearer that interfaith marriages will, in all likelihood, increase.

Table 3 supports this conclusion further because it indicates that,

Table 3

Percentages of college and university students
in 12 groups of schools who dated outside of their religion

Schools	Number of schools	Rarely	Some-times	Fre-quently	Almost always	Never	No infor-mation
All-school	40	21%	39%	20%	9%	10%	1%
Northeastern control	1	7	33	30	17	13	0
U. of Hawaii	1	8	42	29	10	5	6
Catholic	8	35	36	9	2	16	2
Negro	3	15	31	20	9	7	8
Southern	4	22	33	21	10	11	3
Private all-male	3	13	38	22	10	7	10
Private all-female	3	18	37	20	10	5	10
Private coed	9	16	36	18	12	13	5
State U. coed	8	20	39	22	9	8	2
Mountain States	2	8	42	26	13	5	6
Pacific States	3	15	38	24	10	8	5

even though there are certain differences in the "dating out pattern," by far the largest per cent of our students "date out" at some time or other. Our sample indicates that 16 per cent of the Catholic students never date out of their own religion, while 13 per cent of our control group never date out. We also would call attention to the fact that the same per cent of students in privately sponsored coeducational institutions (13 per cent) never date out while 11 per cent of the students in the Southern (all-white) group of schools never date out. It would appear from the "all-school" sample of 40 schools that 80 to 85 per cent of our students date out at some time or other.

I venture the suggestion that "no information" in the replies of the students should be regarded, in all likelihood, as an indication that interdating does take place because it was easy enough to reply "never" to this question. Yet the student chose not to answer the question at all. It is of interest to note that the per cent of students who never date out of their religious group is highest among the students of Catholic schools. Why the Northeastern control group should contain 13 per cent who never date out of their religion is not clear. An examination of the data about these students reveals that 63 per cent come from homes that are "moderate" in their religious influence and further that 67 per cent of the parents, according to these youths, do not object to their interdating. Inasmuch as the opportunities for social and cultural contacts are great in this control school which is located in an urban area, the reason for the comparatively high degree of "never" interdating must be resolved at some other time.

(For a detailed account of each of the forty schools in response to this question, see Appendix.)

In the "all-school" sample consisting of students in forty colleges and universities, only 10 per cent indicate that they never date out and only 1 per cent have not provided any information in this respect. Insofar as the other groups are concerned it should be noted that even when the "no information" column runs as high as 10 per cent as in our sample of all-male and all-female (private) schools, the per cent of interdating with a person of another faith nevertheless is quite high. The fact that the Northeastern Control, like the privately sponsored coeducational schools that have a rather high per cent of students who state that they never interdate, has a large percentage of Jewish students as well as "Eastern Orthodox" religious affiliate. This may, in some measure, account for the rather high percentage. This school is urban in character. Consequently the number of persons of the same faith with whom one can date, is rather large. This fact may also have something to do with the results. Actually, what is of especial importance is the fact that 89 per cent of the forty schools in our sample *do* interdate and

that 87 per cent of the control group, in the main consisting of persons other than social-science students, interdate also.

Insofar as those students who identify themselves with the three major groups are concerned, the per cent of each group, Protestant, Catholic or Jewish, who *never* date outside of their religion is exactly the same—4 per cent. In other words, at least 95 per cent of all three major religious groups interdate "sometimes," "frequently," "rarely," or "almost always." Only 2 per cent of the Jewish students state that such interdating occurs frequently while 7 per cent of the Protestant and 6 per cent of the Catholics reply in the same manner. Six per cent of the Jewish students interdate "sometimes" while 43 per cent of the Protestant students and 33 per cent of the Catholic students interdate at some time or other. Nineteen per cent of the Protestant students say that interdating occurs rarely; 12 per cent of the Catholic students reply in the same manner and only 5 per cent of the Jewish students state that they interdate "rarely."

It is of interest to Catholic schools to note that in this sample, 82 per cent of Catholic students interdate outside of their religion while only 16 per cent never interdate. The fact that the Catholic schools do not control the actions of their students becomes obvious.

In the State University, coeducational schools, 90 per cent of the students interdate at some time or other while only 8 per cent never interdate outside of their own faith. In the all-women's schools, privately sponsored, 85 per cent of the students indicate that they interdate while only 5 per cent state that they never interdate. In this case, we must remember that 10 per cent of the students failed to provide us with information in this respect. In the case of the all-male-school sample, 83 per cent reported that they interdate with only 7 per cent declaring that they never interdate.

Thirty-nine per cent of the students in the "all-school" (40) sample interdate "sometimes" while 33 per cent of the control group (Northeastern University) interdate "sometimes." In the "all-school" sample 9 per cent of the students interdate "almost always" while in the control group 17 per cent answered "almost always."

Catholic, Protestant and Jewish leaders, pastors of churches and synagogues, appear to be aware of the increase in the number of interfaith marriages as we shall see. A majority of the directors of Newman Clubs, Hillel Foundations and Protestant Youth Organizations within our colleges and universities are agreed that intermarriage, interfaith, interethnic and interracial, will increase.

Father John L. Thomas, the noted sociologist, believes that about one-fourth of all Catholic marriages are valid intermarriages. It is estimated by Catholic sources that the number of invalid marriages,

those performed *without* the sanction of the church, is considerably larger than the number of valid marriages.

Insofar as Protestants are concerned, the number of interfaith marriages in which Protestants are involved, is already about 50 per cent of all marriages involving a Protestant.

Jewish intermarriages have, for years, been regarded as remaining at about 7 to 8 per cent. They have, however, shot up to almost 12 per cent in the Washington, D.C., area and have risen to 34 per cent in the Peninsula area of the Pacific Northwest. Whether or not these marriages are only exceptions to the general rule has yet to be proved. It is my belief that they more nearly represent the change which is in the process of occurring insofar as Jewish intermarriages are concerned.

In 1928, Bogardus published his social-distance scale[2] by means of which the attitudes of individuals and groups toward persons of other ethnic, religious, racial or national groups, could be compared and related to each other. This scale has been modified for the purpose of this study. Seven statements of attitudes, indicating "social distance" were considered.

The students in each of the forty schools in our sample were asked to indicate approval by a check or disapproval by offering no response or mark to eleven different kinds of people. We included the three major religious groups, Protestants, Catholics and Jews, as well as various ethnic and racial groups. The groups included in the questions were: Italians, Negroes, Jewish, Japanese, Catholics, Filipinos, Protestants, Mexicans, Greeks, Irish and Polish.

The following statements were made with respect to each of these groups, in order to discover the response of each of the respondents to their "social distance" from each of these groups:

1. I would have as an intimate friend a ————.
2. I would work beside on a job a ————.
3. I would live in the same neighborhood or block with a ————.
4. I would marry a ————.
5. I would bar from my block a ————.
6. I would bar from my social recreation or fraternity, lodge or society a ————.
7. I would date or allow a son or daughter to date a ————.

The social-distance scale, by recording the attitude of each of the 5,407 students toward each of the eleven groups, races, religions, national or ethnic groups, provides us with additional information concerning the readiness of the student to associate in lesser or greater degree

with members of groups other than his own. The attitudes of students in their respective schools were, of course, obtained. Further, the students were classified according to the groups into which they most logically fit. Thus, we obtained the attitudes with respect to social distance of students who were Catholic, or Negro, or all-white Southerners, members of privately sponsored all-male schools as well as privately endowed all-women's schools. The attitudes of students in coeducational institutions as well as those in certain schools in the Mountain and Pacific states were thus obtained. In addition the social distance of the sample of our students at the University of Hawaii and those, too, at the Northeastern University Control Group were recorded as was the average for the students in the forty-school sample. The results, in terms of percentages, are recorded for each group and for each of the eleven religious, racial, national and ethnic groups which we considered. The following tables, 4 through 19, indicate percentage of students in groups of schools based on religion, location, race, all-male, all-female, coed-

Table 4

Modified Social-Distance Scale with Respect to ITALIANS

Schools	Number of schools	1 I would have as an intimate friend	2 I would work beside on a job	3 I would live on the same neighborhood block	4 I would marry	5 I would bar from my block	6 I would bar from my social recreation, frat, lodge or society	7 I would date or allow a son or daughter to date
All-school	40	84%	92%	84%	65%	4%	4%	76%
Northeastern control	1	89	89	83	70	3	2	77
U. of Hawaii	1	62	79	79	40	4	5	57
Catholic	8	88	95	90	79	2	2	85
Negro	3	62	75	65	37	5	6	59
Southern	4	75	88	71	46	6	10	64
Private all-male	3	84	91	83	65	5	4	78
Private all-female	3	87	96	85	63	3	3	78
Private coed	9	87	97	86	64	4	4	75
State U. coed	8	88	91	79	58	2	3	65
Mountain States	2	91	95	75	71	2	3	74
Pacific States	3	81	92	81	59	2	3	74

ucational, private and state universities who agree with the statements in each table.

As Table 4 indicates, while these students do not give any indication of a marked antipathy to Italians, they do not readily accept them. Friendly relations, in terms of accepting them as fellow workers or even as a friend, appear to be quite different from the attitude toward marriage with them. In the case of query number 1, 84 per cent of the all-school sample of students would have Italians as intimate friends, but only 65 per cent would marry one, while 76 per cent would allow a son or daughter to date an Italian.

Further, marriage with an Italian would be less likely to occur if a Negro, a student at the University of Hawaii or one in a Southern all-white school was the other party involved.

The attitude toward the Negro becomes clear when we examine Table 5. Twenty-nine per cent of the students would marry a Negro while only 24 per cent would date or allow a son or daughter to date a

Table 5

Modified Social-Distance Scale with Respect to NEGROES

Schools	Number of schools	1 I would have as an intimate friend	2 I would work beside on a job	3 I would live on the same neighborhood block	4 I would marry	5 I would bar from my block	6 I would bar from my social recreation, frat, lodge or society	7 I would date or allow a son or daughter to date
All-school	40	63%	89%	58%	29%	26%	24%	24%
Northeastern control	1	63	84	50	5	34	21	13
U. of Hawaii	1	43	71	59	6	13	15	32
Catholic	8	58	90	52	6	31	22	12
Negro	3	91	83	84	93	1	1	84
Southern	4	38	70	32	3	55	59	6
Private all-male	3	92	91	67	9	20	15	19
Private all-female	3	72	97	70	10	16	13	27
Private coed	9	73	90	60	13	23	20	25
State U. coed	8	55	87	53	13	28	30	17
Mountain States	2	51	80	48	9	30	34	17
Pacific States	3	48	85	51	16	28	24	20

Negro. In most classifications of student groups (excepting the Negro) the idea of interracial marriage with a Negro is opposed. In the all-white Southern Schools, interdating or allowing a son or daughter to date with a Negro is looked upon askance. The students at the University of Hawaii, it will be noted, also look with disfavor upon marriage with a Negro. It must be remembered in this connection that 72 per cent of these students are themselves "other" than white or Negro.

As was to be expected, students in our group of all-white Southern schools were the most strongly opposed to marriage with Negroes. We must point out, however, that, as in all cases we have studied, there is a considerable difference between the attitude of students toward interdating with Negroes and their attitude toward interracial marriage. Two to five times as many students in most of the groups would interdate as would intermarry with Negroes.

Jews, as Table 6 indicates are far less acceptable as marriage partners in our all-school sample (37 per cent) than are most other peoples,

Table 6

Modified Social-Distance Scale with Respect to Jews

Schools	Number of schools	1 I would have as an intimate friend	2 I would work beside on a job	3 I would live on the same neighborhood block	4 I would marry	5 I would bar from my block	6 I would bar from my social recreation, frat, lodge or society	7 I would date or allow a son or daughter to date
All-school	40	85%	93%	84%	37%	6%	12%	60%
Northeastern control	1	77	87	77	38	11	7	59
U. of Hawaii	1	57	72	65	24	9	5	45
Catholic	8	72	90	78	17	6	17	36
Negro	3	63	78	72	32	3	6	55
Southern	4	77	86	82	29	6	24	56
Private all-male	3	87	93	84	48	3	7	63
Private all-female	3	92	97	87	42	2	8	64
Private coed	9	85	94	89	53	4	7	77
State U. coed	8	80	95	83	31	9	14	55
Mountain States	2	86	93	84	36	7	14	77
Pacific States	3	79	93	80	35	6	11	54

although 60 per cent of this sample would date or allow a son or daughter to date a Jew or Jewess. In this sample 85 per cent of the students would have a Jew as an intimate friend with 6 per cent ready to bar Jews from their block. The question of who creates ghetto walls is in part answered by the reply of the all-school sample to the statement, "I would bar a Jew from my social, recreational or fraternity, lodge or society." In this case 12 per cent of the students support this view. The highest degree of opposition to Jews in social clubs, etc., comes from students in the all-white Southern schools with the next highest percentage opposition (17 per cent) coming from the students in Catholic-sponsored schools. It is obvious that anti-Jewish sentiment is still rife.

One might have expected a higher degree of opposition to relations with the Japanese, but Table 7 indicates that this is not generally the case. Marriage with a Japanese might for some represent frowned-upon interracial marriage. It might also represent marriage with a former military enemy of the United States. Yet our results indicate that, in but

Table 7

Modified Social-Distance Scale with Respect to JAPANESE

Schools	Number of schools	1 I would have as an intimate friend	2 I would work beside on a job	3 I would live on the same neighborhood block	4 I would marry	5 I would bar from my block	6 I would bar from my social recreation, frat, lodge or society	7 I would date or allow a son or daughter to date
All-school	40	72%	90%	74%	24%	8%	11%	46%
Northeastern control	1	70	84	64	23	11	5	36
U. of Hawaii	1	90	93	87	73	4	4	83
Catholic	8	64	86	68	20	9	9	31
Negro	3	59	73	65	21	4	9	49
Southern	4	59	84	60	16	9	24	15
Private all-male	3	80	90	80	40	6	5	34
Private all-female	3	82	97	82	21	6	7	47
Private coed	9	77	92	80	28	7	9	46
State U. coed	8	71	69	71	20	11	16	31
Mountain States	2	70	94	72	23	10	14	42
Pacific States	3	68	88	70	19	13	15	29

few cases, is there an overwhelming opposition to interdating with Japanese and this, as is the case generally, comes from the students at all-white Southern schools.

In our all-school sample 46 per cent of the students indicate that they would interdate or allow a son or daughter to interdate, while 24 per cent would intermarry with a Japanese. Only 8 per cent would bar a Japanese from living in the same neighborhood or block while 11 per cent would oppose any social interrelationships with them. As compared with student attitudes to Jews, the Japanese rate higher. They are not looked upon negatively as are Negroes. As was to be expected the highest degree of acceptance of Japanese in marriage (73 per cent) and interdating (83 per cent) comes from the students at the University of Hawaii. They appear to be least acceptable as "dates" to students on the Pacific Coast (29 per cent) and once again to the Southern Schools' students (15 per cent).

The attitudes toward Catholics are indicated by Table 8.

Table 8

Modified Social-Distance Scale with Respect to CATHOLICS

Schools	Number of schools	1 I would have as an intimate friend	2 I would work beside on a job	3 I would live on the same neighborhood block	4 I would marry	5 I would bar from my block	6 I would bar from my social recreation, frat, lodge or society	7 I would date or allow a son or daughter to date
All-school	40	92%	95%	83%	56%	1%	3%	73%
Northeastern control	1	91	93	91	68	2	1	81
U. of Hawaii	1	73	85	84	42	2	2	68
Catholic	8	97	86	95	85	2	2	94
Negro	3	75	80	77	53	1	2	71
Southern	4	94	95	92	30	1	1	81
Private all-male	3	92	93	91	51	1	4	63
Private all-female	3	71	71	69	32	1	1	55
Private coed	9	92	95	94	49	2	4	77
State U. coed	8	94	97	97	52	1	7	69
Mountain States	2	95	96	96	53	1	2	84
Pacific States	3	91	97	94	50	1	19	54

Differences in attitudes appear to depend not only upon religious factors (Jews and Protestants reared in their respective faiths would not be likely to choose Catholics as mates any more than Catholics would choose Protestants or Jews), but upon regional and class factors as well. In all but three cases, 49 per cent or more of the respondents declare that they would marry Catholics (University of Hawaii students, with 42 per cent of its students declaring that they would marry Catholics, Southern all-white students, with 30 per cent and students in privately endowed all-women's schools, 32 per cent), representing, I believe, social-status and class factors which might affect their attitudes to a marked degree. The readiness to date or allow a son or daughter to date a Catholic appears to be quite marked also except for the University of Hawaii, privately sponsored all-male schools as well as all-woman's school students. In no case does the opposition to Catholics living on the same block go beyond 2 per cent while in but four instances (Pacific States school sample, 19 per cent; state university coeducational students, 7 per cent; private school coeducational students and privately endowed all-male school student sample, 4 per cent) is there really any indication that attitudes toward Catholics is unfriendly insofar as social life and activity is concerned.

It is my opinion, based on the percentages recorded here and upon personal observation as well that Catholics, although a minority, are generally well received. The social distance from Catholics is certainly far less than it is from Jews.

Insofar as the three major religious groups are concerned, Protestants are certainly better received than either Catholics or Jews. An examination of Table 9 makes this clear. In the all-school sample only 1 per cent of the students indicated that they would bar a Protestant from living on the same block, while another 1 per cent would bar a Protestant from their social or recreational life. Eighty-three per cent of the students would date or allow a son or daughter to date a Protestant. We must remember that there are 12 per cent Jews, 47 per cent Protestant and 31 per cent Catholics in this student sample, indicating that religious lines would not influence these groups as much where Protestants are concerned as when Catholics or Jews are involved.

Stereotypes and prejudices continue to exist to the hurt of the three major religious groups and particularly to the minorities—Catholics and Jews. It is most significant that these stereotypes appear to exist in our college student sample. Students who are supposedly receiving a "higher" education are obviously prejudiced also. This, I believe, should cause us our greatest concern in that education has not proved to be a panacea for intolerance and bigotry as we had assumed. But, of course, the Hitlerian era with its most bitter anti-Semitism emanating from

Table 9

Modified Social-Distance Scale with Respect to PROTESTANTS

Schools	Number of schools	1 I would have as an intimate friend	2 I would work beside on a job	3 I would live on the same neighborhood block	4 I would marry	5 I would bar from my block	6 I would bar from my social recreation, frat, lodge or society	7 I would date or allow a son or daughter to date
All-school	40	92%	95%	96%	74%	1%	1%	83%
Northeastern control	1	93	93	91	71	3	0	81
U. of Hawaii	1	85	81	87	77	4	4	83
Catholic	8	90	95	94	45	2	2	66
Negro	3	78	80	80	68	1	2	75
Southern	4	92	96	95	86	1	1	89
Private all-male	3	95	94	95	84	0	2	89
Private all-female	3	95	96	96	88	0	1	95
Private coed	8	95	97	96	80	1	2	82
State U. coed	8	84	97	97	78	1	1	92
Mountain States	2	97	95	96	88	2	0	90
Pacific States	3	95	96	95	86	0	1	90

university students (and professors, too) should still be fresh enough in our minds to make the point quite clear.

The response of Negro students to Protestants (see Table 9) ought to be of special interest inasmuch as Negroes are generally identified with some Protestant denomination. Yet, only 68 per cent of our sample in the Negro schools would marry a Protestant and 75 per cent of this sample would date or allow a son or daughter to date a Protestant. I suspect that these figures indicate a resentment by Negro Protestants against white Protestants. Perhaps it may even be regarded as a rebellion against Christianity which would be understandable in view of the seeming refusal of white Protestants to lead in the fight to break down the race barriers that presently exist.

Table 10 indicates that insofar as our sample taken from the Southern Schools is concerned, Filipinos are not socially acceptable. Only 15 per cent declared that they would marry a Filipino. The same degree of social distance from Filipinos was true of the student sample

Table 10

Modified Social-Distance Scale with Respect to FILIPINO

		1	2	3	4	5	6	7
Schools	Number of schools	I would have as an intimate friend	I would work beside on a job	I would live on the same neighborhood block	I would marry	I would bar from my block	I would bar from my social recreation, frat, lodge or society	I would date or allow a son or daughter to date
All-school	40	69%	89%	73%	24%	11%	12%	42%
Northeastern control	1	69	84	65	3	10	7	38
U. of Hawaii	1	59	56	71	37	12	9	44
Catholic	8	64	80	70	20	14	12	35
Negro	3	58	73	65	27	5	6	56
Southern	4	63	83	82	15	12	25	31
Private all-male	3	78	90	78	38	6	5	54
Private all-female	3	78	95	80	24	6	6	47
Private coed	9	70	93	80	30	8	10	50
State U. coed	8	67	88	68	22	15	12	33
Mountain States	2	67	89	76	27	12	8	41
Pacific States	3	61	89	63	15	13	16	26

in the Pacific State Schools. In no case did more than 38 per cent of the students state that marriage to a Filipino was acceptable and this figure is recorded for the University of Hawaii where it might be understood in view of the many Filipinos in Hawaii. Nor would most of our sample date a Filipino. Indeed, our all-school sample indicates that only 42 per cent of the student sample in our forty schools would date a Filipino. This opposition expresses itself further in our all-school sample where 11 per cent of all the students would bar a Filipino from living on the same block and 12 per cent would bar him from participation in social or recreational life. The opposition to the Filipino is highest in the Southern Schools (25 per cent) and next highest in the school sample of the Pacific States (16 per cent).

The attitude toward the Mexican is also generally unfriendly.

Our all-school sample indicates that less than one-third of all our student sample of 5,407 would marry a Mexican while 45 per cent would date or allow a son or daughter to date a Mexican. Fourteen per cent of

Table 11

Modified Social-Distance Scale with Respect to MEXICAN

Schools	Number of schools	1 I would have as an intimate friend	2 I would work beside on a job	3 I would live on the same neighborhood block	4 I would marry	5 I would bar from my block	6 I would bar from my social recreation, frat, lodge or society	7 I would date or allow a son or daughter to date
All-school	40	68%	88%	66%	31%	14%	15%	45%
Northeastern control	1	67	83	65	35	15	10	46
U. of Hawaii	1	51	71	61	24	8	8	43
Catholic	8	67	86	64	32	14	12	37
Negro	3	63	74	62	34	10	10	62
Southern	4	60	80	70	18	20	29	31
Private all-male	3	75	87	65	41	5	8	55
Private all-female	3	72	90	67	51	10	9	50
Private coed	8	76	90	73	37	13	12	46
State U. coed	8	67	77	61	24	19	21	40
Mountain States	2	64	82	56	25	22	24	37
Pacific States	3	60	85	58	19	19	18	35

the all-school sample would bar a Mexican from living on the same block while 15 per cent would bar him from any social or recreational life in which the average student in our sample is involved. The social distance of our student sample from Filipinos and Mexicans varies in detail, but in many respects it is the same. Clearly neither Filipino nor Mexican is *persona grata* to the average American college or university student.

Persons of Greek origin are, however, fairly well received by most of our student sample.

Only 4 per cent in our all-school average would bar Greeks from living on the same block while 6 per cent would bar them from more personal social and recreational contacts. Insofar as dating with Greeks is concerned, 64 per cent of our sample would do so while 50 per cent would marry a Greek. The social distance between Greeks and the general American university student does not seem to be very great. In only a few cases do we find exceptions. In the Southern Schools 21 per cent of our student sample would oppose the reception of Greeks into their

Table 12

Modified Social-Distance Scale with Respect to GREEKS

Schools	Number of schools	1 I would have as an intimate friend	2 I would work beside on a job	3 I would live on the same neighborhood block	4 I would marry	5 I would bar from my block	6 I would bar from my social recreation, frat, lodge or society	7 I would date or allow a son or daughter to date
All-school	40	80%	93%	82%	50%	4%	6%	64%
Northeastern control	1	81	87	76	52	3	1	64
U. of Hawaii	1	55	75	68	31	4	5	56
Catholic	8	74	94	84	56	4	5	67
Negro	3	63	72	72	34	3	4	57
Southern	4	72	89	82	27	5	21	39
Private all-male	3	86	89	82	44	2	4	72
Private all-female	3	91	97	90	69	1	1	83
Private coed	9	82	94	86	55	4	5	62
State U. coed	8	81	95	89	50	4	5	64
Mountain States	2	84	94	82	53	1	3	70
Pacific States	3	78	92	81	47	4	5	62

social clubs. Yet even here, where we have encountered a higher degree of provincialism than in any other section of the country, only 5 per cent of the student sample would bar a Greek from living on the same block. In this group, 39 per cent would date Greeks while 27 per cent would marry a Greek. Despite religious differences, the Greek does not appear to be on the lower rungs of the status ladder.

Our all-school sample was highly receptive to the Irish.

Excepting for the Negro school sample there appears to be a marked readiness to accept the Irish in marriage, to date with them and, in general, to treat them as equals. In the all-school sample only 2 per cent of the students would bar the Irish from living on the same block while 3 per cent would oppose more intimate social and recreational contact with them. But this does not appear to be large as compared with certain other groups we have studied.

At the University of Hawaii, our student sample appeared to take quite a different attitude toward the Irish. Nine per cent of these stu-

Table 13

Modified Social-Distance Scale with Respect to IRISH

Schools	Number of schools	1 I would have as an intimate friend	2 I would work beside on a job	3 I would live on the same neighborhood block	4 I would marry	5 I would bar from my block	6 I would bar from my social recreation, frat, lodge or society	7 I would date or allow a son or daughter to date
All-school	40	87%	95%	88%	64%	2%	3%	77%
Northeastern control	1	86	91	87	73	3	0	79
U. of Hawaii	1	65	82	64	54	9	4	58
Catholic	8	89	75	91	78	3	3	82
Negro	3	62	74	66	32	3	5	52
Southern	4	86	90	84	58	2	3	71
Private all-male	3	85	91	86	65	2	3	59
Private all-female	3	93	97	92	40	1	2	84
Private coed	8	87	95	85	64	3	3	75
State U. coed	8	90	94	89	70	1	2	80
Mountain States	2	84	94	86	53	1	3	65
Pacific States	3	88	95	89	65	1	2	78

dents would bar them from living on the same block while 4 per cent would bar them from their clubs and other recreational facilities. Yet, 54 per cent would marry an Irish person while 58 per cent would date them. It is difficult to explain why the Irish should not be well thought of by these students other than that personal contacts with certain persons of Irish origin or descent, position on the social ladder plus difference in religion may have some effect upon their attitudes. Such elements are always present and must be acknowledged.

It is worthy of note that the Irish appear to be more acceptable to the students in our Southern School sample than almost any other group. Fifty-eight per cent would marry a person of Irish origin while 71 per cent would date or allow a son or daughter to date a person of Irish origin.

Although so many Catholics are of Irish origin, it is surprising to discover that not all Catholics would "accept" the Irish. Three per cent of the students in our Catholic sample would bar Irish from living on

the same block while 3 per cent would bar them from social and recreational facilities. It may well be that our Catholic sample was making distinctions between "kinds" of Catholics, between, let us say, "lace curtain" and "shanty" Irish. These distinctions, subtle though they may be, are nevertheless real—even important—and seldom ignored.

Although 65 per cent of the student sample in our all-male schools would marry a person of Irish descent and 59 per cent would date an Irish girl, there are still 2 per cent of this student sample who would bar the Irish from their block and 3 per cent would bar them from social and recreational clubs. Three per cent of the student sample in the privately sponsored coeducational colleges would do the same. Yet, in the latter case, 64 per cent would marry a person of Irish origin and 75 per cent would date such a person.

Generally speaking, this table indicates that the Irish are well received. There is little social distance between them and most of the other students in our sample.

What we have noted concerning the attitude of students toward the Irish holds equally true for their attitude toward Poles. Excepting for the students at the Negro schools and the student sample at the University of Hawaii, the attitude toward Poles is generally favorable.

In our all-school sample, 61 per cent of the students would marry a person of Polish origin while 72 per cent would date such a person.

Insofar as the student sample at the University of Hawaii is concerned, while only 25 per cent would date a Pole 33 per cent would marry a Pole; 4 per cent would bar a Pole from living on the same block while 5 per cent would oppose their participation in the same social or recreational clubs. It is difficult to understand why this should be true because the number of Poles in Hawaii is certainly not large or even noticeable. I suspect that, here again, stereotypes play their deadly game with humans, creating images about Poles that have little to do with facts and much to do with emotions.

Through this modified social-distance scale we hope that we have made clear that the greatest distance exists socially between white persons and non-whites, with the greatest social distance registered by white students against the Negro. Next in order of prejudice are those of minority religious groups against religions other than their own. National and ethnic differences are still extant, but they appear to play less of a role than they once did.

How ought we to deal with such situations? Can we ever narrow the social distance that presently exists (despite the fact that the students in our sample are alleged to be "liberal" because they have been exposed to one or more courses in sociology, anthropology, etc.)? Obviously "education" in colleges and universities does not appear, in

itself, to change attitudes to any marked degree. The tolerance and understanding shown by parents, Church and Synagogue leaders and the society in which one lives play their roles in either making for or reducing prejudices and social distance.

Table 14

Modified Social-Distance Scale with Respect to POLISH

Schools	Number of schools	1 I would have as an intimate friend	2 I would work beside on a job	3 I would live on the same neighborhood block	4 I would marry	5 I would bar from my block	6 I would bar from my social recreation, frat, lodge or society	7 I would date or allow a son or daughter to date
All-school	40	83%	93%	83%	61%	3%	4%	72%
Northeastern control	1	84	88	82	67	3	0	73
U. of Hawaii	1	56	75	67	33	4	5	25
Catholic	8	88	94	89	77	2	2	84
Negro	3	64	74	60	26	4	6	47
Southern	4	69	84	69	41	4	8	55
Private all-male	3	83	94	83	65	2	4	59
Private all-female	3	86	96	80	64	2	4	79
Private coed	8	86	93	86	61	4	4	74
State U. coed	8	84	94	85	56	3	4	74
Mountain States	2	86	90	78	61	2	4	70
Pacific States	3	78	93	82	57	3	3	71

A careful review of the results obtained through our modified social-distance scale makes it clear that, whatever their educational attainments, or however "liberal" they believe themselves to be, the number of persons, in our student sample at least, who are really free from bias of one kind or another against some group, racial, religious, ethnic or national, is limited. It seems clear that social-science students are as guilty of bias, in one form or another, as are students who major in other fields of study. It is not evident in any instance that social-science students are much more liberal in their views of other peoples, races, or religions than are others.

Jews and Catholics, in that order, appear to be the victims of a

greater bias than are Protestants. However much we may insist that "religion makes no difference to most people," the fact is that a bias against other religious groups appears to result from indoctrination of one kind or another in homes that identify themselves with particular religions. Of course, one need not be a devout Protestant, for example, to react negatively to Catholics or Jews. But religious homes do not appear to lessen bias against persons of other religions. It will obviously require much more than "good-will" meetings, conferences and dialogues to overcome the prejudice that exists even among persons exposed to higher education in our colleges and universities.

We discover, too, that minority groups, religious or racial, can be prejudiced and biased in their own ways. They can build walls around themselves to protect themselves from the bias they fear so much. We find, also, that antipathy toward other races and religions can result from a sense of frustration and insecurity. Certainly Negroes in our student sample give evidence of this type of reaction as do Jews and Catholics. Being a member of a minority group, religious or racial, is *still* very much of a problem.

Interdating, according to our sample, is very much in evidence. In most cases it appears to be almost twice as great as the receptivity of these same students to intermarriage. It remains to be seen whether "interdating" will ultimately prove to be the major factor that conquers prejudice.

The provincialism of our student sample at the Southern (white) schools is also obvious from this study. Perhaps the only word that can be added to what our percentages clearly demonstrate is that even though contact with persons of many different religions and colors cannot guarantee a more liberal attitude, it may, in degree, be of some assistance in that area. Sectionalism is often limiting as is clear in the case of these Southern-school students.

In another phase of our study an attempt was made to discover which of five types of marriage would prove most difficult to accept. Our student sample in the forty colleges and universities were asked whether they thought marriage outside of their own (1) religious, (2) national, (3) economic, (4) educational, or (5) color group would be hardest for them to accept. One of a five-point scale consisting of (a) hardest, (b) next hardest, (c) not quite so hard, (d) fairly easy, and (e) easiest, were suggested as a possible answer.

Only 9 per cent of the students in our all-school sample of forty schools indicated that they would regard marriage outside of their own religious group as "hardest." Although this per cent was comparatively small, 41 per cent of these students stated marriage outside of their own religion would seem "next hardest." It is interesting to note that

Table 15

Per cent of students in various types of schools
who would marry outside of their own RELIGION group

Schools	Hardest	Next Hardest	Not Quite So Hard	Fairly Easy	Easiest	No Inform.
All-school	9%	41%	24%	14%	13%	1%
Northeastern control	6	57	19	12	5	1
U. of Hawaii	17	16	27	16	20	4
Catholic	17	60	11	7	3	2
Southern	3	31	33	18	14	1
Negro	7	15	22	20	34	2
Private all-male	6	45	25	16	8	0
Private all-female	3	27	29	20	19	2
Private coed	6	41	24	13	13	3
State U. coed	5	40	27	14	13	1
Mountain States	5	29	29	16	20	1
Pacific States	5	33	31	15	16	0

13 per cent of these students believed that marriage outside of their own religion would prove to be the easiest.

As one examines Table 15 it is clear that, with but two exceptions (the sample at the Catholic-sponsored schools with 17 per cent and

Table 16

Per cent of students in various types of schools
who would marry outside of their own NATION group

Schools	Hardest	Next Hardest	Not Quite So Hard	Fairly Easy	Easiest	No Inform.
All-school	4%	12%	23%	23%	35%	3%
Northeastern control	2	9	25	33	31	0
U. of Hawaii	10	24	25	21	20	0
Catholic	1	5	16	19	58	1
Southern	2	38	25	16	18	1
Negro	26	22	22	17	13	0
Private all-male	1	11	23	34	30	1
Private all-female	5	9	22	27	36	1
Private coed	1	14	24	22	39	0
State U. coed	2	22	25	21	28	2
Mountain States	1	20	23	25	30	1
Pacific States	2	28	23	22	25	0

those at the University of Hawaii with 17 per cent), marriage outside of the students' own religious groups would not appear difficult.

A small percentage (4) of students in our sample (excepting the Negro students in all-Negro Schools) state that marriage outside of their own nationality would be "hardest." In the case of the Negro students, 26 per cent think that marriage outside of their own national group would prove "hardest." In all cases except that of the Negro students we are told that such marriage would seem easy. Nation differences, then, are in all cases with the one exception already noted, of little or no significance.

Inasmuch as marriage into a different kind of economic group might be regarded as a difficulty, we checked on this factor as well.

Table 17 indicates the results obtained.

Table 17

Per cent of students in various types of schools
who would marry outside of their own ECONOMIC group

Schools	Hardest	Next Hardest	Not Quite So Hard	Fairly Easy	Easiest	No Inform.
All-school	3%	10%	23%	31%	33%	0%
Northeastern control	4	11	18	33	31	4
U. of Hawaii	6	16	21	26	31	0
Catholic	1	5	24	44	25	1
Southern	2	10	18	33	37	4
Negro	16	20	23	18	23	0
Private all-male	1	7	16	29	46	1
Private all-female	0	9	33	29	29	0
Private coed	2	8	21	36	32	2
State U. coed	2	9	20	33	34	2
Mountain States	1	10	24	31	33	1
Pacific States	2	12	22	31	33	0

Here again we found that marriage outside of one's own group would (with one exception) not appear difficult. The exception in this case, as well, was the Negro group. In the all-school student sample only 3 per cent of the students regard marriage outside one's economic group as likely to be "hardest," but in the same all-school sample, 33 per cent regarded such a marriage as potentially "easiest." Sixteen per cent of the Negro sample regarded marriage outside of their own economic group as "hardest" while 23 per cent thought of such a marriage as "easiest." In most cases over 30 per cent of the students in the various

group samples looked upon marriage outside of their own economic group as "easiest."

Educational differences, too, may be looked upon by some persons as "hardest," hence the student sample was asked if marriage outside of their own educational group appeared likely to be "hardest." Here are their replies:

Table 18

Per cent of students in various types of schools
who would marry outside of their own EDUCATIONAL group

Schools	Hardest	Next Hardest	Not Quite So Hard	Fairly Easy	Easiest	No Inform.
All-school	9%	22%	30%	25%	14%	0%
Northeastern control	4	16	30	26	23	1
U. of Hawaii	17	20	20	26	13	4
Catholic	3	16	46	26	9	0
Southern	6	16	24	33	21	0
Negro	24	22	18	25	11	0
Private all-male	7	27	30	23	13	0
Private all-female	10	44	22	15	9	0
Private coed	10	25	29	23	13	0
State U. coed	8	22	22	27	21	0
Mountain States	7	34	22	25	12	0
Pacific States	7	21	24	29	19	0

Nine per cent of our all-school sample state that they believe marriage to a person of a different educational group would prove hardest. But only the students from primarily Negro schools thought that educational difference would be a major source of difficulty (24 per cent) with the student sample at the University of Hawaii running them a fairly close second with 17 per cent.

The percentage of students who believe that educational differences in marriage would be no problem at all and who term it "easiest" is 14 per cent of the all-school student sample. However, 23 per cent of our control group declare that such a marriage would be easiest while 21 per cent of the student sample at the Southern schools hold to a similar opinion. In all cases, however, educational differences are not generally taken more lightly than religious differences.

Insofar as color differences are concerned, it is clear that such a marriage is regarded as "hardest" for most of our all-school student sample (with only the Negro, 29 per cent, and the students at the Uni-

Table 19

Per cent of students in various types of schools
who would marry outside of their own COLOR group

Schools	Hardest	Next Hardest	Not Quite So Hard	Fairly Easy	Easiest	No Inform.
All-school	80%	11%	3%	3%	3%	0%
Northeastern control	84	4	4	2	3	3
U. of Hawaii	44	31	10	10	5	0
Catholic	79	13	4	2	2	0
Southern	88	8	2	0	2	0
Negro	29	21	16	19	14	1
Private all-male	83	8	4	1	3	1
Private all-female	86	7	3	1	3	0
Private coed	80	9	5	2	3	1
State U. coed	83	8	4	2	3	0
Mountain States	84	7	3	3	3	0
Pacific States	86	6	3	2	3	0

versity of Hawaii, 44 per cent) disagreeing with the majority. In both
cases, it will be noted, we are dealing with color groups (72 per cent of
the student sample at the University of Hawaii were "other" than Negro
or white). Eighty per cent of our all-school sample stated that they
thought marriage to a person of another color would prove "hardest"
while another 11 per cent believed that such a marriage would prove
"next hardest." Only 9 per cent of the all-school student sample felt
that marriage outside of their own religion would prove to be "hardest"
while another 41 per cent stated that they would regard such a marriage
as "next hardest." Color difference, is, then, the most important factor
among our student sample of 5,407 students throughout the country.

If we combine the first two columns ("hardest" and "next hardest") the student attitudes toward these various types of marriages becomes even clearer. The results are as follows:

91 per cent of the students in the all-school sample do not favor
marriage to a person of another *color*.

50 per cent of the students in the all-school sample do not favor
marriage to a person of another *religion*.

31 per cent of the students in this sample do not favor marriage to
a person of another *educational group*.

16 per cent do not favor marriage with a person of another *nationality*.

13 per cent do not favor marriage to a person of a different *economic class*.

Color differences are, then, the most important to our student sample, while religious difference is next, but far less as important as the former. Educational differences are looked upon as having considerable importance while nationality and economic differences bring up the rear.

When we reversed our procedure and checked to discover which of these five types of marriage was "easiest" or "next easiest" to these students, we found the following order:

1. Economic differences (64 per cent)
2. Nationality differences (58 per cent)
3. Educational differences (39 per cent)
4. Religious differences (27 per cent)
5. Color differences (6 per cent)

The nature of our society which makes vertical mobility a possibility—indeed some persons think of it as the very core of the American way of life—explains why economic differences do not appear to trouble many persons insofar as marriage is concerned. The opportunity to come into contact with persons of many different nationalities is pronounced. That is why, it seems to me, that national and even ethnic differences appear to be lacking in importance to the student thinking of marriage. However, differences in education, religion and color appear to be of considerable importance. But of these five, the only one that seems clearly to be a stumbling block insofar as marriage is concerned is color difference.

The percentages of the students in each of the forty schools tested is recorded in the Appendix. A careful examination of the results obtained indicates that they do not differ markedly from the group percentages we have obtained and the implications of which we have considered.

The attitudes of the college and university youth in our sample are clear. Although we note a degree of intolerance and prejudice as represented by our modified social-distance scale, we do not believe that these evils are especially virulent in our day. They exist as latent forces that may erupt if some thing or some person stirs them up. However, on the basis of this study, I do not regard them as dangerous to the welfare of our society. Indeed, the readiness to accept interfaith marriage appears to counter the argument that religious differences make intermarriage unlikely. Much as I personally disapprove, I am obliged to state that religious loyalties of Protestants, Catholics and Jews (in that order) are not as great as the proponents of each faith would like.

The attitude of the parents of our student sample, as these young people view the matter, is also clear. Parents may not be pleased, but their sons and daughters think that parents would not, in the last analysis, disown a child who enters upon an interfaith marriage. Young people believe that their parents are permissive. They see no special problems associated with securing parent consent for such a marriage. They believe that they would receive the parental blessing in the case of an interfaith or interracial marriage, even if, at first, parents appeared to be unhappy or distressed.

Today, parents say—and their children are quite aware of it—"No matter what happens we must not lose our children." Whereas, in a former generation, parents would unequivocally oppose an interfaith or interracial intermarriage and actually cut off an "errant" child from further family contact, this seldom happens today. Catholics, as we shall see, make provision for a compromise arrangement in the case of an interfaith marriage, as do Protestants and Jews.

Today, these college students in our sample appear to be receptive to all forms of intermarriage except interracial. They see or know about intermarriage among their friends. As we have indicated 40 per cent of the students in this sample state that intermarriages exist at the present time within their own families. The trend toward the acceptance of intermarriage appears to be growing. Whether these attitudes constitute a threat to the well-being of the individual, society, family and organized religion is, to some, debatable. In my opinion intermarriage is such a threat. I do not believe that it holds forth the promise of a happier or brighter day for mankind. Many sociologists, psychologists and teachers of religion generally support this view as we shall discover in the succeeding chapters.

CHAPTER 3

FACTORS AFFECTING THE RATE OF INTERMARRIAGE

There are many factors that influence the rate of intermarriage. It is, in fact, hardly possible to enumerate all of them because they vary almost as much as do the persons who intermarry. Further, the weighting of these factors may change according to the characteristics of the personality being studied. Cultural, environmental, physical and psychological factors play significant roles in the rate of intermarriage. In particular cases it may be one factor or a combination of factors with which we may be concerned.

No social scientist has yet been able to enumerate all of the factors, physical, social, or psychological that determine our reactions and ultimate decisions. Nor does it appear likely that one ever will. Not only do the factors vary in each individual, they vary, too, in degree. The influence of our heritage, the tales told us by mother and father, the prejudices entertained, the biases adhered to, the values acquired or rejected through religion and home life—all these affect us and make us different from each other. These differences, however slight, however major, may change the course of our lives and that of our society as well. If we but knew all of these many factors and the exact degree of their influence upon us, we would know far better than we do now how to conquer our tendency to dislike the unlike and the unfamiliar.

However, certain of the more prominent factors and combinations of factors—sociological as well as psychological—that appear to have effected an increase in intermarriages merit our consideration.

The family is certainly one of the major factors determining the values that its individual members will represent throughout their lives. It may, in fact, be regarded as the "transmission belt" for values. The influence of parents, grandparents and others within its structure are generally much greater than we realize. The religious, social and cultural values that prevail within a given family are of sufficient importance to influence persons outside of the family as well as each person within it. Most families would like to see others act in accordance with their own values. Families that regard marriage as sacred will, in all likelihood, respond to the institution of marriage differently from those to whom marriage is more in the nature of a societal "arrangement."

The family remains the nuclear institution of society because the individuals who comprise it are molded, shaped and influenced by it in marked degree to meet the demands that the larger social environ-

ment makes upon them. Parents influence their children by direct and indirect efforts to instruct them in the ways of the world. The "values" they regard as basic to good and proper living are taught by both precept and example. Children learn about society and its demands not only from their parents but from brothers and sisters and others as well. Whatever the way, from formal instruction to personal example, the learning process continues. The family sets the values which it deems worthy of emulation even as it makes clear those which it looks upon with disapproval.

Important as the family is in a biological sense, it is almost equally important as the agency through which social controls may be applied, helping, hindering, or changing the course of the lives of individuals and of society.

The emotional ties that exist between parents and their children often go beyond the immediate family and may be noted, too, in the extended family. Grandparents, uncles, aunts, brothers and sisters, cousins, in-laws—all who are related by blood and legal ties—play their interrelated roles in affecting the religious, social, cultural, political and economic, moral and ethical values of each member of the family.

The influence of the family upon each of its members must then be regarded as the principal means of socialization in our day. Parental authority, by means of which socialization occurs, is generally accepted by the children within the immediate family. The authority of "elders" within the extended family is also recognized for its socializing influence. The role of both the primary and the extended family is of such major importance that it is no exaggeration to say that it has generally been regarded as responsible in large measure for shaping the course of human history.

But if the responses of our college youth are to be believed—and there is no reason to doubt them—today's young people are far less inclined to accept parental attitudes with respect to social, cultural and religious values than is generally believed. Youth's tendency to "rebel" against the ideas, opinions and practices of their elders is obvious. However, that rebellious spirit has seldom been made as manifest with respect to religion as it is in our generation. Religio-social institutions have directly or indirectly prescribed conduct with respect to such important matters as the choice of a life partner in marriage. They have generally opposed intermarriage with a person of another and different religious faith, racial or ethnic group. Matters once generally regarded as settled and fixed by custom and tradition are today, in ever-increasing degree, openly questioned and traditional attitudes are often disregarded. In-group marriages that were formerly assumed to be normal are today

increasingly questioned. The admonitions of parents, of family and of the church are no longer accepted without debate. Intermarriage with a person of another religion, color, class, or ethnic group is far less unusual in these days than it was but a generation ago.

Descendants of Old World families in America differ markedly from their first-generation precursors. Where families were traditionally patriarchal, native-born parents tend to be equalitarian. Today's families are increasingly urban and mobile. The degree of in-group solidarity is less marked. Families have grown smaller. There is a far greater emphasis upon equal or near-equal education for daughters and for sons. Romantic love is assumed to be both natural and normal. It seems less necessary or desirable to live within neighborhoods that consist entirely of one's own ethnic or religious group. Participation in the social, cultural and political affairs of the larger community is expected today on the part of both males and females within the family. Opinions and decisions with regard to major issues involving the individuals within the family are seldom, if ever, made by the parents alone. Not only are such decisions the result of family discussion, but decisions made by young people are frequently quite independent of opinions held by parents and, what is even more important, they are respected even if parents do not agree with them.

The family, in an earlier day, an integral part of the community, "fixed in a framework of numerous links and knots that held each individual within it in his place" [1] has been succeeded by the family that regards itself as quite independent of all other families. As the generations continue here in America, we have evidence to support the thesis that the social controls of the family are shifting considerably in their emphasis. Indeed there is considerable support for the view that the social control of the parent with respect to the children, and particularly the maturing youth, has actually weakened.

Where, in past generations, the goals of the individual, broadly speaking, were determined by one's parents (in David Reisman's terms —"inner direction") they are, today, determined by one's peers ("other direction"). Parents certainly have far less control of their children than they had but a generation ago.

The family as an institution has weakened to a marked degree. And that weakening confronts us with serious social problems. Support for this view is provided by The Family Service Organization of America[2] which offered the following evidence:

> A tripling of the rate of illegitimacy in the last two decades (1940-60).
> A divorce rate of one in four new marriages.

A delinquency rate tripled since 1940.

An annual admission rate to mental hospitals of more than 200,000 persons.

It is acknowledged that these social ills are "but a small part of the syndrome that constitutes the over-all debilitating disease we call family breakdown." We might just as easily point out what is so obvious to so many—that the control the family was able to exert over its members has been markedly reduced in each decade since World War I.

Family solidarity, so characteristic of the Jewish family over the centuries, is weakening also. Brav[3] includes among the factors that produced that solidarity:

> (a) a continuance of culinary habits and tastes, including observance of the dietary laws
> (b) intimacy between members of the family circle which included the extended family
> (c) great concern for the education and personal welfare of one's children and their achievements
> (d) an intense interest in the future and fate of the Jewish people and sincere desire to do everything humanly possible for its survival and enhancement
> (e) The influence of the Past with its biblical and historical associations with this People.

Although culinary habits remain and Jewish cuisine has a "style" all its own, the dietary laws are observed by no more than 10 per cent of America's Jews. Though intimacies between parents and children may still play a considerable role, the extended family (*Mishpocho*) is less directly involved. Concern for the Jewish future takes the form of philanthropy. The State of Israel, a source of great strength and pride to many Jews, becomes far less of a reality in the lives of the children as the time-distance from the creation of the new state increases. The State of Israel is to many Jews little more than "just another State." Concern for the Jewish future expresses itself more with saving refugee Jews in lands where they are ill treated, where anti-Semitism is rife, than with the ancient covenant or a Land of Promise. The education of children is of major concern to Jewish parents, but this refers primarily to secular education. Fifty per cent of Jewish children receive no more than a one-day-a-week Sunday-school education. When the vastness of Jewish learning and values is considered, it is obvious that one-day-a-week schooling can provide little religious education or help in building loyalties.

The Jewish family, generally regarded as the most cohesive of all family groups in contemporary times, is weakening. Even though it

may be stronger in certain respects than Protestant and Catholic families, it is gradually settling down to a standard that must be regarded as American (national) rather than religious. Catholic and Protestant American-born families are increasingly less authoritative, less disciplined and far more permissive.

The attitude of most American families toward religious intermarriage is in the process of changing. A generation ago, Jewish parents, for example, would "cut a child off" in the event that he or she married a non-Jew. Jews might mourn the traditional period of seven days (sit Shivah) as if the intermarried child had died. Today this is seldom the case.

In one study of various attitudes of New Haven Jewry,[4] 57 per cent of the Jewish respondents stated that it would hurt them very much to see their child marry a non-Jew. Another 22 per cent stated that they would accept the marriage provided the children were brought up as Jews, and 18 per cent declared that it would not matter to them; only 4 per cent of the sample would cut their child off in the event of marriage to a Gentile. Jewish parental attitude, although clearly unfriendly to the idea of intermarriage, is far less intransigent than it was a generation ago.

Intermarriages often occur when weak endogamous feelings exist in one of the parties. If there is little or no feeling of identification with a particular religious group or family, or if there are conflicts with parents, tensions with others resulting from displeasure or shame because their gestures, language, accent or manner (to mention but a few of the irritants) differ from those of the majority; if there are personality problems, job difficulties or a host of other such causes of conflict, exogamous marriage is frequently the way chosen to break away from one's past. The desire to "live one's own life," to move up the social or economic ladder, or in some cases to assimilate completely into another way of life often produces the same result.

The decline of religious authority and of observance in the home (a fact attested to by the religious leaders of the three major faiths) as well as the substitution of schools for the example formerly provided by parents in the religious, moral, and ethical education of children, tend also to loosen the ties that bind young people to their religio-cultural heritage. This culture is likely to be replaced by a national culture in which all things American are unquestioningly regarded as "right."

Another factor with which we must be concerned is the nature of the family itself, for today's family is "open." Where young people once married only those persons whose familial, ethnic, social, or traditional background was similar to their own, marriages often take place with

little or no reference to such considerations. In this sense, the family is "open."

Class distinctions are, in theory, and to some degree in actual practice, less emphasized in American than in European society. Not only are individuals here assumed to be free and equal, but they are free to rise to a social or economic status utterly different from that of their parents. The Horatio Alger theme is part and parcel of the American's beliefs about himself and his opportunities. He may, as a consequence, move from a "lower-lower" class status to an "upper-upper" status. We are an open-class society, not only in terms of economic or political opportunities, but in terms of the social aspects of life as well. A man who has moved up the economic scale is generally looked upon as a likely partner in marriage for a woman whose cultural and social heritage may be far superior to his own. Such a man may, on the other hand, marry a woman socially and intellectually inferior to him because of her physical attraction and his emotional response. Such factors make for an increase in marriage between persons from different classes, educational backgrounds and different religious faiths as well.

"Love at first sight" is also generally regarded as a unique American value. The idea of "romantic love," which has nothing whatever to do with the "reasonableness" of that love, is characteristic. Whereas, in an earlier day, matches were arranged by parents and marriage brokers, the potential partners not even seeing, meeting or getting to know each other prior to the formal engagement, today such procedures are almost totally unknown. The literature of our day, the movies, the stage and television have romanticized marriage. The emphasis is upon physical attractiveness and emotional longing rather than upon family background or educational standards. There is thus a likelihood that intermarriages will occur in greater frequency under such circumstances. Here, too, belief in the "equality" of all humans is assumed to mean that there are really no significant differences between people of varying backgrounds, that whatever differences there may be are without importance.

The increasing homogeneity of this nation's population has affected our attitudes toward many things, including intermarriage. Of the country's total population in 1961 (179,325,671) 94.6 per cent were native-born while only 5.4 per cent were foreign-born. What is more, 81 per cent of those born in the United States have native-born parents, and only 8.2 per cent have mixed parentage (one, native-born and the other, foreign-born).

Of the 7,625,273 students who completed four or more years of college education in 1960, 94 per cent were white while 6 per cent were listed by the United States Census of Population (1960) as "non-white." A decade ago (1950) the number of white students who had completed

four or more college years was 5,340,337 or 96 per cent of the total with 4 per cent (181,721) non-whites. An increase of 2 per cent in the number of non-whites is thus noted.

The family's role is changed considerably, too, when mothers engage in work outside of the household. The 1960 Federal Census reports indicate that over a third of the women of working age in the United States are either employed or are seeking employment. This fact, compared with the 1890 Census, which indicated that less than one-fifth of women of working age were employed or actively seeking employment, makes it clear, among other things, that the opportunity for the two sexes to meet in industry and other places of employment has increased greatly. Increase in contacts of this kind leads to increase in social contacts as well. A subsequent increase in marriage between persons who would otherwise not have met thus becomes a reality.

Religious influence in all the major religions has been reduced considerably in our day, due not only to the increasing influence of scientific thought, but to the growing number of persons who, paradoxically, are affiliated with Churches and Synagogues but appear to be quite indifferent to their prescribed standards and values. The social control once exerted by Church and Synagogue is, therefore, less marked in our day. There is a growing influence of so-called "secular" institutions upon our lives. Public education, in the main secular, and public educators exert a far greater degree of control of contemporary values than is generally recognized. Lerner[5] suggests that success, power, prestige, personal glorification are the values Americans esteem most today. These are obviously not the "values" of religion. While these values are in the ascendancy, religious values appear to have waned.

In this connection, we must note, too, that however much the effort is made to reconcile supposed differences and contradictions in point of view between religion and the modern science, science has had a major effect in undermining religious faith. The greater the achievements of scientists, the more remote (and the less real) does God appear to be to an increasing number of people. Although opinion polls regularly remind us that over 95 per cent of Americans "believe in God" or that more Americans are officially affiliated with Churches and Synagogues today than ever before in our history (60 per cent), there is ample reason to question the reasons for Church or Synagogue identification. Ministers, priests and rabbis are in the forefront of those who question the nature of the "religious revival" that is said to have occurred in our day. At best, God is, to many, a remote God, far removed from the actual happenings in our daily lives. According to many of those who are awed by science and scientific discovery, God simply does not matter. He may "exist," but He does nothing in the world because

everything in it, including man's own actions, are due to natural, utterly impersonal causes. Such a view of God and his relation to man provides little or no warmth for man's spirit because, whatever God may have had to do with the act of creation millions of years ago, He is not now generally regarded as being near to modern man. Many—not all—of the appurtenances of religion are discarded by young people because they see little or no relevance of religious values and practices to their lives. More often, it is identification with and loyalty to parents and kinfolk that results in some continuing formal religious affiliation by young people rather than a strong faith in a God who is near to them.

Under these circumstances it matters little or not at all with which religion one identifies himself. Church and Synagogue assume a secondary importance if they assume any role whatsoever. "Indifference" is the word which best describes the basic attitude of many if not most people today to religion.

As the years pass Americans are, as I see them, becoming less religiously oriented. Church or Synagogue affiliation is still, for some, a matter of values, a distinctive way of life, based upon a faith and a creed. But for most Americans, the Church or Synagogue represent a method for securing fellowship and "fun," an opportunity for making friends through activities and meetings. There is general agreement among thoughtful men and women that secularism, which is *non*-religious (not *anti*-religious) in character, is, in fact, the source of American values.

Dr. Nahum Goldmann[6] has correctly summarized the human condition of our day, insofar as the Jews are concerned, with the following comment:

> The two decisive forces and motivations which secured Jewish existence and identity in past centuries, namely, the strength of the Jewish religion which dominated the totality of Jewish life on the one hand, and the persecution of the Jewish people which were a menace to its physical survival on the other, *have lost their effectiveness today.* The major part of the Jewish people is no more guided in its day-to-day life by the laws and regulations of Jewish religion, and imminent physical danger by persecution does not exist for the overwhelming majority of the Jewish people. Under such conditions the Jewish people can easily lose its Jewish identity for the lack of incentives and motivations which would impel it to remain Jewish.

What Goldmann calls "the process of erosion" and what I term "indifference to Judaism" is far more characteristic of contemporary Jews than they are ready to admit. What Goldmann has reported for Jewish life is equally true of Protestants and in lesser degree, of Catholics.

Lenski, discussing the religious practices of Lutherans in the city of Detroit in our day, reports that only one-half of the 192,000 nominal Lutherans in that city are church members and of these, 40 per cent never read the Bible.[7] He states: "Though the Lutheran Churches of Detroit are growing, many who call themselves Lutherans seldom or never attend church. Almost a third of those interviewed reported they seldom if ever attend, while 15 per cent claimed to attend only once a month."

The same attitude might be reported for most other Protestants. Insofar as Catholics are concerned, ritual observance is not necessarily "religiosity" as Protestants and Jews understand it.

National and ethnic churches too, are also far less effective among the native-born than among foreign-born Americans. The effectiveness of the Greek Orthodox, Lutheran, Polish, and Russian churches, for example, as a means of maintaining the cultural as well as the religious solidarity of the group has been weakened. Roman Catholic divisions between Irish and Italians, for example, are considerably reduced although not wholly eliminated. Among Jews the ethnic Synagogue (synagogues were once known as "the Polish Synagogue," "the Russian Synagogue," "the Lithuanian Synagogue") has, with but minor exceptions, disappeared. Only the "Spanish-Portuguese Synagogue" in New York City and several others of similar ethnic awareness around the country are still extant. And, even in these, members of ethnic origins other than the Spanish-Portuguese are to be found. (For the first time in its long history, the congregation's rabbi is not a member of this ethnic group).

Maier and Spinrad[8] reporting on the comparative religious values of Protestant, Catholic and Jew, at a "large urban state university" have indicated that if the criteria of (a) belief in a personal God, (b) frequency of prayer, (c) frequency of church and synagogue attendance, were utilized, Roman Catholic students would rank first in religiosity with Protestants a considerable distance behind them, and Jewish students, far to the rear of both.

According to this study, 66 per cent of the Catholics believe in a personal God, whereas 41 per cent of the Protestants hold to this belief, and 24 per cent of the Jews accept this concept. Seventy-eight per cent of the Catholic students attended church services once a week. This was true of 36 per cent of the Protestants while not a single Jew attended synagogue once a week.

In the matter of frequency of prayer, 44 per cent of the Catholics said that they prayed daily; 41 per cent of the Protestants did likewise. Only 8 per cent of the Jews prayed daily. Thirty-six per cent of the

Jews rarely or never prayed while 12 per cent of the Catholics and 13 per cent of the Protestants were in that category.

And yet, it should be noted, these Jewish students were definitely ready to identify themselves with the Jewish people, for only 10 per cent of the Jews would consider marrying outside their faith. Twenty-seven per cent of the Catholic students and 45 per cent of the Protestants, according to this study, were also ready to marry outside of their own faith.

Of significance is the fact that the Jewish students were far less likely to emphasize "loyalty to God" as the greatest of all loyalties. But 11 per cent of the Jews replied that loyalty to God was most important while 74 per cent of the Catholics and 50 per cent of the Protestants replied in the same way.

However, 74 per cent of the Jews reported that they owe their greatest loyalty to the family, as compared with 24 per cent of the Catholics and 39 per cent of the Protestants.

The relationship of Jewish students to family serves to explain why—despite their seemingly unorthodox religious position—Jews, to date, have had a lesser degree of interfaith marriages than either Catholic or Protestant students. This interpretation is further supported by the replies the students of each of these major religious groups gave to the question: "Can culture exist without positive religion?" While 8 per cent of the Catholics and 15 per cent of the Protestants replied in the negative, 35 per cent of the Jews answered "yes."

A random sample poll of student attitudes at Harvard University and Radcliffe College was taken in June of 1959.[9] Here, too, student responses clearly indicated that the religious ties of the three major religious groups had weakened. Less than one-third of the Protestant students questioned felt themselves in "substantial agreement with the tenets of their faith." Many of the others continued their religious tradition either with reservations or rejected it completely. Twenty-six per cent of the students born into Protestant families have rejected their religious heritage. Of the Jewish students only 35 per cent agreed that they "professed Judaism as a religion, agreeing wholly or substantially with its beliefs and traditions." Forty-two per cent of all Jews polled did not believe in a "one-person God." Yet 40 per cent of the Jewish students regarded themselves as Jews because they were "born of parents who considered themselves Jewish even though they may have discarded certain theological or other Jewish values and practices."

It is obvious that those Jewish students, while rejecting most of the doctrines and practices of their faith, still identify themselves with the Jewish people and regard themselves as Jews.

Because the number of Catholic students who replied to the ques-

tions asked on the poll was so small (twenty-three), no assurance can be given concerning its representative character, yet one-fourth of these students, although reared as Catholics, declared themselves to be "agnostics" or "atheists." Another sixth retain their formal affiliation with the Church but "partially withhold intellectual assent or seem lax in their practices, though they have no particular disagreement with Catholic theology. The remaining sixty per cent of those replying seem quite orthodox in their Catholicism." [10]

Only 28 per cent of the students based correct ethical principles upon religious faith. This number expressed the belief that "a genuine knowledge of man's moral obligations does not involve a belief in a God!" Twenty-four per cent believed in "a God about whom nothing definite can be affirmed," except that this "Presence" was sometimes sensed as permeating all mankind and nature. [11]

An examination of the views and attitudes of these Harvard and Radcliffe students leads to the conclusion that the ties to traditional religion, in all major respects has weakened considerably. These students are, then, not much different from other college and university students we have already discussed.

In yet another study, undertaken to discover "What College Students Think," [12] four social scientists reported the views of students at eleven universities. Included in the survey is student opinion from Cornell, Dartmouth, Fisk, Harvard, Michigan, North Carolina, Texas, University of California (Los Angeles), Wayne, Wesleyan and Yale Universities.

Out of a total of 2,975 students, 48 per cent indicate that they "Believe in a Divine God, creator of the Universe, who knows my innermost thoughts and feelings, and to whom one day I shall be accountable." Twenty-seven per cent claimed "Belief in a power greater than myself which some people call God and some people call Nature." Twelve per cent indicated, "I am not quite sure what I believe." Fifty-two per cent of the total replies, then, were definitely not orthodox even though faith of some kind was expressed.

While 27 per cent[13] of the total number of students indicated that they attend religious services once a week or more, 25 per cent reported that they "never or almost never" attend services. Another 21 per cent reported that they attend religious services "mainly on important Holy days." The place of prayer or worship in the lives of these students can hardly be said to be especially marked. If one considers, too, the likelihood that in at least one of the universities, chapel attendance may be required, the 27 per cent figure does not appear impressive.

A "Religiousness Scale" included consideration of student opinion with respect to: (1) Religious Faith, (2) Belief in a Divine God, (3)

The Church or religion as a personality, (4) Attendance at Religious Services once a week or more, and (5) Religion as a major source of satisfaction in life. This scale was used to measure the religiosity of 368 Catholics, 179 Protestants and 429 Jewish students. Catholic students constituted 52 per cent of those regarded as the most religious and next to the most religious positions on the scale. Thirty-one per cent of the Protestants were regarded as belonging to the "most religious" category while Jewish students constituted only 14 per cent in this group. Except for the Catholic students (and then, only by a very small percentage margin), Protestants and Jews rated poorly according to this scale.[14]

Goldsen et al [15] report that, even though the college students they interviewed believe in God and appear to be aware of a need for some kind of religious faith or personal philosophy, "theirs is more in the nature of a secular religion." Religion provides them with a "sense of belonging but if religious belief is widespread, their religious commitment is rare." [16]

The Congregational Christian Church[17] in a recently conducted survey of 4,095 of its members in twelve Congregational Christian Churches in North Central and Northeastern states,[18] declared through Dr. Yoshio Fukuyama, the denomination's director, that about one-third of the denomination's members are only nominally religious. "Of the two-thirds who showed a stronger religious feeling, the largest number approached religion as an organizational activity rather than an intellectual, creedal or devotional experience." This response is similar to that discovered by other students and researchers in contemporary religiosity. The secularization of marriage and of family life has resulted from the "removal of sacred sanctions from behavior" as Simpson[19] correctly points out. The traditional association of the family with such sacred sanctions is breaking down or, at the very least, weakening.

Another indication of the weakening of religious ties is suggested by Jacobson[20] who reports that "one-fourth of all marriages performed in the U.S. are now performed by civil ceremony. Of these, about one-fourth may ultimately be followed by a religious ceremony." Here we have additional support for the belief that the bonds of religion and of the family have weakened sufficiently to permit young people to accept a marriage without a religious ceremony at the very outset.

Little wonder that the mid-twentieth century is frequently described in such terms as the "post-Christian" or "post-Protestant" era. The influence of Christianity, of Judaism and of religion generally, is waning. Religious pluralism is said to be generally accepted in America today. Herberg[21] has declared that it is natural to the American way of life. I suspect that what passes for religious pluralism is nothing more than

an increase in religious indifference in our day that makes the religious views of others relatively unimportant, hence, not to be argued about.

> It really doesn't matter what religion you are. They are all the same and none of them really matters!

The belief that we are all the children of God is more manifest today than ever before. The reduction of distinctions between men and their religions makes universalism as a way of thinking, and as a way of life, all the more likely within the next generation or two. This, too, is a factor that makes for an increase in intermarriage. The survival of particular religious traditions is, then, by no means assured. Religious learning and the belief in the uniqueness of one's religion, so character-istic of former generations is less evident today. The Americanization process and a sense of at-homeness in America is at once a blessing and a danger insofar as survival of minority religious groups is concerned.

> How is this world going to become "one world" if we persist in maintaining our differences? I'm tired of that. Religion divides us. It doesn't unite us despite all this talk about the Fatherhood of God and the Brotherhood of Man. There have to be some souls in this world who are sufficiently brave and strong to break down these barriers men have erected and I, for one, intend to marry "outside" my own religious group in order to prove once and for all that this is or ought to be one world.

Considerable attention has been given to present-day attitudes to-ward religion because of the erroneous impression that organized reli-gions are really gaining in strength. I believe, on the basis of the evi-dence already noted, that affiliation with Church or Synagogue is not to be regarded as synonymous with commitment to any religion. It appears to me that there is rather an increasing degree of indifference to all organized religions accompanied by a growing desire for and belief in the Brotherhood of Man and creation of "one world."

Let us note, too, that in 1900 only 4 per cent of the college-age group, twenty to twenty-four attended college. That number increased to 35 per cent in 1956. It is anticipated that 45 per cent of this age group will be attending college by 1966. Indeed, in some areas of the country, notably suburban and upper-middle class, over 80 per cent of the young people of college age are presently enrolled in our colleges and universities.

The school population continues to rise not only because there are more children of school age but because, in our day, a greater value is placed upon learning and technical skill than ever before.

Significant, too, is the fact that more females are attending colleges

and universities than ever before. The total number of college and university students is increasing in our time and percentage of females receiving a college education continues to grow apace.

What does this change mean in terms of the family and marriage? And what other implications may this change have for us?

First of all, higher education for women in such proportion means that, assuming college and university training to be valuable in itself, the education of both husbands and wives at the present time is about equal. Allowing for the technical skills acquired by males in universities, medical knowledge, specialized training in the physical and natural sciences, etc., women have become or are, education-wise, fast becoming the equals of their mates.

Further, young men and girls now meet and fall in love while attending the same schools. The number of college romances and subsequent marriages continue to increase each year, as more girls attend colleges.

Bossard [22] has correctly pointed out that "the college years are the marrying years." The attitudes of college youth with respect to intermarriage is, therefore, of major significance. Not only are there more young people now going on to colleges and universities than in the past ten years, but people are marrying at an earlier age and their views of dissimilarities in religion and even of color are hardly as conservative as they were but a decade ago. Similarities in educational background do, in fact, tend to draw people together, however different their religious, racial or ethnic backgrounds may be.

The equalization of educational and economic status among peoples of various religious, ethnic and racial groups tends to increase the likelihood of intermarriage. Young people of varying backgrounds who attend college together have this education and environment in common, and are less likely to concern themselves with differences in family background, origin, or religion.

The increase in college and university attendance is certainly more than likely to widen the circle of marital choices open to students. Popenoe[23] found that one-fourth of the several thousand couples he had studied had first met in schools. About 18 per cent of all of the marriages studied resulted from a first meeting in the home of friends; about 13 per cent came about through business contacts, and about 10 per cent resulted from contacts made through a church or a church organization. It should be pointed out that Popenoe's observations were recorded in 1932. In the past three decades, opportunities for contacts in schools, homes of friends and business remained the major sources of contact that ultimately lead to marriage.

Insofar as Jewish youth are concerned:

Two out of every three young Jewish men and women of college age in the United States are enrolled in institutions of higher learning today. The percentage will probably increase further during the next decade. . . . Nearly two-thirds of the Jewish community of America are or will in the near future be college graduates.

These words by Professor William Haber,[24] Chairman of the National Hillel Commission of B'nai B'rith, provide us with something more than information concerning the enrollment, present and future, of Jewish youth in American colleges and universities. They help to explain why, with ever-increasing intermixture of Jewish and non-Jewish students on the various campuses, in fraternities, sororities and eating clubs, there is the feeling, insofar as some Jews are concerned, that there will be an increase in interfaith marriages involving Jews.

Intermarriages will tend to increase not only because more American young of varying religious, ethnic, and racial background attend our colleges and universities, but also because the policies of fraternities and sororities have been liberalized. The number of exclusive fraternities and sororities is being reduced every year. Colleges and universities are officially urging and even insisting upon such policies. When Jews, Negroes and other minority groups are no longer barred from college fraternities and sororities, we may expect a greater degree of co-mingling that must inevitably lead to a greater degree of intermarriage.

Minority groups that advocate the letting down of barriers in fraternities and sororities must accept the responsibility for an increase in intermarriage that follows naturally therefrom.

Some Jews and Catholics are disturbed about this latest development in fraternity and sorority policy. They believe that there is a place for purely sectarian youth organizations on college and university campuses. They feel that the desire to establish campus "equality" should not require the elimination of Jewish, Catholic or Negro fraternities as such. They believe that at this point in the life of young people, when religious and racial bonds ought to be strengthened, it is unwise to discard them and thereby increase the tendency toward assimilation. They point out that incentive to intermarriage increases as fraternity bias decreases.

National fraternities, in response to the requests of their local chapters as well as the demands of the colleges and universities, are eliminating the bias clauses which have prevented their acceptance of Negroes and other non-Caucasians as well as Jews and other religious or cultural minorities. Although great gains have been made in this direction, it must be noted that the problem of *de facto* limitations often remains. National fraternities eliminate a bias clause from their consti-

tutions but continue to enforce discriminatory practices as an unwritten rule. Many institutions of higher education, well aware of this tendency, have warned such recalcitrants that continuation of such practices may serve to bar them from their campus. Although it hardly seems possible that discrimination will be entirely eliminated, the great gains that have, thus far, been made, should be noted. The social life of the fraternity and sorority makes increasingly closer contact between the races and religions inevitable.

We live, too, in an "Age of Rebellion" when the conservative values of parents, Church and Synagogue are often opposed with great vigor by our young people. We are witnesses to something more than the age-old conflict between the generations. The spirit of rebellion has never gone quite so far or manifested itself so strongly as it has since World War II. The reasons therefor go beyond the matter of emancipation of young people from parental and family controls. They seem to have some direct relationship to the kind of world youth feels it has inherited.

> Why should I listen to the advice my folks give me? What have they done to make me feel that their advice is any good? All I have inherited from them is a world filled with anxiety and fear, a world of A-bombs and H-bombs—a world of fall-outs and bomb shelters, a world either at war or on the brink of war. I can't do any worse by following my own ideas than my parents have done.

Such is the psychology of many young people today.

But intermarriage is not always an act of rebellion against parents or their values. It is often reluctantly entered into because circumstances brought together two young people whose love for each other developed before either was fully aware of what was happening. Such intermarriages are not the result of defiance, revolt, rebellion, hostility. They are rather the product of urbanization, mobility, propinquity and other such factors that play so significant a role in our society.

We Americans are a mobile people. We go from the farms and rural areas to the cities in vast numbers. In 1960, 70 per cent of the total United States population was urban while but 30 per cent was rural. Now Americans are moving from the large central cities into suburban areas. Negroes and whites are moving out of the South and into the Northern and Western states. The degree of mobility today is very high. The proportion of the native population living in a state other than the state of birth was higher in 1960 than at any other time since data on this subject was first collected in the 1850 census. In 1960, 26 out of every 100 persons, in the native population, were residing in a state different from the one in which they had been born. A

little more than one half of the population of the United States was living in the 213 urbanized areas delineated for the 1960 Federal Census.[25]

America has become a primarily urban nation. The opportunity to communicate with persons of other faiths, ethnic and racial groups continues to increase. The influence of religion and of the social caste system appears to be weakest in the large cities. The opportunities for communication between persons of different religious, cultural, economic, and social background are greatly improved in the urban centers. Mixed marriages are, therefore, most common in large cities. In addition, the degree of mobility *within* urban areas is highly marked. The automobile and the plane make it possible for families to move quickly from one area to another. The opportunities for travel, for recreation in new and even far-off places increase the opportunities for making new friends, not of one's own group. Young men in the armed services, moving from one country to another, make new friendships possible. Higher education for more young people and longer periods given over to formal education serve, too, to increase intermarriages. World trade, opportunities for migration, world-wide travel—all these help to create one world. Differences between peoples tend to be increasingly minimized, similarities are stressed. An increase in mixed marriages of all kinds thus becomes highly probable.

The number of Americans who "move up" on the economic scale, and as a consequence, on the social scale as well, is increasing. More and more people move from the lower economic class to the lower or upper middle class. The gap between classes is less marked than it once was. The number in the middle-class group is much larger, hence the opportunity for social intercourse afforded by mobility itself is increased as well.

The greater the degree of mobility, the more numerous are the opportunities to become acquainted with people whose ways may be different from our own. Religious, national and even racial barriers are considerably reduced. Under these conditions groups tend to be less suspicious of or hostile to one another than they were only a generation ago.

In 1950, Negroes constituted 35 per cent of the population of Washington, D.C., while in 1960, they were 53.9 per cent of its population. The mobility of the whites in the same city resulted in their movement into the surrounding suburbs. What is true of Washington is also true of 23 out of the 25 largest cities in the United States (the exceptions being Memphis and San Antonio).

The opportunity for easy social contacts is obvious today. Americans may meet not only at socials, dances, parties, but within churches

and synagogues as well. People of different backgrounds may reside in the same general neighborhood. "Contacts Unlimited" is indeed the characteristic American way.[26] There are no longer many "isolated" families who have no relationships with other families. Schools, societies, churches and a vast assortment of other societal groups have made isolation quite impossible in our day.[27] The greater the degree of contact between groups, the more likely are exogamous marriages.

When any ethnic or religious group is in a minority in a given area there is the tendency to marry out of one's own group. Thomas[28] has pointed out that, insofar as American Catholics are concerned, a low per cent of Catholics to the total population of the community in which they reside is an important factor which influences an increase in Catholic intermarriage. He believes, too, that the presence of cohesive ethnic sub-groups within the community and the socio-economic status of its Catholic population tend to influence the increase in intermarriage.

Using the American Catholic as an example, Bossard [29] states that "in selected Catholic Dioceses where the Catholic population is 20 per cent or less of the total population, the per cent of mixed marriages ranges from 60 to 70; when the Catholic population consists of 50 per cent or more of the total population, the per cent of intermarriage falls below 20 per cent, in some cases, to below 10 per cent in others. The relation of the size of the minority to the total population thus contributes to the increase of interfaith marriages.

Further, when the number of males within the group is markedly different from the number of females, the tendency to intermarry with persons of another religion or color is increased. Unbalanced sex ratio as well as small numbers often lead some groups and their respective members into intermarriage. Physiological factors tend to increase the desire to intermarry under these particular circumstances, and the smaller groups are likely to be absorbed, assuming the willingness of the majority groups to intermarry with them.

Panunzio believes that sex ratios and culture are, in fact, the most basic factors involved in intermarriage. Well-balanced sex ratios tend to cause people to marry within their own group. If the sex balance is unequal, then the nature of one's culture will play a major role in determining the selection that will be made.

Propinquity is another factor that plays an important role in cross-marriages. People who live in the same neighborhood are more likely to become acquainted and ultimately to marry. Hollingshead[30] has pointed out that residential propinquity is one of six important cultural factors that may affect the selection of a mate, the others being (1) ethnic origin, (2) race, (3) religion, (4) socio-economic status, and (5) social characteristics.

In 1938, Koller[31] reported that in a study of 1,132 cases in Columbus, Ohio, 51 per cent of the marriages occurred where the male and female were living within twelve standard city blocks of each other. A 1946 [32] study reported that 50 per cent of some 1,200 men selected women who were living within fifteen standard city blocks of each other.

The second, third, and fourth generations of Americans differ greatly from their predecessors in their mental and emotional attitudes. They speak "another language" even as they represent a distinctive and American point of view. They have become homogenized.

Not only are these young people "American" in the sense that America is their homeland and its ways their ways, but also their knowledge of the foreign languages their parents knew and spoke so well—Yiddish, Polish, Russian, etc.,—is limited. In most cases, young people are, in fact, quite unfamiliar with these languages. Distinctive types of humor associated with ethnic groups is fast disappearing. Although there are Yiddish jokes, for example, the youth seldom understand them. Hence, two processes are occurring at the same time. There is more Americanization and a reduction in minority influence in the lives of our youth. As a consequence, young native Americans, whatever their religious background, are more likely to have similar standards and values than do their foreign-born parents. Interfaith marriages, then, appear to increase as the homogeneity of Americans of all religions and racial backgrounds becomes more marked.

Certainly, the gradual but perceptible reduction in religious and racial discrimination in our society—still not as much as we would like —tends to increase mixed marriages as social and economic discrimination, too, become less pronounced. As ghetto walls continue to weaken and fall, as segregation in housing is reduced, as the job opportunities for persons of different religions and races are equalized, we may expect further intercommunication and intermingling between different religious and racial groups.

The barriers that separate individuals, religions, ethnics and races from each other must, in the view of many young people, be broken down. Some believers in "one world" assume that nonidentification with their parental groups will hasten the day when prejudice, hatred and even war will be vanquished. How realistic such a view is remains questionable. It is equally uncertain whether, by the elimination of these religious and other divisions presently existing among men, we shall gain more than we may ultimately lose.

The breakdown of old forms and patterns of behavior, so characteristic of our day, and the consequent growth of individualism must certainly be regarded as a factor contributing to the increase in mixed marriages. When there is "a decrease of influence of social rules of

behavior upon individual members of the group" [33] social disorganization is evident. The current belief that whatever one does is one's own business, and is only indirectly of concern to society, assures a steady increase in the number of interfaith and interracial marriages.

The happiness of the individual is today regarded as the prime factor in marriage. The choice of a mate is no longer made by well-intentioned parents. Nor are they asked for "permission" to seek the hand of a daughter in marriage. Parents are "told."

> Parents are lucky these days if they know very much about their future sons- or daughters-in-law. Such things as talking matters over with parents doesn't take place any more. Ask youngsters why they don't talk to parents and they tell you, "It's my life and I can live it as I want." So there you are.

Romantic love has come to be regarded as a natural right. Such love is defined by Waller and Hill [34] as "an ungovernable impulse, a wholly normal and even sought-for state of grace in which one is unable to think of anything but the loved person—a great tenderness together with the most extreme delusion as to the value of the loved person and a striving toward her sometimes attended by extravagances of jealousy and morbid despair if one does not prosper in his suit." Young people tend to regard the questioning of their judgment when they are "in love" as highly immoral. Certainly, few parents dare oppose "love." The right of the individual to be "happy" is regarded as superior in importance to all other issues that may arise.

Aware as we are of the many physical and social factors that tend to increase the number of intermarriages in our society, we have not yet explained why some people, confronted in the main by similar factors, will intermarry while others do not. In addition to those influences which we have already enumerated, there must also be certain psychological factors at work, to which each person responds differently— resulting in intermarriage in some cases and not in others.

The marital choice is, according to psychoanalytical theory, related to one's years of interrelationship with parents and members of the immediate and extended family. Emotions and reactions first awakened in early childhood are said to affect the ultimate choice of mate. Warm and happy reactions to a parent, according to this theory, result in an unconscious desire to choose a partner who is regarded as similar in all respects. Unfavorable reactions tend to bring about a choice utterly unlike such a parent. Winch suggests that the marital choice is related to the degree in which it is believed one's maximum need will be gratified.

With these and other theories, we can only point out that the number of exceptions that can be found to them supports the view that

the marital choice of a given person can seldom be predicted with any degree of accuracy. We simply cannot be sure of the motivations in all cases. No hard and fast rule, principle or "law" regarding marital choice can be established.

Resnick[35] has classified Jews who intermarry on the basis of the individual's conception of himself, of his group and his relationship to his group. He classifies them, as follows:

(1) The *emancipated person* who has freed himself from the Jewish religious influence.

(2) The *rebellious* person who intermarries in order to remove his identity as a Jew.

(3) The *detached person* who has broken away from the Jewish primary group, resulting in a weakening of the old standards opposing intermarriage.

(4) The *adventurous person* who does not care about the identity of his spouse while regarding marriage as a new experience.

Slotkin[36] added four other types to those suggested by Resnick. They are:

(1) The *unorganized* or *demoralized person*. His nonconformity is expressed through intermarriage.

(2) The *promiscuous person* who develops affection for a person outside his own religious group.

(3) The *marginal person* who intermarries in order to raise his status or that of his children to that of the majority group.

(4) The *acculturated person* whose newly acquired standards cause him to believe that there is no one in the Jewish group who is any longer acceptable to him and who, as a consequence, intermarries.

Thomas'[37] four basic wishes—the desire for new experiences, security, response and recognition—have also been suggested as the possible reasons for intermarriage.

The Levinsons[38] have divided the intermarried into two groups: (1) the reluctants and (2) the emancipated.

There appears to be no reason to accept any of these suggestions as valid for all kinds of intermarrieds. In some instances the suggested types overlap or duplicate each other. To date all that we can state with any degree of accuracy is that no one has yet been able to present a typology of the intermarrieds that is valid under all circumstances.

Religious differences may be used either consciously or subconsciously by young people to hit out at parents. Rebellion against parents, for whatever reason, is known to express itself sometimes in intermarriage. It is assumed that marriage with a partner of another faith or race "will teach parents a lesson," that their authority or whatever else a son or daughter may consciously or subconsciously object to, will

head for a fall. Marriages involving the "rebellious" are unfortunate and can hardly prove successful because the rebellious are often emotionally unhappy young people.

The psychoanalyst may see still another interesting idea that is associated with such marriages. One analyst, in conversation with me, pointed out:

> There had always been a seductive relationship between this Jewish youth and his mother. He had gone out with Jewish girls and every single time he did he became sick. You see his mother is his first love. There can be no one other than her. In his sincere desire to break this hold his mother had on him and out of his indirect desire to avoid incest, it is almost inevitable that he will go out with non-Jewish girls and ultimately marry such a girl. A Jewish girl would make him think of his mother. It is the hold his mother has upon him that he must break.
>
> When there is an unusually close relationship between father and daughter or mother and son, the likelihood is that they will either not marry or that they will marry someone outside of their group in order to escape from an incestuous situation.

The authors of *Black Metropolis*[39] indicate that, insofar as Negroes in Chicago are concerned, those who intermarry most frequently appear to be: (1) intellectuals and bohemians; (2) religious and political radicals; (3) members of the "sporting world"; and (4) the stable middle-class. They point out, too, that sometimes the interracially intermarried is a foreign-born person, completely unassimilated into American life and not aware of the meaning of such marriage in American life.

Intermarriage is often assumed to be the result of a desire to "escape" from parents, particularly from a mother's domination, or from ties to a religious, cultural or social pattern. It is viewed, too, as a form of "rebellion" or as a desire to hurt a loved one. Neurotic motives may sometimes be rightly attributed to the intermarrieds, but it is questionable whether such motives are always associated with intermarriages. Such marriages may be entered into in order to secure financial gain or social advancement. But, as the generations succeed each other on the American scene, I believe that intermarriages will take place far more frequently because people, by some fortuitous circumstance, happen to meet, fall in love and—as the result of the general weakening of contemporary family and religious ties as well as the possession of similar educational, economic and social backgrounds—decide to marry.

Some persons, born of Protestant parents, feel that they require authoritative direction in religious matters. On occasion this increases the tendency to convert to Catholicism.

Maybe it's just as well that I marry a Catholic girl and have my children reared as Catholics. They, at least, will have the Church make their religious decisions for them. I have always been a confused kind of Protestant anyhow. There are just too many different varieties of Protestantism—all of which proves that not one of them really knows the answers to certain basic and fundamental questions. Well, the Catholic Church says it does and that is good enough for me.

We know that, in some cases, the intermarried are marginal people who live in two cultures. In other cases they are rebellious or escapists or filled with a deep hatred of self and of group. In still others we are obviously dealing with completely emancipated, independent persons, with no ties to family, people or tradition. This attitude may be highly rational or may sometimes prove to be neurotic. Some students suggest that intermarriage is the end result of many external social forces acting upon the individual; others believe that the intermarrieds are often active agents who selectively use and, in some degree modify, social reality in accordance with their own capacities and purposes.

Marriage with a person of a different religion or color may sometimes occur because there is a desire to degrade one's self or one's family. Deep resentment against parents, rejection of them, the desire for revenge, the wish to hurt some member of the immediate family, or to give formal support to an inner revolt against family, group, religion, or race—all these are sometimes expressed through intermarriage. But it would be a mistake to assume that all intermarriages are the result of these or similar psychological factors.

The Levinsons, in their fascinating study of the socio-psychological facts that influence Jews who intermarry,[40] to which we have already referred, believe that their subjects may be divided into two groups. The first consists of those persons who "have retained a high degree of emotional investment in Jewish traditions, values and religion. Being Jewish has great meaning and significance to them." They feel strongly about wanting their children to have "a clear sense of their own Jewishness." These persons disapprove of intermarriage on principle. Upon meeting their future spouse a period of great anxiety and inner conflict sets in. They are torn by doubts and misgivings, but ultimately they arrive at the decision to intermarry. Such persons, the Levinsons term "the reluctants."

A more careful examination of the lives of these people usually indicates that the families from which they spring are culturally unassimilated, that they belong to a lower middle class, live ghettolike existences within the Jewish community, that their contacts with non-Jews have been few and their attitude toward them is generally "distrustful and prejudiced." The Levinsons find, too, that there is often a

very close tie to parents, particularly to the mother, and to family and communal standards as well. Frequently, however, there is an abortive rebellion against parents, standards and traditions, even a desire to escape from the past. It is during such a period that men make first contacts with Gentile girls. But what promises to be rebellion and escape is often succeeded by a sense of guilt and an "incomplete" return to the traditional parental and family patterns. The "incompleteness" consists of a return in all but one's relations with Gentile girls, who are believed to be sexually attractive. Reluctant to discard the past, yet equally reluctant to give up the relationship with Gentiles, which has been both pleasant and exciting, such persons find themselves in a situation from which they never quite emancipate themselves. The Levinsons believe that "all of the 'reluctant' intermarrieds have had emotional difficulties that have contributed significantly to their cross-ethnic marital choice."

The "emancipated" among the intermarried are those persons whose religious, social and cultural ties to the Jewish group are weak, if not completely broken. The traditional forms of Jewish life and values have little or no meaning for them. They "object to all barriers between groups and to restrictions on individual freedom of choice." [41] Their partners, although of different religio-ethnic background, are either "similar or complementary to themselves in values, life goals and personality." [42]

The validity of the Levinson typology has yet to be proved. The sample in the case of both the "reluctants" and the "emancipated" appears to be far too small to generalize therefrom. Further, it is my experience that the "neurotic exogamy" which is said to characterize the "reluctants" may be equally true of the "emancipated," for few persons, if any, are able to cut themselves off completely from all values, standards and traditional environmental factors to the point where they can at a given point in their lives begin anew, utterly free from their backgrounds.

Heiss[43] believes that "those who are dissatisfied with their early relationship with their parents are more likely to intermarry than those who were satisfied." He has hypothesized that persons whose early family life was "strifeful" or whose parents had a weak tie to religion were more likely to intermarry than those whose families had been harmonious or had strong ties to religion. Persons whose ties to their families have been tenuous and those who, at the time of their marriage, were emancipated from their parents also appear more likely to marry out of their own faith.

Fichter's[44] typology of all Roman Catholics includes the "nucleus," the most faithful among Roman Catholic believers; the "modal," the

normal, practicing Catholic; the "marginal," who conform to a bare minimum of the Roman Catholic pattern expected of them; and the "dormant" who, "in contrast to the nominal Catholic is the person who has completely divorced himself from the practices of the Church."

Intermarriages between persons of different religious or racial groups are known to take place, too, when one of the parties to the marriage wishes to repudiate his own religious or racial group and relate himself psychologically to a person of another group in which he desires membership. He may feel so intensely about the matter that he develops a condition that Kurt Lewin[45] has called *"Selbsthasse"* (self-hatred). He may hate himself and the in-group of which he is, perforce, a part. The intense desire to relate to a group other than his own may, in itself, cause him to seek interfaith or interracial marriage as a way either of (a) expressing his hatred of the group to which he and his parents belong, (b) relating to the out-group to which he is attracted, or (c) doing both (a) and (b) at the same time.

Allport[46] comments: "Yet, conditions, customs of the community, force him to live with, work with or be classified with . . . the in-group. Under such circumstances he may, against his will, retain membership in his in-group but marry outside of his own group as a means of expressing his psychological rejection of the in-group even though he has not been attracted to an out-group."

When people cannot or will not relate to their in-group, and are not accepted as completely as they would desire by the out-group of their choice, they may be regarded as "marginal" for they find themselves falling between two groups. They belong neither to one nor the other. Such persons are certainly to be discovered among the intermarried. It is difficult if not impossible to say how frequently this marginal quality reveals itself among them.

"Selbsthasse," so graphically described by Lewin and others for the Jewish group, is characteristic of the attitude of certain members of other minority groups (ethnic and religious, *e.g.,* Italian Catholics, Irish Catholics). However, it is less virulent today than it was a generation ago. The acceptance of differences—religious, cultural and racial—by the American people as Herberg[47] has pointed out; the rise of a new nationalism associated with the development of the United Nations, where member-nations, no matter what their size, are accorded recognition and consequently, status; the substitution of structural and cultural pluralism for the melting-pot theory have all helped to reduce the incidence of self-hatred. Among Jews, pride in the accomplishments of the State of Israel within the past fifteen years has superceded the tendency to cringe or bemoan one's fate in being a Jew. Israel's achievements, culturally, militarily, socially, economically, have converted many of the

self-haters into uncritical chauvinists. The new nations in Africa, who were looked upon as primitive only a generation ago, are today the source of respect and admiration. American Negroes, who had looked upon their lot as a misfortune, are now pointing with pride to the new African nations and their leaders and basking in reflected glory.

"Repudiation of the family pattern," is certainly, as Duvall[48] suggests, also one of the major reasons for intermarriage. Why some children rebel against their parents and their families is not easily comprehended. Yet such repudiation occurs with startling regularity. Psychological difficulties are frequently noted in these "rebels." How and why they occur is not easily explained, for each of such personalities must be studied as an individual and the particular circumstances involved must be carefully considered.

Why one son or daughter discards the parents' standards and values when other children in the same family do not respond in that manner is not readily known, but it happens with far greater frequency than we realize, as marriage counselors, members of the clergy, psychologists and psychoanalysts will attest.

Intermarriage may serve as a symbol of defiance of one's parents on the part of one or both of the parties to the marriage. It may occur, too, when one of the parties, moved by ambition more than by love, decides to improve his or her position economically or status-wise and when the opportunity to marry a person who represents improved social or economic status presents itself. Such a person regards this as the great "opportunity." In a sense, it also represents this person's honest view of his own parents' economic and social status, indicating that the parents are considered to be on a lower level than is the contemplated marriage partner.

The goals, conscious and unconscious, that human beings set for themselves, some attainable and others not, may play their role in the choice of a marriage partner. If, for example, the New England Yankee has become "the symbol of the integrated American at his best, we may seek out a mate from that group, however different our own cultural and ethnic background may be."

Just as the fear of impotence is known to drive some men to become Don Juans or Casanovas in their desire to prove it false, so other secret fears that we entertain about ourselves, our personalities, gifts or talents may force us to try to prove such fears unfounded. So manifold are these psychological and, at times, neurotic needs, that it is quite impossible to list all of those that induce mixed marriages.

Whatever the typology thus far proposed, the factors that influence one person's reaction to another are so diverse as to make it unlikely that the prediction of one person's response to another can, in all

cases, be undertaken with any degree of accuracy. The "rebellious" may be all that the name implies, yet the rebellion may express itself in an altogether different way than through intermarriage. This is equally true of the "emancipated," the "reluctants" and all the other types to which reference has been made. I have seen among all the major religions many persons who must be regarded as "nuclear" yet whose love for one of another faith is so great that family reactions and church or synagogue affiliations assume a secondary role in their lives.

Are mixed marriages solely the result of rebellious attitudes, self-hatred, neurotic tendencies, escapism, immaturity, and other psychological factors, as some sociologists and psychologists have suggested? Or are they due to such factors as unbalanced sex ratios or social mobility, both vertical and horizontal? No one knows for certain which factors invariably produce such marriages. The factors, causal and psychological, appear to be so numerous and so different from case to case that we must conclude that all the factors we have mentioned play some role, but we must add that the factors differ in individual cases. That is why no general rule can be laid down with any degree of accuracy. Whatever the factors may be, individuals respond and react differently to them. What may affect one person adversely may appear to have no such effect on yet another person, or at the most to affect him slightly. It is, then, the nature of the particular individual with whom we may be concerned that must be clearly ascertained.

The major factors that make for intermarriage vary not only with the society and environment, but with the individual as well. Some factors appear to act at certain times, under certain conditions and upon certain individuals, with greater speed and ease than they do at others. But reaction depends—and this must be stressed—in large degree upon the individual's psychological make-up.

We may speak of the factors that appear to make for intermarriage as catalysts in the sense that they serve as reacting agents, tending to produce certain results and changes even as chemicals would react upon each other.

I have found that intermarriages between young people of different religions take place surprisingly often even when the home is a thoroughly religious one, even when parental pressure does not drive a sibling out of the home in an effort to escape a dominant mother or father or an all-too-strict religious or moral standard.

Intermarriages in the main occur, I believe, because people in our American society, in ever-increasing number, come into contact with each other, socially, industrially, educationally, culturally, politically. The price that we must pay for living with persons of religions other than our own is the increasing likelihood of intermarriage. Unless we

wish to create a separate ghetto for Jews, for Catholics, and for Protestants we are obliged, in the American society of which we are a part, to take our chances with intermarriage.

Even though we have pointed out many factors, both causal and psychological, that tend to encourage intermarriage, we must also point out that there is another side of the coin—there are also factors at work that tend to reduce the possibility of intermarriage. There are numerous such "controls" in our society and, even if they do not operate as effectively as they once did, they are, nevertheless, generally influential.

Among such controls are the legal and religious prohibitions which societies and religions have established against marriage. The legal statutes that prevent marriages between persons of different colors constitute one type of social control used by our society. The organized opinion of the citizens of a community or state, thus expressed, represents a powerful form of control because the violation of such laws subjects the violators to fine or imprisonment. Under the impression that the preservation of our society depends upon such methods, over half of the states in the Union have such laws on their books.

Religion, too, because of its desire to preserve its own way of life, uses the statutes of its codes to prevent marriages outside of the religious group. Punishment for the violation of its will usually expresses itself through Church, Synagogue and family. Not only are sancta prescribed for violation of the group standard, but unofficial procedures involving group ridicule, scorn, or ostracism may be utilized to enforce the group's attitudes.

Despite all of the freedom and independence of each individual we are nevertheless limited in all possibilities. The controls, social and personal, that are exerted over us by parents, friends and society are considerable. Only a few of us do exactly what we want to do. An ambivalence resulting from the desire to please parents, to conform to the norms of our society and religion and to fulfill our own wishes as well is always apparent. Most people steer a course that lies fairly close to conformity. Some few may ignore controls and express their independence, however much they may "hurt" parents and other loved ones.

Group survival in large measure depends upon the careful and deliberate use of isolation devices. Uniforms, lodge pins and badges, flags, distinctive religious rites and ceremonies, all help to develop "consciousness of kind," as did the establishment by the early Christians of the Lord's day (first day) to distinguish them from Jews who observed the Sabbath (seventh day). They are useful means by which to achieve the ultimate purpose of distinctiveness and control.

The group provides a certain degree of personal security. Identification with the group becomes a psychological necessity for most indi-

viduals. Both the group and the individual gain strength by strengthening each other.

We may say, then, that we "belong" to groups and we identify with them as a means of *maintaining our own security*. We humans are gregarious animals. We benefit from contact with others even as they gain from their association with us. Our emotional and intellectual stability requires that we live as part of the group, which, in turn, derives its sense of purpose from the individuals who comprise it. If the persons who are members of a sub-group are clearly identified with it, and if the integration within the group is sufficiently well developed, the desire for ever-increasing cohesiveness through unique uniform practices, ceremonies, rites as well as common memories, hopes and ambitions will manifest itself. Such a sub-group will attempt to avoid complete integration and ultimate assimilation by a larger group. Jews, Protestants and Catholics are all members of sub-groups (the group being "religious people") and become assimilated when they no longer identify with the behavioral patterns, practices and ideology of their own group but adopt the patterns of a more dominant group. When intermarriage with a member of a different group takes place on a non-discriminatory and nonpreferential basis, the cultural assimilatory process has been completed.

Boas[49] saw the overwhelming tendency toward endogamy as an expression of ethno-centrism—concern for the perpetuation of one's own ethnic group. Idealization of one's own group is regarded as natural because of the desire to perpetuate its values, to help maintain its uniqueness, to assure the purity of its ideology (freedom from foreign values) and its physical and racial purity as well. Every effort is made, therefore, to maintain solidarity. Marriage outside the group is generally frowned upon and even opposed because it may, in some ways, weaken the group.

The family, with all of its weaknesses, is still an important and powerful influence in our lives. Eating, visiting together, the performance of various family rituals, the counseling that occurs within the family—all tend to strengthen family controls. Family mores are still strong enough to cause many young people to hesitate before they marry outside of the family religion.

The creation of all-Catholic, or all-Protestant, or all-Jewish neighborhoods, characteristic not only of Suburbia, but of the core city as well, serves to reduce the number of interfaith intermarriages because the opportunities for social contact with members of other groups are thereby reduced. Glorified ghettos of the organized ethnic sub-groups within metropolitan and suburban areas, consisting of Poles, Italians, Jews, Catholics, Mexicans, Chinese and other minorities serve to per-

petuate these groups even as—by control of public opinion, attitudes, religion, foods, language, culture—they affect directly or indirectly the views of the individuals, young and old, who reside in their midst.

Lenski[50] has correctly observed that parents and the clergy are still very close to most young people. Therefore parental and clerical attitudes toward other peoples and their religions naturally affect the attitude of the young toward intermarriage.

Inasmuch as the mate choices of the young people are most important to the elders in a given society, parents seek to control the choices that young people make. They do so, in certain societies, by supporting child (or early) marriages in which the elders choose the mates for their youth. They arrange matches on the basis of family, cultural, economic or other factors. They separate male and female adolescents, making them inaccessible to each other. They exercise close supervision of their young, and define marriage as a duty and an alliance rather than a matter of romantic love. They invoke societal and religious standards and traditions, enforcing their decisions by causing the treasonous youth to feel guilty of an offense against either or both. They urge conformity to these traditions and standards as means of preserving the group.

In the main, these controls may be said to have characterized European and older societies. They were certainly far more powerful among first- and second-generation families of European descent living in America than they are among Americans of the third or fourth generations. Many of these controls have already disappeared while others are disappearing slowly.

Although persons who are neither religious nor affiliated with a religious group (even those who are quite ignorant about the religious group with which their parents are affiliated) may object strongly to intermarriage, they do so, I believe, on grounds of racial, national or familial loyalties.

Opposition to intermarriage may also be based entirely on family pride. Parents may object strongly and effectively to an intermarriage because the child contemplating such a union is acting contrary to the parents' wishes—however rational or irrational those wishes may be. Their own societal character is made to seem better, more correct, or "special" than that of any other group. They find within their own group unique qualities and values that seem to them especially worthy of perpetuation. There may be many who deny the quality of uniqueness to any group other than their own and who state that the group has a special significance for its own members and provides a positive motive for its continued existence.

It is not enough for those who derogate such ideas to point out that each subdivision in our society believes in its own uniqueness and

"chosenness." The Jews who regarded themselves as "chosen" were not alone in their ethno-centrism. The ancient Greeks spoke of themselves as the "Darlings of the Gods" and, indeed, other peoples and religions, in antiquity and contemporary times as well (German, British, American) do likewise. Catholics claim to possess the Truth and insist that all other religions are "in error." All, in one way or another, believe implicitly in their own uniqueness. That certain ideas or values are universally held by our society does not necessarily prove a sub-group's contentions to be false. It may, in fact, support the thesis that each group, however much alike others it may be in most particulars, is nevertheless "different" and hence unique (*i.e.,* distinct and separated from the other groups) in some detail that has special significance for that group.

Giddings who spoke of "consciousness of kind" as reason for the continued existence of our sub-groups, was talking about an empirically proven fact. The group, the family and organized religion consciously seek to establish this awareness of kind in the minds of their members. Devices are consciously chosen to isolate one group or one religion from another.

Even though the family, the Church and Synagogue may be weakening, there is still a basic need on the part of most individuals for identification with someone, some group and/or some Church and Synagogue. Whatever may have happened to the distinctive ideologies of these institutions insofar as the average individual is concerned, the need to belong is as great as it ever was. It is still not easy to discard this last vestige of affiliation. What other persons think about us matters greatly to many of us—to the vast majority in fact. To marry someone of another religion is often regarded as a form of desertion.

In his study of the Detroit area, Lenski[51] confirmed this view. Family and friends appear to oppose intermarriage because, to them, it symbolizes the desertion of one's own group. Lenski reported that 96 per cent of the Jews; 87 per cent of white Catholics, and 75 per cent of white Protestants believed that their friends would discourage them from "joining another group." So great is the effect of family and friends upon the choices we ultimately make even in marriage.

Catholics, Protestants and Jews respond in much the same way. The religious teachings emphasizing the unique, if not the superior and distinctive, qualities of each of these religions clearly urge young people to marry within their group in order to maintain these special qualities.

Lenski[52] in discussing the Jews in the Detroit area said that 77 per cent of them reported that all or nearly all of their friends were Jews. In the case of Catholics, he indicated that 79 per cent reported that all or nearly all of their close relations were Catholic while 44 per cent

declared that all or nearly all of their friends were Catholic. As for white Protestants, 76 per cent of his sample reported that all or nearly all of their close relatives were of the same faith, while 38 per cent declared that all or nearly all of their friends were Protestant.

Lenski's observations support the thesis that, however weak organized religion may be in our day, it is still very much of a vital force, particularly insofar as it affects the matter of marriages. Marriage partners are generally chosen from among one's own religious group. The influence of parents and the Church and Synagogue in this area has weakened, but it is clear that their influence as a deterrent to mixed marriage is still marked.

Despite seeming indifference to distinctive theological ideas and ceremonial practices of Judaism, young American Jews believe that the Jews should continue as a group. The "Riverton Study" of 1958,[53] comparing the attitude of Jewish youth with the responses of their parents in one Eastern urban community (Trenton, New Jersey), indicates that 35 per cent of the children gave as their reason for the continuation of the Jewish group, "We should keep our Religion alive," while only 3 per cent believe that "differences between Jews and Christians are "unsurmountable" as compared with 9 per cent of their parents. Yet 95 per cent of these youth believe that Jews ought to continue as a distinct group as compared with 93 per cent of their parents. Whereas their parents were 81 per cent "Orthodox," 11 per cent "Conservative" and 5 per cent "Reform," the children declared themselves 17 per cent "Orthodox," 42 per cent "Conservative" and 30 per cent "Reform."

Among Jews there is still a general but definite attempt to maintain a Jewish kinship order. If intermarriage appears to be inevitable, conversion to Judaism is generally insisted upon.

Jewish youth are regularly reminded by parents, family, Synagogue and the Jewish community of their obligation to maintain the Jewish kinship group. Public opinion within the Jewish community is definitely opposed to intermarriage. This means of social control is still highly significant and serves to retard assimilation and proselytization.

Hitler's inhuman methods forced even those Jews who regarded themselves as liberated from what they called "the tribal rites" of the Jewish people to reconsider their position. They discovered that, however emancipated they might consider themselves to be, Hitler still viewed them as Jews. They were, therefore, obliged to examine their position anew. Many turned back to the Jewish community, their loyalty to the Jewish people reinforced by Hitler; still others, moved by the establishment of the State of Israel, by the heroism of its defenders and the imagination of its leaders, turned inward toward the Jewish people.

Their sense of pride in their newly discovered brethren brought them closer to the Jewish people than ever before in their lifetimes.

When Jewish parents followed the practice of "sitting *Shivah*" (formally mourning) for an intermarried son or daughter, the youth was dramatically reminded that parental objection to intermarriage was something more than a whim or passing notion. Young people were thus informed that most parents would not reconcile themselves to intermarriage in their families even if it meant cutting of a son or daughter from the family itself by the extreme and formal act of sitting *Shivah*. Today, such acts happen rarely. Young people believe (and are generally correct) that parents, however much they may oppose intermarriage prior to such a marriage involving one of their own children, will somehow eventually become reconciled to it. When such a reconciliation occurs, parents once again accept an intermarried child.

Two generations ago the Jewish community could and did apply such sanctions effectively. Sons and daughters, aware of the open hostility to intermarriage generally refrained from interdating lest it might lead to intermarriage.

Antonovsky,[54] in his study of the second generation of Jews of New Haven in 1953, reported that only 4 per cent of his sample would "cut their child off in the event of marriage to a Gentile." Yet, 57 per cent report that an intermarriage "would hurt them very much." If, however, the children of an intermarriage were brought up as Jews, 22 per cent of the parents would accept the intermarrieds. In 18 per cent of the cases the intermarriages of their children would not matter. Antonovsky believes that the "moderates" (the 22 per cent) and the "neutrals" (the 18 per cent) among the parents would, as a consequence, no longer serve as a deterrent to the intermarriage of their children.

Although Jewish religious law permits formal conversion to Judaism and states that such a person is a Jew and is so to be regarded, Jews do not generally take kindly to conversion because, as Goldstein[55] has pointed out "an alien element has been introduced."

Protestantism appears to be equally opposed to intermarriage. It regards marriage, particularly to Catholics, not only as dangerous to its own survival but as an affront to Protestantism, particularly because of the Catholic Church's present insistence that children of a Protestant-Catholic marriage must be reared as Catholics. Whatever its attitude, this has not prevented about one-fifth of all married Protestants from entering into marriage with Catholics and persons of other religious backgrounds as well. About 80 per cent of Protestants marry Protestants. The Protestant Church has weakened its control, but it has not lost its power

to evidence disapproval of exogamous marriages and, what is more, the vast majority of its adherents heed its counsel.

The Catholic Church, as we have already noted, frowns upon interfaith marriage. Yet, it tolerates valid mixed marriages under conditions which it believes may assure the survival of the true religion of which it is a part. Catholic churches are neighborhood churches. Catholics are urged to live near the church, to send their children to its parochial schools and to participate in all-Catholic group activities in order that the preservation of a distinctive way of life may be assured. The control of the Catholic parent, Church and parish may have weakened, but it has certainly not disappeared. As with the Jews and Protestants, identification with the Catholic community is urged and is made both socially desirable and commendable. Endogamous marriages are urged upon young Catholics. Family and Church alike are important forces seeking to control the actions of their young people. Whatever controls they can use effectively are attempted.

The urgings of one's own family or religious group to conform to all of its values and standards may not be wholly adhered to, but its conventions will seldom be completely ignored because it is quite impossible to do that. The influence of the kinship group has a marked effect upon each of us. Inasmuch as our own security often depends upon the degree of acceptance we receive from our families and our own people, it is understandable that a lack of Church, Synagogue or family acceptance, sooner or later causes many of us to wonder about the wisdom of our acts. This is certainly true of interfaith marriages. It is even more true of interracial marriages, where the prejudices of society against persons of different skin colors as sex partners is so great.

Even though affiliation with Church or Synagogue is not, in these days, to be mistaken for total acceptance of its ideas, values or attitudes, the fact that approximately 60 per cent of Americans are directly affiliated has some significance.

The social controls of Church and Synagogue are far from passé. They bring about reactions of various kinds: fear in some persons; and, on the part of others, pleasure in having conformed when the dicta of organized religion are adhered to.

Prejudice and bias against other peoples and religions are not to be ignored as an important factor controlling the number of intermarriages that take place. Family admonitions, the tendency to caricature people of other nationalities, ethnic groups and religions continues to exist as a potent factor in reducing the number of intermarriages. The tendency to look down upon others, to believe in one's own superiority and to teach these ideas to children, even by indirection, tends also to reduce intermarriage. It is in part through prejudice, then, that

the course of marriage may be controlled. Prejudice must, therefore, be listed as one of the inhibiters of exogamous marriage.

The inhibiting factors, strong as they are, do not appear to be powerful enough to overcome the many positive factors that seem likely to increase the number of intermarriages in each of the three major religious groups. At the most, they indicate that the rate of intermarriage is slowed but not stopped. The factors making for intermarriages and the catalysts that are presently at work, are, in my opinion, more than likely to increase the intermarriage rate within the next two decades.

CARLOTTA AND ABRAM

Carlotta, a Catholic from Brazil, is married to Abram, an American Jew. Both are physicians and Abram is a professor at a medical school where Carlotta was his pupil. Both are very much in love, but problems persist. How will Carlotta, who has formally converted to Judaism, ultimately find acceptance by the Jewish community? Will these two ever achieve a "normal" Jewish life?

CARLOTTA

I have been converted to Judaism over ten years. I have lived a good life as a Jewess. My husband and I are happy together. Our young children bring us great joy. They regard themselves as Jews. There has never been any question about that. I have tried faithfully, sincerely, to live a good life as a Jewess. I observe many of the Jewish rituals. I kindle the Sabbath candles and attend Sabbath services with my husband regularly. I work with all possible devotion for Hadassah, the Women's Zionist organization and many other specifically Jewish organizations. Practically all of our friends are Jewish. I do just about everything I can to bring honor to the Jewish name and yet I am unhappy, very unhappy. Why, please tell me, do so many Jewish women, who are far less devoted to Judaism than I, still regard me as a "stranger"? Why do they still ask me: "How does it feel to be married to a Jew?"

I must confess that this disturbs me very much. Will I never *really*

be fully accepted? Despite the fact that I was formally converted, are people always going to remind me that I was not born of Jewish parents? What are they going to do to my children? What effect will they ultimately have on my husband?

Let me tell you about myself and my childhood. I am one of six children. I was born in Brazil and reared in an upper-class Catholic home. My parents were very superior people. My father, now dead, was a man of considerable wealth. My mother was one of the most communally active, charitable, and emancipated women in the country. My family has always been looked up to in our country. In addition to having great business ability, my father was also a political figure of some note.

My family is Catholic. They are in fact, strong Catholics. There are nuns and priests in my family. My mother goes to church every morning. She is, I think, a very religious person. My father was not as religious as my mother. Back home, you see, it was not like here where men go to church on Sunday. Back home it was not stylish for the men to go to church. My mother used to beg my father to go to church and he would go—maybe once a year, or maybe he wouldn't go in ten years, but men didn't think they should go to church. You would never find a man with a prayer book. You certainly never would see the whole family going to church like in this country. It just wasn't considered very manlike for men to go to church. If men went to church regularly, other men would make fun of them.

My mother was a very advanced woman in every way. She was, however, very religious. She was a very brilliant woman who read a lot and knew a great deal about music and art. She was determined that her daughters should have a good university training. She was certainly one of the first in our country to think or to act that way. All of my sisters went to universities. My oldest sister is a lawyer. She was the first woman to go to a university and the first woman to get a degree. She was active in trying to get the right for women to vote. Another sister went to medical school as I did. They are all very talented people and they have made it clear that women are deserving of every right that men have. My parents never objected to our studying medicine. They were unusual, perhaps, but that was their conviction. I have yet another sister who is a concert pianist. She studied with some of the greatest teachers in the world. She came to New York City to study. She also studied in France with Madame Nadia Boulanger. This will, I hope, give you some idea of how advanced my parents were. When I was young, I remember that my mother found a school that was very good, but it was an all-boys school. My mother arranged it so that we girls could go to that school. I still remember how the priest in my home town denounced my mother for permitting us to go to a school with all those wild boys, but that didn't make her change—even though the priest embarrassed her by his public statements.

With all of this liberality, my mother was a good Catholic and a good church woman. When my parents went to church together, they had a front pew. Everybody looked up to them. That is, everyone except the

priest who once delivered a sermon in which he attacked my parents, especially my mother, because he said that women who send their daughters to such and such a school should be excommunicated. Well, this was a terrible shock to my mother. She was a religious person, but she didn't agree with everything the priest did and said.

My mother talked to the Bishop about what the priest said and the Bishop, who was a much smarter man, said, "This is terrible." And he said that the priest was an ignoramus. So she felt better. But all the while my mother was seeing to it that her daughters got the best kind of education whether our priest liked it or not. So much about my mother.

I got my medical degree in Brazil. But I decided that, in order to be a really good doctor, I ought to do postgraduate work and was accepted in a University in New England. It was while I was there that I met Abram. He was one of my teachers. I didn't even know at the time that he was Jewish, but I liked him right away.

The religion of other people did not mean very much to me. Even though I was a Catholic, I always studied other people as if they had no religion. Other people's religion just didn't matter. All the members of my family were the same. I remember that there were a few Jews in the town I came from in Brazil. They were good people. They had their own church, or whatever you call it, and they were nice and friendly. They did not belong to the same clubs my parents belonged to. Jews had their own club. But I never thought about it very much. The Jewish girls of one family attended the same school as I. When the priest came to the school to give us instruction in religion, the Jewish girls would not make a scene about it. They would go to the library or do their homework. They were separate. They and we knew that they should be Jewish and nobody made any fuss about it.

When I came into the medical class and listened to the lecture by the man I later married, I was impressed with him. When I wrote to my mother that I had a Jewish professor, she thought it was a terrible thing. But I didn't really pay much attention at that time. All I knew was that the man was one of my teachers and I admired him very much.

One of my sisters was in the United States when this Jewish professor invited me to go out with him. I talked it over with my sister and she said that she wouldn't go against it. I mean she wouldn't take sides, one way or the other. Since then my sister has married a Catholic lawyer and she now lives in Brazil.

It was about this time that my mother made her annual visit to the United States to visit my sister and me. When she heard about my continuing to go out with this Jewish professor, she became very upset. Later, when my husband-to-be came to lecture in Brazil and paid a visit to my parents, my mother was courteous to him, but very cool. At that time, my marriage to him was still uncertain.

You may notice that I am speaking most about my mother's reactions and saying little about my father. That's because my mother was the "strong one" in our family. She had definite ideas on many subjects. She was the

religious one. My father had made much money and was respected. We girls all loved him very much, but it was always my mother's ideas that were followed in our family. Things were the way she said. It was she who was most determined to give her daughters a very superior education and have us work in fields where only men had been before—like my studying to be a doctor, for example. So, if I talk about my mother most, it's because of the influence she had on us and, let me say, too, on our home community. She was a dynamic, cultured, dominant person. She wanted to preserve her ideas. My husband feels that it wasn't always that she felt that her ideas were absolutely the best, but rather because they were *her* ideas. She couldn't very easily change her mind because her ego was involved—not because some particular value or set of values was involved.

My mother was a good Catholic, not just because Catholicism was absolutely the best, but rather because it was good enough for her parents and her grandparents. So, even if she deviated from some Catholic practice it was, I think, not associated with any change in her thinking. She still felt that she was observing the religion of her parents even though, in certain respects, she moved far away from it. But she had a fierce pride. Catholicism was hers and she interpreted it to suit her pattern of thought.

My father was a very quiet person. He didn't like to get involved in things if he could avoid it. He had some strong reactions to some things. But when it came to my marriage later on, all he said to me was, "You do what's best for you. If you love the man, that's all that matters!" My father was very devoted to us girls. He came from a long line of fine Spanish people. He had become quite wealthy. Later, he lost it all. But my mother took hold and made enough money to see to it that her daughters went to colleges. I always feel that I really never got to know my father as well as I should. This is one of the great regrets of my life.

To get back to the main theme, I must say that it wasn't easy to make a decision as to what to do about marrying Abram. He was such a wonderful man. It wasn't just that I admired him. I loved him. I was sure of that. The more I saw him, the more convinced I was that he was the man for me. I knew that his religion was going to be a problem and I was not unmindful of my mother, who had some very definite ideas on the subject of religion. I had considered myself a good Catholic. But when it came to a matter of love, I felt that it was more important that I marry the man whom I love so very much. That's why I decided to convert to Judaism. If I loved Abram enough, it was important that I be the kind of Jewess who would make him happy in every way. And that's why I have formally converted to Judaism. I have tried to live up to his standards all the while. My mother had a hard time of it, but she finally accepted my decision. I simply wasn't going to change, and she knew it. So she accepted the fact that I was going to convert to Judaism. I think that I studied and prepared myself very faithfully. I did everything the rabbi asked me to do and I did it wholeheartedly. I was really in love with Abram and I still am. I have tried to live a good Jewish life. I have broken off every connection with Catholicism. My mother has accepted the fact that this is my choice and

there are no arguments from her. My sisters had an even harder time of it, but they accepted Abram and, really, they like him very much. My only problem is that after all these years, when I have tried so very hard to live a good Jewish life—and, I think, live it better than many Jews I know—some Jewish women who do not observe much, if anything, Jewishly still regard me as a Catholic. How long is this going to continue?

I won't have any objection whoever my children may decide to marry. Today they are young and they are reared as Jews. But if they decide to marry a Protestant or Catholic, I won't interfere. That's their concern. I think that I have done the right thing. I married a Jew. I gave up my own religion, and I'm glad that I did what I did. All that disturbs me, makes me unhappy, has nothing to do with Abram. It has only to do with these women I work with in the Jewish community. Why do they persist in making me feel that I am an outsider? That I don't really belong?

When I told my mother that I was determined to marry Abram, a Jew, I thought she would die right at that moment. But I have discovered that people have more sense than we give them credit for. Suddenly my mother realized that she could not live my life for me, that I had to do what I thought was right—and she understood. That was all the problem I have had with my mother. Maybe she is unhappy, but she really doesn't show it. She is a great woman. She knows what it means to be in love and she respects me because I am in love. But it's more than love. I am a Jew and I want to be a Jew. I remember when I was at home in Brazil that whenever our family got together we would never talk about Catholicism. But whenever Jewish people get together they talk about Judaism. I can understand that because being part of a people is so important. The Jews are really strange. They are a people and a religion all in one.

What annoys me so much to this day is to hear my little boy ask my friends who come to the house: "Are you Catholic? Are you Jewish?" I don't even know where he learned about Catholicism. But he seems to know that I was not born a Jewess. Please tell me what to do about him!

I gave up Catholicism because of Abram. But as I think about it, I was ready to give up Catholicism because I really no longer believed in it. I wanted to find a way of life, a theology, in which I could believe and that proved to be Judaism. This is what is so disturbing. When are these Jewish women, who know far less about Judaism than I, going to stop looking down on me and accept me as a Jewess? That is what I am and what I hope to be all the rest of my days. Yet, when I did a really good job for Hadassah, what do you think the women said: "Isn't it wonderful? Carlotta is not a Jew and she did such a big job." To them, I'm still not a Jew.

ABRAM

I occupy an important medical teaching post in one of the great medical schools here in the East. As a doctor, I have acquired a good reputation

for which, I must confess, I have worked very hard. I have loved medicine all these years and with God's help, I have done well. I am consulted on cases from all over the country. I have been teaching for many years and, I must say, I wouldn't trade my life with anyone. That's how really happy I am in my work.

I was born in Philadelphia. I was the oldest of two boys. My family are plain hard-working people. My father is a civil-service employee. He has been on his special job for many, many years. My brother is a doctor, too. He is considerably younger than I. We have always gotten along well. And we both get on fine with our parents.

My folks are not especially religious Jews. They go to the synagogue only on the High Holy Days. My mother keeps a kosher home, but she does eat out—and not always kosher food. She certainly regards herself as Jewish, however, and the same is true of my father. In fact, I think that they would be insulted if anybody raised any questions on this score. They even call themselves "orthodox."

I used to go to a Hebrew School when I was a youngster. Of course, I attended the public elementary school and high school not too far from our rented apartment. My folks were always concerned about our getting the best of education. They lived for us boys. There was absolutely nothing we could possibly have needed or wanted that my mother and father wouldn't get for us. No sacrifice was too great.

My parents were both born in Europe. My father's people were manual laborers, not educated Jewishly or secularly. He was and is a good man. About the time he married my mother, he was trying to learn the plumber's trade and then, when he saw that things weren't going too well, he got a job with the government—a civil-service job and he has been on that all these years.

I believe that it was my mother even more than my father who had the great ambition for her boys. She was anxious for us to become doctors. Perhaps my father, more realistically, was aware that all this kind of training required money—the kind and amount he just didn't have. But we boys used to work on Saturdays and earn money at odd jobs all the time. We would put the money away to be used for our education. In our family "education" meant "to become a doctor." As I look back over those years, I realize the errands we used to run, the flowers and vegetables we used to deliver. My father wouldn't take a cent from us boys. Everything was for "education."

I went to college in Philadelphia and worked at some job all through my college years. With many boys this is not unusual and we certainly didn't regard it as unusual in any respect. When I graduated from college, it was in the very depth of the depression, but I had managed to get a good job and it paid very well. I happened to be good in laboratory work and one of the professors gave me a job helping him. I held another job, too, helping a man buy his produce for the vegetable market. I would go to the market for it at 2 A.M. and I would help him distribute it. Then I would go home, take a cat nap and go back to the lab to work. In this way I saved

enough to make it possible for me to get along when I had an internship in one of the better hospitals.

My parents were very much alike in their concern for us boys. But my father was the realist. He was always concerned with where the money would come from for our education. But my mother just took it for granted that, somehow, the money would be there when we needed it. But an education we *must* have!

In another way, too, my parents were quite different from each other. Take the question of intermarriage. Now my father had made up his mind on this subject. He had once told us how he felt about it. He was plainly and simply against it. To him, there was only one way to deal with this subject. Once, he talked to me about it and his whole philosophy can be summed up in one word: "Don't!" As for my mother, such things as intermarriage could happen to other people's sons, but *never* to hers. I'll wager that the thought never entered her mind that I might ever intermarry. She would not believe it possible for her boys to do anything like that.

During my years in medical school, I was doing very well. I devoted every single waking hour to my work. I was soon recognized as a good doctor. And all the while I was earning my medical degree, I went out with a girl on but a few occasions. You can't imagine how important it was for me to do well in my chosen field. My whole life was tied up with it. I became a good enough doctor for an important medical school to offer me an assistant professorship shortly after I was graduated. Of course, I was thrilled. That was a great moment in my life. But if you think it was a great moment for me, you should have seen my folks at that time. It was the greatest thing that had ever happened to them. I couldn't have done anything greater, if I had become President of the United States. Both my father and mother were so thrilled, so happy. So you will understand why it is important that I tell you about their reaction. At that time, I had attained such a position that in their eyes I couldn't possibly do anything wrong. Whatever I wanted was good. Whatever I said was right. And that was the way they looked up to me all these years!

I guess they believed that I was going to remain a bachelor because I never wrote them about going out with girls and they never heard from anyone that I was going out. It was one of those situations where parents wait to hear. Maybe they expected that someday I would marry some wealthy man's daughter and all would be fine. They were content to see me to the top in the medical teaching profession. That was all they wanted.

When Carlotta came to our medical school as a postgraduate student and we were attracted to each other, it was as much a surprise to me as to anyone. She was a brilliant student, and why she accepted my advances, I don't know. I am older than she is. We had such utterly different backgrounds, and our religions were different, to name but a few of the things that really separated us. But we began going out on occasion. And it wasn't long before we found ourselves enjoying each other's company so much. We had wonderful times together.

My mother had heard that I was going out with a Brazilian Catholic

girl. My brother, it seems, told her about it. But her letters to me never mentioned it. I still cannot understand how she managed to avoid mentioning the possibility of my intermarriage when I know that it must have been very important to her. I guess her love for me was really very great and I know that she was concerned about my happiness. Yet she was a proud Jewess and it must have hurt her very much.

You won't believe this, I'm sure, but it hurt me, too. I could never imagine that I would marry a non-Jewess and, of all people, a Catholic. I was essentially a religious person, a religious Jew. I knew I was a Jew and I wanted to be a Jew. Even though I was single, I had become a member of a Synagogue and I was rather active in its program. I used to go to services on Friday nights very often.

It all meant a great deal to me. And Carlotta was also a very religious person. She attended church every Sunday. She was a devoted Catholic. And what's more, I respected that in her and used to drive her to church every Sunday morning.

Once I came home to spend a few days with my parents. They were delighted to see me and made such a fuss over me. I was the "Professor." I'm sure that my visit at that time meant a lot to them. I had already heard, through my brother, that my parents knew about my romance with Carlotta, but neither of them said anything about it. Oh, yes, only once do I recall that my mother hinted at it in much the same way that a parent says to a small child going out into stormy weather: "Don't forget to put on your rubbers." All my mother once said is *"Mine Kind* (my child), I'm sure you'll think twice before you marry a non-Jew." And that was all. It was a passing comment and no more. But she didn't have to say more. It had its effect.

Now I was a Jew. I was an active Jew, a positive Jew. I was active in the Jewish Federation. I was the Chairman of a B'nai B'rith Lodge. I was active in the Brotherhood of my Synagogue. I was always identified with Judaism and the Jewish people. All the students at the medical school knew me as a Jew. I actively helped Jewish students who came to me because I was Jewish. Here we were—two people of different religions, more and more in love all the time. We were talking all the time about our differences —Carlotta and I. What would happen if we had children? What should we do about ourselves? Should we convert? Should I go to Brazil and convert there? What? I even went to Brazil to see if I could somehow feel that I should convert to Catholicism. And after all the inner conflict I had with myself, I decided that the only real answer was for Carlotta to convert to Judaism. I simply could not give up my Jewishness. I knew that it would come pretty close to killing me to do so. When, after many months of discussion, we both agreed on this, Carlotta went to the rabbi with me and told him how we felt. The rabbi was understanding and, after months of instruction, Carlotta accepted Judaism and was converted to it.

Carlotta and I have been very happy together. I think that she is a good Jewess. We have two lovely children. They are being reared as Jews, of course. Carlotta lights the Sabbath candles and I make the Kiddush each

Sabbath Eve. We go to synagogue services regularly. I am still a member of the same Synagogue. And no one has ever said anything to me about our marriage. I think that our marriage has succeeded very well.

What would I do if my children decided to marry a non-Jew? After all that I have told you, you must realize how difficult it is for me to answer that question. I'm sure that I made my own parents unhappy and yet I know that I did the right thing. So I may not be happy if my children marry outside of our faith and yet I can understand it.

I think that whatever the kind of marriage, the parents ought to be of the same faith. This is essential. If my son falls in love with a Protestant, I hope that the girl he loves will convert to Judaism because, in my opinion, Judaism is really the best religion. I cannot imagine my children marrying someone who retains his or her own faith. It would be bad not only for them but for their children as well. I hope that my son will want, above all else, to learn. I hope that my son will marry a person who loves him. And I have observed that this isn't the rule in marriage. I hope that whatever the religion, there will be one religion in the family, not two.

I don't know how my children are going to react when, as they grow up, they realize that I, a Jew, married a Catholic. Maybe they will realize how much we love each other to make this sacrifice. Maybe they will not realize it and think only that their mother has made life more difficult for them by marrying a Jew. I don't know just what they will think. But I think that I have done the right thing. I have always been a Jew and a very strong Jew. I couldn't think of being anything other than a Jew.

MAUREEN AND JACOB

Maureen O'Brien Weinstein, a Californian, of Catholic-Protestant parentage, but herself unaffiliated with any church, fell in love with Jack Polster. Not until three years after their marriage did she realize that her husband was a Jew. Prior to their marriage, neither had identified with any Church or Synagogue. Following the birth of a daughter and the return of both parents and child to the East Coast, where warm relations were established with the husband's family, Maureen decided that whatever her husband's ideas might be on the subject, their daughter should be identified as a Jewess. Accordingly, Sunday school and a Jewish temple affiliation were sought. Shortly thereafter Maureen was formally converted to Judaism. Her husband's sudden death did not change Maureen's attitude toward her identification as a Jew.

Now, almost three years later, she has remarried—and this husband, too, is a Jew.

But Maureen is troubled about how genuinely her daughter will feel the need for identification—and particularly with Jews. "Above all else," she says, "I want a united family front. There should be but one and the *same* religious identification in a family."

MAUREEN

I am a San Franciscan. I was born and raised out in California. My father was Irish Catholic and my mother was a Protestant. So you see, I am the product of a real mixed marriage. I have seen so much heartache and conflict caused by a difference in religion in my parents' home that, long ago, I made up my mind that this would not happen to me if I could help it.

My folks met and married out in San Francisco. My mother's family is pre-Revolutionary War American. My father was a second generation Irish Catholic. My mother's family had come from Maine in the 1860's. They were liberal Baptists. There were three or four Baptist ministers in the family, back East. My parents were married in the Catholic faith. Mother was *not* converted to Catholicism, but she promised to bring up the children as Catholics, which she had to do in order to be married by the priest. However, my mother later decided that she was *not* going to rear her children in that faith. Something must have happened in my parents' relationship to cause this change. But whatever it was, we children were reared as Unitarians. My younger brother was reared as was I, but when later, in his early manhood, he decided to become a Lutheran, he just went ahead on his own. He is a fairly ritualistic and observant Lutheran. His wife was born a Polish Catholic, but she was converted to Lutheranism. I don't think there were any major principles involved. They lived in Iowa at the time and, I believe, it was then merely a matter of environment. The young people whom they knew were predominantly Lutherans and they joined that church.

To get back to my childhood days, my mother's decision to have us children raised as Protestants wasn't readily accepted by my father and his parents. In fact, there was heavy, very heavy objection. So much so, that my mother tried to appease father and his family by sending me to a Catholic school, which I attended in the seventh and eighth grades. To this day my father's family keeps this thing very much alive. Whenever they see my mother or me or my brother, the matter of why we are not Roman Catholics becomes a major issue. But we have no real ties with my father's family whatsoever. It didn't even matter to them when they knew that I was married to a Jewish man. They chose to ignore that fact. They still felt that I belonged to them and that I should formally become a Catholic.

I'm sure you will want to know something about my interests—what they were and what they are now. First of all, after the usual high-school education, I matriculated at the University of California at Berkeley and got my Bachelor's degree there. I was a sociology major. I also took advertising courses. And the next thing you know, I found myself working in the advertising business for many years, beginning almost immediately after my college years.

That's when I met my first husband. He had been in the advertising business and we became good friends in a short time. We decided to get married in a civil ceremony in San Francisco. You see, neither one of us gave much thought to religious affiliation. This will surprise you, I know, but it is an absolute fact that I didn't know that Jack was Jewish. I had never thought to ask him and I just didn't know until three years after we were married. You see, Jack had no association with the Jewish community —absolutely none. We knew lots of Jews, but we knew lots of other people as well. Jack had originally come from the East. I knew none of his family. He was only eighteen when he left Portland and he was out of touch with his family. At that point, I wasn't even a practicing Unitarian, so the question of religion simply never arose. It's only now, upon reflection, that I realize how many Jews we knew, but no one of us ever thought or talked about religion.

Perhaps part of this lack of interest in religion was due to the environment itself—San Francisco is such a cosmopolitan city—and the fact that we were in the advertising business where you see and meet all kinds of people and think nothing of it.

About three years after our marriage, World War II broke out and San Francisco became a port of embarkation. All of a sudden, out of his past, there came friends of my husband and of the family from the East Coast— all of whom were shipping overseas. I shall never forget that day when he told me that a relative of his was coming to San Francisco on his way overseas and he asked me to join them at lunch. Somehow, Jack picked the moment before we met this young fellow to say: "I have something to tell you—I'm Jewish!" I don't think that it was ever a case of Jack denying his Jewishness. It was rather that he had found himself separated from his family and from his tradition and he simply felt no reason to identify with it. Then came the war and this sudden appearance of his Jewish past in the person of friends and family.

Even the Nazi picture hadn't made him think in terms of identification as a Jew. He had been naturally, like all human, civilized beings, extremely resentful of the whole Nazi picture, but no more so than when other liberal friends were so concerned with the Spanish Civil War.

Now, Jack's telling me that he was Jewish came as a surprise, but I wasn't shocked, upset, disturbed, or anything else. I knew Jews—fine, intelligent ones. I didn't know that any of my Jewish friends lived in a ghetto or anything else that would make me think twice. San Francisco is a very free and liberal town.

Not long after Jack told me that he was Jewish, our daughter Marg

was born. Well, I can't explain what it was that happened to me, but I rather felt that Jack and I ought to go East to visit his family. I think I was moved by the idea that it was about time to have my daughter come to know her father's family. I think, too, I wanted to meet them and show them our child. Well, Jack was ready for it and agreed very quickly. I'm happy to say that, just as I liked Jack's family, so they seemed to like us. Because these were war years and it was so difficult to get across the country again, and because we both liked the East, we stayed on.

Jack's family had always been identified with the Jewish community. They were not religious Jews in the sense that there was much ritual and ceremony in their religious life, but they did belong to a Reform Jewish Temple. And I remember going to temple with the family on the High Holy Days. We also attended the family Seder on Passover. It was a nice feeling to be close to the family even though they took me in "with reservations." Up to that time, I had not really thought about joining a Temple or even converting formally to Judaism. Margie, our daughter, was then going to nursery school. One day she came home in tears because "everyone had a Jewish holiday but Margie." That's when I remember saying to Jack, "This is the time when we have to join a Temple." Now, you may have noticed that all this while, Jack was saying nothing at all about religious affiliation of any kind. He had a good job in the advertising business. I, too, had gotten a fine position. But Jack wasn't a religious man. He had rediscovered his family and his background but not his religion—and he never did. I suggested different Temples and in each case Jack had some reason for not wanting to join. Finally I said, "Let's join Temple B'nai B'rith because that's where the rest of the family belongs and Margie can then go to Sunday school there." Well, he accepted that idea, and we joined. I'm not very much given to following ritual. I never was. But we observed certain of the Jewish holidays, and we lit the Hannukah candles. We did the things which you do for a child. However, I did not really "do" a Sabbath dinner or the more conventional things that go on in a Jewish home.

Now all this while, I was learning something that was very important. I decided that everything that would help my daughter to feel more at home—identified with the Jewish people and her family—was what I wanted to do. I saw her go through those stages where she was very happy in her Sunday school and at other times very unhappy. I was more concerned than many Jewish parents because I knew that I wasn't Jewish and that her father, even though he was born into a Jewish family, wasn't really identified with the Jewish religion. So I felt I had to work harder at this whole business of being a Jew. I didn't want my daughter to be a marginal person. I joined some evening study classes at the Temple. I wanted to learn more about Judaism than I knew till then and, quite frankly, I worked at it. Now this year Margie is going to be confirmed and I feel that this really is a religious experience for her as it surely is for me.

Jack died about five years ago. That was hard for me to take, you may

be sure. We were happy together. We made a good team. There was now the question of what I would do. I had my work, so there was no worry about that. But just because I could now give up the relationship I was developing with Jews, and, I think, because some people really expected me to drop everything and declare myself a Unitarian, I wanted to make my attitude very clear. I decided that this was the time for me to be formally converted to Judaism. I thought it was right for me and especially right for Marg. I thought I could help her to know that there was no uncertainty or equivocation insofar as I was concerned. She was going to a very good private school, but there were very few Jewish girls there. You see, she could have turned either way.

When I asked the rabbi about the preparation for conversion, he was kind enough to say that he knew me well enough to believe that I would not require a long period of study because I had already been attending adult Jewish education classes and generally conducting myself as a Jewess. I was formally converted with the appropriate Reform ceremony. But now, even though many Jewish people know that I have been converted, they still seem to think that I am not a Jewess. About that kind of attitude, I must confess, I am quite unhappy. But I know and the rabbi knows that I am now a Jewess. I even have a new Hebrew name, Ruth, to prove it. Ruth was the Moabite who, according to the Bible, was a righteous convert to Judaism, and I feel honored to have this Hebrew name. What's more, I feel that this has helped my daughter to find herself. She had needed the steadying influence.

I think a united front in the matter of religion in a family is not only desirable but necessary if there is ever going to be real stability in the home. The "going" is too difficult when there is a divided home. All I need to do is to remember my childhood and the dreadful scenes I witnessed because in our case there was a divided home. Religious conflict is dreadful. I didn't want a recurrence of that at any time. My father was a devout Catholic. His loss was truly great because his children weren't raised as Catholics. I have always wanted stability and certainty. When I came East, I found acceptance by Jack's family and by the community. They are solid, good people. I made friends and they became important to me. They deserved the loyalty that I could show them by—well—saying that I wanted to be like them and that included their religion, too.

There is one other fact in my life that I would like to talk about. Just a short time ago, I got married again—and this time it is also to a fine Jewish gentleman. So, you see, this way, too, I have made it perfectly clear how I want to identify myself. Marg is living with us, of course. And it's good for her to have this good influence in her life. I have tried to make it clear to my husband that our home is definitely going to be Jewish. I have put a *Mezzuzah* on the door-post of our house because the *Mezzuzah* is the outward sign of a Jewish home, so the rabbi told me. I want my husband and Marg to see it and to understand why it is there. To me it is a way of identifying myself and my family with the Jewish people.

Margie has Jewish friends, but she also has many non-Jewish friends. She is not finding it as difficult these days to be a Jewess as she did some years ago.

Your question as to what advice I would give my daughter if she were to meet and fall in love with a non-Jewish boy, interests me. Frankly, I would accept anyone except a Catholic boy. Yes, I know. You're going to remind me that my father was a Catholic. Maybe that's why I feel as I do. I would not be fearful about any intermarriage if it were with a Protestant or any non-Catholic. In our family we have an Episcopal-Jewish marriage which has gone Episcopalian. There is also a Christian Science-Jewish marriage. The wife is a Christian Scientist; the child and father have nothing. I have a friendship with two people, the man, a Catholic and the girl, Jewish. The girl converted to Catholicism. I've been around enough, met people in many different walks of life and classes, to feel that if there is to be a marriage between people of different religious backgrounds, one—whoever it may be who is the weaker in loyalty—should convert to the faith of the other and do so sincerely, otherwise the intermarriage should not take place. It is better for two people to start with, let us say, nothing—I mean that neither one is religious. That kind of a marriage is better, than for one to be religious and the other one not be religious. The trouble with my mother's religion was that it wasn't strong enough. She only found her strength after her marriage and after she had made a pledge to raise us as Catholics. No wonder my father was so hurt. But in his case, he really believed that none of us could be "saved" except through the Church, *his* church, and this attitude caused even deeper resentment.

I've still got my fingers crossed about my daughter. I only hope that I have done enough to date, by example especially, to have her follow a course, when the time comes for her to get married, that will make her see how important it is for the members of a family to be united in religion as in all other things. But, as I have said, I still don't know which way she will turn. Marg still seems undecided, despite her Jewish confirmation. Her affiliation at this point is still not clear and unequivocal. Anything may happen and I suppose, it will!

INTERFAITH MARRIAGES

Dear Dad:

I am aware of and believe I understand the difficult situation I have created by my decision to marry Jim. I am writing to you because I want you to understand several things. Although I have tried very hard to control myself when I am with you and therefore may have appeared not to care how you feel or what you think and say, it upsets & hurts me very much that I am hurting you so greatly. I want you to understand that Jim and I love each other very much, that we have considered very carefully and I feel that we understand the responsibilities & difficulties involved in marriage to someone of a different religion.

We have known each other for three years; we know that we are not just infatuated with each other. We know that we have similar views on the basic and most important issues we will have to face in marriage. We want very, very much to make each other happy, and we sincerely believe that our characters and ideas are such that we can do so. We want, too, more than I can express, to make you and Mother happy, also. We hope and pray that you can come to comprehend why we are getting married, that we can show you that our decision has not been based on unfounded beliefs, and that time will prove that we made the right decision.

One thing I would like to make particularly clear to you is that by marrying Jim I am not abandoning my religion. I beg you, Dad, to try to believe that Jim will be a good religious person when I marry him, that our home will be a religious home, and that any children we have will be raised in our home in accordance with our faith.

Jim and I both believe that children should be brought up to have a thorough understanding of religion; in order to reach this understanding they must experience and learn about the entire religious tradition. I do not wish to lose either heritage or my family nor does Jim wish to lose his, and I sincerely hope that both of these forces will play important roles in helping us achieve the goals I have stated above.

Jim is an extremely intelligent young man, willing to learn, completely devoted to me (as I am to him), and as anxious and determined as I am that our children be brought up with the kind of background and understanding that will enable them to know who they are and to make wise & intelligent decisions about their own lives. Because he is willing to learn and because I have a good religious background, I believe that I can teach him a great deal.

I also believe that you and Mother could be a most helpful example to us and that Jim could learn a great deal from you also, if only you can bring yourself to believe that he really wants to consider himself as a Catholic. I cannot beg you enough to please, please try to understand what a great help you could be to us.

Please believe me, Dad, when I say that I am terribly sorry and

most upset that I am causing you & Mother such pain. I only hope that in the future I can show you how sincerely I mean all these things I am saying and that we will not have to lose each other but rather you will gain a son who will be a good Catholic husband and father.

Love,
Dora

This letter, altered only to preserve the anonymity of the writer, will help us to understand the nature of the problems that interfaith marriages often present. The anguish and heartache that caused a lovely young lady to write such a letter as well as the utter dejection and opposition of loving and loved parents, are apparent in this single letter.

According to the United States Census[1] study of religion (1957) 8.6 per cent of all Protestants were married to persons of other religions, 21.6 per cent of all Catholics and 7.2 per cent of all Jews were intermarried. This study, however, is far from adequate and does not, either statistically or psychologically begin to tell the full story.

Heiss,[2] in 1960, on the basis of an area-probability sample in midtown Manhattan (New York), reported that 21 per cent of the Catholic, 34 per cent of the Protestant and 18 per cent of the Jewish marriages involved a person of another religion. Although intermarriages involving Catholics, Protestants and Jews will be specifically discussed in succeeding chapters, the degree of intermarriages that currently take place in the United States ought to be recorded at this point in order that the nature of the problem should be correctly understood.

The frequency of interfaith marriage is attested by the following facts:

The Roman Catholic Church has reported that over 27 per cent of all marriages involving Catholics in 1961 were interfaith marriages.[3]

Studying the intermarriage patterns of 51,671 families distributed in thirty Catholic parishes in a large urban population, Thomas[4] found that by 1955 the percentage of mixed marriages had increased considerably in the middle and upper classes. Whereas the per cent of such marriages found in these parishes at the time of the study was 8.5 per cent in the "lower" class and 9.1 per cent in the "mixed lower and middle" class, the per cent of mixed marriages jumped to 12 per cent for the "middle" class, 16.3 per cent for the "mixed middle and upper" class, 17.9 per cent for the "upper" class and 19.3 per cent for the "suburban" class.

In 1953 the state of Iowa began to use statistical forms for the report of the religious denomination of the applicants for marriage licenses as well as for divorces. Two years later, in 1955, Chancellor and Monahan, reported on the information they had been able to glean

from these new forms. They concluded that, in 1953, 42 per cent of all marriages involving a Catholic were mixed. Most Protestants in that state in the same year seemed to marry Protestants. Ninety-two per cent of the husbands were Protestants while 91 per cent of the wives were Protestants. The large percentage of Catholic intermarriage may be due to the fact that the percentage of Catholics in proportion to the total population of the state is not high. The number of intermarriages increases when the percentage of Catholics in a given community is small in relation to the total population.

The Iowa study indicated further, that there were about twice as many divorces among Catholics married to non-Catholics as there were in families where both husband and wife were Catholic. The high percentage of divorce in this case supports the theory that divorce is more likely when two faiths are involved in a marriage.

Goode,[5] in a study of divorced women in Detroit, found that persons of different religions seemed to be more prone to instability in marriage than were persons of the same religious faiths. He speaks of religion as a contributing factor in these divorces.

Inasmuch as there are no federal government statistics on this subject for marriages involving Jews, we can only point out that the number of such intermarriages varies greatly in different parts of the nation. Although it was generally believed that the rate ran from approximately 7 per cent (New Haven) to as high as 34 per cent (Marin County, California), we now know that in the period of 1953-1959, in the State of Iowa, 42.2 per cent of all the marriages involving Jews were intermarriages.

Eric Rosenthal reminds us in the *American Jewish Year Book, 1963* (p. 51) that while the rate of Jewish intermarriage in the cities of Iowa with a population of 10,000 and over was 34.2 per cent, it was almost twice as high in the towns and rural areas of that state. In the towns the rate of intermarriage involving Jews was 64.1 per cent and in the rural areas it was 67 per cent.

Insofar as the 250 Protestant denominations are concerned, we can only point out that many Protestant denominations are gravely concerned with the subject of interfaith marriage, particularly insofar as Protestant-Catholic marriages are concerned. (*See* Chapter 5.) Inasmuch as most of the Catholic intermarriages involve Protestants as well, interfaith marriage is certainly an important problem to Protestants as it is to Catholics and Jews.

Interfaith marriages are comparatively recent in our society. The Roman Emperor Constantine prohibited intermarriage between Jews and Christians in A.D. 339. Such marriages were, in fact, in A.D. 388

declared to be adulterous. Opposition to interfaith marriages has continued throughout the centuries. On occasion it has also included marriage between various denominations among Protestants.

Religious intermarriages were first recognized and permitted only after the separation of church and state occurred in certain European countries in the eighteenth century. There were, nevertheless, strong protests from the churches in those lands. Even though interfaith marriages were then permitted, many questions remained unresolved. In 1825, the Prussian government decreed that all children who were born of interfaith marriages should be reared in the religion of the father or, at least, in the religion the father chose for his children.

It was also forbidden for a priest to exact any promise from parties to an interfaith marriage regarding the religious affiliation of any child born of such a marriage. This resulted in a major controversy between the government and the Bishop of the Rhine province and of Westphalia.

A law similar in many respects to that of the Prussians was passed by the Austrians in 1868. In Czarist Russia, as well as in the former Austrian Empire, intermarriages between Jews and Christians were not permitted to take place unless the Jew was first baptized.

In Poland control of such marriages continued until 1940. Intermarriage between Catholics and Protestants was also controlled. The male children born of such marriages were to follow the religion of the father while the female children were legally obliged to follow the religion of the mother. Lithuania and Yugoslavia, like Poland, prohibited religious intermarriage prior to World War II.

Although the reasons may have changed, there is still organized Church and Synagogue opposition to interfaith marriage. That opposition expresses itself through individuals, families and churches alike.

In his Detroit study, Lenski[6] has pointed out that among white Protestant laymen 75 per cent favored marriage with their own "kind," while 93 per cent of the clergy favored them. Among Catholics, 31 per cent of the laity supported the view that close friendships should be restricted to one's own group while 53 per cent of the clergy supported this view.

Despite the accusations directed against religious leaders of the three major faiths for their negative attitudes toward intermarriage, it is important to note that their opposition is, I believe, not based solely on their desire to perpetuate their own religious group for selfish reasons. Their contention is that marriage between persons of different faiths appears to have less chance of being happy or successful. This view is indirectly supported by a recent Landis study[7] which indicates that the distance of the children from their parents in any given family

appears to depend upon the success or failure of the parents' marriage. The happier the marriage and the fewer the number of divorces within a group, the more closely identified are the children with their parents and with their parents' religion. This holds for Jewish, Catholic and Protestant families. In this study Landis found that Jewish children were the closest to their parents, with Catholics next and Protestants in third place. But all three were, in fact, "close" to their parents. A further and more exact interpretation of the study led Landis to conclude that the degree of devoutness of the parents and their religiosity, had a positive correlation to the degree of closeness of children to their parents.[8]

This study indicates too that "there is a higher conception of self associated with growing up in a devout religious home, especially for females." [9] The children of religious parents tend to be more devout than are the children of parents who are indifferent to religion.

The degree of family religiousness, according to the same author, appeared to be closely associated with the attitude of children insofar as their willingness or unwillingness to marry a person of a different faith is concerned.[10] In the Jewish group, which had the least number of females who would intermarry, only 12 per cent of those who came from devout families would intermarry, while in Jewish families that were indifferent to religion the percentage rose to 60. Jewish males were more ready to intermarry than Jewish females. In the case of devout Catholic families, 69 per cent of the females expressed a willingness to intermarry, while 77 per cent of the females from "indifferent" families expressed that willingness. Seventy-two per cent of all the Catholics declared that they would marry outside their faith, but only 13 per cent of the Catholic females and 7 per cent of the Catholic males expressed a willingness to change their faiths.[11]

A fifteen-year survey conducted by Notre Dame University tells us very clearly what happens to religious beliefs of people when they are married to persons of the same religion and when they enter into mixed marriages:

> If both parents are Catholic, 92 out of 100 persons cling to some religious faith (not necessarily Catholic) when they grow up.
> If both parents are Protestant, 68 out of 100 hold to some religious faith. If, however, it is a mixed marriage (Catholic-Protestant) the evidence indicates that only 34 out of 100 retained a religious belief.

Marriage between persons of different faiths apparently weakens the ultimate religious beliefs of such persons. What such marriages may do to the religious beliefs of the children of these mixed marriages must be even more startling.

Elmer's[12] studies lead him also to believe that, when people of different religious groups marry, religious interest fades and often is lost. He concludes that "if a child marries one who is of the same religion as either parent was originally, it strengthens that religious preference. If a child of a mixed marriage marries one with a strong religious belief, that child will turn to that group. If a child marries a person of about the same religious indifference, he or she will tend to affiliate with whatever group is predominant in their social group or area."

Church and Synagogue, representing the religious traditions of society, believe that the moral and ethical traditions taught and upheld by them through the centuries should be preserved and further enhanced by married couples. Believing in the value of the religious way of life, they expect those who identify with religion to strengthen that way of life. They fear intermarriage because they believe that the likelihood of failure to adhere to a religion's tradition is thereby increased.

The argument that the Church and Synagogue are selfish, that they are not sufficiently concerned with the personal lives of their congregants and much too concerned with their own survival, is, I believe, hardly fair to organized religion or its institutions, which have a basic purpose. It is, simply put, to serve God to the best of their ability and through their teachings to bring a greater degree of peace and harmony into the lives of men. If the institutions that represent this idea are weakened or destroyed, the opportunities to teach these values are as a consequence reduced as well. Organized religion requires whatever spiritual strength it can legitimately acquire from its adherents. Its insistence upon loyalty to its teachings, it is claimed, is not the result of lack of concern for the individual. Rather, its solicitude for the individual and his peace of mind and soul is so great as to oblige it, like a good parent, to take a definite position with respect to intermarriage, even though it may not always satisfy each and every individual.

Priests, ministers and rabbis are generally well aware of the problems created because, in many cases, Church and Synagogue forbid them to officiate at any mixed marriage (where there has been no conversion or agreement reached). A minority of the members of the clergy (Protestant, Jewish and Unitarian-Universalists) take the stand that they owe a duty to the young people who ask them to officiate at their marriage. They believe that if young people want to be married with benefit of clergy rather than by a civil ceremony the clergyman owes it to them as well as to his Church or Synagogue, to officiate. They argue that children born of such a marriage are likely to become affiliated with a religious institution, because the parents do not look upon religion with unfriendly or cynical eyes. These clergymen insist that they are not

simply providing a "convenience" for such young people or their parents by officiating; that it is, in fact, psychologically sounder for them to officiate than to refuse to do so.

The more traditionally minded clergy, on the other hand, Protestant and Jewish, believe that, such marriages only tend to weaken religion generally and their own denomination in particular. One says:

> It is better to turn such people down even though I may be certain they are very much in love than have them look upon me or the Church as a tool to be used whenever one has a mind to. I represent a certain view of life. I am pledged to preserve that way in sincerity and truth. I cannot give it all up to satisfy these people while I destroy my own religion.

Clergymen report that a considerable number of young people, contemplating mixed marriage, believe that they can resolve family problems associated therewith if they arrange for two separate religious ceremonies, each in accordance with the wishes of their own parents. Salving their own family conscience thereby the couple often has little interest or concern, at the time of the marriage, with either religion. If clergymen will not "lend" themselves to such a procedure, these young people often turn to a church leader whom they regard as a "liberal" —whose religious philosophy is neither clearly Christian nor Jewish. Although the person officiating at such a marriage may be liberal, it is quite likely that the parties to the marriage are, in fact, indifferent to religion and seek only a kind of neutral religion which, in their view, makes no demands upon them.

Often laymen, out of their desire to belong to something they can call their "own," identify with what they regard as "compromise" movements. They believe that Unitarian-Universalist Societies, Ethical Culture Societies, or Community Churches represent such compromises. Unhappy, for whatever reason, with their inability to identify with the religion of a parent, they seek a new direction and a new identification. Unable to identify with the older traditions of parents and family, they seek a different path. In the process of seeking out such identification they often cause misunderstanding and even heartache for parents and family. This may, on occasion, be the price of progress. Often it is the price which a burdened, insecure person pays for his marginality.

The sociologists Zimmerman and Cervantes[13] define a "successful" family as one that (1) avoids family disruption by divorce or desertion, (2) avoids interference by the police and (3) keeps its children in school. They declare that one of the fundamentals in family organization is religion.[14] Its influence upon family behavior was marked. In their sample of over 42,000 families, they found that 15 per cent of

this number were intermarried. On the basis of their definition of the successful family, they declared that "the mixing of faiths within the homes of successful families is much less than the general public's but, nevertheless, is very common." [15] Of particular interest is the observation that there are fewer interfaith marriages among "successful" families than is true for the population as a whole.

Zimmerman and Cervantes, comparing unmixed and mixed marriages with particular respect to divorce and desertion rates in the five cities studied in 1955 found that, in all cases, the rate of divorce and desertion among mixed marriages was higher than the unmixed.

In Boston, in cases where both parties were of Protestant faith they found that the percentage of divorces and desertions was 7.3. However, that rate increased to 11 per cent when the husband was Protestant and the wife was of another religion. In New Orleans, the per cent of divorce and desertion was 11.4 for unmixed Protestant marriages. It increased to 14.6 per cent for marriages involving a Protestant husband and a wife of another faith. In St. Louis, the rate of divorce or separation changed from 9.8 in the case of unmixed Protestant marriages to 18.9 when the husband is Protestant and the wife identified with another religion. In Denver, the rate soared from 5.5 per cent to 17.7 per cent under similar circumstances; while in Omaha, it increased from 6.4 per cent for unmixed Protestant marriages to 16.9 per cent in the case of mixed marriages involving a Protestant husband and a wife of another religion.

The same kind of evidence is cited in the case of Catholic marriages. Where the husband and wife are both Catholic, in Boston, the divorce and desertion rate is 4.3 per cent. When *only* the husband is Catholic the rate increased to 13.5 per cent. In New Orleans, the rate went from 5.1 per cent in the case of unmixed marriages to 13 per cent in mixed marriages where only the husband is Catholic. In St. Louis, the rate changed from 4.2 per cent in the case of unmixed marriages to 12 per cent. In Denver, they indicated that under similar circumstances the rate of desertion and divorce went up for the Catholic group from 6.1 per cent to 15.9 per cent, while in Omaha the rate increased from 3.8 per cent to 16.7 per cent.

Insofar as the Jews in this study were concerned, their statistical evidence is not much different. In Boston, the rate of divorce and desertion where both parties are Jews was 4.7 per cent. It rose, however, to 25.4 per cent where only the husband was Jewish. In New Orleans the rate rose from 33.4 per cent to 57.4 per cent. (In this instance there were only 108 cases involved in the sample, hence the rate of divorce or desertion in this city for unmixed Jewish marriages was unusually high.)

In all cases and in all religions, this study indicates that in interfaith marriages where the religion of the husband is held constant and that of the wife is different, the divorce and desertion rate is considerably higher than that of those persons who are of the same religion.

In the case of those families where husband and wife had no religion, the rates for divorce and desertion were from two to ten times higher than the all-Protestant and all-Catholic rates in the same cities.[16]

Here, again, the evidence indicates that interfaith marriages, if we use divorce and desertion as criteria of judgment concerning the success or failure of marriage, must generally be termed unsuccessful.

Further, Zimmerman and Cervantes[17] reported that of nine thousand mixed marriage cases studied:

(1) "Couples with different religious affiliations have fewer children as compared with those who marry within their own faith.

(2) "These children are less likely to finish high school than those whose parents are of the same faith.

(3) "Six out of every ten children of a Catholic-Protestant marriage end by rejecting all religions.

(4) "About half of the Catholic men who marry outside of their faith abandon their faith.

(5) "The divorce rate of the intermarried is higher than that for those who marry within their own faith. When one of the parties is a Catholic, the divorce rate is three to four times as high; when it is a Protestant, the rate is two to three times as high, and when one of the parties is Jewish, the divorce rate is five or six times as high.

(6) "The teen-age arrest rates for the children of mixed marriages are much higher than is true of the children in families where both parents are of the same faith. In the case of the children of a Catholic married to a non-Catholic, the arrests of teen-age children doubled or tripled. The children of Jewish husbands married to non-Jewish wives in Boston, St. Louis, Denver and Omaha were involved in four to ten times as many arrests as the children of all-Jewish marriages in the same cities. Protestant men who married non-Protestants in St. Louis, Omaha and Denver had children who were involved in twice as many arrests as were the youth in marriages in which both parties were of the same faith."

(7) If a person *without* any religious affiliation married a person who had a religious affiliation, the chances of divorce, desertion, and delinquency are generally twice as high as marriages in which both parties are religiously affiliated.

(8) If a person without a religion marries another person without religious affiliation, the chances for divorce, desertion and delinquency are four times as high as marriages in which there is religious affiliation.

Protestant-Catholic marriages, according to Cervantes,[18] are four times as likely to break up as are marriages in which both parties are Protestants. Most studies of such marriages indicate a divorce rate that is nearly three times higher than marriages in which both parties are of the same religion.

Locke[19] on the other hand, comparing 200 divorced couples with 200 happily married couples in a sample taken from an Indiana County, does *not* believe that religious difference constituted a significant factor in the divorced group.

Mixed marriages, according to the studies of Landis,[20] Weeks,[21] and Bell,[22] are likely to be less stable than marriages between persons of the same faith.

In Bell's[23] Maryland Study of 13,528 families, the divorce and separation rate where both parties are Catholics was 6.4 per cent; where both were Protestants, the rate was 6.8 per cent; where the marriage was mixed, *i.e.*, (Protestant-Catholic) the per cent increased to 15.2. Where neither party "had" a religion the divorce rate rocketed to 16.7 per cent.

Week's[24] Study of Spokane, Washington, indicates that where both parties are Catholic the per cent of divorce was 3.8 per cent, where both are Protestant, 10 per cent. Where there is a mixed marriage (Protestant-Catholic), the divorce and separation rate increased to 17.4 per cent. There is a 23.9-per-cent rate of divorce where neither party identified with a religion.

Landis'[25] study of 4,108 marriages of the parents of students at Michigan State University indicated a divorce rate of 4.4 per cent for all-Catholic marriages; 5.2 per cent for all-Jewish marriages; 6 per cent for all-Protestant; and 14.1 per cent for mixed, Protestant-Catholic marriages, while the rate of 17.9 per cent was reported for cases in which both parties had no religion. In addition, he indicated that 20.6 per cent of the marriages failed when they involved Catholic men and Protestant women.

According to Landis: "Mixed marriages or non-religious marriages have two to six times as many divorces and separations as intra-religious marriages."

In another important study, involving college students, Landis[26] found a close "positive association between religiousness and success in marriage." Being "religious" (and of the same religion) is likely to draw the parties to the marriage together. This, then, is one factor that must be remembered by those persons who contemplate marriage. Landis found, too, that, in his sample, 5.5 per cent of the devout parents, as assessed by their children, were either divorced or separated; 8.9 per cent of the "religious" (apparently moderate in their religious

ideology) and 19.8 per cent of the parents indifferent to religion ended up in divorce or separation. The chances of failure in marriage, as measured by divorce or separation, are, according to Landis,[27] greater when there is no religious preference. He found that 10 per cent of those who were Protestants; 7.7 per cent of Catholics, 3.3 per cent of the Jews and 18.2 per cent of those with "no faith" among the parents of his student sample were either divorced or separated.

He[28] found, too, that the readiness of students to marry a person of another religious group is closely associated with the family religiousness. The atmosphere of the home, including the religiousness of parents, appears to have a direct affect upon the attitude of children insofar as intermarriage is concerned. Indifference to religion was found to be closely associated with willingness to marry outside their faith by 67 per cent of the religiously indifferent female students; 57 per cent of the slightly religious; and 48 per cent of the devoutly religious. Insofar as male students were concerned, the results were not far different. Seventy-one per cent of the "indifferent" males were willing to marry outside their faith while 57 per cent of the "slightly indifferent" and 43 per cent of the devout reported a similar attitude. Jewish females from devout families seemed least willing to marry outside of their faith (12 per cent); 60 per cent of Jewish females from families indifferent to religion were willing to intermarry. Devoutness of parents obviously plays an important role in the prevention of intermarriage even though it may certainly not guarantee such parents that interfaith marriages involving their children will not occur.

Landis[29] has pointed out that "willingness or unwillingness to marry a person of a different religious faith is closely associated with family religiousness. . . . Jews are the least willing to marry outside their faith." This view is supported by my studies as well. However, "religiousness" is not easily definable. In terms of attendance at religious services, for example, Jews generally rate lowest, yet their record of refusal to marry into another faith is greater in degree than Protestants' or Catholics'. (The rate of desertion among Catholics is much higher than that of Protestants or Jews because divorce is prohibited by the Church.) When both parties to the marriage were Protestant, the rate of desertion was 22.9 per cent. It increased to 33.9 per cent when the husband was Protestant and the wife a non-Protestant, and remained at about the same figure (33 per cent) when the wife was Protestant and the husband was a non-Protestant.

Heiss,[30] comparing a sample of 304 persons who had married outside their faith with a sample of 863 persons who married within their faith, reported that among the intermarried (a) the tie to religion was less, (b) there was a greater dissatisfaction with the early relationship

with parents, (c) there was greater strife in the families (parents and children) of the intermarried, (d) there was a lesser degree of early family integration and (e) there was a greater emancipation from parents among the intermarried at the time of the marriage than was true of the intramarried.

Locke[31] reported that, in the case of the "happily married" men of his study, only 1 per cent "frequently or almost always disagreed" with their wives on religious matters, while among the divorced men, 11 per cent frequently or almost always disagreed on religion.

Locke[32] has further pointed out that the frequency of church attendance is positively correlated with the probability of marital adjustment. He declares that "the happily married attended church more frequently than did the divorced" and "that never go to church was without question associated with marital maladjustment." Whether "marital maladjustment" produces the "never go to church" attitudes or vice versa is not clear from this evidence.

The noted author and executive director of the Philadelphia Marriage Council, Dr. Emily H. Mudd,[33] commenting on religious differences among married couples, stated:

> Any difference is potentially a problem in marriage. Differences in religion, though, usually present more of an emotional problem than differences in such matters as age or education. Peoples' attitudes alone determine whether all differences can be resolved or will become acute.

Religious differences seem definitely to add to the problems that a married couple must deal with. There is no absolute way of determining whether the intermarried are emotionally mature enough to be able to cope with such problems. The role which religion plays in our lives is different in the case of each individual. That role may actually become different *after* marriage than it was prior to marriage. These are some of the major difficulties and problems that the intermarried must inevitably face.

Kirkpatrick,[34] in analyzing the "Factors Associated with Marital Adjustment" also suggests that among the premarital factors "roughly in descending order of scientific verification" are the following:

1. Happiness of parents' marriage
2. Adequate length of acquaintance, courtship, and engagement
3. Adequate sex information in childhood
4. Personal happiness in childhood and approval of the marriage by parents and others
5. Engagement adjustment and normal motivating toward marriage
6. Ethnic and religious similarity
7. Higher social and educational status

8. Mature and similar chronological age
9. Harmonious affection with parents during childhood

Among the postmarital factors which Kirkpatrick suggests may influence the success of the marriage is "harmonious companionship based on common interests and accompanied by a favorable attitude toward the marriage and spouse."

"Common interests," which most certainly include religion, are once again pointed out as vital to marital success.

E. W. Burgess and L. S. Cottrell [35] proposed five components that would make for marital success. They are:

(1) Agreements and settlement of disagreements
(2) *Common interests and activities*
(3) Demonstration of affection and confiding
(4) Satisfaction with marriage
(5) Absence of feelings of unhappiness and loneliness

Mixed marriages are by their very nature, divisive. They destroy or weaken the faith and the values that with good reason have been emphasized by organized religion. They often create rather than resolve problems in human relationships.

Young people see no special problem in interdating with persons of another faith because they are convinced that, in their case, intermarriage will certainly never result therefrom. What possible harm can come from friendly social contacts with persons of another faith? Mayer[36] has pointed out that, as a rule, persons who interdate are convinced that they will never intermarry. Indeed, he speaks of many such persons as "reluctants," because they never intended to marry outside their faith.

Parents are often unaware of the romances in which their children are involved. We have found that even when a child hints at an "affair" involving a person of another faith, parents refuse to believe that their child can be serious about it. Hence, little, if anything, is said or done by them. The hope is that if the romance is not disturbed "something will happen to break it up."

Mayer[37] states: "of the sets of parents who had been opposed to the relationship, over 88 per cent were either unaware of its existence initially and/or failed to keep abreast of its future development."

A college professor (Protestant), discussing his daughter's marriage to a Catholic, offers some fascinating comments about the problems that mixed marriage creates, even for liberals:

I was born in a rural, Midwestern community. My father was not interested in religion. He never went to church. My mother was a

believer and a good church-goer. I was reared in a liberal home. I could take religion or leave it alone. But I did belong to a Methodist Church and my wife and I have always maintained our relationship with the Church even though we have had other interests, particularly those associated with the college campus on which I taught for three decades.

When my daughter began going with John who came from one of our town's finest families, neither my wife nor I gave it much thought because we were used to having people of all kinds around. The fact that John was a Catholic didn't mean very much to me at that time. When they got serious about each other though, we *did* have our worries about it because we knew that John's family was very close to the Catholic Church, whatever his own opinions on Catholicism might be. But our daughter's happiness mattered so much to us that we were willing to let her make whatever choice she wished.

John told Mary that he knew that his family expected him to be married as a Catholic and however little he regarded himself as a good Catholic, he felt honor-bound to be married "in the church." This was a difficult decision for Mary to make and you can bet that Mary's mother and I were sick at heart over the whole situation. However liberal we thought we were, we just didn't relish the idea of our daughter converting to Catholicism. Strangely John never asked her to convert. I guess his family's influence must have been considerable for a special dispensation was obtained from the church and Mary and John were married by a Catholic priest in our home. Mary insists that she never made any promises to the priest about how her children would be reared. At any rate, John never attended the Catholic Church nor did Mary. Shortly after their first child was born, they moved to another town, away from both sets of parents. John's parents, particularly his mother, were very unhappy because neither John nor Mary attended the Catholic Church, but they kept on hoping that something would happen to bring both John and Mary to their church. When they moved away from our town, John and Mary made friends with young people who belonged to the Christian Church, which, you know, is Protestant. Before we knew it they joined that church and are still members. I suspect, however, that they are "social" rather than "religious" members even though their two children now attend that Sunday school.

But even though Mary is happy and all seems well, I know that John is still in conflict with himself over the situation. He doesn't want to hurt his father and mother, yet he cannot, in all conscience, remain a Catholic. He has permitted his children to be reared as Protestants, and he wants to be so regarded himself. John's mother is really quite hurt about what has happened to her (and our) grandchildren. I suspect that when she sees John she keeps on reminding him of his "duty," but she is fortunately the kind of woman who will not do anything to make either Mary or John really unhappy if she can help it.

I cannot understand why my wife and I should have been so unhappy when we felt that Mary might convert to Catholicism. After all, we are liberals! But I can understand how unhappy John's parents are because John, Mary and the children are not Roman Catholics and that makes us, too, unhappy for them. I suspect that John and Mary will

never turn back to the Catholic Church. They are strong and good people.

Even in intermarriages such as this where all the persons involved are good people, I'm afraid that someone must get hurt. In this case the direct victims are John's parents. Indirectly, John and the children may suffer.

The evidence points to the following facts:

1. The tensions that result from mixed marriages are produced not only because of religious and cultural differences between the intermarried, but because of their families as well. Inasmuch as no two people, no matter how much in love, live in a vacuum, the ideas, opinions and values of in-laws and family have a direct effect upon them, and that effect under circumstances involving intermarriage is often negative.

2. The problem is not resolved, as some would suspect, by "giving up their religion." Such a process may lead to resentment and recrimination.

3. The children of the intermarried may suffer even more than their parents because the need to identify with some religious group is ignored or denied by the intermarried.

4. Partners in a mixed marriage who believe that by refraining from direct affiliation with any religion their "problem" will be resolved are only fooling themselves. Two "negatives" will not make a "positive."

5. Parties to an interfaith marriage often declare that, if they were left to themselves, they might solve their problem, but there are no isolated islands, physical or mental, and they are not likely to resolve their differences any faster even when they are away from parents and in-laws. We humans are gregarious. We need other humans to complement our lives. It is a serious mistake to believe that there is really any "escape" from our families. Sooner or later we turn to them once again for they are so much a part of each of us.

6. The social obstacles to intermarriage are, indeed, many. There may be religious differences. There may also be class, ethnic, national, or racial differences—all of which are likely to create barriers to a successful marriage. It is easy enough to say that these differences ought not to exist. It is quite another thing to find a society where, in fact, they do not actually exist. Differences like these cannot be wiped out with the wave of a hand. They must in practice be taken into account and dealt with realistically.

The reasons for marital failure may include such matters as differences in social or class background, educational standards and levels, sexual compatibility, personality, the complex of values, alcoholism and a host of other factors. Religious differences, which may be one among

the many sources of conflict, are often assumed to be the major cause for the failure of a marriage to work out successfully. No one can state with any degree of certainty, that religious differences will be the primary cause of marriage failure. Yet differences in religious affiliation often appear to be present in such failures quite frequently. It is, therefore, not wrong, I think, to conclude that this type of difference is much more important than many of us suspect. As long as it remains one of the factors that seem to be closely associated with many marriage failures, it seems proper to call attention to it and to indicate that it plays a role in the failure of many marriages.

VIRGINIA AND PAUL

Virginia, of Polish descent (and now a Congregationalist) is married to Paul, a Jew, who apparently has no strong convictions about Judaism, but who definitely identifies himself as a Jew. Affluent, well-liked and thoughtful upper-middle-class people, these two have been married for twenty years. Although their personal regard for each other was always manifest, in-laws, parents, brothers and sisters have presented major problems that have yet to be completely resolved. Two children, a boy and a girl, react as marginal people generally do. Grave uncertainties concerning their identification with Judaism or Christianity are evident. Solutions for their problems, particularly that of the daughter, have yet to be found—if ever they can be!

PAUL: Virginia and I have been married for almost twenty years. We live just outside of Springfield in a suburban community that we like very much. I am what is generally considered to be "a successful businessman." Over the years, my several brothers and I have done very well. Virginia and I have two children, Joyce, age 16, and Robert, age 18. I little realized when we started going together that there would be quite as many problems for us to solve involving ourselves, our religions, our families, our children and in some sense even the community, but the fact is that, to this date, some twenty years after our marriage, we still have some way to go before we will really overcome them. New ones, particularly with my daughter, now seem to be cropping up.

But first, before I discuss the problems, I will say something about my personal and family background.

My parents were both born in Russia. My father came to this country over sixty years ago. He started off as a peddler and earned enough to

bring my mother and my sister over within just a few years. My brother and I were born here. Neither of my parents received any formal education in this country, but my father had a really good Hebraic background. He could speak four or five languages. He was always a highly respected member of the Jewish community.

Our home was strictly orthodox. My mother was from a family where there were many rabbis and in my father's family, too, there were learned Jews who knew the tradition of the Jewish people intimately. My parents observed the Sabbath all through the years. My mother still does. My father died about thirty years ago in Springfield. They observed the dietary laws within our home and all other ritual that one would expect of good orthodox Jews. I do remember that even though my father was so particular about *kosher* food in his own home, he would eat in other peoples' homes, even in the homes of non-Jews. But the food that he ate was, I believe, never non-*kosher* even then. My mother was all that you can imagine the typical Jewish mother to be. She "looked well to the ways of her household" as Proverbs says. She was and is a good mother. She is well over eighty years old. We all love her very much. My brother and I went into the wholesale grocery business. My father had been in that business. But we have expanded so that today we are in about a half-dozen different businesses. And, I'm happy to say, we have done very well.

My brother and my sister are both married to Jews. There have been no other inter-marriages in our family as far as I know.

VIRGINIA: Now that Paul has started, it's going to be easier for me to talk about my background and our problems. I was born in Springfield. My father, who is Polish, had lived near Philadelphia. Then he and my mother, my sister and brother moved to Springfield. My mother, too, was Polish. She, like my father had been born in Europe, but she was brought here when she was one year old. My father's family came to the United States and to Springfield when he was a very, very young child.

My father's family were originally Roman Catholics. I say "originally" because his parents were sort of "non-practicing" in any church. They just weren't church-going people, but they observed Holy Days, and they believed in religion. Still, from all that I can gather about them they did not regard themselves as Catholics or anything else. I would say that I remember my grandfather as being rather anti-Catholic. Somehow they drifted over to the Presbyterians, although they still really weren't church people.

Now, mother's family, too, had an interesting religious history. They, too, had been Roman Catholics, but when they came to America they regarded themselves as Protestants. My mother's mother is in her eighties. Every once in a while—maybe it's because she is fast becoming senile— she talks about seeing a priest or wanting to talk to one. I think it's the fear element that is bothering her because she is nearing death.

PAUL: It's a most interesting family. Really, it's very much different from mine in so many ways.

VIRGINIA: Paul's is a very warm family. My family is far less so. My mother died some years ago, but my father's family is definitely on the cold side. There was quite a difference in this respect and in others as well between my mother and my father and their parents. It was my mother who had wanted some affiliation with a church, not because of religious reasons, but because the church was the center of social activities.

I remember that for a short time we lived in a small town not far from our present home, where the townspeople didn't have enough to pay the ministers of the two churches in town. One was Congregationalist and the other was Methodist. They hit on a grand idea. For two years they had a Methodist minister and for two years thereafter they had a Congregational minister. This satisfied the people in that little town. It didn't make very much difference to us because, as I say, we needed the church only because it was the center of social life. I guess that's what church really meant to my mother. It didn't even mean that much to my father. When I was old enough I used to teach Sunday school. I learned, too, to play the organ.

My mother had been quite ill for a long time. But she enjoyed the church. She played the violin in the church service. She was quite active. My father contributed financially to this church, but not of himself.

PAUL: My religious education was more concentrated than Virginia's. I attended a small Hebrew School every afternoon after regular school hours. I think I attended until a short while after my Bar Mitzvah at age thirteen. We studied the Five Books of Moses and the Prophets in Hebrew. Of course, the first thing we did was to learn to read Hebrew. I regarded myself as quite an orthodox Jew when I was a kid. In addition to the schooling, I remember attending the *Shule* (synagogue) very faithfully every Sabbath morning with my father and my brothers. When I was about fifteen years old, I remember helping out in the store on Saturdays. But my father never went to business on Saturday. He kept on going to the synagogue.

We had a nice family relationship. Not only my parents and us kids, but uncles and aunts and cousins as well. We visited a lot with each other and, of course, I had my own gang of boys who went to Hebrew School with me. All in all, I would say that I kept very much in the Jewish Community. None of us really had many outside contacts with non-Jews except in a business way.

VIRGINIA: In my case, there wasn't very much contact outside of the family. For one thing, my mother was ill so much of the time. I didn't tell you very much about my mother, but I ought to because she was a very unusual person. My mother was brilliant, very talented and very attractive. In those days it was very unusual for a girl to have a college education. Yet she went to Hunter College. She was a trained librarian and worked in the college library. I believe I mentioned that she played the violin. She was really a talented violinist and a good vocalist as well. She came from a poor Polish family and her folks were really very proud of her. They pushed her. They were excited about her talents. I think that she was a genius.

After my mother became ill, her parents who lived but a short distance away from us came even closer in order to take care of her.

My father was very different. He was the real boss in our family. He had the old European feeling that a woman's place is in the home. He never particularly cared for my maternal grandparents. He felt that they were a falsely proud family. Of course, they were poor, humble people. But my father was very much different from them. I suppose, too, my father may have been a little jealous about my mother's education. I think that made him feel less adequate. But apparently he fell in love with her because of her attractiveness and her talents. My mother's family had sort of pushed her into this marriage because he was rather well off, compared with them. He had a little manufacturing plant. In addition, my father's family was bossy. All through my mother's life, they were the ones to whom we listened more than to our parents.

PAUL: Well, our relationship was different. It was really very good. My father and mother got along well and we children got on very well with them. We all listened to our parents. I think we could really be called obedient children. None of us rebelled—certainly not when we were children. But I was growing up fast and I was getting to the point where I was going to express my own ideas on a lot of things in my own good time. As I look back now, I realize that in my case as well as in Virginia's there were strong family controls. We knew that what our parents said was law and that controlled all of us pretty completely.

VIRGINIA: But, with all the controls, we children were growing up and beginning to express our independence. I think I became a much more self-reliant girl when I went away to college. With all of my father's attitudes, he *did* want me to get a college education. There, among other girls, and pretty much on my own, I think that my own ideas began to take form.

PAUL: And my independence began about the time when I, after a couple of years at the university, was given a chance to help run one of the family businesses. Our business had grown and I was sent up to New Hampshire to take charge. Well, when you are on your own, you learn. You just have to. I drifted away from the close ties I had had to the Jewish religion during that period. I spent most of my time with non-Jews. I dated non-Jewish girls. I became part of a non-Jewish community. It wasn't that I ever regarded myself as anything other than a Jew. I knew who I was, all right. But Jewishness generally came to have less meaning for me. I came to learn more about other people's religions through my contacts with these people.

Now, this is strange, but it's true, that never once, during all the time I was in New Hampshire did any member of the family (my father had since died) ask me whether I was going out with non-Jewish girls. Not even my mother. I suppose they took that for granted.

I must have you understand, too, that even though my family's contacts were primarily with Jews, my sister, for example, did have non-Jewish friends as well. In fact, it was through my sister that I met Virginia.

VIRGINIA: I was through college and I was working as a private secretary and administrator for a large firm in Springfield. I had somehow come to know Paul's sister. It happened that I had taken ill and Paul's sister came to call on me just to see how I was.

PAUL: Just before she went over, my sister asked me if I would care to come along. I had just finished a long period of work in New Hampshire. Many of my friends had drifted off. There wasn't too much for me to do in my own home town. So I accepted her invitation and went along.

VIRGINIA: I happen to know that I wasn't the only non-Jewish girl Paul's sister knew. I remember her telling me that during her high-school days she also went out with boys who were not Jewish on occasion.

PAUL: Certainly, nothing was ever said about it, or thought about it. If my mother knew—and she must have—she never said anything. During my years in New Hampshire, I had found myself getting serious about a Christian girl. There was quite a bit of objection when the members of my family heard about it.

VIRGINIA: My family would have objected very strongly if I ever became serious about a Jewish boy. I'm certain that there would have been no objection whatsoever if I became interested in either a Catholic or Protestant. These, at least, were Christian. As I grew older, my independence expressed itself in that, as far as I was concerned, it was not really very important whether I married a Christian *or* a Jew. I didn't think that it was the most important thing in my life or ever would be. Since I had lived with many people outside my own faith and had a liking for people, as people, I just felt if it did happen, it would happen. I was not really concerned with what my father or grandparents or anyone else would think on this score. While I was arriving at this decision, I was meeting Jewish people and not even aware of their Jewishness. It never occurred to me to ask and besides I was never so close in friendship with any of them that it would have been important to know. I have probably dated Jewish boys during those years and didn't even know that they were Jewish.

PAUL: Virginia and I started dating on occasions. It was about two years before we really became very serious. And then when the family began to take notice of it, there were many objections. Now, the family, my mother, my sister, my brothers, knew Virginia and they liked her very much, but it was one thing liking her—and quite another to have a Christian girl in the family as my wife. I tried to talk it through with them, but they objected and very strongly, you may be sure.

VIRGINIA: My father had met Paul and he was extremely fond of him. I think it was only because of the kind of person Paul is and not because of his religion. Had it been any other Jewish boy, my father would have had very serious objections. Now there was very much prejudice in my family against Jews in general, but not this one, meaning Paul, in particular. When I told the family that I was thinking seriously of Paul, my father astounded me by actually saying that he was delighted. My mother was then so ill that I couldn't talk it over with her. Despite the prejudice against Jews, good common sense won out, in my father's case. But he, too, realized that there were likely to be problems that were in part caused by our different religious and family background and training. So he advised me to talk to a rabbi to see if we could be married by him in a religious ceremony and help to make Paul's mother feel better about it all. You see, religion really didn't mean very much, if anything, to him. But he knew that it did to Paul's family even if it didn't mean very much to Paul. So he was really trying to be helpful.

In my family the objection to my continuing to go with Paul came from my sister. She was not then a regular church-goer. She *is* now. During those years, she was like a mother to me because our mother had been so ill. She took all the burdens on her shoulders and tried to advise me. But, as I look back at it now, I think that here, too, religious differences didn't play so much of a role in her thinking. I think that she was much more concerned about the social pressures that could result from my marrying a Jewish boy. She knew that this would be quite great—and, I must say she was right in this respect.

While I was talking things through with my father and sister (my brother was away at school), my grandparents sort of kept a "hands off" policy, but it was clear that they, too, were worried about what might happen. They didn't want me to get hurt.

I guess that I was so busy thinking about myself and my family in connection with the possible intermarriage that it just never occurred to me that there was any negative feeling on the part of Paul's family. Certainly Paul never spoke of it to me. I just never knew. I knew that they liked me, but I just didn't guess that "liking" is one thing and marriage into the family is something else again.

PAUL: We actually were married while I was in the army. This was during World War II. The family just didn't know when we were going to get married. They may even have hoped against hope that we would not marry. Because of the way things were between my mother, brother, sister and myself, I decided to go ahead on my own without any more conversations about it. Oh, yes, I forgot to say that my family was so much upset that they asked the local rabbi, whom I knew and respected, to take a trip down to the army camp where I was stationed, to see if he couldn't talk me out of marrying Virginia. Well, the rabbi did come down and we had a very honest, forthright talk. I was very frank with him and I told him that I had made my mind up. I suspect that all the while I was rebelling against

my family more and more. The last straw was the rabbi's visit, although he was only doing his duty as he saw it. I felt that in time, when my mother and the others really got to know Virginia, the thing would iron itself out.

VIRGINIA: But Paul was always a nonconformist in his family. And they didn't like that. As I look back at it, I realize that I should have been smarter than I was and understood what was happening—that there was a breach a mile wide developing between Paul and the others. In fact, when his sister was married, I who had been a friend—not the closest perhaps—but certainly a friend, wasn't invited. I was hurt, but not really desperately upset at all. It was only when Paul burst into my home that evening. He had left the wedding party because he was so angry and hurt, too, that I had not been invited. He admitted that night what the real reason was for my not getting an invitation.

Like Paul, I decided that we would do what we thought was right, regardless of others. They had shown no consideration of me as a person. But time heals many wounds. I think I understand them far better today. They *did* like me as a person, but they felt an obligation to perpetuate a certain religious way of life and in having to choose between these two—myself and their religion—they chose their religion.

PAUL: A Protestant army chaplain officiated at our marriage. We never thought about having a Catholic priest. And, insofar as a rabbi was concerned—well, here are the circumstances. They were building a new chapel at the camp and all the colonels insisted that mine was going to be the first wedding in the chapel. They worked overtime just to get it ready. Virginia's father attended the wedding, but no member of my family came. One of the reasons—the most important—is that I had not informed any of them when we would be married.

VIRGINIA: That's not exactly true because, on the day of the wedding, there was an announcement in the Springfield papers.

PAUL: Well, anyhow, the point is, we got married! I was in the service about six months following our marriage. I had been overseas for several years and back in the States. I was slightly wounded in battle in Europe.

VIRGINIA: While Paul was overseas, I lived with my sister. When Paul returned, we moved into my father's home.

PAUL: You may wonder why, upon my discharge I didn't go back to Springfield and into the family business. After all, that would have been the natural thing to do. Well, the answer is that there were "hard feelings" between one brother and myself. I didn't want to embarrass him by bringing home a wife who would not have their regard, nor did I want to embarrass the family friends. You see, my family had become very well known in our

city. This would just reopen a wound and nothing good would come of it. In fact, I had heard that my brothers didn't really want me to return because they said it would be too hard on them and on my mother. For a while I took another job, but it really didn't work out too well. I guess that my brothers were trying to wear me down. I had the impression that they thought that I had disgraced them all. One day, however, I guess the old adage "blood is thicker than water" proved to be true, for I got a phone call from one of my brothers asking to see me. Well, I went down and we really had it out. Of course, it wasn't easy, but I think I made it clear that even though I loved my mother, my wife came first and if he wanted me to return to the business, he would have to accept my wife, too. None of us was too happy about our conversations in those days, but Virginia and I decided to take our chances. So we returned.

VIRGINIA: It was at that time, the pressures being so great, that I decided that I would convert to Judaism. It wasn't that important. I would convert for the sake of peace. I felt that this would be the easiest way out. Then I consulted a rabbi. I went for instruction twice a week and I passed my test and everything else. I studied with the rabbi about six months. But there was no conversion ceremony because the rabbi told me that one of the concluding steps toward conversion involved the Ritual Bath or "Mikvah." That's when I just flipped completely. To me the whole idea was repulsive.

I guess the rabbi had not explained the ritual properly so that I understood it. I didn't feel that there had to be a formal time for a conversion. Whatever the reason, whether I was right or wrong, I never went through with it. I guess all the conditions laid down by Paul's family troubled me. Not only about the conversion, but the insistence that I keep a *kosher* home. Now, all this while Paul had not even once suggested that I be formally converted, nor did he ever think about a *kosher* home because Paul had been away from that for years. But the pressure was building up again so, this time, I decided that I would talk with a Reform rabbi. He was a very friendly and nice person and I told him exactly how I felt about the whole thing. He responded that it would be foolish for him to work with me toward conversion because he felt that I would be a hypocrite if I converted when I did not really feel that way, and he would be very much of a hypocrite if he helped me under these circumstances. So, upon his suggestion, I just dropped the whole thing and that was the end of my conversion.

PAUL: As far as the Jewish Community is concerned, it doesn't know whether Virginia has or has not been converted. She goes along with me to the Temple on the High Holy Days and contributes to certain Jewish woman's organizations, but she doesn't attend meetings or anything like that. There has never been any real question of her acceptance socially.

VIRGINIA: Actually now we live outside of Springfield and, on occasion, rather rare to be sure, I go to a Congregational Church. My daughter Joyce

who attends the Jewish Sunday School likes to attend Friday evening services there. On occasion I go with her.

PAUL: I get along very well now with my brothers and sister. I know that they and my mother would all be happier with Virginia had she converted to Judaism, but she must not do it unless she means it—and I know that she doesn't.

VIRGINIA: Now I think Paul and I have reached a plateau insofar as our relations with family and community are concerned. I think we have done as well as we have because we are both independent people. I cannot say how I would have reacted to the idea of conversion had Paul been much more like his mother and brothers in his Jewish religious convictions. Perhaps things would have been different.

At this point, I think our problem revolves around our children. My daughter Joyce regards herself as a Jewess. As for my son, Bob, there is a question about his religion. He has been shying away from identifying himself with anything Jewish. Even though he was Bar Mitzvah and stayed on for confirmation, I think I can say in all truthfulness that he wants no part of it. Of course, some years back, the children did go to the Congregational Sunday School not far from where we live. Joyce is a pliable youngster. She enjoys whatever she does. But Bob rebelled. We quite literally had to *make* him go. The children pray, but they do not use Jesus' name in their prayers.

PAUL: We had quite a time with our son about his Bar Mitzvah. We explained to him the reasons for it. His mother reminded him that I am Jewish. So there was no rebellion. He took private Hebrew lessons. I think he built up more resentment at that time, not because of his opposition to Bar Mitzvah but because it took time away from his sports program. *That* is his major interest. When, following the Bar Mitzvah, we insisted that he continue through confirmation, he vowed that, once he finished with confirmation, he'd never set foot in a Temple again. I think that it's just a matter of time before he'll come around. He knows that he will be labeled as a Jew. He was medically circumcised—not by a *mohel*. He has been given no Hebrew name nor has Joyce.

If Joyce should fall in love with a nice boy from an Orthodox Jewish family, she will have a problem, but she is going to have to work out her own salvation. The fact is that we have children whose identification, Jewish or Christian, is not too clear. I just hope that it doesn't create special problems for them.

As an example of the kind of special problem I mean, let me tell you about what Bob did recently. He's shopping around for a college these days. About one Southern school that seemed to have everything, Bob said that he was sure that he wouldn't be accepted there because they didn't want Jews or Yankees. And he resented it deeply. On another occasion, in filling out a college application, there was a question about his religion—which he

could fill out or not fill out. There was no requirement about it. But Bob sat down and wrote a lengthy explanation of the fact that his father was Jewish and his mother is Congregationalist and that, on occasions, he attends either service. What I'm trying to say is that he really doesn't know *what* he is. I guess he thought his chances for admission would be better if the college did not regard him as a Jew.

VIRGINIA: And, yet, Bob is extremely devoted to Paul's mother. He really adores her. He accepts my father and likes him very much, but there is not that warmth that he has with his grandmother. If Bob married a non-Jewish girl, neither Paul nor I would object, but it might cause trouble in our business and Bob would in all likelihood get squeezed out of it. As far as Bob is concerned I do feel that if he is allowed to work out his own problems without outsiders interfering, he's going to get along very well.

PAUL: But that is the largest IF you can find.

VIRGINIA: If he's going to go into the family business, then there will be a real problem.

PAUL: Well, there is a good deal involved not only in the case of Bob and Joyce or even in our own case, but in all cases of intermarriage. There is the problem of the personality of the persons involved. How strong are they? Can they stand up to difficult situations. Then there is the economic factor, too. It plays an important part. Can you *afford* to be independent? And that is an important question. I think, too, there is the intelligence problem. How intelligent are the two people? Can they build their lives together? Not every couple can face problems or be honest with each other. I know the whole problem is rather tough, but for us at least it was the right thing to do—I think! If someone were to come to me for advice on the whole question of intermarriage, I would say that there are, of course, problems in any kind of marriage and *it doesn't make it easier* to marry outside of one's religion. You've got to work much harder to make the marriage work. The formal trappings of religion are not very important to me, but this makes it more difficult for my children. They do not know definitely whether they belong to one group or are identified with another. It's not easy for them. They're going to have to think things through for themselves.

VALERIE AND CHARLES

Charles, a Jew in name only, marries a Catholic who out of love for him converts to Judaism. Many factors ultimately bring about the

"destruction" of their marriage. Valerie, unhappy and upset by the unfaithfulness of her husband, seeks comfort in the Catholic Church and, even though formally converted to Judaism, asks for formal return to the Catholic Church.

Charles, a confused and unhappy Jew, is suddenly faced with the problems associated with the future of his children.

CHARLES

"It was the *Mezzuzah* that symbolized the difference between us. I would put a Mezzuzah on my little boy each day and my wife would keep on pulling it off. She made a promise that our children would be reared as Jews. Why didn't she keep it? She studied for almost a year and was formally converted to Judaism. Why did she turn back to Catholicism? Why did her priest come into my home and tell me that she wouldn't go to Heaven unless I, mind you, I, converted to Catholicism, was married by a priest and the children were reared as Catholics?

Religious differences weren't the only things that eventually ruined our marriage. There were other things. I have a temper. I may have done and said things that she didn't like, but it seems to me that it was our religious differences that put our marriage on the rocks.

Now it's a very strange thing that religion played any role in my life at all. My parents were orthodox Jews, but they weren't Sabbath observers and Synagogue-goers. My father was in the family business and I have followed him. We were associated with quite an orthodox Synagogue when I was a youngster. I'm not so sure that he understood the Hebrew services too well. Maybe that is why, some fifteen years ago, he joined a Reform Temple. I was Bar Mitzvah at the orthodox Synagogue. I went to Hebrew School up to that time—when I turned thirteen—and then I quit. I also went to high school and had two years of college. But I really wasn't very much interested in college.

I enlisted in the army just after I graduated from high school. It was as part of the army program that I was sent to the university where I was given an engineering course. During World War II I was in the States. I never got to go overseas. I got out of the army when I was just under twenty years old.

I hadn't done too well in school, either high school or college, and I didn't want to go on. So when I had the opportunity to go to work for my father immediately after getting out of the army, I was happy. I was too impatient a person to go on to college. I just didn't have the desire to study.

Now during all those years I wasn't particularly close to the Jewish people or to Judaism. I didn't understand it, I guess. As for being Jewish,

that is something that you are and you don't change. It was there, but I didn't relate myself to Judaism because I didn't really understand it.

I don't recall any time since I began going out with girls that I didn't interdate with non-Jewish girls. There never was any violent objection to it on the part of my parents, although I'm very certain that there was some objection. As I look back I believe that most of my friends were Jewish. In schools, the groups were mixed. I remember bringing non-Jewish boys to our home, but no girls. Had I brought them to the house, I imagine my folks would have objected.

My parents were quite different from my grandparents on my father's side. These grandparents were outspoken, devoted Jews, particularly interested in Zionism, but they weren't particularly observant of Jewish ritual either. It was my mother's folks who were very observant. But none of it seemed to have impressed itself on me.

How did I meet the girl I married? Well, I was working in my father's business. One day I happened to meet her in the office of one of my business friends. She was a secretary, working in his office. At first it was just a matter of saying "hello." There was nothing serious. One day quite by accident, I met her outside the office and we got to talking. We found that we knew certain people in common. It was quite accidental. But I did invite her out that night and we had our first date. She was Catholic, but at that time I didn't know or care particularly.

I called her again about a week after our first date. During this time I was going out a good deal, dating other girls, Jewish and non-Jewish.

My folks knew that I was out practically every night, but they didn't know who I was dating. I never discussed such things with them. If they had thought I was serious about any non-Jewish girl, there would have been a major question. But if they thought it was nothing more than a lark, there would have been no questions.

Of course I learned eventually that this girl I was dating was a Catholic. But insofar as I was concerned I was only dating a nice, pretty girl, and I wasn't taking it too seriously. After about seven or eight months had passed, I found that I was becoming serious about her.

I never discussed her with any of the members of my family—my parents or my brothers and sisters. There just was no problem in my mind about her religious affiliation. I guess part of the reason was that when our talk got around to religion, she would always say that, as far as Catholicism was concerned, she felt that there was a lot to be desired. She didn't agree with much of it and I guess she didn't understand some of it.

Her parents were good Catholics. They went to church regularly. When they heard from her that she was going with a Jew, they didn't like it at all. In fact, she used to tell me that she was having a bad time at home with her parents. I would say that conversation between her and her parents became strained. There was a strain in the whole family relationship. All the other children in her family went to a parochial school, for example. I could tell that she was having a rough time of it at home, but that didn't sway me from my thinking. I didn't see why I should drop her. Insofar as the two

of us were concerned, we got along very well, but I never went into her home. To this day I have never met her parents. I never had anything to do with them or they, with me.

After we had decided that we were going to get married, I knew that her folks would never forgive me because she was going to divorce herself from Catholicism and her family in order to marry me. She said she wanted to study Judaism and then be converted. Now, remember, she *volunteered* it! It would have made a real difference to me if she had not converted. I would never have married her.

You're surprised about that, aren't you? I wasn't very much of a religious Jew then because I didn't understand it and appreciate it, but there was something that would not allow me to marry her unless she was converted. At that time my attitude was that I could marry a non-Jew, but that she would have to convert first to Judaism.

I felt that as long as the girl converted that would be satisfactory.

My folks were most unhappy when I told them that I was going to marry this girl. It was definitely a matter of religion that upset them. My mother cried a good deal about this. My father was firm. He said, "You shall not do this!" The folks took it very hard, but I had made up my mind.

Insofar as my friends were concerned, nobody said anything one way or the other. Nobody entered into this discussion at all.

I had explained to my parents that the girl was going to convert and I couldn't see why they were still so upset about it. Of course, the same thing was happening to my girl in her relation to her folks—only worse, I think. She was giving up her own Catholic faith. This just about made her a very serious problem to her folks and all her family.

At this time I was no longer working for my father. I was working on my own and I guess that's why I finally got my parents to accede. Come to think of it, my grandfather played a major role in my marriage because, after I had gone with the girl for well over a year and a half, and she was taking lessons in Judaism from a rabbi, it was my grandfather who more or less swayed my parents. He said, "If she wants to be Jewish and if she will bring up her children as Jewish, let them get married. Why are you standing in their way?"

Even though my parents were opposed to my marriage, I would have married the girl. I was determined to go ahead.

It had taken about one-half year before we became serious enough to talk about the whole idea of conversion. We went to the rabbi of my congregation and talked about it. The rabbi was very helpful. The girl agreed to be converted. I wanted her to be, of course, and she knew it, but it was she, not I, who made the decision. It was absolutely agreed that if we had any children, they would be reared as Jews.

The rabbi didn't accept her as a pupil immediately. He didn't seem too anxious to convert her, but after seeing us together a few times in his study he agreed, providing we both studied together. I remember that when the rabbi asked us to define our religious ideas at that time, both of us gave answers that must have been regarded as comical. Neither one of us under-

stood either the Catholic or the Jewish religion, nor were we able to give intelligent answers. That rabbi met with us regularly and he taught us both. And what he said about the religion and about the beliefs of Judaism interested me. He gave us a book to read and study. I think it was *Basic Judaism*. We would read and then come back to him. From him we learned what Judaism meant. My girl became very interested in all this and she was very fond of the rabbi. We started to go to Temple services on Friday night. A word about the rabbi. We studied with him once a week for a period of about five months. Sometimes he kept us as long as three hours. Time didn't make any difference to him. My girl was truly appreciative of the fact that his time was ours. She used to comment that whenever she spoke to her priest, he had always seemed to be in a hurry. I guess that's why this meant a great deal to her.

My girl friend had many friends. There was nothing withdrawn about her. Except insofar as the matter of religion was concerned, she got along well with her folks, too. She didn't convert or want to marry me in order to escape from her family. Nor did I regard my marrying a Catholic as a form of escape from my family. I never even thought of that. Neither one of us did.

After we had studied together for those five months, there was a formal conversion ceremony about two or three weeks before the wedding. The conversion took place in the Temple before the Ark. The ceremony was not orthodox. There was no "immersion" rite. My girl then signed a document agreeing to rear any children we might have as Jews.

After my folks saw what was happening, they agreed that they would not stand in our way and the wedding was arranged. My folks and all my family attended. In fact they "made" the wedding. But none of my wife's family attended. Neither her father, mother, brothers or sisters. I don't believe that she was too disturbed about this because she had not expected them. They opposed the marriage and that was that!

Of course we bought a house and set up a very nice home. For about nine years everything went fine. We had two children, a girl and a boy. The girl is the older of the two. I think that we got along as well as couples generally do. We went to the Temple services on occasion. The children knew that they were Jewish. They went to Sunday school. They would go to children's services. They are learning Hebrew. We would attend the Passover dinner which my parents always had. But I never said *Kiddush* in my home nor did my wife ever light the Sabbath candles. I can't say that it was just because we weren't interested. Perhaps it was because, in the wintertime, we went away every weekend. We would leave on Friday afternoon and go skiing. In the summertime we would go out to the beach or boat which I own.

We got along just fine, I think. Sure there were problems. There was a problem about other women from time to time. (*Editor's note:* There were also problems of bitter arguments and his temper and tempestuous outbursts which Charles did not discuss.)

One day I came home from work to find a priest sitting in my living

room. It seems that my wife had gone to a Jewish lawyer and discussed the problem of a particular woman I am alleged to have gone out with and the next thing I know this priest, a friend of the lawyer, turned up at my home.

This priest told me that my wife had a problem and that it was a basic problem that involved religion. He told me that my wife wished to return to the Catholic Church. I asked my wife if this were so and she said, "Yes." So I asked her at that time, in the presence of the priest, to answer some questions about Catholicism, basic questions any Mohammedan should be able to answer if he knows something about basic Catholic beliefs—you know, she couldn't answer. She didn't know what to answer. She understood nothing of Catholicism except that after several consultations with this priest she had decided that she wanted to return to Catholicism.

I told the priest about her formal conversion to Judaism and that our children were being reared as Jews, but that didn't seem to make any difference to him. As far as the priest was concerned, she was living in sin. In order for them to take her back into the Catholic religion, she would have to be married in the Catholic Church, which meant that I was expected to go through a Catholic ceremony and also sign a statement that all future children would be brought up as Catholics. I wouldn't do this. I just couldn't do it.

My children regard themselves as Jews. They always have and they do now. My wife insisted that I be married in a Catholic ceremony or else she wouldn't go to Heaven. I tried to find out if there was any way in which she could be satisfied, where she could continue to go to church and leave everything else alone. The priest to whom I spoke said he couldn't guarantee that she would go to Heaven. I explained to him that this was going to ruin a marriage. But nothing helped to solve the problem. According to him there was only one answer.

Oh, yes, I *did* start talking about the *Mezzuzahs* and my children. Let me tell you the story:

Last year the children came home from Sunday school one day and said, "Daddy, will you buy us a *Mezzuzah?* They are selling them in the Temple and we want them." So I got the children *Mezzuzahs*. That's what they wanted and that's what I bought them. They were really very pleased.

They wore them with great pride. But my wife got angry about it. We had a tilt about it. She tried to pull the *Mezzuzahs* off the children and they refused to take them off. Well, when I heard about it, you can imagine that there was quite a tilt. My wife and I really had a battle about it. I said that the children were going to be brought up as Jews and the *Mezzuzahs* meant something to me and to them. But she wouldn't leave them alone. She was determined to rip them off the children.

It may be that she was so irked with me that she sought security in the Church. Then she became determined that the children wouldn't be reared as Jews. My children have been very much upset because they saw no reason why she should try to change their religion. They were Jewish. They had an identity and they are pleased with going to Sunday school.

They get excellent marks. They would rather do their Sunday-school homework than their regular school homework. It's amazing!

My wife sued me for divorce and the divorce has just become final.
I get to see the children every Sunday between the hours of nine in the
morning and six in the evening. That's so I will be able to have them go to
a Jewish Sunday school and my former wife won't be able to take them to
church. I don't want them to be influenced by Christian symbolism or
Christian practices.

My former wife once tried to take the children to her church, but
they refused to go. Every Sunday morning I take the children to Sunday
school. My son often asks me to go into the Temple and he asks me to
put on a *Yarmulka* (skull cap) which I do. We go into the Temple and I
show him the Holy Ark and tell him what's behind it, what the Torah is.
We say the *Shema* (a prayer proclaiming the unity of God) together. He
is quite moved by this experience and so am I.

Up until the time of our divorce, the business of ripping off the *Mezzuzahs* took place regularly. I used to buy *Mezzuzahs* by the gross (144
of them) in order to have replacements when she ripped one off. I am not
forcing the children to wear them. That is what *they* want. They *want* to be
Jewish.

I don't think that religious difference is the sole factor that broke up
our marriage, but when the going got tough, it was religious difference that
came to the fore. She no longer wanted to be a Jew. She was anxious that
the children should no longer be Jews.

I would have worked something out if the Church had given me half
a chance. Even if she had wanted to go back to the Catholic Church, I
would not have minded, but when I was told that I would have to marry
her in the Catholic Church and agree that any future children would have
to be reared as Catholics, I wouldn't have anything to do with it. It ruined
our sex life because I was not going to permit a situation where I might
get her pregnant. She was constantly talking and arguing and asking, "Why
won't you marry me in the Catholic Church? Why? It's not such a terrible
thing. We've got two Jewish children, why can't we have a Catholic child?"
I don't know why it was so important for my wife to have a Catholic child,
but it certainly was.

The priest certainly was an important factor in our eventual break-up.
He was determined to have my wife return to Catholicism. Now I know
that she invited him into the situation, but it seems to me that he ought to
have had some respect for the fact that we were married *as Jews;* that my
wife converted to Judaism. All he could say is that my wife was living with
me "in sin."

If my children should come to me at a later age and tell me that they
want to marry a non-Jewish person, Protestant or Catholic, I would object.
I think it is a mistake. In fact, today they say to me, "Daddy, when we get
married, we are going to marry someone Jewish so we don't have the
problems you have."

I happen to have met a Catholic with whom I fell in love. I think that

I would not have married anyone of another faith had I really understood my religion. Today, I am opposed to interdating on any level. I am opposed to intermarriage, of course. If my children fall in love with non-Jews, I will not disown them, but would be very much disturbed and unhappy. I think that if children are educated properly, given a good understanding of their religion and of other religions so that they can see the difference, they would be better Jews. The likelihood of intermarrying would be reduced. You need more than knowledge about Judaism to avoid intermarriage. You need a genuine appreciation of Judaism. I wish that I had had it years ago. Today, whatever my weaknesses, I feel that I am more of a Jew than I ever was before. Maybe it is my intermarriage that taught me what I could never have learned otherwise.

THE PROTESTANT POSITIONS

Protestants, generally, look with disfavor upon marriages that involve a partner of another faith. They view with special disapproval intermarriage with Roman Catholics. Such marriages are officially frowned upon through the media of resolutions and formal statements drawn up by various Protestant church denominations. Individual clergymen as well make their displeasure known when such marriages are contemplated.

A sampling of Protestant ministers who serve all kinds of churches, urban and rural, from all parts of the country included in this study confirms this impression. While recognizing that "there is nothing to keep young people of other churches from falling in love with Roman Catholic friends,[1] the National Council of Churches of Christ has published a booklet since 1945 which deals with this problem and which unequivocally declares its opposition to mixed marriages in general and to such marriages involving Roman Catholics in particular.

The Protestant position, as represented by the National Council is recorded in "If I Marry a Roman Catholic," [2] and declares:

1. Of course Roman and non-Roman Christians share in the values of the great Christian stream of culture and of American democratic life. They are, nevertheless, shaped to different patterns and their convictions about family living do not always fit together well.

2. Christians who are not Roman Catholics have something that is quite as precious to them as the teaching of the Roman Church is to its members. Why should they not stand for the preciousness of their faith and resist the exactions of a church which attempts to make all the rules for any marriage in which one of its members is involved?

3. When intolerable conditions are introduced, the young person should reject them even if it means delaying one's marriage until an equally attractive person of one's own faith can be found.

4. Recognizing that the Roman Catholic Church has the right under the freedom of religion to promulgate its teachings about marriage in any way it sees fit we are compelled to emphasize the fact that we of other churches have freedoms and convictions that are inexpressibly precious to us.

Protestants are generally indignant about Roman Catholic marriage laws because they require that the non-Catholic must promise to

rear children, born of a mixed marriage, as Catholics if a priest is to officiate. These requirements are regarded by Protestants as unjust, oppressive and divisive. They declare that such requirements are both humiliating and unfair. It is believed, too, that the Roman Catholic Church, by its refusal to recognize marriages performed outside of the Church indirectly makes for an increase in desertion by Roman Catholic husbands of their non-Catholic wives. Protestants also suspect that marriages performed outside of the Roman Catholic Church are viewed lightly by Catholics. They point to the restrictions of the Roman Catholic Church recorded in its 1918 Code of Canon Law which look upon invalid (non-church approved) marriages as nonexistent.

Protestants generally believe that the Catholic Church has imposed "intolerable conditions" on mixed marriages when it obliges non-Catholics to sign statements that children born of the intermarriage will be reared as Catholics. They object, also, to the requirement that the Catholic shall be obliged to attempt to convert the non-Catholic to Catholicism.

A recent editorial in the liberal *Christian Century*[3] states the case well:

> . . . By sharply increasing the restrictions of the church in regard to mixed marriages the 1918 code of the Canon Law subjected non-Catholics to intolerable and unfair religious pressures, to personal humiliation and, in the case of many non-Catholics, to desertion by their Roman Catholic husbands. The fact that it is not the intent of the Canon Law to encourage Catholic males to desert their non-Catholic wives does not alter the fact that the church's refusal to recognize mixed marriages performed outside the church does encourage Catholics who are thus married to view the bond lightly. As a result of the 1918 Code millions of legally valid marriages between Protestant and Roman Catholics are considered by the Roman Catholic Church to be nonexistent. The non-Catholic who marries a Catholic has to choose between a marriage which the church claims non-existent and a marriage in which the non-Catholic must state in writing that he will not interfere with the religious practices of the Catholic spouse—including the efforts of the Catholic to convert the non-Catholic. If Roman Catholics cannot understand why Protestants find these regulations offensive and repugnant, they have little imagination and little sensitivity to the feelings of other people.

Protestants appear to be critical of Catholics on grounds of their alleged Catholic intolerance of other religions. However, there are other and equally important reasons for opposition to interfaith marriages involving one Protestant partner. Ideological and theological ideas of Protestantism often come into direct conflict with Roman Catholic and Jewish thought as well. The belief that interfaith intermarriages are not

healthy for the survival of Protestantism is not to be ignored, for such marriages may indeed weaken the religious foundation upon which the Protestant Church is built.

Protestants in America have no means of regulating or controlling interfaith marriages except by official resolutions and declarations. It is hoped that these attitudes, as interpreted by clergymen in their parish churches and the families of church members, will deal with this problem in their own effective ways. But here, too, the controls exerted by Church and family are greatly reduced in efficacy. The right of the individual to make choices, even the wrong ones, is respected even though there may be wide disagreement with the decision arrived at.

Protestant Church organizations are generally opposed to interfaith marriages because they believe, too, that the members of a family who are united around a single religion are more likely to be stronger and better as people and as a family than families that are religiously divided. They believe, too, that the Church's view of life, man and God would be materially weakened by families that are divided on matters of religion.

Inasmuch as it is believed that a religious philosophy makes for human betterment and brings man close to the Kingdom of God, they seek to maintain as high a degree of religious unity as possible.

The Protestant Church bodies declare that they have reason to oppose intermarriage on grounds other than ideological differences or resentment against Catholic insistence upon control of the religious lives of the children of the intermarried. Their opposition is associated, too, with the Church's desire to perpetuate itself as distinctive with values and ideals both unique and highly important, according to its view, if the will of God is to be done by Man on this earth.

Basically Protestant in character, after a study of 743 mixed marriages, Leiffer's report[4] that of a total of 444 men involved in such marriages, 52 per cent (234) "appear to have withdrawn from their churches and of 449 wives, 151 or approximately one-third have done so"—makes it clear that the Protestants lose in numerical strength as the result of interfaith marriages.

Of the 250 varieties of organized Protestantism in America today, the vast majority have expressed their disfavor of interfaith marriages through church documents. There are even those denominations that oppose marriage between members of their own group and certain other Protestant sects. Fundamentalists and literalists most often urge their disciples to refrain from marriage with liberals. Protestant liberals I have known generally frown upon such intermarriage because the chasm between the two Churches is obviously so great.

The official views of certain major Protestant denominations

with respect to intermarriage are excerpted and recorded in order that
their positions may be made clear:

Congregational Christian Churches and the Evangelical and Reformed Church recently merged into the United Church of Christ. As
yet, these merged churches have not issued any pronouncement on this
important subject. Organizational matters presently occupy their agenda.
However, the Evangelical and Reformed Church issued an important
pronouncement on this subject which is representative of the thinking
of its large membership.[5]

THE EVANGELICAL AND REFORMED CHURCH
Interfaith Marriage

. . . "It is abundantly clear that the realization of God's purpose for
married life—like every relation of Christian people to each other and
to their fellowmen—is grounded in and sustained by a sincere faith in
God and a constant devotion to Christ and His church. The marriage
relation is strengthened and sanctified when both man and wife meet
the joys and sorrows, the stresses and strains, the successes and dis-
appointments of their lives with a shared Christian faith and worship.

Marriages between Christians and non-Christians, therefore, present obvious obstacles to the realization in marriage of the full purpose
of God. Even marriage between Protestant and Roman Catholic Christians involves difficulties arising out of different and partly incompatible
interpretations of Christian truth. Because such a marriage puts obstacles in the way of realizing a union that can be compared to the
union of Christ and His church, we call attention to the problems involved.

Then, citing the problems of mixed marriage with special emphasis
upon the marriage of a Roman Catholic to a member of this Protestant
Church denomination, the statement continues:

Protestant Christians will not surrender their faith lightly; and
they ought not to do so. They will also do well to ask whether a marriage entered into under the conditions imposed by the Roman Catholic
Church provides a sound spiritual basis for happy and successful family
life. Unless one himself believes in the Roman Catholic interpretation
of Christianity firmly enough to become an honest and sincere adherent
of that faith *before* marrying under the conditions prescribed by the
Roman Catholic Church, it is wrong to whole-heartedly embrace. It is
equally wrong to withhold from them the Protestant's freedom and joy
of direct access to God.

Protestant Christians need to be on guard against two false ways
of escape from the problems raised by mixed marriages. One false way
is to take any vow lightly or to subscribe to it with mental reservations.
All vows are responsible acts in the sight of God. Taking a vow with
the mental reservation that one does not intend to fulfill his promises is

dishonest. It does not constitute a "solution" of the difficulties created by the conditions imposed by the Church of Rome.

A second false way is for the parties to a mixed marriage to fall into an attitude of religious indifference. A right relationship with God is the chief end of our lives. It is certainly not attained by indifference to God.

There appear to be no resolutions or pronouncements on the subject of mixed marriages by Congregational Church bodies. The secretary of the Massachusetts Congregational Christian Conference, Reverend Myron W. Fowell, explained the reason therefor in a personal letter:

> I presume the reason for this is the deep commitment of Congregationalism to ideals of freedom and liberty. Only as a people exercise their freedom, at least occasionally, to move out of positions, religiously, politically, etc., into which they were born, into positions of their own adoption, is there sure evidence that the springs of freedom are functioning. I doubt very much if any responsible Congregational body would take a position to the effect that people ought not to marry, across religious lines.[6]

Yet, the Reverend Mr. Fowell, in the same communication, sent two pamphlets "which have been used rather extensively in Congregational Churches to help young people to understand the particular problems identified with mixed marriages." Neither pamphlet is written by a Congregationalist, however much they may be used by their clergy. Both pamphlets urge young people to consider carefully the implications to them and their faith, especially of marriage to a Catholic. The Congregationalist ministry seeks, thereby, to help young people to understand the extra problems and difficulties inherent in such marriages.

The merger, on June 28, 1962, of four Lutheran denominations: (1) Augustana Lutheran Church with 630,000 members; (2) the United Lutheran Church with 2,500,000 members; (3) the Finnish Evangelical Lutheran Church with 36,000 members; (4) and the American Evangelical Lutheran Church with a membership of 25,000, has resulted in the establishment of the new Lutheran Church in America. Bringing together Lutherans of Swedish, Finnish, German and Danish background and ethnic origin, the new organization has not yet issued statements representing their joint thinking on such matters as mixed marriage. However, the Lutheran position with respect to this subject is well known. It is unequivically opposed to it.

In June, 1956, the Augustana Evangelical Lutheran Church declared its opposition to intermarriages between the members of its Synod and Roman Catholics. It declared that such marriages "often result in marital unhappiness and disruption of normal home life for the children

effected . . . . create situations having far-reaching psychological, social, economic and spiritual consequences . . . very often involving the danger of the denial of faith."

Bossard and Letts'[7] study of "Mixed Marriages Involving Lutherans" helps to explain the reason for the concern of this church about this subject. These researchers reported that between 1946 and 1950, intermarriages in which one of the parties was a Lutheran had increased to 58 per cent of all marriages involving Lutherans. Almost twice as many Lutheran women (64.1 per cent) as men (35.9 per cent) contracted such marriages. Of each 100 marriages in the 9,963 cases studied, 20 were with Roman Catholics; 57 were with other Protestants; 19 were with other non-Protestants and 1 was with a Jew.

Of the cases examined, 35 per cent remained active in their own Lutheran Church; 40 per cent brought their mate to the Lutheran Church; 10 per cent left their church and joined a non-Lutheran Church while 7 per cent of both parties dropped out of any church affiliation.

This study also stated that mixed marriages affect the religious rearing of children. "Of 5,796 children involved, 63 per cent were reared in the Lutheran Church; 18 per cent were reared in the church of the non-Lutheran; 7 per cent were reared in a church other than that of either parent and 10 per cent were not reared in any church."

The position of the Lutheran Church, Missouri Synod, as adopted at its 44th Regular Convention in San Francisco, California, June 17-26, 1959,[8] follows:

STATEMENT ON INTERFAITH OR MIXED MARRIAGES

In Compliance with the request of Synod (Proceedings, 1953, pp. 345, 346) the Family Life Committee of the Board for Parish Education submits the following statement for the guidance of pastors and congregations with regard to interfaith or mixed marriages.

1. General Principles

Marriage in the Christian view, as ordained by God, is the personal and sexual union of one man and one woman in a continuing relationship of mutual love and service based on fidelity toward each other (Matt. 19:4-6; 1. Cor. 7:10,11,39). The purpose of this lifelong union is fulfilled in the intimate one-flesh relationship in mutual helpfulness, and in the procreation and rearing of children. This marriage union involves physical, economic, social, psychological, and spiritual factors which may lead either to unity or to divisiveness. . . .

Concern for the spiritual welfare of the members of the body of Christ should cause parents, teachers, pastors, and leaders of young people to be sensitive to the urgent need of providing in the home, in the church, and in the educational program such instruction as will enable youth, before or as they arrive at the age of forming intimate friendships between sexes, to understand and appreciate the divergent

teachings and interpretations relative to marriage and other doctrines held by different religious bodies. As a church, we are to be concerned that our young people do not enter into marriage relationships which would make it impossible for them to enjoy a wholesome Christian family life or which would require them to compromise or surrender their personal Christian convictions and responsibilities (Joshua 24:15; John 8:31,32) or which would hinder them from speaking the Word of God to each other (Col. 3:16).

2. Lutheran-Roman Catholic Marriages

Marriages between Lutherans and Roman Catholics raise serious and special problems for the following reasons:

a. The two faiths differ in fundamental doctrines. Of special note is the fact that the entire spirit and way of thinking in the Roman Catholic Church is different: the church and its interpretation is placed above the Bible and guides the conscience; while for the Lutheran the conscience instructed by the Word of God is the guide.

"The Roman Catholic Church is the one true church. There is no such thing as equality of religions from the Catholic standpoint. Therefore, to have offspring reared in another faith is a catastrophe, since it denies to the persons for whom one has the greatest love the grace of the sacraments and solaces of Roman Catholicism in life and death." —Father John J. Kane, *Marriage and the Family* (New York: The Dryden Press, Inc., 1952), p. 152.

Lutherans cannot accept such Roman Catholic teachings as their doctrine of the church, the adoration of the Virgin Mary and of the saints, the false Roman Catholic Mass, and the erroneous Roman Catholic doctrine regarding good works. . . .

b. Under conditions imposed by modern Roman Canon Law, the required premarriage agreement which the non-Catholic party must sign if the marriage ceremony is to be performed by a priest, binds the Lutheran party to the promise that all children of the marriage are to be reared in the Roman Catholic faith and that no attempt to dissuade the Roman Catholic partner will be made by the non-Catholic. In fact, the Roman Catholic party must promise by a signed pledge to do all in his or her power, by means of word and example, to bring about the conversion of the non-Catholic spouse to the religious faith of the Roman Catholic Church. Before the actual dispensation to marry is granted, the non-Catholic party is usually urged by the parish priest to take instruction in the Roman Catholic religion.

The religious factor which, under normal circumstances, should contribute to keep all the members of a family together and which should be of great help in facing and overcoming prayerfully the sometimes inevitable problems between husband and wife, parents and children, is bound instead in a marriage like this to become an insurmountable wall dividing the parents from each other and the children from their parents.

The promise which the non-Catholic party must make places a burden upon his conscience and silences his witness. No one, we believe, should do anything contrary to his religious convictions or the voice of his God-instructed conscience (1 Tim. 1:19; James 4:17). If

one signs the pledge with no intention of keeping it, this act should be classified as a morally dishonest one (Mal. 3:5). . . .

3. Marriages between Lutherans and other Protestants

Although the marriage between two Protestants of different denominations may not present the same practical and religious difficulties as the marriage between a Protestant and a Roman Catholic, yet religious agreement between husband and wife is undoubtedly one of the major factors in securing that peace and harmony which makes possible the normal function and development of Christian family life (1 Cor. 12:13).

The differences in both doctrinal beliefs and outward practices within the various Protestant denominations are sometimes such that essential agreement is difficult or impossible to achieve. Theological differences, differences in the actual form of worship, and differences in the ethical expression of the Christian faith may involve the central teachings of the Christian faith and hence become unquestionably vital. A faithful Lutheran married to a partner who does not believe in Infant Baptism, who attends public worship on Saturday, or who believes that the Old Testament law is still binding on the Christian people of the New Covenant, may have to live in a religiously divided home where subjects vital to a Christian are seldom discussed and where Bible reading, prayer, and family worship are greatly hindered or entirely neglected. Christians whose faith is clearly founded in Holy Scripture cannot compromise their fundamental beliefs (1 Cor. 1:10; John 18:37).

4. Marriage between Lutherans and Non-Christian Partners

. . . It is obvious that in a marriage between a Lutheran and a non-Christian there can be no spiritual unity between the married partners, and the Christian training of the children usually will suffer serious limitations. The relation of the husband and wife and children is to be "in the Lord" (Col. 3:18,20). Christians are admonished to "take a wife in sanctification and honor" (1 Thess. 4:3-7). Christian widows, if they marry, are to marry "in the Lord" (1 Cor. 7:39).

Marriages with Jews present both religious and cultural difficulties that may involve a compromise of the evangelical faith. While the opportunity exists to witness to the saving faith in Jesus, the Christ of Old Testament prophecy, religion may be an area of tension which even silences a clear Christian witness and thwarts the true unity of the family. Heartaches come to homes where faith cannot be openly confessed and practiced.

Bossard[9] reported also that, of almost 400 Lutheran pastors who replied to his questionnaire, 17 per cent would refuse to officiate at a marriage ceremony in most cases if the marriage involved either a Catholic or a Jew: 6 per cent would excommunicate those persons whose marriage ceremony was performed outside the Lutheran Church, while 18 per cent would require both parties to join one church before marriage. Nineteen per cent of the clergy would require guarantees that

the children born of a mixed marriage would be reared as Lutherans, particularly in the case of marriage to a Catholic or Jew. The remainder either "assumed no official position or considered the issue a private matter."

Yet, despite the opposition of the Lutheran Church to mixed marriages, the per cent of Lutherans who marry outside the church continues to increase. Bossard[10] reported that, in a fifteen-year period (1936-1950) the increase, measured in five-year periods was as follows:

$$1936\text{-}40 = 46 \text{ per cent}$$
$$1941\text{-}45 = 47 \text{ per cent}$$

Within the past decade (1951-60), intermarriage has continued to increase. Twice as many Lutheran women as men married outside the church.

In 1956, The United Lutheran Church in America[11] published its official attitude with respect to mixed marriages. It deserves our attention:

MIXED MARRIAGES

The increase of marriages between people of different religious faiths constitutes a special problem. The adjustments necessary in any marriage are, of course, made more difficult if major differences in economic, educational, and cultural levels are in the background of the marriage partners. These differences also affect the acceptance of the marriage by in-laws and friends. In interracial and interfaith marriages, the attitude of the community also complicates the adjustments. These facts ought to be studied in preparation for marriage and in marriage counseling.

Of major concern here is the significance of religious differences in marriage, especially differences in attitude toward marriage of Roman Catholics and Lutherans. Roman Catholics stress celibacy as a higher way of life than marriage. In marriage they maintain that procreation is the chief justification of the sex relation though there is some recognition of the place of the sex relation in binding the couple together. However, the enjoyment of the sex relation is always looked on with suspicion. This stands in contrast to the evangelical view of marriage in which sexual pleasure is integral to the primary purpose establishing a one-flesh relation and is viewed as a good gift from God. This accounts in part for the difference in attitude toward conception control, which may become of major significance in mixed marriages. . . .

Marriages with Jews present great difficulties also and involve compromise of the evangelical faith. In marriages with unbelievers there is an opportunity to confess one's faith and bear witness to it. However, one should be fully aware that this itself may be a source of difficulty, which may persist all through the marriage and thwart the true unity of the family. St. Paul's admonition concerning marriage "in the Lord" is not to be taken lightly.

The church should give increased attention to education and counseling about mixed marriages. Where religious differences are a factor in a proposed marriage, the non-Lutheran should be informed of the Lutheran view of marriage and family life by the Lutheran pastor. Young people should be led to face the issues involved and helped to see that true love of another person should persuade one to desire the other's spiritual welfare and to wait for marriage until religious unity is assured. To do other than this is to violate the Christian view of marriage and invite unhappiness.

At its regular convention, in 1959, the Missouri Synod adopted a statement on Interfaith Marriages that discouraged marriage with Roman Catholics because the Lutheran "must not submit to church laws which are inconsistent with the Gospel." It also opposed marriage with other Protestant groups and marriage with non-Christians.

Some Protestants are very much concerned about the marriage of Protestants of one denomination to a Protestant of another denomination. In 1939, the writer even read a letter written by a Lutheran minister in the Midwest to one of his parishioners, urging her to "date" only young men from the same Synod because, in his view, the members of another Lutheran Synod were not as devout as they should be. This, of course, is an extreme case, yet conversations on this subject with Protestant ministers of denominations other than Lutheran often induce a frown, a pained expression, or the raising of eyebrows at the very thought that such a mixed marriage might occur. The growth of ecumenicism, beginning with the latter half of the 1950's, suggests that there may be a reduction in this kind of thinking. However, it is suggested that, despite the ecumenical effort, splinter groups, some old and some very new, spring up as a result of the desire to perpetuate distinctions they regard as meaningful and significant within their own denominations. Hence, there appears to be no reason to believe that Protestants will be likely in the near future to accept other Protestants of different sects or denominations in marriage without some degree of opposition.

The opposition that Protestants express to Protestant-Catholic marriages is very much like that which the Catholic clergy expresses against Catholic-Protestant and other non-Catholic marriages. In the meantime, *both* Catholics and Protestants are continuing to intermarry at an ever-accelerating rate.

A portion of a statement, prepared by the Committee on Research and Social Action of the American Lutheran Church entitled "Toward an Understanding on Marriage, Divorce, and Consistent Pastoral Practice," deals with "mixed marriages" as follows:

Particularly difficult is the request to officiate at the marriage of a man and a woman markedly different in such characteristics as religion, race, age, and cultural background. Such a marriage presents complex problems fraught with difficulties. The pastor should insist that the couple examine carefully the consequences of their marriage for themselves, their children, their families, their congregations, and their community. Only when the pastor is firmly convinced that the two are sufficiently strong and mature, both spiritually and emotionally to overcome the hazards to Christian marriage which their marked differences in background, experience, and outlook impose, should he officiate at the desired marriage.[12]

The Constitution of the United Presbyterian Church in the U.S.A. offered the following on Marriage and Divorce:

"Confession of Faith"
Of Marriage and Divorce

Christian marriage is an institution ordained of God, blessed by our Lord Jesus Christ, established and sanctified for the happiness and welfare of mankind, into which spiritual and physical union one man and one woman enter, cherishing a mutual esteem and love, bearing with each other's infirmities and weaknesses, comforting each other in trouble, providing in honesty and industry for each other and for their household, praying for each other, and living together the length of their days as heirs of the grace of life. . . .

Ministers are admonished to emphasize the need of spiritual and ecclesiastical compatibility in marriage. Lack of harmony on the part of parents in the training of their children when they differ in the essentials of the faith endangers the happiness of a truly Christian home.

Children have a God-given right to be well born. Therefore, those contemplating marriage should be bodily and spiritually fit for such a relationship. It is the duty of parents and of the Church to train their children and youth in an adequate understanding of the sacred meaning of Christian marriage, that they may determine most carefully before entering into the marriage relation whether they have reason to hope for such a married life as shall receive the constant blessing of God.

PRESBYTERIAN, SOUTHERN

This Church body, in a pastoral letter,[13] recorded in the Minutes of its General Assembly, in 1946 (p. 165), declared its opposition to mixed marriages as follows:

While the Roman Catholic laity accept Presbyterians as fellow Christians, their priests do not recognize our ministry as valid or our Communion as a part of the Church of Christ. This creates a deep and wide gulf which at once appears in the marriage rite itself.

If a priest of the Roman Catholic Church performs the ceremony,

the Presbyterian party to the marriage is required to promise to do nothing to change the faith of the Roman Catholic party; altho the Roman Catholic is expected by his Church to win the Presbyterian. Also the Presbyterian is required to sign away the unborn children to an ecclesiastical organization that will forever forbid them to worship with their parent in the Presbyterian Church.

We call upon our members to stand uncompromisingly in this matter, to resist resolutely this unfair demand and refuse to make such a promise, especially in an hour when they are not truly free but are under the emotional compulsion of romantic love. Having acted under that compulsion, the non-Catholic henceforth lives under a promise which a conscientious Christian will find it increasingly difficult to observe without mental and spiritual strain, threatening the peace and stability of the home. . . .

THE METHODIST CHURCH[14]

In 1960, a resolution on "The Christian Family" was adopted by the General Conference of the Methodist Church. It is printed in the Doctrines and Discipline of the Church as Paragraph 2021. In that paragraph of the Discipline, we read:

> Mixed Marriages—Religious convictions should be a strong tie in marriage. Recent research has emphasized the importance of common cultural and religious backgrounds as the foundations of successful marriage. It is therefore strongly urged that each young person consider carefully before becoming engaged to anyone who does not have a similar religious background. It is important that Protestant youth discuss this problem with their ministers before it is too late. Ministers are urged to discuss with both youth and parents the likelihood of failure in mixed marriages.

The General Conference of the Methodist Church meets every four years and is composed of ministers and lay members in equal numbers, elected by the annual conferences.

THE AMERICAN BAPTIST CONVENTION

In 1956 the Convention of this Church body took the following view:

> Critical social and moral conditions exist in our country which threaten the basic structure and unity of the family and are revealed every day in the startling numbers of arrests of children and youth. . . .
> We are also aware that there is a growing tendency for young people to take a tolerant and permissive attitude towards inter-faith marriage, as well as towards easy divorce and separation, and that many American Baptist youth are entering into marriage without adequate pre-marital counsel and spiritual guidance. . . .

Southern Baptists

In June, 1951, the Southern Baptist Convention declared:

Whereas the Roman Catholic hierarchy has adopted a policy to discourage mixed marriage and said church has sought to exact from non-Catholic parties to mixed marriage pledges that said marriages will be performed only by Catholic priests, and that children born to that union shall be brought up in the Catholic faith; therefore, be it

Resolved, first, that we, with our Roman friends, give public warning of the dangers to harmonious home life in mixed marriages. . . .

The Protestant Episcopal Church

The attitude of Episcopalians to mixed marriages, including Catholics and persons of other religious affiliation, was recorded in 1949 [15] in the following resolution and report:

The conference earnestly warns members of our Communion against contracting marriages with Roman Catholics under the conditions imposed by modern Roman Canon Law, especially as these conditions involve, among other things, a promise to have their children brought up in a religious system which they cannot themselves accept.

Disciples of Christ

In October, 1950, the following resolution was approved by the International Convention of Disciples of Christ, in Oklahoma City, Oklahoma:

Whereas, mutual religious convictions, a common philosophy of life, and a similarity of cultural backgrounds are factors which contribute to a happy marriage; and

Whereas, mutual respect for and sincere tolerance of differences on the part of both persons entering the union are indispensable, so that marriage can be a union of equals; and

Whereas, some religious bodies (notably the Roman Catholic Church) officially forbid their adherents to enter marriage with non-adherents except on the condition that non-adherents subscribe to certain agreements, particularly that the children of such a union be trained in the faith of the adherent, which in effect destroys any basis for tolerance and equality; . . .

That we urge our young people to stand on their rights as self-respecting Christians, and that in no event they enter into a marriage contract which places them in a position of disadvantage in their family relationship and in the training of their children.

LATTER DAY SAINTS

Young people in this church are reminded that the "doctrine of the church may be compromised and the marriage weakened unless young people marry within their own denomination." Marriage even with other Protestants is discouraged.

"The Reorganized Latter Day Saints have a ban on marriage with those outside their own communion. That this ban has not prevented marriages with non-Mormons is seen in the Study booklet 'The Latter Day Saints and Family Life' by Roy A. Cheville (Herald House, 1957). Dogmatic edicts against mixed marriages have not sufficed, he points out, and young people want to know why their elders laid down such laws." [16]

ADVENT CHRISTIAN

In two resolutions (July 3, 1946, and June 21, 1950) this Church has made known its antipathy to marriages of its adherents to Roman Catholics:

> *Inasmuch* as the problem and sorrow of marriages between Advent Christian young people and Roman Catholic young people is a definite and growing danger, due to the facts that the Advent Christian Clergy is not recognized by the Catholic Church as ordained, our church in no sense recognized, and our marriage ceremonies are pronounced not valid. Hence children born of such mixed marriages are held as illegitimate by the ever aggressive Roman priesthood; and moreover, the very home life in many cases is made all but unendurable, be it therefore . . .
>
> *Whereas,* marriages between evangelical Christians and Roman Catholics have so very often proved fatal to spiritual growth in that and succeeding generations, and
>
> *Whereas,* this is not the least among the problems facing the Christian Church today; therefore be it
>
> *Resolved,* that we urge upon our pastors to counsel with our young people and that we urge them to heed such counsel, so as to discourage and avoid such marriages, with the strong belief that love must not be blind to faith; and that it be further . . .

JEHOVAH'S WITNESSES

According to this sect, any marriage between a Jehovah Witness and any person outside of their group, is a mixed marriage.

Even though Ethical Culturists, Unitarian Universalists and often Community Churches do not regard themselves as Protestants, the official attitudes of these groups are arbitrarily recorded in this chapter.

UNITARIAN-UNIVERSALISTS

The Unitarian-Universalists have, to date, never made an official statement on the subject of mixed marriages. And yet, their position

is clear: "A marriage, either interfaith or interracial is a matter of primary concern to the two contracting parties. The Church would certainly support the action of those persons who, whatever their difference in religion or color, would wish to marry." This view, expressed to the author by an official of these merged church organizations appears to represent the general view of its clergy.

In response to a questionnaire addressed to fifty Unitarian-Universalist ministers, twenty-nine responses were received. Of these, eleven are from men who occupy prominent pulpits in the East, four are from the Midwest, and two are in the greater Washington (District of Columbia) area. The other twelve responses came from the Pacific Coast and the South.

It is noteworthy that, in response to the question: "About how many intermarried members are there in your church?" each correspondent replied that the number of such persons was considerable. In a Wisconsin church, for example, consisting of about 400 members, some 30 members are intermarried. Of these, 11 were Jewish and 4 had been Roman Catholics. In a Minnesota church approximately 75 out of a total of 610 members are intermarried. Of these, about 50 were formerly Roman Catholics and 25 were Jewish. In the several churches in the District of Columbia area, one reports that 26 out of a total of 144 members are intermarried, while the other reports about 12 intermarried members, most of whom were Roman Catholics and one of whom was Jewish.

In practically all of the Unitarian-Universalist Churches, the number of former Roman Catholics appears quite large, with the number of Jewish members about one-third that of Catholics. The remainder consists of those families who have been Unitarians or Universalists for a generation or more and others, formerly associated with one of the Protestant Churches, who have joined the Unitarian-Universalists.

These Unitarian-Universalists are divided in their opinion as to whether their church serves as a kind of compromise in an effort to find middle ground. About 40 per cent agree to this characterization. The remaining 60 per cent hold to the opinion that "more and more people are marrying across the faith lines and are looking for religious institutions which will accept this and which will find a ground on which to stand which does not cause either one to reject his background.

"This coincides with another development which is the corollary of the scientific age, namely, that more and more people are taking a position outside of any single faith requirement and judging all faiths from the viewpoint of the understanding of modern scientific knowledge and an objective, rather than subjective, approach." [17]

Unitarian-Universalist ministers generally favor interfaith and in-

terracial marriages because their emphasis appears to be on the two individuals who are contemplating marriage rather than upon the survival of any religious organization or institution, including their own. The opinions of these ministers vary. Representative ideas as suggested by these men follow:

I never think about mixed marriage because we accept it as a matter of personal preference which has no bearing upon our church relationship with the individuals involved. When these couples come to me, I believe that they are serious about making their life together a real success. They come to the Unitarian church because neither they nor their children are made to feel "different" here. We do not criticize them nor do we decry the religious orientation from which they came. They find no rejection in our religious Society, only support and appreciation of them as individuals and families. I advise them to weigh carefully all the factors which will make their lives easy or difficult. They know that they will always be welcome in a Unitarian Church. If there is strong family pressure against the liberal orientation, I counsel patience and necessary concessions without compromise. I think that official opposition to intermarriage is absurdly provincial. This argument about "purity of the faith" is specious, in my opinion. We reject such provincialism. To us the individual is of paramount importance, whether he be white or colored; Christian, Jew, Moslem or Hindu. I cannot imagine denying a congregant the sanctuary of his faith because he chose a wife who was used to a different interpretation of Scripture. Is not God one? Is not humanity of one blood? Can we divide God or presume to divide man as God did not? [18]

It all depends upon the persons involved, actually. I neither favor nor oppose. I believe that people of different faiths have greater difficulties in marriage, have to work a good deal harder to make the marriage succeed, have to develop insight and understanding to a greater degree than people of the same faith background, but it has been my observation also that often the differences of background make the marriage richer and the extra effort required makes the marriage a better marriage.

I cannot generalize about interfaith marriages. So much depends upon the individuals involved. I tend to discourage such marriages when the couple have failed to apprehend or discuss the prospects that lead to tension.

I favor interfaith marriages so long as both members to the marriage are *not* devout believers in their own particular religious background.

I always urge couples with mixed backgrounds to find a *common* faith first. There are tensions enough that exist to make marriage difficult without adding to the problem by expecting one of the parties to capitulate to the faith of the other.

The opinions expressed by these men may be regarded as typical of Unitarian-Universalists. They emphasize the individualistic, non-conforming attitudes of ministers who, religiously, are far to the left of the Protestant and Roman Catholic Churches and of the Jewish Synagogue.

ETHICAL CULTURAL SOCIETIES

There is no opposition to mixed marriage by the Ethical Culture Societies because of doctrine. Whatever feeling there may be arises as a matter of personal concern alone. Algernon D. Black,[19] one of the chief spokesmen of the Ethical Cultural movement, writes: "Only continuous increase in the communication between members of religious groups and only unceasing education for understanding and respecting differences can overcome the resistance and conflict over such inter-marriages."

Now that we have looked at the opinions, official and personal, of the spokesmen of various church bodies, it is important to look, too, at the attitude of those men who represent Protestant youth organizations at universities representative of those attended by our own sons and daughters.

Twelve clergymen—leaders[20] of Protestant Student-Youth Organizations on representative Eastern college and university campuses—were asked to express their opinion with respect to the possibility of an increase of intermarriage. The question specifically asked of them was: "In your opinion, is the number of students who discuss the possibility of their intermarriage increasing? _____ about the same? _____ decreasing? _____ than there were about five years ago?" In reply, six of these men indicated that intermarriage was increasing on their campuses while four declared that it was "about the same," and two offered no opinion.

In reply to the question: "Do you believe that interfaith marriages can, in the main, work out successfully?" two clergymen replied "yes" while eight replied "no." Two other replies were conditional in that they said, "It would depend upon the circumstances in each case."

Reasons for these replies, both affirmative and negative, as stated by these clergymen follow:

I think that intermarriage leads to an increasing area where there is the tendency to "soft pedal" strongly held convictions. The problem is doubly difficult in the raising of children. Somebody is "left out" or there is nothing to be left out of this homogenization process.

The surface arrangement whereby each of the parties goes to his own faith never seems to be such a neat and simple thing; nor does it do

anything toward bringing the family together as a unit in worship or otherwise.

Intermarriage cannot occur without loss of an important dimension in human relationships. People can live together and share significantly, but they can't share at the point where they should and most need to share. The religious climate of family life will suffer.

They can only work out successfully if clear decisions regarding religious involvement are made prior to the marriage.

The intermarriages *can work* out, but the statistics indicate more tensions than elsewhere. Still I note that most of the intermarriages *do* work out.

Although I have seen more intermarriages that have worked out than those that haven't, I would say it depends on the propinquity of in-laws and the degree of real devotion to religious life (it is easy for the non-committed person to intermarry) but is this an argument for it?

It depends upon how strong the religious opinions of the parties to the intermarriage really are. A strong Catholic and a strong Protestant (who intermarry) will have trouble.

If the "faith" means anything to either or both parties the issue (of difference in religion) will eventually come up, especially if and where there are children. My advice is that it be worked out first.

I am against interfaith marriage because I believe the family ought to be based and grow around one faith. Separate faiths mean that man and wife and children cannot share their religion. I believe that interfaith marriages *may* work out O.K., but it all depends on how strong the faith of each partner is. Two strong and differing faiths have little chance. Usually one partner is weak or indifferent, faith-wise, and thus conflict between the partners is lessened.

There is no reason why anyone, on moral grounds, can oppose inter-religious marriages. Every person is free to marry whom he chooses. I think, however, that the more variant the factors are in the personality and background of two people in a marriage, the greater is the chance for difficulty and probably marital failure. I would caution against intermarriages which cause such added difficulties— On the other hand, if a couple can "live above" the possible added difficulties of an intermarriage, I believe that such marriages have considerable value in promoting religious tolerance and understanding. Each case must be dealt with individually and even then it is difficult to make a judgment.

Of the two clergymen who stated that "interfaith marriages can, in the main, work out successfully," one gave as his reason:

My non-clinical observation is that the difficulties in interfaith marriages do not find their cause in religious differences even though it may appear to be the case. I feel that interfaith marriages will be as successful as the other marriages.

In the second affirmative (Unitarian) reply, the reasoning is as follows:

Modern man no longer exists in groups of isolated cultures. Increased communication and association plus a startling increase in the number of members in the human family have caused a rapidly developing single homogenized, universal *human* culture to appear and to evolve. I believe that cross-fertilization of ideas and races is healthy and will result in creative bursts of energy and ideas such as the world has never known. The dawn of Universal human history is beginning. Should I fight it?

Seven of the twelve replies indicate a belief that the elimination of religious and color bars in fraternities will play a positive role in increasing the number of mixed marriages. Yet these clergymen suggest other factors which will, in their opinion, tend to increase such marriages. Among them are: premarital sexual "involvement"; "a drift away from the family background faith into a watered-down irrelevant faith; emotional insecurity," "the prevalent view of 'romantic love' as the only criterion of marriage"; "sentimental attitude toward the possibility of solving difficulties (in the intermarriage situation)"; "social climate and opinion"; "the prevailing attitude among young people that there are really no differences in the faiths and that one is just as good as another"; "the pluralistic situation of our society"; "a Herberg Protestant-Catholic-Jew Amalgam."

In ten out of the twelve replies, it should be noted, mention was made of the weakening of religious ties and "no commitment."

Attitudes toward interracial marriages, as expressed by these clergymen, include the following:

There are certainly no religious or ethical grounds for opposing Negro-White marriages. In fact, I think it is morally and ethically wrong to oppose such marriages on the usual basis. I favor each person marrying the person with whom he falls in love. However, when people of different races marry they should consider the difficulties which they will face and be sure they can surmount them before going through with the marriage. I have known some very successful inter-racial marriages. I have also known some very unsuccessful marriages of people of the same race and cultural background. Therefore, each situation must be judged on its own merit. (Church of the Brethren)

I have no objection to inter-racial marriages provided that the persons involved are well aware of the *social* problems they will face

and provided, too, they are strong enough to face them fearlessly. (Presbyterian)

I am in favor of inter-racial marriages theoretically, ideally and, in some cases, actually. The chief barrier to such marriages is cultural and social, not racial. If a couple is mature, strong, realistic and plan to live in some fairly open culture or section of society, inter-racial marriage is O.K. (Episcopal)

Replies in the case of interfaith marriages were generally less equivocal and uncertain than were those involving the question of inter-racial marriages—a characteristic noted in the Catholic and Jewish clergy as well.

The views of pastors in congregations throughout the country not directly associated with colleges and universities was also sought.

Forty-nine Protestant ministers, representing major denominations, all of whom have served congregations over a period of many years, in all areas of the country were invited to answer certain questions put to them by the author. Of these 42 responded. Included in the denominations are Presbyterian, Episcopal, Methodist, Church of God, United Church of Christ, Lutheran, Reformed Church in America, and Baptist. These clergymen were chosen, after consultation with the Reverend William Genné of the National Council of Churches of Christ in America. Each was asked to indicate if there were intermarried Protestant-Catholic, Protestant-Jewish, or other couples affiliated with his church. In every case, the answer was in the affirmative. Of interest, too, is the fact that the degree of mobility from one Protestant denomination to the other appears to be high. In one case (a Presbyterian) the reply interpreted "intermarriage" in an interesting manner:

I consider all marriages to be intermarriages. Everyone comes from a different religious background just by being different. The important point is whether or not they can find a common culture and way of life for the future.

In 37 out of the 42 responses, these Protestant clergymen expressed opposition to intermarriage involving Catholics or Jews. Some of their comments follow:

Marriage involves the *whole* of one's life. There must be common interests and common purposes. The children are entitled to and must be given a religious education by both parents. This cannot be done if the children are required to attend the church or synagogue of one of

the parents and are excluded from attendance upon the other. Obviously to attend both, makes for confusion. I am very much opposed to intermarriages between Protestants and Jews or Protestants and Roman Catholics. I am strongly opposed to inter-racial marriages of whatever kind and would not officiate at one. The problems are too great.

I oppose out-group marriages generally. Actually, I view each partnership specifically. I feel that the marriage bond is further strengthened by common interests and affinities commonly associated with the in-group relationships.

The studies I have seen indicate that intermarriages have fewer chances for happiness. Too frequently there must be compromises that make religious life difficult if not impossible for the intermarrieds.

If there is a basic difference in the religious orientation of people then every decision is a potential point of disagreement. Further, it is really not only individuals that marry but families!

Intermarriage is a source of division and ultimate conflict between people. It produces either indifference or complete abdication of the religious life for the entire family. There is no unified religious perspective for the family by which they can acquire strength.

For persons of strong religious faith, problems in an inter-religious marriage are unavoidable. It is our responsibility to see to it that young people are discouraged from entering into such a relationship. If they do intermarry let them know what they are getting into.

Such marriages make for confusion for children, a lack of sharing worship experience and increasing indifference toward religion of one or the other faith.

Parents need a united religious life. There is more than likely to be conflict in the training of children. The demand of the Roman Catholic that the Protestant give up the right to train children born of the marriage, makes me angry.

Partners in marriage ought to have a common faith. The idea of "one-flesh" relationship in marriage set forth in the Bible makes that clear.

Whom one marries ought to be a personal responsibility rather than a church responsibility. Yet two faiths cannot merge unless one party is only a nominal believer or unless one or both of them compromise. Yet a decision will have to be made on how to rear the children of an interfaith marriage. I can only see the likelihood of heartache and the possibility of a house divided against itself.

From four clergymen who did not oppose intermarriage, we have the following comments:

Much depends upon the circumstances. I would urge that the couple go in the direction of one church. But if I feel the relationship between these two can be a genuine one and if the couple understands fairly well the problems that may arise, I try to help them make the adjustment.

Marriage can bring understanding, tolerance and co-operation within the membership of previously isolated groups. Old lines of group superiority are breaking down rapidly and marriage between differing religious groups helps the process along.

I have neither encouraged nor opposed interfaith marriages but have tried to help those contemplating such a union to understand what is involved. I have great faith in the abilities of persons to meet such situations successfully.

I think that we must try to help these young people. We ought not to keep people who love each other apart. It is our duty to help them enrich their lives and whatever counsel I can give them that will help them to meet admittedly difficult situations arising out of interfaith marriage, I want to provide.

Each of the 42 Protestant clergymen believes that interfaith marriages will continue to increase within the next decade. These ministers indicate an increase in the number of young people who come to them to discuss such a possibility. All are opposed to interracial marriages and give a variety of reasons therefor. They seem to agree that if interfaith intermarriage is likely to be difficult, marriages involving persons of different colors would be even more difficult. Yet, they venture the guess that interracial marriages, too, will increase within the next decade. They speak of the problems that the children of interracially married people might have. They express the hope that such marriages are not entered into as a means of demonstrating rebellion against parents. In no case do they decry such marriages as "contrary to the will of God." (There was but one Southern clergyman in the sample.)

Intermarriage between Protestants of one denomination and another, between Protestants and Catholics and, in lesser degree, between Protestants and Jews is obviously increasing. Most intermarriages involve Protestants and Catholics because the latter happen to be members of the largest minority religious group in America (almost 20 per cent of all church members) and the opportunities for social contacts are greater. Despite formal opposition to interfaith marriages by

Protestant Church leaders and contrary to the formally stated position of most of the Protestant Church bodies, intermarriages involving nominal Protestants continue at a fairly rapid pace.

LUCY AND TOM

Lucy and Tom have been married for eight years. They have three children. Both are college graduates and Tom is a resident in surgery at a major hospital. In addition to the usual problems that often confront young marrieds, these two have a "special" problem, for Lucy has always identified herself as Protestant while Tom is a devout Catholic. They were married by a priest because Lucy, though not converted to Catholicism, pledged herself to rear their children in the Catholic faith. The two refuse to call their marriage a "success." Both Lucy and Tom are now seeking guidance from a marriage counselor. Lucy has also been psychoanalyzed. Unhappiness and tensions between these two are obvious. Lucy's personal insecurities, pique with parents, even rebellion, seem to have moved her toward marriage with Tom, whose religious convictions and church affiliation, aided by a happy childhood home, provide him security and strength.

LUCY

Our marriage is not an unqualified success. I must say that at the very beginning in order to make clear how I really feel. I have every hope that our problems—my problems—will be resolved. But I'm afraid I must say what my heart tells me. The truth is that, so far, things haven't worked out.

As for me, I'm afraid that I can't explain it all. But perhaps, as I tell my story I will understand things better than I have up to now.

Let me tell you about my early years. I was born in New York City. For many years during my childhood I lived in a suburb not far from Boston. During my teens, I lived in the city of Buffalo.

My early school years were spent in the suburb. Later, when my parents moved to Buffalo, I went to a private school for a few years. The last two years of my high-school days were spent in a Buffalo school. I don't know

why I went to the private school. It just happened. My folks may have thought that it would be a good place for me to learn something but when, for no reason that makes sense to me, I told my parents that I wanted to complete high school in a public high school, there was no problem about it at all. I simply enrolled in the fall of the year and that was that.

I have one sister who is older than I. She lives in New York, Greenwich Village. She regards herself as a writer. I would say that unofficially she is a writer. But officially she is a clerk in a large department store and hates every minute of it. Someday she may begin to sell her stories, but to this date she hasn't. She is not married. There are, as yet, no prospects of marriage, either.

As for me, I attended Barnard College in New York City. I must say that, even though I did rather well in my studies, I did not have an easy time arriving at a decision concerning what my major would be. For two years, it was anthropology and then I kind of drifted into English. Although I graduated about ten years ago, I don't feel that I got all that I could have out of my college years. It was a good school, but somehow I couldn't find myself. I graduated, as I say, but I should have done much better than I did.

I met the boy to whom I am married when I was a student at Barnard. He was at Columbia College—just across the street. In fact, we happened to take a course in music appreciation together. I forgot to mention that I lived in the dorms with the exception of my junior year when I got a "room and board" job outside the dormitories. It seemed important for me to be on my own as much as possible. Even though my parents were comfortable, economically speaking, and had certainly never raised any question about my working, I felt that it was the thing for me to do and they never objected.

My parents are very well regarded in their community. My father is the executive director of a major social service agency. He is regarded as one of the city's leading citizens. My mother never graduated from a college or university, but she did attend a New England finishing school. My father is a graduate of a New England college. He was born in a small New England town and later, from there, went on to college.

I don't really like talking about my family. I think I would rather talk about how I met Tom and what happened. [*Editor's Note:* Lucy talks instead, about her parents.]

I can't say that I or my parents were ever regular church-goers. My mother had been reared as a Congregationalist, but she had no ties to any church. My father, too, came from New England stock, but there wasn't very much of religion in him either. My father was very much of a public figure. Ever so many important people knew and liked him. He was everybody's friend. But, I must say, I always saw a whale of a difference between his publicly expressed ideas and those he expressed in private. I think I began to rebel against both of my parents, perhaps more so against my father. It was never that he appeared to try to direct me, but there was something disturbing, to me at least, in the way he acted with my sister and me and the things he said in public.

The rejection of my father by my sister was even stronger than mine. She just didn't want to have anything to do with anything he represented.

I do remember that I went to a Congregational Sunday School as a very young child and that, as an older child, I went to an Episcopalian Sunday School, but there was never any strong or cohesive kind of feeling about church upbringing. I feel as though I just drifted through, I guess.

As I look back over the years and try to figure things out, it seems to me that the feeling that existed between my parents and myself must have resulted from a clash of personalities. My father was very domineering. My mother was not. I came to regard my father as a—hypocrite. Yes, that is the word that describes it. I remember that once, when I had gone on a date with a Polish boy, my father, who always gave everyone the impression that he was the most tolerant, understanding man on earth, said to me, "Must you always pick people from minority groups to chum with or go with?" I recall how shocked I was at this kind of question, especially because he had always prided himself on having a Catholic bishop as a dear friend. They were on a first-name basis. Whether my father really feels that the Anglo-Saxon white is the only breed that should survive is hard to tell. But that is what he said to me and I shall never forget how it shocked me. I feel that anyone who acts this way should at least be honest enough to admit that he is acting. Anyone can see the split between what he said to me and the way he acted in public.

When I was younger, I suppose I noticed these things, but I never gave voice to my disagreement with them. But as I grew older, particularly during my college years, I think I openly rebelled, as did my sister.

There was something more. He refused to discuss things after he had made one of his mighty pronouncements. He was absolutely close-minded. He didn't want to be disturbed in his thinking. Even when I openly gave expression to my opposition to his ideas, I never felt that either my father or my mother paid very much attention or gave any consideration to my ideas. I became quite distant from them both. Someone described this as "rebellion" on my part. Well, perhaps it was, but I only felt that I was withdrawing myself from them as had my sister. As I look back upon that period of my life, it is especially difficult to understand it because I know that people in our community generally regarded our family as a good and happy one. But insofar as I am concerned, we weren't that at all. During the last half of my high-school years and practically all of the time I was in college, I think I had rejected my parents. My mother was strongly aware of it. She felt hurt with me and rather confused by it all. She didn't know why I was so hostile. As for my father, I used to think that he wasn't aware of it at the time, but now, as I look back on it, I think that perhaps he was, only he said and did nothing to straighten matters out with me and my sister.

When I met Tom, I had no idea that he was a Catholic. It really made no difference to me—or at least, so I thought. I had no firm religion or church affiliation that was more than nominal and as long as Tom was a person whom I liked and respected, that was really all that mattered. Tom

and I dated for about a year before we got serious. There had never been any real discussion between us about religion, but I knew that he was a Catholic, a convinced Catholic and a liberal Catholic. I was somewhat attracted by that, too. I think I kind of envied Tom his strong belief in a strong institution—the Church.

When I told my folks that I was planning to marry Tom, there was considerable opposition. It was one thing to like Catholics in theory and quite another to marry one. My father, in his domineering way, insisted that I break it up. But my mother approached matters more subtly. She asked me if I realized that being married to a Catholic I would not only not have anything to say about the Church my children would join, but that it was against Catholic principles to practice birth control. There were discussions and arguments, but nothing proved effective. I had made up my mind.

Tom and I were married in the Church, the Roman Catholic Church, that is. I gave my consent to having our children reared as Catholics. I knew that my marriage to a Catholic made my parents unhappy. However, I feel that my mother's objections were so completely unrealistic. She believed in all the old wives' tales that are told about Catholics. She even said that being a Catholic was not something to be proud of. But she and my father, seeing that I had every intention of going through with the marriage, attended the service which was performed by a priest.

I still cannot understand why they should have been so obviously disturbed about my marriage to Tom. I had always dated boys of other religions. Besides, as I told you, religion didn't mean much to me or to my family. My roommate at college had been Jewish. I had had many Jewish friends there and at high school. Why all the excitement? At least, Tom has something he can call his own. His religion gives him peace and it is his. I know that I just don't have anything like that.

Although I was not a Catholic when I married Tom, I remember that for some time *after* our marriage I experienced a slight degree of pressure from Tom's mother to change to Roman Catholicism. It was intimated early in our marriage that it would be nice if I could. Her point was that she felt it would be much better for the children as well as for the family unit. But her talks to me were never conducted in an unpleasant manner. I guess Tom's folks would not really press me on this point. Tom's brother has married a girl who used to be Protestant and she has since converted to Catholicism.

For a while I thought maybe my problems were directly associated with the fact that Tom was doing all this medical-school work and then interning. We were living on money that came from our folks. And I was having children. I now have three—two girls and a boy. All the housework and the scrimping seemed to upset me and make me very nervous. Of course, most of the money we lived on came from Tom's G.I. bill. You see, Tom had been in the navy. I take it out on people these days—my children, and my husband, I take it out on myself, too. My oldest child is certainly aware of my bursts of anger and irritability, but the younger ones are not yet

aware of it. Tom gets a lot of my anger. I'm trying to find out why I should be this way. I've visited a psychiatrist and I've been analyzed by an analyst.

My relations with Tom's parents are really very good. At the beginning of our marriage I felt that the relationship was, in fact, better than with my own father. Insofar as my parents are concerned, I was withdrawn with my mother also. After our marriage I know that my mother often felt hurt because I seldom, if ever, phoned her, and when she called me, I was very rude and very short with her. Even if we were together an afternoon would end up by my being in a fury with her.

Matters have improved a bit in my own family relationships in the past several years. I seem to have developed some kind of feeling for my own parents I never had before. I'm not sure exactly why or how this has happened. I think I feel a greater sense of sympathy for their position on many matters, perhaps even including religion that I did not understand clearly before.

Of late, things have gotten so difficult that together Tom and I have been consulting a marriage counselor for some time.

My reactions may have something to do with Tom's religion or with the promise I gave to rear the children as Catholics. I'm not really very sure about it. I do think that Tom's upbringing and schooling had much more of an organized flavor about it—it was much more parent-directed than mine was. I feel as though my parents never directed me. I seem to be torn between a feeling of rebellion against my parents and a rebellion, too, against some of the very direction I respect so much in Tom's parents. I'm sure that I have nothing against Tom's religion. But there is the feeling that, good as it may be, am I not being *directed*? Am I being obliged to do certain things about my children's upbringing that are not really what I want? Even though I solemnly agreed to it before our marriage and certainly intend to live up to my pledge, it is difficult to take.

Whether religious difference is *the* irritant, I cannot say. I just don't know; it may be one of many things.

How could someone like myself, with rather loose convictions on religion—or a lack of positive religious convictions—marry a very convinced Catholic? Well, for one thing, I feel that Tom is a good Catholic and a liberal Catholic. Before we were married, I didn't feel drawn to the Church, but I did *not* feel repelled by it. I would say, rather, that I was somewhat attracted by it. I think I kind of envied Tom his strong belief in a strong institution. Since we have married, I find myself becoming a great deal more prejudiced against the Church and Catholics than I ever was before I was married. Sometimes I rather feel that my anti-Catholic feelings are actually "anti-Tom" feelings. There may even be a bit of jealousy in my attitude, for I sometimes feel that Tom's relationship to the Church is stronger than his relationship to me.

I do not think that I can describe our marriage up to this point as successful. Yet it may be that, given time to straighten things out, we can make a go of it.

We just came back from a vacation during which we were quite tense with each other. Yet, I wouldn't have wanted to be there alone and I can't think of anyone else I would rather have been with than Tom. So, for that reason, I feel that basically, our marriage is going to be happy. But when? I can't say.

TOM

Lucy and I have been married for eight years and as I sat here listening to her I was thinking how much I have forgotten about her and her problems and how much, too, I need to refresh my own memory about myself and my background.

I was born in Hyannis, on Cape Cod. My mother is a Catholic and Dad is not, although he insisted that I and my sisters, both are younger than I, be brought up Catholic. I attended a parochial school in a nearby town through the sixth grade. Then I went on to public school for the seventh and eighth grades as well as for high school. I'm certain that my folks would have wanted me to continue in parochial school had it not been that in the junior high—that begins with the seventh grade—they added shop and science courses which weren't available at that time in the parochial schools. The family must have felt that it would be a better thing for me to go to the public school. When I graduated from high school, I went on to Columbia and graduated from there. My major was biology. My sisters, in accordance with our parents' wishes, went to a Catholic university.

Now, I mentioned that my father is not a Catholic and I can see that you have been wondering about that. My father, who is a successful business executive, was never converted to Catholicism. He and my mother were married by a priest and I know that could happen only if he gave his solemn pledge to rear their children as Catholics. Somehow, though, I don't believe that his acting as he did with respect to us and our religious education depended altogether on that pledge because Dad would go to church—the Catholic Church—every Sunday, with us or with Mother. Dad supports the Catholic Church and has supported it financially all these years. Although it is very definite that he is not a Catholic, he goes to Mass with us, too. It is because of his sense of regard for the Church. I still do not quite understand what it is that he doesn't accept about the Church because he certainly knows all the liturgy of the Mass and many of the beliefs much better than even I do.

Mother's folks have always been Catholics and she certainly is a good one. She is devoted to the Church. My father, who came from a Protestant family background, met my mother at the beach. Their parents had adjoining cottages.

I'm told that my mother's parents definitely opposed their daughter's marriage to a non-Catholic. Still they ultimately accepted the marriage which must certainly be regarded as a happy one. Now, this isn't just my opinion about it. Let me tell you what happened one day when I was attending a Catholic Youth Organization meeting. A priest was talking and the subject of mixed marriage came up every so often. We had discussion groups on this subject and I always took the stand that there was nothing wrong with mixed marriages. One night, after I had made that statement, the priest took me aside and said, "Now, look, you are never going to understand what would be wrong with a mixed marriage because you've got an example of one that has worked out very well." Perhaps that is really why I feel that mixed marriage can work out well. Even though there are overtones of this problem in my own marriage, I still believe that such a marriage can work out.

I have been and, in fact, am a practicing Catholic. I go to Mass regularly; I follow the practices of the Church and I observe its ritual. I've done so all through the years and I still do. I find a certain satisfaction, a certain peace in being a Roman Catholic. I have talked with Lucy about it occasionally, but this is something that I feel is lacking in her. She doesn't respond to religion as I do. To paraphrase, the Catholic Church says: The purpose of life is to do good here on earth for eternal happiness in Heaven. Now, Lucy doesn't feel that way at all. She doesn't feel that she is doing good on earth for happiness in Heaven. The idea doesn't move her, yet it moves me. Even though our children will be brought up as Catholic, because, in a formal sense, that is settled—it was settled when we were married by a priest, there *is* a difference between "bringing up children" and "bringing them up as Catholics," and I don't think Lucy quite accepts the full implications of that. I feel that to bring up our children as Catholic will add *purpose* to their lives as it has to mine.

I don't know if it is really a point of friction between us, but it seems to be. I try to have the children go to church and it seems to be a burden to Lucy to get them ready to go to Mass on Sunday mornings.

After I graduated from Columbia, I spent three years in the navy. Lucy and I got married while I was still in the service. I was a commissioned officer. As soon as I finished with the navy, I started medical school. Lucy and I had seen a good deal of each other in college. We had dated for about a year before we really became serious. It had occurred to me that she was a Protestant and I was a Catholic, of course, but it did not seem to be of special consequence because there was never any discussion between us about this difference in religion. There are several other reasons why the subject didn't loom so large in my thoughts. The first is that, in our family, there had never been any talk about my dating non-Catholic or Catholic girls. Neither of my parents was shocked when I told them I was dating a girl of Protestant background. All that I can recall mother saying is, "It would be nice if she were Catholic." But there was no pressure on that score from anyone, including other members of the family. And here I come to yet another reason why I think the whole idea proved to be so

easily acceptable and understandable to my parents. Not only was my father a non-Catholic, but there were other non-Catholics in my mother's family. One of her sisters married a Protestant and another married a Protestant who converted to Catholicism. So, you see, the family had rather grown accustomed to the idea. And one of my sisters will be marrying a boy who used to be a Protestant and has converted to the Church.

There had been physicians and surgeons in my family. I hadn't really given much thought to any profession until a cousin suggested that my interest in biology could very well lead on to a medical career. Perhaps I'm easily influenced to act on the basis of such a remark, but I felt that my cousin was quite right and I'm glad about the profession I've chosen and I'm reasonably certain that I'll do fine. Well, after I got my M.D. degree, I decided to go back into the navy for internship, which was fine with Lucy, because I would be getting some training and at the same time be able to build up a dollar surplus which we needed badly. I was stationed in Boston which was fine for the both of us and our children as well. Our oldest child was born before I got out of the navy. The other two were born while I was in medical school. I now have a residency in surgery in a major hospital.

To come back to my parents again, I have always gotten along very well with them and with my sisters. I would say that where I think of my parents with affection—that's the correct word—Lucy tells me that whenever she thinks of her parents, she is filled with tension.

Sometimes I believe that our problems—and we *do* have them—are due to the fact that in a mixed marriage there can be serious doubts about decisions one has made—such as rearing children as Catholics. At other times, I feel that our basic problem stems from Lucy's attitude of rebellion against her parents. Lucy believes that I'm always wary of her ideas on the subject of religious upbringing, but she has told me many times that there's no question in her mind about our children going to parochial school. She says "by prior agreement they should go to parochial school." That is so. The matter should be settled, but deep down, I'm still not so sure it has been. When the children have all been enrolled in parochial school, *then* I'll be certain.

I think that the matter of religion probably, in some way or other, affects our marriage adversely, but there are other factors as well, that might be called variables. Lucy agrees with me on this point. Religion is always an area of possible conflict. It's one of those things you have to try to skirt because the lighting of a match might blow up the whole thing. I had always assumed that in such a marriage as ours—with Lucy having no set beliefs or convictions—it would be easy for her to accept or live by my convictions, but this is merely an assumption. I'm certain that I could never have married a non-Catholic who was a firm believer in any other religion.

I can't jump up and say dramatically, "Yes, ours is a successful marriage." But I can say that we are both trying to work out our problems, our differences, personal, financial and religious. I'm still hoping things will work out.

THE CATHOLIC POINT OF VIEW

The position of the Catholic Church with respect to intermarriage is clear. Interfaith intermarriages are opposed unless a pledge is given that the children born of a marriage involving a Catholic and a non-Catholic will be reared as Catholics. Other conditions must also be met to the satisfaction of the Church before a priest will consent to officiate at the marriage service. The participation of a priest in the marriage service implies that all requirements have been met. The marriage is then "valid" inasmuch as it has some degree of Church sanction.

Valid mixed marriages, though sanctioned by the Church, must still in some places be performed in the rectory and not in the church. The rite of the Nuptial Mass and the Nuptial blessing is forbidden, nor may the banns be published. In this manner a distinction is made between the marriage of two Catholics and the marriage of a Catholic to a non-Catholic. Half-hearted approval of valid mixed marriage is thus indicated.

Marriages are termed "invalid" when they have not been performed by a Catholic priest because the conditions for such a marriage have not been met by either or both parties, or if a non-Catholic minister or civil servant officiated at the marriage service. Inasmuch as marriage is regarded as a sacrament that can be administered only by a priest of the Catholic Church, public officials and other civil authorities may not officiate in a religious sense (though they have the legal right to do so). Such a marriage is regarded as nonexistent or null and void in the eyes of the Church.

Schnepp designates the term "mixed marriage," in Catholic terminology, as a marriage between a Catholic and a non-Catholic who does not subsequently become converted to Catholicism in one of two ways:[1]

(a) *Mixta-Religio*—a mixed marriage in which the non-Catholic was validly baptized;
(b) *Disparitas Cultus*—a mixed marriage in which the non-Catholic was not validly baptized.

Father John Thomas defines a "mixed convert marriage" as a marriage between a Catholic and a non-Catholic who subsequently becomes converted to Catholicism.

A "validated mixed marriage" is a term used to describe a marriage

149

between a Catholic and a non-Catholic which was originally invalid but was later regularized by a priest.

An "invalid mixed marriage" is one at which a non-Catholic or a civil officer has officiated because the requirements of the Catholic Church have not been fulfilled.

Twenty-six and one-half per cent of all marriages in the United States in 1962 were, according to the *Official Catholic Directory* for that year valid mixed marriages.[2] In the twenty-six Archdioceses in the United States, the *Directory* indicates that 24 per cent[3] were (valid) mixed marriages. In the Dioceses (covering smaller areas than the Archdioceses) 29 per cent[4] of the marriages were (valid) mixed marriages.

The Catholic Church cannot report the number or per cent of *invalid* mixed marriages in which a Catholic is involved because it has no official way of gaining such information.

As we have already noted, the Catholic Archdioceses represent those areas which have the largest number of Catholics. The opportunities to meet and associate with other Catholics are greatest. Yet, it is estimated that almost one-fourth (24 per cent) of the marriages involving a Catholic in these Archdioceses are "invalid." The suggestion then that the total number of such marriages represents at least half of all marriages involving a Catholic seems reasonable.

Father Thomas[5] believes that the number of invalid marriages in the United States involving a Catholic, is, in fact, higher than those that are "valid." In his study of 29,581 mixed marriages[6] in 132 parishes in the East and Middle West, he reported that 39.6 per cent were "invalid."

He found further that,[7] "in 6,744 divorces involving Catholics from the Middle West region, 60.4 per cent of these unions were based on invalid marriages in the first place." He states also that he believes that "two out of five (of the mixed marriages) are invalid throughout the nation."

The National Catholic Family Life Convention,[8] held in 1956, stated that it believed that one-fourth to one-third of all marriages involving a Catholic were mixed marriages.

One-third of all Catholics now marry outside of their faith and, of these, according to Cervantes,[9] "four out of every ten are lost immediately . . . since their marriage is outside of the Church and hence invalid, of the remaining six . . . two more are ultimately lost because their interest and conformity gradually evanesce."

The number of mixed marriages involving a Catholic is believed to be increasing. Kane[10] predicts that the number of valid mixed marriages will increase to 50 per cent. What the number of invalid mixed

marriages will be within another decade can only be guessed at. It would seem, on the basis of the evidence already presented, that the number of such marriages will also continue to increase.

The number of Catholics in America has increased so markedly that, for every one Catholic in the year 1790 there are now almost 1,000 Catholics. The number of Jews has also increased, so that they constitute about 3 per cent of the nation's total population. Inasmuch as these two minority groups have, in ever-increasing numbers, become members of the middle and, on occasion, upper classes, we may understand why they have become more acceptable and more tolerated and, further, why their social contacts with each other and with Protestants will continue to increase.

One of the reasons for Catholic opposition to interfaith marriage is suggested by Kane's report that, in mixed marriages between Protestants and Catholics, where neither party changed his religion, 50 per cent of the children born of these marriages were reared as Protestants, 45 per cent were reared as Catholics and 5 per cent were reared without any religion.[11]

In another study, Schnepp[12] reported that "of every 10 children whose parents were *both* Catholic, 6 married a Catholic, 3 married a non-Catholic and 1 married without approval of the Church. He further points out, on the basis of evidence gathered from the study of one large parish on the Atlantic Seaboard that where only one of the parents was a Catholic, the proportion of mixed marriages among their children was about 50 per cent.

Fichter[13] believes that all evidence points to the fact that even valid mixed marriages eventually "represent a loss to the Church of the Catholic spouses and the children born to them" because so many drift away from the Church. He believes that the number of persons who, having been born of Catholic parents, contract invalid marriages, is exceedingly high, and regards them as a serious loss to the Church because here, too, so many break their ties with the Church as the result of their marriage.

This view is further supported by Elmer's[14] study of a Catholic parish in the city of Pittsburgh. He indicated that in the case of 480 all-Catholic families, 15 per cent missed Mass regularly. In the case of 61 valid mixed marriages in which the woman was a Catholic, 20 per cent missed Mass regularly; of 20 valid mixed marriages in which the man was a Catholic, 40 per cent missed Mass regularly; in 43 invalid mixed marriages, 53 per cent of the Catholics missed Mass regularly. Further, Elmer[15] has pointed out that the Catholic education of the children of mixed marriages is definitely different from that of the children of all-Catholic families. In these 480 all-Catholic families, 63

per cent of the children attended parochial school while 37 per cent were in public schools; in 61 valid mixed marriages where the woman was a Catholic, 45 per cent of the children were enrolled in parochial schools, while 55 per cent were enrolled in public schools; in 20 valid mixed marriages where the man was a Catholic, 30 per cent of the children were in parochial schools, 70 per cent were in public schools. In the case of 43 invalid mixed marriages only 20 per cent of the children were in parochial schools while 80 per cent were in public schools. The effect of mixed marriages, both valid and invalid, upon attendance of children at parochial schools is thus regarded as unfavorable.

The mother's influence, whether or not her "equality" has been established in the religious training of her children, is always marked. It becomes especially significant in the case of mixed marriages.

Landis[16] reported that in the case of mixed Catholic marriages, "less than half of the children (of valid mixed marriages) are brought up as Catholics." Whatever might have been the pre-marital agreements, the most common policy was that the mother took all responsibility for the religious training, resulting in the situation where "approximately 65 per cent of the boys and 75 per cent of the girls follow the faith of the mother." When the mother was the Catholic partner of the marriage and the father was Protestant, "the mother took complete charge of the religious education 38 times as often as did the father. When the father was Catholic and the mother, Protestant, the mother still took complete charge of the religious education 6 times as often as did the father."

According to the report of the Bishop's Committee of the Roman Catholic Church,[17] in 1943, the written promise to rear as Catholics children of Protestant-Catholic marriages at which a priest has officiated is not kept in 30 per cent of the valid mixed marriages. There is reason to suspect that the number of such unkept promises may be much larger for, as Father Francis J. Connell[18] pointed out, there have been "terrible inroads on the Catholic faith caused by mixed marriages."

The number of mixed marriages (valid and invalid) involving Catholics appears to be directly associated with the number of Catholics there are in a given community in relation to the general population: the larger the number of Catholics, the smaller the number of such marriages; the smaller the number of Catholics, the larger the number of mixed marriages.

Wherever the Catholic population is small, the number of exogamous marriages increases. An examination of the records of the *Official Catholic Directory* indicates that, in 1959, in such dioceses as Atlanta, Georgia, there were 170 mixed (valid) marriages with but 101 all-

Catholic marriages; in Charleston, South Carolina, of a total of 370 marriages performed, 233 were "mixed" (even though validated), while 137 were all-Catholic. The scarcity of prospective Catholic mates in certain areas of the country generally results in higher rate of mixed marriage. This is especially true when ethnic and other differences within the total population do not prevent contact between Catholics and non-Catholics. Even in such large communities as Buffalo, New York, where 4,977 marriages involving a Catholic were performed, 1,193 were "mixed" marriages (where one of the parties was a non-Catholic). In Brooklyn, New York, one of the largest Catholic communities, for the same year, 13.3 per cent of all Catholic marriages were "mixed." And in Boston, Massachusetts, where the Catholic population is reputed to be well over 75 per cent of the total population, the number of valid mixed marriages was 2,607 out of a total of 13,512 or about 19 per cent of the total number.

Whether or not the intermarriage will be valid depends not only on the proportion of Catholics to the total population but upon the relationship of the particular Catholic to his Church, his intensity of feeling for it, his acceptance of its ritual, his devotion to Catholicism as a particular religion of unique significance.

The number of Catholic females who will intermarry with non-Catholics is likely to be larger in a community where the number of Catholics is small because the desire to marry will continue to take precedence over one's religious identification.

Yet marriages between Catholics and non-Catholics are frowned upon by the Roman Catholic Church, which contends that, whatever else marriage may be, it certainly involves a contract between the parties. "A contract demands the meeting of minds, an agreement of view points, a joint resolution to pursue a common end, exactly defined." [19] To insure a happy marriage there must be a meeting of minds on such issues as birth control, divorce, the existence of children for this world alone or for another world as well, the meaning of life, good and evil, the nature of God, Catholicism argues.

Each of the issues mentioned above has a religious implication that cannot be ignored. Religious differences may imply lack of agreement on issues regarded as major. The likelihood of happiness in such mixed marriages is, therefore, not as great as it is where there is complete agreement between the parties. To the Catholic, marriage is both a contract and a sacrament that is under the control of the Church. The Church regards it as its right to apply and interpret the Divine Law, derived from Jesus himself.

The Church regards a marriage between a Catholic and a non-Catholic as a "communion in sacred things with those outside the

fold." Thus, such a marriage degrades the holy character of matrimony.

Inasmuch as the Church alone has the right to interpret the Law which is Divine, the Church, through the Council of Trent, declared that all "marriages" between Catholics and non-Catholics are null and void unless they are entered into before the proper ecclesiastical authority, namely the Roman Catholic Church.

The Church, while recognizing that not all mixed marriages are unhappy, believes that "a happy mixed marriage would be happier still if religious unity were added." [20] Because such marriages are "founded on compromise rather than communion" they constitute, at best, a "very inferior substitute."

The Church opposes mixed marriage not for reasons that may be regarded as sinister or even because of hatred or contempt for those of other faiths. It insists that its opposition is based on a "laudable and intelligent anxiety to insure the happiness of the wedded life of those who marry." No one can be certain that marriage between persons of the same religious faith will always prove to be happy, but both parents and the Church believe that in mixed marriages the odds against happiness are greater. The Church warns its members that their unions with non-Catholics will never be completely comfortable.

Despite its prohibition against mixed marriages in general, the Church may grant an exception or dispensation, allowing a Catholic to contract marriage with a non-Catholic. Dispensations may be granted from those laws that have been enacted by the spiritual rulers of the Church, the pope and the bishops, for the spiritual good of the Church members. Inasmuch as the Church, rather than God himself, initiated such ecclesiastical laws, the Church can grant a relaxation from their observance. Enacted by human beings, such laws must admit of exceptions. A dispensation implies that there are in a particular case circumstances present that would make the application of the law more harmful and beneficial. The Church finds that in the case of a weak Catholic, refusal to permit marriage to a non-Catholic will often result in the abandonment of his faith. It believes that if a devout Catholic is granted permission to marry a non-Catholic, the conversion of the non-Catholic will "sooner or later" [21] occur.

Historically, excepting for the New Testament which offers no prohibition against intermarriages other than those with heathens,[22] there gradually grew up a body of tradition against marriages with non-Christians, i.e., Jews; the prohibition later extended also to marriage with Protestants.

Despite its distinction between "valid" and "invalid" mixed marriage, it is important to remember that the marriage of a Catholic to a

person not formally converted to Catholicism is definitely frowned upon.

Pope Pius XI, in his encyclical, *Caste connubii* (Sections 82 and 85) made the position of the Church clear:

> This attitude of the Church to mixed marriages appears in many of her documents, all of which are summed up in the Code of Canon Law: "Everywhere and with the greatest strictness the Church forbids marriages between baptized persons, one of whom is a Catholic and the other a member of a schismatical or heretical sect; and if there is added to this the danger of the falling away of the Catholic party and the perversion of the children, such a marriage is forbidden also by the divine law." If the Church occasionally on account of circumstances does not refuse to grant a dispensation from these strict laws (provided that the divine law remains intact and the dangers above mentioned are provided against by suitable safeguards), it is unlikely that the Catholic party will not suffer some detriment from such a marriage. . . .
>
> Assuredly, also, there will be wanting that close union of spirit which as it is the sign and mark of the Church of Christ, so also should be the sign of Christian wedlock, its glory and adornment. For, where there exists diversity of mind, truth and feeling, the bond of union of mind and heart is wont to be broken, or at least weakened. From this comes the danger lest the love of man and wife grow cold, and the peace and happiness of family life, resting as it does on union of hearts, be destroyed.

A Catholic priest may officiate at the marriage of a Catholic and a non-Catholic if a "dispensation" or waiver has been obtained from the Catholic hierarchy. The dispensation is given only if there are "just and grave causes." Among others, these causes include (a) concern for the Catholic who resides in a community with a small Catholic population where the possibility of marrying a Catholic is, as a consequence, highly restricted, (b) fear that the couple might be married by a Protestant minister or civil magistrate unless the dispensation is granted. Written assurances must be given by the Catholic that every effort will be made to try to convert the non-Catholic to Catholicism after marriage, and that if the priest officiates at the marriage ceremony there will be no other (non-Catholic) ceremony.

The non-Catholic must promise in writing that (a) the Catholic partner to the marriage will be permitted to practice the Catholic religion and (b) that children borne of this marriage will be unconditionally educated and reared in the Catholic faith. If there is any question of the sincerity with which these promises are made, the Catholic partner is obliged under pain of mortal sin to break the engagement. The law

prohibiting marriages which may menace the faith of the Catholic is regarded as divine. A dispensation may not be granted under such circumstances. In some Catholic dioceses, the non-Catholic is required to accept a series of lessons or "instructions" from the priest, concerning Catholic doctrine as well as the duties of married life as understood by the Church.[23] The Catholic party to the marriage is also required to attend these classes, for it is believed that the chances of marital happiness are increased thereby.

A non-Catholic who wishes to have a priest officiate at his or her marriage is certainly not forced to agree to the premarital guarantees. It is his or her right to refuse to agree to these conditions, in which case it is equally the right of the Church to refuse to officiate. The Catholic Church states that it does not engage in coercion of the non-Catholic. Its conditions are clear and openly stated. Refusal to accept them is the right of any non-Catholic.

It must be understood that a Catholic who marries a non-Catholic without a dispensation commits a deadly sin according to his Church. He is forbidden to marry before any civil official even as he is prohibited from having a Protestant or other clergyman officiate at his marriage. Such a marriage although legal is done in sin and is, in the Catholic view, entered into under the displeasure of God. Intermarriages improperly entered into were termed "abominable marriages" by Pope Pius IX. Dispensations are given by the Church "with sorrow and to prevent greater evils."

What are the specific conditions under which a valid mixed marriage may take place?

The Church requires that an agreement be signed by the non-Catholic party if a priest is to officiate. The wording of the agreement may vary slightly in different dioceses. Its essence is as follows:

ANTE-NUPTIAL CONTRACT AND PROMISES

To be signed in duplicate in the presence of the priest by the parties entering a mixed marriage, and by two witnesses.

To be signed by the non-Catholic party

I, the undersigned, not a member of the Catholic Church, wishing to contract marriage with the Catholic party whose signature is also hereinafter affixed to this mutual agreement, being of sound mind and perfectly free, and only after understanding fully the import of my action, do hereby enter into this mutual agreement, understanding that the execution of this agreement and the promises therein contained are made in contemplation of and in consideration for the consent, marriage and consequent change of status of the hereinafter mentioned Catholic party, and I, therefore, hereby agree:

1. That I will not interfere in the least with the free exercise of the Catholic party's religion;

2. That I will adhere to the doctrine of the sacred indissolubility of the marriage bond, so that I cannot contract a sacred marriage while my consort is still alive, even though a civil divorce may have been obtained;

3. That all the children, both boys and girls, that may be born of this union shall be baptized and educated solely in the faith of the Roman Catholic Church, even in the event of the death of my Catholic consort. In case of dispute, I furthermore, hereby fully agree that the custody of all the children shall be given to such guardians as to assure the faithful execution of this covenant and promise;

4. That I will lead a married life in conformity with the Law of God and the teaching of the Catholic Church regarding birth control, realizing fully the attitude of the Catholic Church in this regard;

5. That no other marriage ceremony shall take place before or after this ceremony by the Catholic priest. In testimony of which agreement, I do hereby solemnly swear that I will observe the above agreement and faithfully execute the promises therein contained, and do now affix my signature in approval thereof.

The signature of the non-Catholic is required. Thereafter, the four promises to be made by the Catholic party are listed, preceded by a preliminary statement similar to that given above. The Catholic promise:

1. That I shall have all my children, both boys and girls, that may be born of this union, baptized and educated solely in the faith of the Roman Catholic Church. I understand that in case of my death or in the event of a dispute, the custody of all the children shall be given to such guardians as to assure the faithful execution of this covenant and promise;

2. That I will practice my Catholic religion faithfully and will strive, especially by example, prayer and the frequentation of the Sacraments, to bring about the conversion of my consort;

3. That I will lead a married life in conformity with the Law of God and the teaching of the Catholic Church regarding birth control, realizing fully the attitude of the Catholic Church in this regard;

4. That no other marriage ceremony shall take place before or after this ceremony by the Catholic priest.

It will be noted that four important promises are included in this agreement:

1. The promise that the Catholic party to the marriage will not be obstructed or hindered by the non-Catholic party in the practice of the Catholic religion.

2. The promise that all the children born of this marriage will be baptized and educated solely in the Catholic religion.

3. The promise that there will be but one marriage ceremony and that it will be a Catholic service (not Protestant or any other religion).

4. The promise that every effort will be made to convert as well as baptize the partner of such a marriage to Catholicism.

In addition to the above, some agreements include the promise that contraceptive devices will not be used contrary to the teachings of the Roman Catholic Church.

A convert to Roman Catholicism officially accepts the faith and practice of this Church. If the non-Catholic has already been baptized, a second baptism is not required, but a profession of faith is required. If there has been no prior baptism, then both baptism and a profession of faith are required.

The parish priest through whom the "petition for dispensation" must be transmitted to the Hierarchy of the Church, must give assurance that "every reasonable effort has been made to dissuade the Catholic party from this marriage, but without avail." [24]

The above agreement, according to the Church, can be broken only by death.

The moral force of the Ante-nuptial Agreement is very great even if it has no definitely legal binding upon the parties. A recent ruling[25] (June 6, 1961) of the New York Appellate Division points up the legal factors that are often involved:

> The Appellate Division ruled yesterday that three small children could remain with their Protestant mother even though she had made a pre-wedding agreement with her husband to rear them as Roman Catholics. The couple is now separated.
>
> The mother has asked the court for permanent custody of the children on the ground that the agreement was unconstitutional. However, the court said it would not pass on the enforceability of the agreement.
>
> The father had earlier received custody of the children from the State Supreme Court. Justice ———— then ruled that the pre-nuptial agreement was binding . . . In their decision, the justices said:
>
> In reaching this decision we do not pass upon the enforceability of the pre-nuptial agreement. The question may be presented at a later time when the children have reached the age which makes them less dependent upon mother care and which gives them sufficient maturity to receive religious instruction.

The Church demands that all children born of a mixed marriage shall be reared as Catholics. It denies, however, that it makes such demands because of a desire to control and dominate. It says that the sacrament of matrimony was instituted by Jesus "principally for the replenishment and growth of the religious society which He organized.

. . . Hence, if the Catholic Church solemnized the marriage of a couple who intended to deprive their children of an education in the Catholic faith, the Church would be party to an assault on the very nature of matrimony; she would be guilty of hideous disloyalty to the Founder of Christian wedlock. . . . To request the Catholic Church to officiate at a marriage wherein the man and wife have agreed to frustrate Christ's purpose is to ask the Church to preside at the desecration of one of her own sacraments. She simply must refuse." [26]

We emphasize the fact that there is an obligation upon the priest who has granted the dispensation to see to it that the signed agreement is kept. It is his direct concern that the children of the mixed marriage be reared in the Catholic faith. The Church is aware of the great influence of the mother upon the religious upbringing of her children. When the mother is a non-Catholic, the responsibility to keep her aware of her obligations rests with the priest. The Church believes that "there is no such thing as equality of Religion." [27] If, then, children are reared in another faith they have been deprived of their right to the true faith. This is, of course, "catastrophic." [28]

The Catholic Church is further opposed to interfaith marriages because it is also concerned with its own survival and with the strengthening of the Church through its adherents. Intermarriages may weaken the Church structure. The number of faithful, devout Catholics may be considerably reduced through parents who are divided in their loyalties. In Fichter's[29] study he found that about 30 per cent of all marriages performed over a ten-year period, in those parishes he studied were mixed marriages. However, a study of the census reports revealed that about 18 per cent of the couples actually living in the parish were partners in mixed marriages. He assumed that the difference between these two figures represents a loss to the Church of Catholic spouse and their children. These figures represent only valid mixed marriages. The number of those who have entered into invalid mixed marriages if added to the first figures, would suggest that the rate of loss to the Church of parents and their children must be at least 25 per cent. Catholics, like the other major religious groups, are concerned because they believe that "the absence of intimate union and mutual harmony" [30] between husband and wife is more likely to occur when their religious views and backgrounds differ.

Determined to do everything that can possibly be done to reduce the "loss" to the Church in the person of the children particularly, the Catholic priest is advised to attempt to reduce this loss to a minimum by accepting the inevitability of the marriage while, with unflagging kindness, urging the non-Catholic to become familiar with Church doctrine, with the hope of making a convert. Even if the non-Catholic does

not enter the Church, he or she will acquire "a better appreciation of the Church and the danger of perversion on the part of the Catholic will be lessened." [31]

Catholic youth are, nevertheless, urged to avoid dating non-Catholics.

> Suppose you're married to a non-Catholic. What's life like? You and your mate hold conflicting ideas over the most basic beliefs of your existence. Frequently there is little agreement on what life is all about—why you were born, what kind of life you are supposed to lead on earth, what you are supposed to do in marriage, what will happen to you after you die. . . . Other differences arise almost every day of your life. You must abstain from meat on Friday in memory of our Lord's sacrifice in giving His life for mankind. Your non-Catholic partner thinks the practice is silly. You want to arise early on Sunday to attend Mass. Your partner urges you to roll over and go back to sleep. . . . Instead of encouraging such sacrifices, your partner by word and deed indicates that they're totally unnecessary.[32]

A detailed account of the many differences in faith and practice between Catholic and non-Catholic is given in order that Catholic youth may be reminded of its religious responsibilities. Finally, they are reminded:

> The way to avoid a mixed marriage is at the beginning. Don't date non-Catholics and you'll never marry one. It's as simple as that.

Father John A. O'Brien[33] after listing twelve factors to be kept in mind when an interfaith marriage is being considered, says:

> The chief purpose of this presentation of the facts about mixed marriages is to show that they are replete with hidden dangers to the stability and success of the marriage, lead to religious indifference and loss of faith on the part of the parents and offspring, and bring various degrees of unhappiness to both the partners. These are not theories but facts distilled from the heartaches, headaches, and tears of persons who have contracted such marriages. . . .

The above statement is essentially the same as that made by most Protestant and Jewish religious leaders.

The "values" of the Church are also at stake in mixed marriage. Father Thomas[34] has pointed out that Catholics clearly "embrace a distinct set of family values." "Such [invalid] marriages lack the unity of belief and outlook necessary for happiness in marriage, because they involve risks to the Catholic's faith and morals and because they make the proper religious upbringing of children very difficult." [35] The

Church's attitude with respect to birth control is well known. It is not a simple matter to ask a person, however much in love he or she may be, to accept a new and different attitude and practice in this area of values when a violation of the Church's prohibition against birth control is regarded as a "sin." The Church's opposition to divorce is equally well known. A violation of the Church's injunction on this score is also sinful. Hence, a radical (to a Catholic these attitudes are certainly 'radical') change of attitude is difficult if not impossible. The fundamental differences that exist within the value systems of each religious group are not easily resolved. The problem then, although it may begin with the Church, reaches far beyond it.

My own experience with a goodly number of mixed marriage families, makes it clear that many such persons upon the birth of their first child, began to find "reasons" why promises and pledges made prior to marriage should not be honored. The emotional responses and even traumatic experiences of persons who, in good faith, prior to their marriage, have promised to rear their children as Jews or Catholics, and suddenly found it psychologically impossible to comply, must be recorded. Such experiences are not uncommon, as rabbis, ministers and priests will attest. Emotional responses after marriage vows have been made may not be the same as those *prior* to marriage, however honorable and well-intentioned the parties may be because the family and its religious values somehow play a more important role than young people are ready to acknowledge.

According to Father Thomas,[36] mixed marriages involving Catholics occur more frequently in the upper social class of society. In one large city, among 51,671 Catholic families, 8.5 per cent of the mixed marriages occurred in the lowest rental areas, whereas the rate jumped to 17.9 per cent in the highest rental areas and increased to 19.3 per cent in the suburban areas.

The number of mixed marriages involving a Catholic is, in fact, so large that Father Thomas has expressed his disagreement with the view of Kennedy[37] that "religious endogamy" (marriage within the same religious faith) will continue while marriage along nationality lines will decrease. He declares that the "triple melting pot idea is untenable insofar as Catholics are concerned" in that, as we have already pointed out, 39.6 per cent of all Catholic mixed marriages took place *outside* of the Church.

Is mixed marriage ultimately responsible for most annulments and separations among Catholics or are there many other factors that are even more responsible?

His Excellency Eric F. MacKenzie,[38] Auxiliary Bishop of the Archdiocese of Boston, who is in charge of The Tribunal of the Archdiocese,

where all matters pertaining to marriage, separation and annulment are ultimately presented, believes that "religious differences are practically never a matter of conscious difficulty. The proximate causes for separation fall into the usual categories of drinking, gambling and infidelity. A deeper-seated reason [than religious difference] appears to exist in practically every case: a serious degree of selfishness and callous disregard of the rights of the other party. Sometimes 'in-law trouble' is present and, in this connection, the religious background may strongly color the picture." He concludes with these words: "I am, however, convinced that most of the marriages break up for all the other reasons, and not because of the different religious beliefs of the parties."

Father Thomas[39] holds a similar view. He found "religion" to be but 2.9 per cent of the factors resulting in the breakdown of the Catholic marriages he studied; while 29.8 per cent involved "drink" and 24.8 per cent involved "adultery." The factors that may ultimately have led to alcoholism or even to adultery are not reported because they are not so easily ascertained. He states:

> Religion as a factor in the breakdown of marriage was surprisingly rare, although 17 per cent of the cases (studied) involved intermarriages.[40]

Inasmuch as none of the "cases" with which His Excellency Bishop MacKenzie and Father Thomas were concerned involved divorce, and further, inasmuch as the Church would have no formal knowledge of the ultimate disposition of *invalid* mixed marriages, the above view may prove only that in mixed marriages, where the authority of the Church is accepted, many factors other than difference in religion affect the marriage. It is questionable whether the other reasons for marital discord suggested by His Excellency are, in fact, the causes or the results of the mixed marriage.

The fact that "quarrels over religious difference" [41] do not necessarily cause interfaith marriages to break down does not, in itself, indicate that religious differences and disparate religio-cultural values have nothing to do with the situation. In my experience few persons who talk about their marital troubles ever begin with a discussion, or even an acknowledgement, of the *real* problems. Tangential, peripheral and secondary issues are generally presented completely out of focus, and blown up out of proportion, because it is so difficult for such persons to admit even to themselves, let alone to others, the primary sources of their difficulties.

Statistics here cannot prove what careful observation can suggest. People with problems tend to "beat all around the bush" before the

actual facts are brought to light. Even then, only those who recognize the religious overtones of their vexing problems, who understand that attitudes resulting from religious-value systems may have much to do with their difficulties, will tend to acknowledge the religious factor for what it is, a motivating force of tremendous power. Two values systems, differing from each other, can, I believe, create an impact that may ultimately result in separation or divorce.

Catholics appear more willing than either Protestants or Jews to marry outside their faith but, according to Landis[42] they indicate the least willingness to change faiths. The permissiveness of the Church, despite its insistence upon formal agreements and pledges on the part of the non-Catholic as well as the Catholic, does not affect its teaching that Catholicism is the one true religion. Nurtured with this belief and an awareness of the sinfulness of a change in religious allegiance, as taught by the Church, Catholic youth is hesitant to break affiliations. Protestants argue that the Church's qualified permissiveness with respect to interfaith marriage should be weighed against the attitude which views conversion to another faith as a sin, yet regards conversion to Catholicism in an altogether positive light. Converts to Catholicism, obtained through interfaith marriages, are not only accepted but are heartily welcomed by the Church. This is one of the views to which Protestants seem to object so vehemently. Roman Catholic theologian, Hans Küng[43] acknowledged this fact when, speaking in Chicago in April of 1963, he stated that his Church's canon law condemning mixed marriages solemnized in non-Catholic rites creates "a very sad and tragic situation" which is good neither for such marriages nor for the Church.

The official views of the Roman Catholic Church toward interfaith marriages both valid and invalid have thus been presented.

It seemed important to secure, also, the opinions of priests who serve Catholic youth directly, as leaders of Newman Clubs in a variety of universities throughout the country, as to whether interfaith marriages were, in their opinion, increasing, decreasing, or remaining about the same in number. Accordingly, I invited 30 Catholic priests who serve as directors of this official Catholic student organization to give me the benefit of their opinions.[44] These 30 priests serve 37 different colleges and universities. Of these, 17 say that interfaith marriages are increasing, while 13 believe that the number of such marriages is about the same. The majority (17) indicate that the number of students who make inquiries concerning the possibility of interfaith marriage is increasing. In no case does any priest say that such intermarriages are decreasing!

When asked whether the elimination of racial and religious bars in fraternities and sororities tends to increase the number of interfaith mar-

riages, opinion was evenly divided (16 "yes" and 14 "no"). Asked whether the gradual change in fraternity and sorority restrictions might affect Catholic student attitudes toward interracial marriages, 13 priests answered "yes" while 15 replied in the negative. One reply indicated that, on his campus, the bar against interfaith and interracial fraternity and sorority membership was still up. In one case, there was no answer.

When asked—"Do you believe that the family is as strong a deterrent to intermarriage as it was five years ago?"—12 priests answered "Yes," while 18 replied in the negative. The belief that family ties have somehow weakened within so short a period of time, predominates.

The personal attitude of each priest toward interfaith and interracial marriages was asked for inasmuch as it was believed that such attitudes might "color" the replies given to the other questions. Twenty-five priests were opposed to interfaith marriages with but 4 expressing a friendly attitude. In the case of their attitude toward interracial marriages, 19 of the priests were "friendly" to them; 5 of these Newman Club directors expressed opposition to the idea, while 4 declared themselves "unconcerned." One priest declared that, although he was unopposed to such marriages in principle, he might not favor it in particular circumstances. One priest did not reply to this question.

These priests were also asked if they believed that "such student organizations as Newman Clubs, Hillel Foundations, etc.," tend to discourage intermarriages. Engaged in this student organization work and possibly biased in its favor, 26 out of the total of 30 replied in the affirmative.

The assumption by Roman Catholic parents and the Catholic clergy that attendance of Catholic children at parochial schools would, among other things, have a positive effect upon their desire to marry a Catholic, does not seem to me to be substantiated. The Catholic students in the Catholic-sponsored colleges and universities I have studied, seem to be less certain about their position on this score than either their parents or educators had assumed. I believe that in the case of many Catholics, as is the case with Protestants as well as Jews, identification with their religion is often more formal than it is real. Catholics, like others, "identify" with their religion, observe its rituals and practices, but appear less likely to view Catholicism as a distinctive way of life, different in major respects from that of other religions. Our student sample appears to maintain a kind of nominal identification that is only partially religious and, in greater degree, ethnic.

Intermarriages between Catholics and non-Catholics will, I believe, continue to increase. This opinion is based not only on the obvious statistical increase in such marriages reported by the Church itself, but also upon the evidence that there is an increase in the number of culture

contacts that have been and are being made by Catholics throughout the country with peoples of other religions and cultures. Catholics are, in ever-increasing numbers, becoming members of the middle and upper economic classes. They are less isolated, in home settings, in colleges and universities, in business and in the professions. They now represent the third and fourth generations in America who believe far more in America as the great melting pot than they do in the infallability of the Roman Catholic Church. Catholic youth "dates" outside of its own religious group. It would marry, too, outside of that group if love were truly great. Its identification with the Catholic people and even with the Church has been weakened. These reasons, I feel, suggest that inter-marriages will continue to increase in even greater numbers than they have hitherto.

RUTH AND JOE

Ruth and Joseph, the former, of Catholic origin, and the latter, a Jew, have been married for two years. Prior to the formal announce-ment of her engagement to Joseph, Ruth prepared herself by study of Jewish ritual, for conversion to Joseph's faith.

The experiences of both of these intelligent young people, from good families, who have fallen in love and then realize that there are significant differences in faith and point of view, is discussed in this inter-view. Specific problems encountered with parents, family and friends are pointed out in detail.

The insights and responses of Ruth and Joe are worthy of our attention.

RUTH: It's a rather trying experience, I find, trying to recall some very difficult moments in one's life. But for the sake of the record and for what-ever contribution I can make, I'm going to attempt it. I'll start our story—for it is really not only mine, but Joe's as well—with a few facts about myself.

I have been married to Joe for almost two years. I am twenty-five years old. My husband is twenty-seven. I am teaching school at present and Joe is in business. He will tell you about himself and his work later on.

Before our marriage, I lived just outside of Washington, D.C., in a suburban community. I had the usual parochial school education and then I went on to college. I had planned to be a teacher someday and that was what I was aiming for.

While I was at school I happened to meet Joe on a blind date. One of Joe's friends knew my roommate. I can't say that it was love at first sight or anything like that, but actually I was impressed with Joe, his quiet ways and the fact that he was a gentleman.

JOE: Thanks for the compliment. I might say that I, too, was attracted to Ruth almost immediately. I had graduated from college and was just getting started on work for my M.A. when good fortune and my roommate brought us two together. It was a picnic arranged by the students that helped us to meet. My roommate was going with a girl who was Ruth's sorority sister.

RUTH: From the very start, we seemed to like each other. It never occurred to me that Joe was Jewish.

JOE: And it never occurred to me that Ruth's religion had anything to do with the date. Although I had certainly not made a practice of dating Christian girls, I had not really given much thought to the matter of Ruth's religion because—well, it was just a date. If anybody had ever asked me, "Will you marry a Jewish girl?", I would have been surprised because to me it was always very clear and definite that I would *only* marry a Jewish girl.

RUTH: I was a senior the year that we met. Joe was in the graduate school and within the year he would be graduated. Frankly, it never really occurred to me to ask about Joe's religion. You see, there have been many intermarriages in my family. We—that is, my folks—are quite accustomed to them. My paternal grandmother was Catholic and my paternal grandfather was Protestant. My mother was a Catholic (although she isn't now), and my father is a Lutheran Protestant. My mother's brother married a Jewish girl. They brought up their children as Catholics. My mother's sister married a Protestant who was converted to Catholicism. My grandmother, on my mother's side, was Catholic. And my father's family were all Lutherans. So, you see, we have quite a history of intermarriage in my immediate family.

JOE: Ruth's background is far different from mine. Had anyone ever talked about the possibility of intermarriage in my family, the roof would have fallen on him. My family had not only never had any intermarriages, but I was quite convinced that it just simply couldn't happen. Now, I think that you should know that I feel very close to my mother and father. I always have. The relationship has been very good. I'm sure they will tell you the same thing. But when I first accepted Ruth's invitation to visit her in her home over New Year's, things really began to happen. To put it another way, *the roof did fall in!* It was my father who was especially difficult. When I told my folks that I was going to New York over New Year's Day weekend, my father casually asked me where I was going. He

really didn't do that often. It was just one of those questions that make for conversation. I'm sure that, at that time, he certainly wasn't thinking about me going out with a Christian girl. When he asked me whether the girl I was going to visit was Jewish or not, I sort of hedged. I said that I had never bothered to ask her. Now *that* was a dead giveaway. Both my father and mother knew at once that I was going to visit a Christian girl and you can imagine how much that upset them!

My parents had not known much about my social life. They didn't ask many questions and frankly, I didn't volunteer any information. I can say that, at that time, I really hadn't made up my mind about whether I was really serious about Ruth or not. I didn't see any point in making an issue under those circumstances.

Now, my mother, I guess, rather took it for granted that I dated Jewish girls exclusively. She was really quite right because I seldom, if ever, went out with Gentile girls. Perhaps a few times on a blind date, but really nothing more than that. There was one occasion when I dated a girl whose name I don't even remember now. She was Jewish. This girl had a summer job in a restaurant, which meant that she didn't get out of work until about ten o'clock at night. A couple of times I would leave the house about nine-thirty to meet her after work. Then, I guess that both my father and mother thought that I was going out with a non-Jewish girl and they were quite upset about it.

RUTH: My parents never asked me any questions about the religion of any of the boys I went out with. I guess that's because they weren't religious in the same way Joe's folks are.

JOE: That may be. I think of my father and mother as very religious people. They feel very strong ties to religion. Yet, as I think about it, I'm not quite sure that they were as religious as I imagined. For example, my father certainly didn't go to the synagogue to pray each morning and, in fact, he really didn't pray at home in the morning or at night. But I do know that he felt a great sense of identification with the Jewish people—and so, for that matter, do I. My father and mother have a great pride in their Jewishness. My mother worked hard for many different programs in the synagogue. My father had a high sense of appreciation of the moral and ethical values of Judaism, and, I know, certainly tries to live by them. My mother feels very close to Judaism. It gives her strength. I would say that she is very typical of the old-type Jewish mothers. She is very much like her mother, my grandmother, in that respect. That's the kind of a home we have.

RUTH: Yet, when I came to Joe's parents' home, after hearing him speak about their religious way of life, I was rather surprised that the Sabbath Eve wasn't observed in the way I came to understand it should be—with the Kiddush, or blessing over the wine—and such things.

JOE: Well, not all Jews feel the same way about all the Jewish rituals. Some do more, some observe less. But my parents were and are good Jewish people in the best sense of the term. I have a brother. He's married to a Jewish girl. They live on the West Coast. When all the talk began about my seeing Ruth, my brother tried to help me by convincing my folks that I should continue to see Ruth if I wanted to. Later, my folks told me about that, but frankly, I wasn't impressed because I didn't think that my brother was very religious himself. In fact, I was and still am more religious than he.

RUTH: My parents were not surprised or upset when I first told them that I had invited Joe to visit with me during the vacation. Mother asked me what his name was. I told her 'Werner' and she said, "Oh, is that a German name?" I remember answering, "No, it's Jewish." All she said was "Oh!" There really wasn't any problem for me at all. Neither my mother nor father, nor anyone else in the immediate family who heard about it, raised any question or offered any objections. Oh, yes, now I *do* remember that, about the time our wedding invitations were issued, I worried that some of my relatives wouldn't come to the wedding. And, in fact, *some of them, didn't!* We suspected that an aunt, my mother's sister who is married to a man who was converted to Catholicism, would not come. She's so very strongly Catholic! The idea of my marrying a Jew and being converted to Judaism made her very unhappy. We knew about her attitude, but it wasn't her idea that upset me. I was concerned lest she influence other members of the family and urge them not to come. I understand how she feels even though I don't agree with her. But my grandmother and my other uncle and his wife did attend the wedding in the synagogue. My father's mother, who is a German Lutheran, rather worried me for a time, but there wasn't a problem about her, either. She has a prejudice against Jews. But she met Joe, I think, before she realized that he was Jewish and she liked him right away.

JOE: Ruth's parents are not really religious.

RUTH: That's quite correct. I would say they are not religious *at all!* There is no ritual or ceremony of any kind in my parents' home. My father has an easygoing attitude about everything, including religion. He takes people for what they are and that's that. He believes that everyone else has a right to his own ideas in religion, too, so he never really becomes upset. My mother isn't as easygoing as my father. The decisions in our family are made by her. My relationship with my father and my mother has always been very good. They're warm, friendly people. They understand. They listen and they talk things through. My father's advice is wonderful. When I first told him about Joe and how much in love I was and we discussed the fact that he is Jewish, I remember my father saying, "Ruth, everybody will try to give you advice now on what to do, but intelligent, adult people will listen to all the advice and make their own decisions."

He did say, too, "Ruth, marrying a boy of another religion is a problem. You know you're going to have to think seriously about converting to Joe's religion!" And he, of all people should know, for he is a Lutheran and my mother is a Catholic.

JOE: I'm glad you mentioned the matter of conversion, because I didn't bring it up first.

RUTH: My father once said to me, "Everybody has to face problems of one kind or another. How much of a problem you're going to have is up to you."

JOE: Ruth didn't have to rid herself of certain Christian ideas because she never did hold to them.

RUTH: I did as a child, but I outgrew much of what I was told in parochial school. Now, here I am, telling you that my family is not religious and then I tell you about my going to parochial school. Well, it really wasn't because my mother was so religious or so anxious to make me a good Catholic. I went there because of my brother. He was born in December and he would have missed out on a year of school if he had gone to public school. He only missed out on six months by going to Catholic school. So, when I was to start, I just went to the same school.

JOE: It always struck me as strange that when Ruth and I finally got around to talking about religion, I told her that I was Jewish and asked her what she was, and she couldn't answer.

RUTH: Well, I didn't have a name for my religion. I had been a Catholic, but I knew that I really had not been one for several years. I used to attend Mass during my first year in college, but then I decided to attend chapel instead. I simply realized that I didn't believe in the things that Catholics believed in. I talked to the priest about it. He said that in time my faith would come to the forefront. It was there, but that it had to be discovered by me, so to speak. That was when I decided to attend the chapel which was more or less Protestant, nonsectarian.

JOE: Compared with some of the problems I had, Ruth's seem rather minor.

RUTH: They weren't minor, but they certainly didn't cause so much difficulty for me as yours did for you.

JOE: My father was much more of a problem than I had ever realized he was going to be. I knew that he was close to Judaism, but I certainly thought that I was, too. It was quite by accident that I had met Ruth and come to love her. I thought my parents would understand. Particularly

because Ruth had told me that whether she and I married or not, she was going to study and prepare herself for conversion to Judaism. Now, my father isn't a talkative person. He doesn't say much, but he thinks a great deal. When he heard about Ruth, it was as if someone had hit him with a sledge hammer. I felt that he was just going to go to pieces. My mother was shocked, too, but she was worrying most about the way my father was taking the news. I knew that my parents simply did not want me to marry a Christian girl. I knew that it might break their hearts. So you can imagine the state of mind I was in. One part of the problem was overcome when Ruth told me that she intended to convert to Judaism whether or not we got married. I felt then that Ruth was sincere about it. Truthful in every way. But even this idea didn't fix things up with my folks. I knew that I could never give up Judaism myself, or accept any halfway religion that would be common to us both. I tried talking about it one night at the dinner table and all hell broke loose. My father, especially, let me have it. I love my parents dearly and this was one of the most difficult moments of my life.

RUTH: Joe told me about all that had occurred and we decided to see if, during the summer, we could, perhaps, forget about each other. We agreed that this was the thing to do. It wasn't easy for either of us, you may be sure. But we simply couldn't go on the way things were.

JOE: In order to try to forget about Ruth, I got a good job out on the West Coast. I wanted to get far enough away to really get my bearings. But in about two months, I started to write to Ruth, I missed her so much! We wrote and phoned each other. I was very much in love, but still faced with the very same problem.

While out there, I decided to speak to a rabbi about my problems, but he wasn't very helpful. It was then that I decided to write a letter about all that had gone on, all that was in my heart, to my own rabbi in the congregation to which my parents belong. Had I done that in the first place, I could have saved quite a few heartaches.

RUTH: Joe told me about his idea over the long-distance phone. He would soon have to go into the army. But before he did that it seemed to us that we ought to arrive at a clearer understanding about ourselves and the possibility of our marriage. I liked Joe's idea of talking the matter over with his own rabbi.

JOE: I informed my parents that, although I had tried to forget Ruth, I could not and I wanted to marry her. I further asked them to invite her to be our guest for a few days when I arrived home, before going into the army. And then I wrote a long letter to my rabbi, asking to see him with Ruth when I came home. Shortly after I received word from my parents that they had extended the invitation to Ruth, but it was clear that they did so with heavy hearts. I heard later that about this time my father was talk-

ing about suicide. However, my mother even though very unhappy, was doing her best to calm him down. I know they thought Ruth was a fine person. If only she had been born of Jewish parents! I cannot understand the reason for this emphasis. They wouldn't have asked about a Jewish girl's religious tendencies. Somehow, although my parents really didn't observe very much of Jewish religious ritual themselves, this idea of my marriage simply played havoc with them. What is it that caused them to respond this way? Was it fear of what others in the family or certain friends would say? Was it a sense of shame? Did they think I ever planned to give up my identity as a Jew? Had you been around my parents during those days when I returned from the West Coast, you would have noticed their attitude immediately. Now, my parents are good people, wonderful people. Why did this happen to them?

RUTH: Joe's parents were wonderful to me. They made me feel very much at home and I appreciated it very much. I thought everything was going along fine, until we kept the appointment with the rabbi at his study.

JOE: Well, that session was very difficult: we talked frankly and the rabbi talked frankly to us. He sought to discourage us from getting married. He gave us statistical information on the subject of intermarriage and indicated that if he were betting on the success of such a marriage, he would be obliged to demand very high odds because the chances of successful intermarriage were not too good.

RUTH: I had already talked with the rabbi of one of the synagogues in my home town. He is quite Orthodox. Since he didn't know Joe, it had been a bit difficult, but he was understanding when I told him that it didn't matter whether Joe and I got married and that, under any circumstance, I had decided that I wanted to be converted to Judaism. He gave me some books on Judaism to read. And he offered to meet with me regularly to discuss them and answer my questions. We met for about an hour a week. So it was a shock to me to see the stumbling blocks that Joe's rabbi placed in our path and the questions he asked. He later informed us that, as the representative of the Jewish tradition, he had to be absolutely certain that, if there was to be a conversion to Judaism, the convert should be really serious about preserving the Jewish ritual and the Jewish way of life in the home and out. Now, I can understand it better. But at the time, it was difficult to take.

JOE: My rabbi had always been regarded as a friend and I had a hard time reconciling his attitude at the time with the way I felt toward him. However, after the engagement had been announced and after Ruth had been converted to Judaism by the rabbi in her town, we were amazed by the change in the attitude of my rabbi. He and his wife came to the reception in my parents' home. He had suddenly become very human and understanding of our point of view. As we thought about it more, we began to

understand why, at certain times and under certain circumstances, he had to place his official responsibilities and duties as a rabbi above his personal friendship.

RUTH: There had been a two-year wait from the time we first thought we wanted to get married until we actually did. Those years dragged so I can't imagine living through them again, but as I look back on them, they really were good for both of us. The waiting period made us very certain about what we wanted and why. Despite all of Joe's troubles with his folks, they all came through it very well. Maybe, at first, the whole idea was difficult to accept, but, like some foods, it takes a while to get used to them.

JOE: Ideas are not like foods. It takes longer to digest ideas to which we are unaccustomed. When my parents realized what a fine person Ruth is and that she was very serious about becoming a Jewess and when it was pointed out that her conversion was performed in the Orthodox tradition, that she studied the history of Judaism, its theology, its ritual and ceremony, and that she even learned prayer-book Hebrew so that she might be "at home" in any synagogue, when they realized that she went through the ceremony of "T'villa," the ritual bath——

RUTH: Very much like Baptism——

JOE: ——they began to see that there was every reason to welcome her, no matter what neighbors or friends or relatives might say, and, I think, they have accepted Ruth as a daughter—gladly.

RUTH: When I overheard my mother-in-law speak of me to a friend as "*my* Ruth" then I knew that I was *really* accepted.

JOE: My father is quite a different man these days, too. The rabbi told him that, once a person has been formally converted to Judaism, she is to be regarded as a Jew, the same as all other Jews—and that the children of such a marriage would definitely be regarded as Jews. The bitterness and great hurt of the past two years seems to have disintegrated.

RUTH: Our wedding took place in the synagogue where I had been converted to Judaism. I wanted to make it clear that I was a Jewess and that I intended to be a good one. Of course, a few of our Catholic friends and a few relatives didn't come to the wedding. I guess it's them and not their religion.

JOE: I was surprised that Ruth wanted to be married in the synagogue and my folks were, too.

RUTH: Well, if it was going to be a Jewish wedding, it *belonged* in the synagogue, and not in any hotel or even at home. I wanted it to be a *reli-*

gious wedding in every way. When I told my folks the way I felt, they had no objection whatsoever.

JOE: If I were now to be asked by any young person whether to marry a person of another faith, I would say *no!*

RUTH: I don't understand.

JOE: I think that if two young people of different religions meet and fall in love, one of them should convert to the religion of the other and do so in all sincerity. I can see now why it wouldn't work to have two different religions and religious practices in the same house.

RUTH: I think that, even if one of the parties is not very strong or firm in his religious convictions, it is best if *both* parties to the marriage be of the same religion. One should accept the faith of the other under any circumstance. I think the way we have gone about it has strengthened us both.

JOE: Ruth's parents bear no resentment whatsoever and my folks are much better today, too. There's still a little strained feeling between the two families, but I hope that this will disappear in time. That's a price one must pay for intermarriage. It's one of the things we must grow accustomed to.

RUTH: If I were advising young people on this important subject, I would say "Above all be sure you are really in love." There must be a deep sense of love, otherwise any marriage, and particularly an intermarriage, is likely to fail.

JOE: When friends ask our opinion about dating someone of a different religion we both say, "Stop now if you possibly can. Stop, because if you're not sure that you love each other, no intermarriage can be successful. Don't create problems for yourself. Don't prolong the agony!

THE JEW AND INTERMARRIAGE

Dear Mr. and Mrs. Cohen:

I hope this letter will help you understand some of the things that have happened in the past one and a half years. I am writing it mainly because of your daughter. She loves you both very much and I know you love her equally as much. Love can be a very powerful emotion as both Ann and I have found. We started seeing each other late in 1960 and as you know or guessed we continued to do so through the end of the school year. Then we parted and went our ways. I left New York and started work in Pennsylvania as a chemist. We kept in touch with each other and we saw each other a few times during the summer.

Then Ann went to Pittsburgh. This was, I suspect, the downfall of both of us. We were completely lost. We were about the unhappiest people in the world, even though we both had dated numerous other people. Ann was very unhappy with school, and I couldn't do anything right at work. Finally one weekend I drove to Pittsburgh and for the short period of thirty hours when I was there, there were no happier people in the world.

Since then many things have changed for the better as far as we are concerned. Ann came out here during Christmas, and we found her a few good job offers and a place to stay. When she arrived, we set to work on her apartment and we have made, painted, or overhauled everything that is in it. Because I only live about ten minutes' away, I have been seeing your daughter as much as possible and we are very much in love. I know that "love" is a very big word to fool with and I should use it carefully. But I have been very fortunate or unfortunate in some respects, because my parents have been divorced for almost eight years. To have lived with a mismatch has had many effects on me. I was very uneasy about marriage, and planned on not marrying for some time. My religion also went out the window, not that I am now an atheist, but more unhappy with the religion being offered to me.

Almost four years later, after many girls, I met your daughter, and I wish you could have seen how much happiness we have brought each other.

Now, after many hardships we seem to be on the road toward success. I know we could not get along without each other and we don't plan to. Religion has posed no problem for us because we have a common faith in God, and we have tentatively planned to bring our children up in the Jewish faith. I know your daughter would like to get married in a temple, and this is fine with me.

I am looking forward to talking with you this weekend. It is your future that you have to handle, because I know that we are both old enough to be capable of managing our lives. We would like you to be a part of them.

I hope your love for your daughter is strong enough to enable you to understand our situation, and that our meeting will be a happy occasion.

(Signed) Ralph Johnson

Dear Mom and Dad,

Thanks for the package. It came in perfect order—as if it had been moved across the street.

Saturday was almost 100° (99 to be exact) so we headed for the lake. It's quite a distance, but it was a beautiful beach day (I have quite a tan for this time of the year).

Mom, Dad—I'll keep my letter brief so I may save much of what I have to tell you on Saturday. I am bringing a guest home with me. I think you remember Ralph. We have wonderful things to tell you and we only hope and pray to God that you will be happy with us. Ralph and I have been working very hard together for some time to prove not only our sincere, deep love for each other, but also our compatibility and our potential contribution to the world as a unit. Our progress has been great through our own diligence and the help of some very dear friends. We feel we have attended to all aspects of our lives as mature individuals. Now we need every bit of your understanding of life and compassion for the lives of your children in order for us to exist in complete happiness.

What traits have I looked for in my man?—well let me tell you just a few qualities that Ralph has shown me and every person he meets. He is a chemist for a company here, and is now working part time for his Ph.D. degree. He is a very stable, down-to-earth person who has insight into the character of people and situations alike. Neither of us are obsessed in any way with wealth in the form of money. We are looking for wealth in our happiness, maturity, stability, friendships, and of course in love of each other and our family(s). One thing you both know I regard highly—that is goodness. No other person could ever be so good to me or so understanding. Ralph has an instinctively kind, outgoing nature so that he is constantly giving of himself. He has had the opportunity to help others in diversified ways—aiding different students on many occasions, helping in physical labor, giving sound advice to those who seek it. . . . I could go on bragging forever; instead I want you to open your hearts and see with your own eyes that I exaggerate not one bit. We are fortunate to have Ralph's presence in our lives.

We will be home some time Saturday afternoon. See you then. We're both looking forward to coming home.

Love 'n kisses,
your daughter,
Ann

These letters tell their own story. They were brought to me by Ann's mother and father, who, although normally calm individuals, were obviously highly emotional and distraught. The father's face, flushed and unhappy, revealed the tragedy that he believed had come

into his life. The mother, tears streaming down her face, was equally unhappy about the proposed intermarriage, but also uncertain about her right to interfere with her daughter's happiness. The tensions were indeed great. "What *should* we do?" "What *can* we do?" "What *dare* we do?"

These Jewish parents had, over the years, acquired a point of view about intermarriage. For them it spelled disaster. They believed it meant unhappiness and even catastrophe.

Consider, now, another true story:

> John, a Catholic, married Rebecca, a Jewess. They were married in a civil ceremony because Rebecca was not willing to convert to Catholicism or rear her children as Catholics. They are the parents of three children, two boys and a girl, each of whom regards himself as a Jew. None of the children has received a religious education (the boys have not been Bar Mitzvah or confirmed in the faith of their father). Contacts with the family of the mother are rare inasmuch as Rebecca's folks bitterly opposed the marriage. Her parents "sat *Shivah*."
>
> John believes that his wife's family opposes him because he is not Jewish, but he believes it would be wrong for him to convert to Judaism. He says, "I was born a Catholic and I intend to remain one."

Both the letters and the brief case history call attention to an important phase of the problem of intermarriage in which a Jew is involved. Such marriages directly concern not only these well-intentioned young people, but involve, too, their parents and families as well as the communities from which they come. They are associated with a faith, a sub-culture and a people. They are involved, therefore, with its past, its present and its future.

Before we can understand the nature of the problems Jews see in interfaith marriages, it is necessary to point out that, from almost its earliest days, interfaith marriage, according to the Jewish tradition, was generally opposed. Endogamous marriage, within the extended family, was the general rule among the early Hebrews.[1] At a later period in Hebrew history, however, Moses married a Midianitish woman and later, a Cushite. There was social disapproval for these acts. The condemnation of Moses, for instance, by his brother and sister, Aaron and Miriam, is clearly indicated.

The Book of Ruth, however, implies a more favorable attitude toward intermarriage, a view later severely opposed by Ezra the Scribe. Epstein reasons that the author of the Book of Ruth was saying, "Intermarriage has social disapproval, and as a social standard, it does not distinguish between one kind of foreign woman and another. That . . . is unfair: Ruth is different from other foreign women by her character and

her loyalty." Such a view was generally held in the days of the establishment of the Hebrew people in Palestine. In the days of the later kings of Judah, a much more hostile attitude toward intermarriage developed and became a matter of law as contrasted with the earlier view that marriage outside of one's own people was merely a matter of acceptance of or refusal of a social standard. During this period a people, disconcerted by the degraded cultures and practices of neighboring nations and at odds with them, too, on political matters, included in the Book of Deuteronomy a legal enactment opposing intermarriage.

It[2] expressly forbids the practice of intermarriage and unequivocally states the reason: "For he will turn away thy son from following Me that they may serve other Gods; so will the anger of the Lord be kindled against thee and He will destroy thee quickly." Intermarriage with seven nations—the Hittites, Girgashites, Amorites, Canaanites, Perizzites, Hivites, and Jebusites—was expressly forbidden.

The desire to prevent the Hebrews from adopting heathen practices and thereby degrading their own religious way of life lies at the root of such legislation. *It had nothing whatsoever to do with notions of racial superiority or even of purity.* Such legislation was intended rather to assure the religious and political unity and solidarity of these people.

Later, Ezra the Scribe (444 B.C.E.) believing that the purity of the monotheistic religion and the purity of blood were bound together, viewed intermarriage as a form of defilement and declared that the ancient *faith* was adulterated when the blood of a Hebrew was mixed with that of a heathen. Marriage with the children born of these mixed marriages was also prohibited as was marriage with all non-Hebrew peoples. This form of nationalism, rabid as it was, must be understood for what it was—a desire to re-establish the religious and national entity of the Hebrews. Those families who could not prove their "pure" origin were not affected insofar as their status as Israelitish citizens was concerned. Their members, however, were not permitted to serve in the priesthood and pure-blooded Israelites would not intermarry with them, but they "shared in all the religious and civil rights of the community." [3] Intermarriage was so firmly entrenched in the life of the people that Ezra, despite his teachings and heroic efforts, could not root it out. Nor has it ever been eliminated.

Later, with emancipation from the ghettos of Europe, the Jew came to fear his loss of identity as a Jew by means of the assimilatory process. Opposition to intermarriage was, therefore, intensified. The threat to the survival of the Jew as a member of a minority people with a sacred literature, a distinctive religious philosophy, ritual and observances, proved real and forboding.

Although, at a later date in history, Christians were not regarded by

Jews as either heathens or pagans, intermarriage with them was opposed because it might lead to the loss of the religious identity of the Jew and to his ultimate absorption into the majority as well. Yet—and this is highly significant—intermarriage with persons of another faith was permitted, provided that the Gentile was formally converted to Judaism. By such a ritual which followed weeks and months of preparation and an intensive study of Judaism, the convert was officially accepted as a Jew.

The Jewish insistence upon conversion to Judaism on the part of the non-Jew before a marriage is explained by Louis Finkelstein:[4]

> Because of the special place that the home occupies in Judaism as a center of religious life and worship, almost co-ordinate with the Synagogue itself, Judaism holds it essential that both parties to a Jewish marriage be members of the Jewish faith. There is, of course, no objection to marriage with a sincere convert to Judaism. But it is not possible for the home to function in the manner prescribed by Jewish law unless both husband and wife are of the Jewish faith.

Opposition to intermarriage, as in the post-Biblical period, has continued up to and including the present day. Intermarriage without formal conversion was regarded as a sin against God and the Jewish People. Both the Talmud and the Rabbinical Codes declared that such marriages were punishable by banning, tantamount to excommunication, of the guilty Jewish party.[5] Despite this and later officially expressed opposition and condemnation, religious intermarriages have continued to take place.

When the separation of Church and State in Europe and the consequent introduction of civil marriages came about as a result of the French Revolution, other European states, including Great Britain, Holland, Belgium, Italy, and the Scandinavian countries, Norway, Denmark and Sweden, also introduced civil marriages. In Germany, religious intermarriages were legalized in 1875 although they had been permitted in certain of the separate German States at an earlier date. Legalization of such marriages occurred in Hungary in 1895, and, in Bulgaria, Serbia and Rumania they were permitted before World War I. Only after the Russian Revolution of 1917 was it legally permissible to enter an interfaith marriage in that country. In Austria, official permission was required in order to arrange an interfaith marriage. However, it was readily obtainable.

As late as 1940, when Poland was conquered by Nazi Germany, Jews could not marry Christians in that country. Countries like Yugoslavia and Lithuania prohibited Jewish-Christian marriages before World War II.

The Nuremberg laws, enacted by Germany in 1935, prohibited marriages between Jews and "Aryan" Germans on the basis of supposed blood differences "for its protection of German blood and German honor." The laws prohibited marriages between Jews and persons who had but one Jewish grandparent. The latter could not intermarry with those persons who had two Jewish grandparents unless consent was given by the German Minister of the Interior and the Assistant of Adolph Hitler or the officer appointed by him. Those persons who had but one Jewish grandparent could, however, marry Aryans in order to hasten their absorption into the German people.

The Nuremberg laws were applied in all the countries of Europe that were conquered by Germany. Italy, an ally of Germany, applied these laws to its own people in 1938.

Prior to the Fascist-Nazi years, interfaith marriages involving Jews had taken place increasingly, as the emphasis upon political and social equality was more clearly enunciated. Despite the opposition of Church, Synagogue and State, such marriages came to be viewed as the dawn of a new and better era in human relationships. The arguments of Jewish religious authorities against interfaith marriage proved to be correct, for intermarriage, which occurred most frequently without the conversion of the non-Jew to Judaism, resulted in the further weakening of the ties of identification with the Jewish religion and in the increase of children who, born usually of Jewish fathers and Christian mothers, were reared as Christians.

Intermarriage rates, insofar as they involve Jews in major European countries, provide us with a clear indication of the proneness of Jews to assimilate with non-Jews. For example, of the 3,537 Jewish families who lived in Switzerland in 1950, about 30 per cent (1,240) were mixed marriages. In the year 1953, there were 102 mixed marriages performed and but 80 involving Jews only. In 1954, there were 78 mixed marriages compared to 70 all-Jewish marriages.[6]

Insofar as the Netherlands is concerned, what few figures we have[7] indicate that 3,100 of the 7,000 Jewish families said to be living in that country in 1957 were intermarried and, of this number, 42 per cent had no affiliation with the Dutch Jewish community. During the period between 1954 and 1961 there were a total of 613 intermarriages compared with 469 full Jewish marriages.[8] In 1961 alone, there were 87 intermarriages as compared with 74 full Jewish marriages.

Ruppin[9] reported that the interfaith intermarriage rate for Jews in Germany in 1933 was 43.78 per 100 Jewish marriages (the beginning of the Hitler era).

In 1939 (during the Hitler regime) more than 25 per cent of all marriages involving Jews were said to be interfaith marriages. In Berlin

alone, almost one-third of the marriages involving Jews were mixed and "about 11 per cent of the children of such marriages belonged to Judaism.[10] Since the year 1945, 59.1 per cent of all marriages involving Jews in West Germany have been mixed marriages. A recent study[11] made at Mainz University in Germany indicates that 29 per cent of all newly born children in the Jewish community of West Germany between the years 1951 and 1958, were the products of interfaith marriages.

The degree of intermarriage among the Jews of Hungary was high. During the years 1931-33, 32 per cent of all marriages involving a Jew were intermarriages.[12]

Following World War II, Cohen[13] reports that, in Berlin, nearly three-fifths of the members of the small Jewish communities were married to non-Jews, while in Frankfort-on-the-Main, "almost all of the 400 members of the Jewish community were partners of mixed marriages." Similar reports have been made about other communities in Germany. In Vienna, for example, where 90 per cent of the Jews of Austria lived following the war, three-fifths were intermarried.

In Italy in the early twentieth century as many as one Jewish person in three[14] and in some places even more, had intermarried. This meant not only the immediate loss to Judaism of the person involved, but even more, the loss of future generations when the children of these intermarriages, reared perhaps as Catholics, are considered. Until Italy became a co-partner of Nazi Germany, the number of intermarriages increased. On October 7, 1938, by edict of the Italian Fascist General Council, marriages between Jews and non-Jews were prohibited without regard to the religion professed by either party.[15]

In the hope of escaping Nazi oppression, thousands of Jews "sought salvation in apostacy" [16] but to no avail. Their rate of intermarriage, however, was high long before World War II began.

In 1961, there were about 350,000 Jews in France, the majority of whom lived in Paris. Intermarriage there is said to be "considerable," but no exact figures have been reported. Indifference to Judaism is regarded as a major problem. Conversion to Catholicism by Jews in France is also said to be "considerable." The number of Oriental orthodox Jews in France from Tunisia, Morocco and Algeria, whose existence under French influence in their native countries has been challenged by independence and Arab-Moslem control, has increased almost 100,000 and promises to change the assimilationist tendencies of French Jews—at least for a decade or two.

In Great Britain, interfaith marriages, according to a British-Jewish observer,[17] are now taking place in ever-increasing numbers. Neustatter reports:

Interviews with ministers of religion and experienced representatives of Jewry have shown that intermarriage at the present time has much increased. One informant, well acquainted with the Jews of London in his capacity as a communal social worker has said, "I cannot think of any (extended) family in which no intermarriage has taken place."

Slater,[18] writing about English Jewry and intermarriage has also indicated that intermarriage is increasing rapidly in that country. All signs point to an even greater degree of intermarriage in the years ahead.

When we consider the Jews in the Scandinavian countries, we find that the percentage of intermarriage in Denmark is the highest in all the world. The Jewish Secretariat in Copenhagen has indicated that 50 per cent of the Jewish males have Gentile wives and that 23 per cent of Jewish females have Gentile husbands. Rabbi Marcus Melchior, the Chief Rabbi of Copenhagen, in a personal conversation with this author, in 1960, stated that over 50 per cent of the total Jewish population is intermarried.

Joel Cang,[19] editor of the London *Jewish Chronicle,* believes that intermarriage between Jews and non-Jews in Denmark is, in fact, between 60 and 70 per cent of all marriages involving Jews.

The total population of Denmark is 4,500,000, with a total Jewish population of 6,500, practically all of whom live in Copenhagen. The nation is almost completely free of anti-Semitism.

In Norway, where the total Jewish population consists of but 1,000 Jews, the percentage of intermarriages is said to be as high as that of Denmark.

Sweden has 13,000 Jews out of a total population of 7,300,000. With a population that is truly homogenous, there is no Jewish neighborhood in all of Sweden. According to Rabbi Kurt Wilhelm, Chief Rabbi of Sweden, 45 to 50 per cent of all marriages registered in the Jewish community records are intermarriages. This means that of the 7,000 Jews or 2,300 families registered in the Jewish community, there are about 1,250 to 1,500 intermarriages.

Rabbi Wilhelm believes that these intermarriages are seldom undertaken for the purpose of escaping from the Jewish community. Rather, he suggests, that the small number of Jews in all the Scandinavian countries make intermarriage inevitable.

Although the formal identification of Jews with the Jewish community will, in all likelihood, continue for another two generations, it appears more than likely that, given freedom from anti-Semitism, and other forms of prejudice, the Jewish communities in Scandinavia are likely to die out.

Of the 1,800 Jews in Finland, the former Chief Rabbi of Finland reports that from 1955 through 1960 there were 65 marriages recorded in the Jewish community register; 24 of these involve both a Jewish male and a Jewish female. In addition, there were 5 marriages, representing 45 per cent of all the marriages, where the non-Jewish female was formally converted to Judaism. The remaining 36 marriages, 55 per cent of all the marriages involving a Jewish partner, are mixed marriages, in that the non-Jewish member has not been converted to Judaism. Of the latter group, 26 marriages involve a Jewish man married to a non-Jewish girl, while 10 Jewish girls are married to non-Jewish men.

There are 299 children recorded in the register of the Jewish community (ages, 1-18). Of these, 239 have both parents Jewish while 12 have one parent who, although presently converted to Judaism, was originally a non-Jew. There are 50 children who were born of mixed marriages.

At present there are three Jewish congregations in existence in Helsinki, Turku and Tampere. Before 1940, there was a fourth Jewish congregation in Vipari (Viborg), but it fell into Soviet hands with the Soviet victory over Finland.[20]

Organized Jewish communal life is weak in the Scandinavian countries, as it is in France, Belgium, Holland, Italy, Austria, and Germany. Whether it will survive the next decade is open to question. The influence of "the community" is, as a consequence, little felt by its members and particularly by its young people. The controls over practices and actions exerted by the Jewish community in an earlier day is no longer of great moment. Under these circumstances, interfaith marriages between Jews and non-Jews are bound to increase.

As for the Jewish population of Canada, estimated at 250,000[21] or 1.44 per cent of the total population of the country, about 60 per cent are natives. Of these Jews 218,000 live in the four major cities: Montreal (103,000), Toronto (85,000), Winnipeg (21,500) and Vancouver (8,500). Some 32,000 live in all the rest of that vast country. Seventy-two per cent of all of Canada's Jews lived in Montreal and Toronto.

The Canadian Census informs us that the percentage of mixed marriages involving Jews in Canada increased from 4.9 for the five-year period 1926 through 1930 to 11.7 for the period 1951 through 1955.[22] The rate further increased to about 16 per cent in 1960.[23] Jewish grooms constitute two times the number of Jewish brides. Such marriages are lowest in the city of Montreal which, as we have noted, has the largest Jewish population in Canada, despite the fact that the Jewish community is but a part of the larger, French-speaking, Catholic majority.

Intermarriages between Jews and Gentiles have been occurring from the very beginning of Jewish settlement in the United States, but not without a strongly stated opposition by Jews as well as non-Jews.

The attitude of the Jewish community in the United States toward intermarriage as early as 1845, is expressed in an article in the noted Anglo-Jewish newspaper, *The Occident*,[24] from which the following is excerpted:

> If then we wish to preserve our race, we will not say unmixed, for proselytes are as much of Israel as we are, but still if we wish to preserve our race in our religion, and do not wish to see them incorporated with all or any one of the many denominations of Christians, we must endeavour to prevent, if possible, any of our members from intermarrying with Christians or persons indifferent to any faith. Let us state, in passing, that our using the term Christians must not be ascribed to any illiberality, as though we had a particular objection to them only; on the contrary we employ the word merely because we are surrounded by them on all sides, and even they who believe in no religious system whatever, are nominally reckoned among Christians; and we use therefore this comprehensive term as denoting all dissentients from Judaism.

The constitution of such a noted early American Synagogue as Mikveh Israel in Philadelphia declared that intermarried Jews would be deprived of their rights and privileges within the Synagogue. Inasmuch as the Synagogue was, next to the family itself, a basic Jewish unit of social and organizational life, playing a major role in the development and control of opinion among Jews, its declarations were listened to, even if they were not always adhered to.

The proportion of intermarried Jews who, in the 1900's, became identified with the Christian community or whose children came to be so identified was rather large. The Jewish community in the 1840's, consisting of less than one-half of 1 per cent of the nation's total population, fearful for its survival in a milieu that appeared ready to engulf it, felt duty-bound to exert sanctions such as outlined above. We may imagine how being deprived of synagogal, moral support by the Jewish community, and of social contact with that community as well, affected the intermarried. However, despite the official opposition of Jewish congregational leaders who were, by virtue of their synagogal leadership, also regarded as Jewish communal leaders, intermarriages continued to take place. Marcus[25] believes that by the middle of the eighteenth century, "10 per cent of the Jews in the cities were married to non-Jews."

In a highly detailed study of 942 marriages involving Jews in America, for the period prior to 1840, *where the names of both* spouses were given, Stern[26] states that 150 or 15.9 per cent of the total were marriages of Jews to Christians; of the remainder, 155 marriages were interethnic marriages.

Of the 150 interfaith marriages referred to, 87 per cent "seem to have been completely assimilated into the non-Jewish community." Despite the opposition of the Jewish community, the great majority of those who intermarried ultimately identified themselves with the Christian community. Stern states further that "only 5 per cent of those who did not convert [to Christianity] made any apparent effort to identify themselves with the Jewish community."

Most contemporary Jewish religious leaders, as well as the three major movements in Judaism, Conservative, Orthodox, and Reform remain strongly opposed to intermarriage to this day.

The official views of the Committee on Jewish Law and Standards of the Rabbinical Assembly of America (Conservative) as expressed in their answers to questions put to them by their rabbinical colleagues on the subject of intermarriage are of interest:

1. A Jew who has intermarried does not cease to be a Jew. He may continue to attend synagogue services and perform other commandments of Judaism although he has violated one of the most important of all Jewish prohibitions (Exodus 34:16; Deuteronomy 7:3).

2. It should be clearly understood that in frowning upon intermarriage and in voicing opposition to the choice of a non-Jewish mate, neither Judaism at large, nor Conservative Judaism in particular, expresses any judgment about the morality or character of these non-Jewish men and women.

3. These individuals may be fine, exceptional people. However, unless they are converted to Judaism they cannot wholeheartedly and sincerely help to preserve the Jewish religion, foster its development, and raise their children to be Jews. Children of a non-Jewish mother are not Jews.

4. Judaism is not alone in objecting to intermarriage; so does Catholicism and Protestantism. It should be noted that we feel sympathy for those Christian families whose members have intermarried with Jews and whose family unity has, consequently, been disrupted and, often, destroyed.

5. A person who has married outside of the Jewish community should not be considered a candidate for membership in a Conservative Congregation that is affiliated with the United Synagogue of America even though he applies for membership without his non-Jewish partner.

6. A congregation constitutes a community of Jews who band together to promote their interests and loyalties as Jews. The purposes of the congregation and these interests and loyalties are stated in its constitution, and must always be kept in mind.

7. By the very act of joining a congregation, a Jew agrees to live up to the purposes of the synagogue. He either tacitly, or, publicly declares his desire to follow the laws and regulations of the Jewish religion. Even if he does not adhere to all of the rules and traditions of our religion, by becoming a member, he, at least, recognizes their worthwhileness and importance, and wants them passed on to his children.

8. By joining a congregation he expresses a desire to strengthen Jewish family life and to raise his children in accordance with Jewish teaching. His congregation membership helps to enrich his family life as the head of a Jewish household.

9. In Judaism, the synagogue always leads back to the home, the central institution of Judaism. Husband and wife strive to create the conditions for a beautiful and harmonious relationship based upon the time-honored principles of Jewish practice which they must try to live out together to the best of their ability.

10. Unless both husband and wife are Jewish the purposes of the synagogue, and the reasons for the existence of a congregation, are defeated and destroyed from the outset.

11. Therefore, a person who has intermarried should not be admitted to membership in a congregation, even if he applies for membership singly, without his non-Jewish mate. Husband and wife, since the very beginning of time, are considered "one flesh" and, therefore, "one member."

12. In refusing to accept such a person for membership, the synagogue can help him resolve the problem of his intermarriage by facing the issue squarely, and not avoiding it.

13. If the matter of affiliation is so urgent and important, the non-Jewish partner can convert to Judaism, and, become an active and honored member of the congregation. The Rabbi is prepared to spend time with the non-Jewish person and convert him in accordance with the procedure laid down by the Conservative Movement's Committee On Law.

In 1947, the reform rabbis, by a resolution passed at the Central Conference of American Rabbis, reaffirmed a stand taken in 1909 "that mixed marriages are contrary to the tradition of the Jewish religion and should therefore be discouraged by the American Rabbinate."

At the 1960 meeting of the Conference, complaints were made by some reform rabbis against certain of their colleagues who—despite the official position of the CCAR which discourages rabbis from performing mixed marriages—officiate at marriages in which one of the parties has not been converted to Judaism. This subject is to be reconsidered by the Central Conference Executive Committee.

Reform Judaism's opposition to mixed marriage is, however, officially recorded in the Rabbi's Manual[27] as follows:

MIXED MARRIAGE

Reform Judaism is opposed to mixed marriages—by which is understood the marriage of a Jew to a non-Jew on essentially religious grounds.

The very nature of the Jewish marriage ritual implies a positive commitment to Judaism by both bride and bridegroom. This is indicated by the formula HARAY AT, "Be thou consecrated unto me as my wife according to the law of God and the faith of Israel."

Other equally cogent reasons for opposing the marriage of Jews

to non-Jews have been expounded by the scholarly authorities of Reform Judaism.

Thus M. Mielziner wrote, "Peace and harmony cannot be expected to reign supreme in a marriage in which the parties belong to religions so widely diverging from each other in regard to certain dogmas. Experience, besides, demonstrates that it is only in the rarest cases of such mixed marriages that domestic life can be conducted and children brought up in the spirit of our religion. Judaism being the religion of the minority, as a matter of self-preservation is, therefore, also opposed to mixed marriages, which, if prevalent, would weaken its influence and endanger its very existence (The Jewish Law of Marriage and Divorce, pp. 47-49 and 52).

David Einhorn held similarly that "such marriages are to be strictly prohibited, even from the standpoint of Reform Judaism" (Mielziner, p. 52). The same view has been expressed by many other leaders of Reform.

At its New York meeting in 1909, the Central Conference of American Rabbis passed the following resolution:

The CCAR declares that mixed marriages are contrary to the tradition of the Jewish religion and should, therefore, be discouraged by the American Rabbinate (*Yearbook*, CCAR, Vol. XIX, p. 170, and discussions thereon pp. 174-184). This resolution was re-affirmed in 1947 (*Yearbook*, CCAR, Vol. LVII, p. 161).

Certainly the Jewish home, which is the object of marriage, must be conducted according to the Jewish principles. A Christian minister cannot consecrate a Jewish home; nor can a Jewish minister consecrate a Christian home; and if a man and wife belong to two different religions, it will be a house divided against itself. Without harmony of views in a matter so vital to the future, there is no real unity. For those who think that the Jewish home needs no religious consecration, the State Law provides that they may apply to the civil magistrate to perform the marriage and have the sanction of the State for their union (K. Kohler, *Yearbook*, CCAR, Vol. XXIX (1919), p. 76).

Of course, a person born and raised in a non-Jewish faith and subsequently converted to Judaism is a Jew in every respect. Marriage between such a person and a born Jew is completely acceptable.

At its 1962 convention the Special Committee on Mixed Marriages[28] of the Central Conference of American Rabbis (Reform) introduced a report on mixed marriage containing views that seem not to have been shared by most of those rabbis present. The recommendation reads as follows:

The CCAR shall adopt the following as its official statement on mixed marriage.

Our deep and abiding concern for the sanctity and the unity of the Jewish home, our profound commitment to the preservation of Judaism and the Jewish people make it imperative that the Reform Rabbinate do everything within its power consistent with the principles of liberal Judaism to discourage mixed marriages.

When called upon to officiate at a mixed marriage, the Rabbi shall make every effort to bring the non-Jewish member into Judaism by way of a sincere conversion.

The CCAR further declares that it is the sacred duty of the Rabbi to insist that mixed couples receive thorough instruction in Judaism prior to their marriage and that they reach a firm pre-marital agreement on the religious climate of the home and the rearing of the children.

Objection by some of the reform rabbis was based on the belief that such a resolution implied an easement of their stand made at prior conventions. The official attitude of the Reform Rabbinate remains opposed to officiation at mixed marriages although it is generally agreed that about 35 per cent of their number perform such marriages.

Orthodox Judaism has not issued any formal pronouncements on interfaith marriage other than to point out its adherence to the ancient Jewish tradition which strongly opposes intermarriage.

The leaders of major branches of contemporary Judaism have also formally expressed their opposition to intermarriage. Among them, we cite the following:

Jews are hostile to intermarriage with people of another faith. This is not too well understood. Jews are not hostile to intermarriage with people of another race, if they are Jews. The basic doctrine here is that the home is a sanctuary. It cannot be so maintained if either the high priest or the high priestess, so to speak, belongs to another faith. That is something Jews do not like—marriage outside of their fold—because it means the children will not be Jews, or will be only half-Jews. Jews feel strongly about the importance of preserving Judaism because there are very few Jews. Judaism does not consider it an unreasonable sacrifice for a Jewish man or woman to shun marriage or even the thought of marriage to a non-Jew.[29]

Dr. Louis Finkelstein, Chancellor
Jewish Theological Seminary of America
(Conservative)

When we say that the Jewish ideal is the brotherhood of man we are not advocating that either gentile or Jew give up his own distinctive historical and religious traditions. Brothers are not identical. Each must have his own individuality. . . . We have little respect for one who is so characterless as to submerge his own personality in that of his brother. Be yourself, be true to yourself is as sound a counsel to religious groups as it is to individuals. Let each be loyal to his own traditions of birth, his own religion and God. . . . for married union to be happy and permanent there must be the maximum of compatibility. This is far less likely to exist and to develope where husband and wife bring to the union incompatible religious traditions. When religious associations and feelings (and they are among the deepest

rooted and strongest feelings known to man) pull husband and wife in different directions, is it to be wondered at that demonstrably a mixed marriage between Jew and Gentile is more likely to turn out unhappily than a marriage between adherents of the same religious group? Divorce figures from various sources show that religious "mixed marriages are three to four times more likely to be dissolved than pure marriages. . . ." Marriage is not a private matter affecting only the one man and the one woman. It affects their parents and family on both sides and as a rule, brings discord or non-recognition into the families who would lightly enter into a religious mixed marriage which is going to cause lifelong sorrow or heartbreak to loved ones who treasure loyalty to religious traditions?" [30]

> Dr. David de Sola Pool
> (Orthodox)

Dr. Mordecai M. Kaplan,[31] noted Jewish thinker and founder of the Reconstructionist movement in Judaism, highly regarded by conservative and reform rabbis, believes that:

> Since Jews are a minority and Judaism is exposed to tremendous disintegrating forces from the non-Jewish environment . . . it cannot approve of uncontrolled intermarriage with non-Jews. If, however, a non-Jew who desires to marry a Jew, after studying what is involved in being a Jew and what are the principles and practices of Judaism is willing to undergo formal conversion to Judaism, he should be given every encouragement and should be welcomed into the Jewish community. Only in this way can we compensate for losses through intermarriage, where conversion to Judaism is not made a condition. It is unreasonable to expect that Jewish religion and culture will be perpetuated in homes resulting from mixed marriages where no such requirement is insisted on. . . . We cannot regard as a proper marriage any union between a Jew and a non-Jew who has not been converted. Though that interdicts the officiation at such a marriage by a rabbi, or any other functionary of the Jewish community, it does not mean that we should regard the couple as living in an immoral relationship. It merely means that the Jewish party to the marriage is guilty of a dereliction in his or her obligation to Judaism.

Seventy-five conservative and reform rabbis serving congregations throughout the country were asked a series of questions about their personal attitude toward the intermarried. Of these, 72 replied that there are intermarried families who are members of their congregations. Only 2, both conservative rabbis, replied in the negative. The other 3 failed to respond.

Of those who responded affirmatively, 38 are the spiritual leaders of conservative congregations, while 34 are reform rabbis. Orthodox

rabbis were not asked to complete the questionnaire because Orthodox Jewish tradition definitely opposes intermarriage. However, this must not be construed to mean that the children of Orthodox Jews do not marry persons of other faiths. What actually occurs is that these children, driven by the "shame" attached to intermarriage within their own families, yet with the assistance of their parents, often seek out conservative and reform rabbis who, after a period of study and formal conversion rites, officiate at such marriages.

Of the 38 conservative rabbis who replied, 14 occupy pulpits in the Eastern States, 8 are in the South, 2 live in the Far West, and 14 serve congregations in the Midwest.

The length of service of these reform rabbis in the active rabbinate parallels that of the others. Of the reform rabbis 13 serve Eastern congregations; 8 reside in Southern States; 9 are in the Far West, and 4 occupy pulpits in the Midwest. In practically all cases, these rabbis serve urban Jewish Congregations. They are men not given to hasty judgments and opinions. Whether or not the reader will agree with their opinions, their ideas are, I believe, representative of those of all American rabbis—orthodox, conservative and reform.

With but two exceptions, the rabbis who responded to our questionnaire were ordained a decade or more ago. Some have served their congregations for over thirty years. All but one expressed *a priori* opposition to the idea of interfaith marriages. They believe that the survival of Judaism is at stake in such marriages if one of the parties to the marriage has not been converted to Judaism. Their varied attitudes and opinions as recorded in their completed questionnaires provide an interesting commentary on the contemporary American-Jewish scene.

Typical of the conservative rabbis' opinions are the following:

> The historic, Jewish, traditional reasons opposing intermarriage hold good in our day as they have in the past. Unless both parties to the marriage are platonic philosophers, nostalgic factors enter to make such a marriage unworkable.

> Intermarriage adds a major area of conflict and difference to a marriage which has enough areas of disagreement to resolve and live with. It confuses the child of such a marriage in later years and serves to divide husband and wife in the most important area for building a peaceful and beautiful marriage.

> Marriages are subjected to enough strains without beginning them with a tremendous cultural and religious strain. Conversion for the sake of marriage may be a very traumatic experience or it may create a climate of religious indifference. Its effect upon an entire family (parents of the couple) may leave severe scars upon all concerned. The

success of such marriages depends upon the kind of religious ties both parties really have. It is somewhat dependent too upon the degree of acceptance they receive in the Jewish and Christian community.

The Home is the chief means of transmitting a culture. It suffers when parents have a divided background. It is so difficult even through formal instruction to transmit one's emotional ties. Despite the laxity in Jewish observance, etc., there is still a strong sense of kinship and mutual identification among Jews. An intermarried couple moves in Jewish circles exclusively and the non-Jewish partner feels overtones of an acceptance that is *not* complete.

There is a greater chance for a happy marriage when there is a similarity of religious background, when there is no family opposition to the marriage as is generally present in intermarriage, where there are no guilt feelings on the part of the person who has been converted. There is an uneasiness and guilt in relationship to parents and family.

Intermarriage undermines the unity of the family and shows little consideration for the basic role that religion plays in a person's life. Hence, I oppose it!

Conversion, in many instances, is merely a formality. If the non-Jew seriously desires to embrace Judaism and not just embrace another Jew, then I am not opposed to it. I have a number of cases in which the couple has been married for some time and, of her own volition, the non-Jew asks to become a Jewess. The social and family pressures that work against the success of interfaith marriages are tremendous.

Because greater adjustment is required in interfaith marriage, the chances for dissension are also greater. The strong sub-conscious influence of early childhood often prevent complete conversion. The Jewish people is the bearer of Judaism. Since I would like to see Judaism survive, I regret any loss to the Jewish people. I think that such a loss occurs through intermarriage. Although differences may attract people to each other, they do not contribute to the ease of adjustment in marriage. Even though the people involved in the intermarriage may not be observant religiously, their religious identification however tenuous is intermeshed with strong emotions. The early childhood, environment and training cannot be erased from the subconscious.

In the long run, interfaith marriage weakens the survival possibility of the Jew.

The youngster who intermarries wants only to marry the one he loves. Twenty years later, he has other concerns, (a) his children's happiness, (b) his identification with the Jewish people. As the years go by following upon his marriage, these concerns become stronger and they may weaken a marriage considerably.

Intermarriage is the greatest single threat to the operating Jewish tradition.

Reform rabbinic attitudes on intermarriage, as recorded in the replies to the questionnaires, include the following:

I have noted with interest that there is an interesting proportion of cases where the Jewish partner to an intermarriage is a girl, and that the economic, social and educational level of the non-Jew (contrary to the majority of cases in earlier decades) is often equal or superior to that of the Jew. I may add that while I continue to follow tradition and decline to officiate at mixed marriages where there has been no conversion, I grow more and more unhappy about the matter. Finally, I may note that in the last year or two a remarkably large number of prospective converts (nearly all planning to marry or already married to Jews) have come to me from outside the congregation. I received five such converts in 1960 (besides others who started but didn't finish), another yesterday, and have several more in process.

Marriage has enough difficulties without taking on the additional one of difference of background with all the subtle nuances this implies. I, generally speaking, oppose interfaith marriages. Such marriages fail when family ties assert themselves, when historic loyalties rise to the surface, when the normal differences and tensions are rationalized in religious and racial terms.

Even though I believe that in a free-flowing democracy people are bound to meet and fall in love, I feel that if they are to establish a family, it is in the best interests of all involved that they begin with a common faith. Intermarriages often fail when there is a lack of interest on the part of the Jewish-born partner to replace the religious experience that his formerly Christian mate has given up with a creative Jewish religious experience.

I am concerned with the preservation of Judaism. I will officiate at an interfaith marriage (where there has been no formal conversion) when an agreement is reached to rear a Jewish family.

One reform rabbi in a large Eastern community expresses his opposition to intermarriage:

Yet, even though I do not require a formal conversion ceremony by the non-Jew, I require that a written agreement be made by the non-Jewish partner, pledging to rear the children born of such a marriage and "to the best of our ability rear our family according to the traditions and faith of Israel."

Other opinions given include the following:

Intermarriage weakens the Jewish community. It raises special problems in adjustment that are not easily resolved. Religious conflict goes beyond theological differences between the two parties. There are also problems involving parents and the difficult problem of securing community acceptance of interfaith marriages.

There are so many problems involving the children of the inter-married. When a child says: "Mother wasn't born a Jew, why should I be a Jew?" just how are you going to answer him? Parents' inter-ference is often so marked and the general indifference to religion simply adds to the problem.

Intermarriage is a challenge to the warmth, viability and ultimate survival of the Jewish home.

I do not believe that such marriages are conducive to personal happiness. I feel too that it weakens the Jewish people.

I oppose interfaith marriage because I am concerned about Jewish survival. I think too that they are unfair to the children, and that the risk of personal unhappiness is greater. Differences in background and one's emotional attitude toward religion affect a marriage. There is the probability that intermarriage was in itself a symptom of emotional immaturity in the first place.

When both parties fail to agree on their religious life together, the chances for the success of the marriage are diminished. But otherwise, this is not so. In fact, in all the years of my rabbinate I have had hardly any divorces from mixed marriages.

Except for rare cases, intermarriages weaken both the intermarried family and Judaism. Whole-hearted participation in the life cycle of ceremonies and religious holidays is quite impossible in the family when there is intermarriage because one of the parents (husband or wife) is bound to get hurt and offended.

One rabbi, himself the parent of a son who has married a non-Jewish (but converted) girl, writes:

Differences in religious background and failure to agree on the religious training of the children of the intermarried make me believe that interfaith marriages cannot, in the main, work out successfully.

A noted rabbi who has officiated at many interfaith marriages (but has always insisted upon formal conversion to Judaism) comments:

I do not officiate at a marriage unless both partners are Jewish by birth or unless there has been a conversion of the non-Jewish party prior to marriage. I find a greater tendency of Jews who are marrying

non-Jews to have them convert to Judaism as I find that there is generally a greater interest in Judaism over the whole of the United States. If I analyze the future correctly, there will be a greater number of conversions to Judaism in the years to come. There are, I believe, psychologically, two reasons for this. One is the impact of the Hitler period, which means that the Jewish partner is reluctant to add to the losses of our people. . . . The other reason is the existence of the State of Israel which has added stature and dignity to the Jewish name. . . . Unless the partners decide on one and the same basis for their marriage beforehand, it runs a greater risk of failure.

The co-operation of the rabbi[32] of the only Jewish (Reform) Congregation in Hawaii, located in Honolulu, has made possible added data from one of the most singular communities in the Western World. Interracial marriages in Hawaii are, as we have noted elsewhere, the normal pattern for that society. It was of interest to know how the 370 families on the current mailing list of Temple Emanu-El (Reform) and their rabbi react to the problem of intermarriage. In addition to these 370 families there are known to be others who have no connection whatever with the Jewish community, and, for the most part, no contact with any other Jews. The intermarriage rate among this group is said to be higher than it is for those who are on the Temple mailing list.

Of the 370 families already referred to, 150 are members of this Temple, signifying thereby their desire for direct affiliation with the Jewish people and Judaism, as represented by the Temple. On the Island 130 families or 34.1 per cent of all the families are intermarried —of the 150 families who are Temple members, 37 or 24.6 per cent are intermarried.

Six Jews who are members of the Temple are married to Orientals (Mongolians) and another 4 are married to Hawaiians (Polynesians). Concerning intermarriage, the rabbi comments:

> It is my conviction that intermarriages can work quite successfully. I think it is a rare case in which difference in religion is the sole cause of marital unhappiness. The continued survival and prosperity of Judaism is linked, at least in part, I think, with a willingness to accept increased intermarriage, for it is bound to come. As to interracial marriages, of course here in Hawaii, these present no problem. . . . As a generalization, though, I would guess that the marriage of a Caucasian to an Oriental or a Polynesian, whether in Hawaii or on the mainland, will be less problem-laden than the marriage of a Caucasian to a Negro.

According to these American rabbis, there will, in all likelihood, be an increase in the rate of interfaith marriages involving Jews. Forty-five rabbis declare that "propinquity" will be the primary cause of this increase; 34 believe that "parents exercise less control over their chil-

dren," while 26 believe that an increase in intermarriage may be due to the simple fact that "more Jewish boys and girls go to colleges and universities." Sixteen rabbis declare that "Jewish youth is less religious today" and 15 feel that the increase will be due to the "more ready acceptance of Jews in non-sectarian college fraternities." Other factors suggested by the rabbis are (a) "America means political and social equality to more people" (6 responses); (b) "a greater loyalty to universal prophetic values" (3 responses); (c) "the feeling that Jewish survival is not important," that there is a "marked decrease in hostility"; "social and psychological distance between Jews and non-Jews has been reduced" and "the inadequacy of the Jewish education (and indoctrinal) program for youth" (3 responses each).

Other reasons for the belief that intermarriages will increase are: "the weakness of religion in the home"; the belief that "intermarriage will happen regardless of what anyone may do because Jews are members of a minority group"; awareness that "when but a few Jews live in non-Jewish communities, the rate of intermarriage is bound to increase"; the feeling that "there is a lack of insight into the implications of assimilation and what it means with respect to Jewish survival," that "Jewish religious institutional life is 'anemic' "; that "Jews are not seriously committed to a way of life (2 responses in each category) and "the liberalizing influence of modern culture"; "rebellion against hypocritical parents"; "a general atmosphere of permissiveness"; "military service draws young men away from the parental religious patterns" and finally "romantic love"—each of which was suggested as a factor related to intermarriage. The only point on which the vast majority seem to agree is that propinquity, going to school together, living and working near each other, tends to increase the likelihood of intermarriage.

> In a free and democratic university setting in which Jews constitute a sizeable segment of the student population, the need for kinship and Jewish fellowship will increasingly lose its importance as a major stimulus to Jewish community life on campus. . . . Today's students are no longer reluctant to affirm their Jewishness. But in most instances they are ignorant of what they affirm. . . . Our central problem today is no longer that Jewish students try to escape their Judaism. The problem is that Judaism is escaping them.[33]

As we have already noted elsewhere in this study, Jewish students rarely seem to have religious scruples about intermarriage. They know that their parents would not approve of it and that is sufficient reason for avoidance of intermarriage although interdating continues. Most Jewish students define their Jewishness in terms of religion, but from point of view of actual fact, have little that can be so defined.

Today, Jewish parents, 85 per cent of whom are American-born and products of the American school system tend to be permissive in their relations with their children. Parents are far less authoritarian in their attitudes than they were a generation or more ago. They strive mightily to "be a pal" to their children. Their determination "not to lose the child" whatever the action or reaction of their children to them or their values serves the younger generation in good stead. Youth senses that parental ideas and values with respect to Judaism are not clear and are even equivocal; that often, parents despite their lip service to Judaism, and its way of life, are really indifferent to it. Youth counts on its own determination and parental softness in a critical moment to gain its end, which often means interfaith marriage.

Parents "give" their children a Jewish education, hoping to develop their self-awareness as Jews, but they do nothing about their Jewishness in their homes. Often their ideals and values are free from Judaism. Yet, they seek somehow, to avoid assimilation. They ask, as did Neustatter,[34] "What would it mean to the Jews if, for example, one out of every six marriages involving Jews were a mixed marriage?"

Basing her speculations on Elliot Slater's statement that one out of every six marriages involving Jews is mixed, Neustatter says:

> If we take no account of the decreasing birth-rate and neglect the fact that the average number of children in a Jewish family is less than two, and if we *disregard moreover the probability that the rate of intermarriage will increase during the next two generations, we may estimate the effect of intermarriage on the Jewish population after two generations. If we assume 60 couples in which there has been no intermarriage and which produce two children each* who grow to maturity and in turn produce two children, the grandchild generation will number 240. If, however, 10 of the sixty couples are mixed and 75% of their children are lost to Jewry, at a constant intermarriage rate of 17 per 100 marriages, after two generations only 183 children would be left to Jewry. . . . there would be a loss of about 25%. Since size of family *is less* than 4 persons on the average and the intermarriage rate is steadily increasing, the cumulative effect of these two factors must necessarily result in a far greater loss. It is even possible that as much as ½ of the Jewish population might have to be written off within two generations as a result of intermarriage alone.

Frischberg[35] said that the statement that "about 75 per cent of all the children born to Jews married to Christians are baptized immediately at birth and only 25 per cent are reared as Jews" is perhaps, not true today, but the fear that this may occur is another factor that strengthens Jewish opposition to intermarriage.

The Greater Washington Study[36] indicates that, in two-thirds of the intermarried families (3,300 out of a total of 27,000 families) the

children are reared as non-Jews; in one-quarter, the children are reared as Jews, while in the remainder, their religious training, if any, is uncertain. The data also makes clear the fact that where families have already experienced intermarriage, it is more likely to occur again.

Twenty-five directors and counselors who minister directly to Jewish student needs through the Hillel Foundations at 28 different American colleges and universities[37] appear to be uncertain about the future of Jewish students' response to the idea of interfaith and interracial intermarriage in the next decade. Thirteen believe that there will be an increase in interfaith marriage in the next decade; 5 do not believe so, while 10 of these persons remain uncertain. As for their attitudes on interracial marriages, 11 directors and counselors (all the directors are rabbis and one counselor is a Jewish University professor) believe that there will be an increase in this category; 5 persons do not hold to this view while the remainder are uncertain about what is likely to occur in this area. Fourteen of these Hillel directors report that more Jewish students are coming to them to discuss the possibility of intermarriage; 9 declare that the number of such students is about the same.

Seventeen of these Hillel directors believe that interfaith marriages cannot, in the main, work out successfully; only 5 believe that they can while the others remain uncertain.

Among the opinions expressed on this subject are the following:

> Interfaith marriages I have seen or to whom I have counselled are not successful. Basic differences arise in the approach to child rearing, family, interference and arguments where the term "damn Jew" is involved. The greatest chance of success comes where one partner is only a nominal member of a religious group. Many problems in intermarriage do not arise until the question of where to send the child, comes up.

> Jewish society is fairly rigid in its expectations of intra-faith marriages and is, in the main "traumatized by deviations." The problems of children increase in interfaith marriages. There is generally less than the usual support by friends and relatives on both sides, resulting in an inadequate number of friends (which in turn, affects the marriage).

> When both parties to such a marriage are mature enough and can share their attitudes, both emotionally and intellectually, toward basic matters, there is no reason why the marriage cannot work out.

> Practical experience has taught me that the chances for the success of such a marriage are much lower than normally—particularly when children enter the picture.

> Marriages in which one of the two parties has not formally changed his or her religion are difficult because such differences are much more

than doctrinal. They represent a whole way of life and thought. As such, adjustment is all the more difficult even though it is, of course, not absolutely impossible.

Insofar as interracial marriages are concerned, 12 Hillel directors believe that they cannot work out successfully, while 3 state that *under certain conditions* they believe that they may be successful. Ten of the directors express no opinion on the matter. Their views are expressed by such replies as the following:

> . . . marriage involves much more than doctrinal differences. It is a relationship between two people and the society in which they live. The reactions of the society must be taken into account.

> Our Society is not willing to accept such marriages and the strain particularly upon the children of such unions would be enormous.

> If the interracially married couple lived in some place where they would be socially accepted and where there are others in the same situation the marriage might work out, but otherwise, I cannot imagine it working out.

> Whether or not an interracial marriage would work out would depend on the maturity of those concerned, the nature of the community where they live, similarity or dissimilarity of religious and cultural backgrounds. Then, given agreement on these points, there is a chance for the success of the marriage.

> Communal pressures complicate the interracial marriage situation. The likelihood of success is reduced because of such community negative response. Public opinion as represented by the community is important and certainly affects the results in such cases as in all others.

> Tradition and prejudice as well as the accumulated centuries of widely different culture patterns render inter-racial marriage extremely hazardous.

Fifteen out of 25 of the Hillel directors do not believe that the elimination of religious and racial bars from fraternity and sorority constitutions will change the situation very much on college campuses with respect to intermarriage, either interfaith or interracial. Interestingly they suggest that the *formal elimination* of such clauses from their constitutions will not necessarily increase the number of persons of different religions or races who are invited into membership, nor will it necessarily increase the likelihood of social contact. There is a certain skepticism which runs through the comments which, drawing on the experiences of Jews and Negroes in both the United States and elsewhere, suggests that constitutional guarantees of equality, political or social, do not assure

such equality in our time. Inasmuch as there is no empirical data as yet to confirm or to deny the correctness of this view, we must wait for another decade before these ideas can be verified or disproved. Yet, the logic of the situation suggests that, if there is an increase in social mixing, there will be greater exposure to possible intermarriage both religious and racial.

For centuries, prior to the American experience, Jews who married out of their faith were looked upon by most Jews as renegades who had deserted their people and their religion. Memories acquired through historical and contemporary events in which Jews suffered physical and psychological pain and anguish at the hands of non-Jewish persecutors were kept ever fresh. Indeed, the day-to-day story of Jewish persecution and suffering, including that of the Hitler era, made it impossible to forget. Intermarriage with persons whose ancestors or families had directly or indirectly been responsible for such acts was generally regarded as equivalent to treason to the Jewish people. Often it had little to do with religious differences in ideologies between Jew and non-Jew. It had far more to do with the treatment accorded a minority people in any particular country.

The nature and quality of the American way of life, its basic principles of liberty and equality before the law, its acceptance of certain Old Testament values—the importance and worth of the individual, recognition of each man's God-given rights as a human—all woven into the fabric of American life, tended to mold Jews and all other Americans into a general pattern of unity of thought.

The means of Jewish identification, particularly insofar as American Jews of the third generation are concerned, have assumed a different character from what they were in the past. Despite the cataclysmic Hitlerian era with its valley of despair, American Jews do not generally think of themselves as members of a people "in exile." Nor do they generally regard themselves as a people apart from all others. Their experience, education, and association with persons of other religions, colors and ethnic groups has had its marked effect. Generally they speak of themselves as Jews by "religion." It is, they often say, religion that distinguishes them from other Americans. Yet they understand the Jewish religion far less in terms of personal ritual and observance than did their parents or grandparents; and much more in terms of identification with the synagogue, philanthropy and other Jewish institutions. Although they are aware of the traditional emphasis which made the Jewish religion coextensive with life, contemporary Jews have acculturated to a marked degree. They are so much like other Americans that even their professed relationship to the Jewish religion is often difficult to discover.

Insofar as the Jew is concerned, Lewin,[38] in 1940, indicated a frame of mind that must ultimately lead to assimilation.

For the modern Jew there exists an additional factor to increase his uncertainty. He is frequently uncertain about the way he belongs to the Jewish group, and to what degree. Especially since religion has become a less important social matter, it is rather difficult to describe positively the character of the Jewish group as a whole. A religious group with many atheists? A Jewish race with a great diversity of racial qualities among its members? A nation without a state or a territory of its own containing the majority of its people? A group combined by one culture and tradition but actually having in most respects the different values and ideals of the nation in which it lives? There are, I think, few chores more bewildering than that of determining positively the character of the Jewish group. It is not easy to see why such a group should be preserved as a separate unit, why it has not entirely given up its will to live, and why the nations have refused to grant the Jews full assimilation.

The Jewish religion is often regarded as but one phase of what it means to be a Jew. It is, therefore, proper to speak of Judaism as religio-ethnic in character. It is only by this means that we can explain why it is possible for persons, born of Jewish parents, without a vestige of religious feeling or concern, yet, identifying themselves with Jews in other matters, cultural, social and philanthropic, to regard themselves or to be termed by others as Jews. Judaism is, in fact, a way of life.

Lois Rubin, a 20 year old Jewish, Bronx stenographer was "going steady" with Thomas Smith, a nominal Catholic. Although the Catholic youth is willing to convert to Judaism and Lois isn't too concerned about religion in general or Judaism in particular (she says she doesn't care about whether she or Tom convert to the other's religion), Lois' parents are very much distressed about the matter. "I'm orthodox, but not strictly," says Lois' father who is not affiliated with any Synagogue. "There's a Temple down the street. It's Shaarey something. No, I don't belong to it." Lois' father has no known Jewish affiliations but he triumphantly pronounced "My wife's as Jewish as rye bread." [39]

It should be noted, too, that, Tom, "the nominal Catholic" was also bitterly attacked, as were various members of his family—younger sisters and brothers—by his Catholic neighbors who regarded his acts as a form of treason to Catholicism for it, too, has cultural as well as purely ritualistic and theological implications for Catholics.

Some Jews themselves find it difficult to understand why deviation from Judaism, in terms of such practices as the Sabbath and the dietary laws, is so easily accepted while the thought of intermarriage with a non-Jew leaves so many Jews utterly horrified. The number of such

intermarriages has never exceeded 8 per cent in the United States as a whole, yet Jews somehow feel as if the survival of the Jewish people were actually at stake. It is the Jewish family, the personal relationships that presently exist between parents and child—between a sibling and other siblings—that is at stake. And these relationships appear to be tremendously important to the Jew.

It may be difficult to understand what impells Jewish parents such as the Rubins to oppose intermarriage. They seldom enter a synagogue from one year to the next. They do not observe the dietary laws or any of the ritual of Jewish life. Their relationship to the Jewish community is only nominal. They do not know Hebrew and can hardly use the language for prayer. Why do they get so disturbed about the possibility of their son or daughter marrying a non-Jew? They sit before me with tears in their eyes and literally cry out, "Rabbi, you've got to save my child!"

Oscar Handlin's sagacious comment in this connection may well be the correct answer to this vexing problem. "A man holds dear what little is left. When much is lost, there is no risking the remainder." [40] Well aware of the distance he has traveled from his tradition and religion—of the practices, rites and ceremonies discarded; the values and "way of life" ignored—the intermarriage of a son or daughter appears to be the very end of the road, the last moment before one is "assimilated," *i.e.,* loses his identity, as a distinct and unique personality. Hence, it often happens that the otherwise religiously indifferent cling to the little that remains.

What is disturbing to the Jewish group is that it has never before lived under conditions so favorable to a full democratic existence. It is also true that never before has the ritual observance of the Jewish people fallen to such a low point. Although there has been an increase in the number of Jewish children receiving an intensive (three to five afternoons a week) Jewish education, percentage-wise the number has not increased. Only half of Jewish children of school age are being formally educated as Jews.

The many factors that cause young people of all religions to view their traditions so dispassionately makes for further concern among Jews. They are less worried about their physical survival than they are about the *quality* of their survival. Intermarriage probably will not destroy the Jewish people in America. It serves, however, as a symptom of the general weakening of ties and the reduction of the sense of empathy for their own people that characterized so many Jews in the past. Studies of various American-Jewish communities reveal pertinent information and provide a self-portrait of American Jews in this connection.

A study of the Jewish community of New Orleans, Louisiana,[41] in 1953, was basically demographic and the question of intermarriage was only incidental. This study indicated that 7 per cent of all married individuals among the Jews of that city in 1953 were intermarried. The accuracy of the above figure may well be questioned because "only those who retain identification with the Jewish community to the extent at least of answering the questionnaire" were included. The number of the intermarried in this community may, therefore, be considerably higher.

In her noted New Haven studies, Kennedy[42] found that, in 1955, 97.4 per cent of all marriages involving Jews in that city were endogamous. In other words, the intermarriage rate involving Jews in New Haven in 1955 was 2.6 per cent. The rate of Jewish intermarriages in that city appears, then, to have leveled off from its high of 7.2 per cent in 1900. The idea that native-born Jews will tend to intermarry in increasing numbers is discounted by this study.

Kennedy's conclusion that "intermarriage does not relentlessly increase in the dimension of time in a smooth, unbroken pattern" challenges those who assert that the assimilation of religious minority groups into majority groups is inevitable or that the three major religious denominations will certainly merge into one amalgam—whatever its name or content will be. That "no mystical force pushes any aspect of intergroup relations in a single pattern," [43] is an important reminder to those who wish to retain their identity as a member of a distinctive religious group that, according to Kennedy, this is quite possible.

Further, Kennedy's belief that "the strength of family influence is positively related to the observance within the family of traditional Jewish values" is supported by the Riverton, Southville and Bayville surveys,[44] all of which indicate that attitude toward exogamous marriages is more receptive among Reform Jews than among the Conservative and Orthodox. Among Reform Jews there is far less ritual observance of the dietary laws and other religiously prescribed behavior than among Conservative and Orthodox Jews. Whether the reduction or elimination of ritual observance induces assimilation, or whether the desire to integrate or acculturate with the majority and hence dominant culture, reduces traditional ritualistic practices and ultimately "values" is debatable. Kennedy's intuition may be correct when she positively relates the observance of Jewish practices and ritual with assimilatory tendencies. Yet it must be noted that the reduction or elimination of these practices results in part from environmental and cultural factors directly related to the scientific age and the generally "liberal" tendencies of the twentieth century. These, rather than the reduction of religious practices alone,

may be the causal factors of assimilation while the minimization of observances is but one result of these new cultural and environmental factors.

In 1948, Shosteck[45] estimated that at least one-tenth of the marriages involving Jews in small towns were mixed. I believe that he has underestimated the actual number of such intermarriages.

Rose, on the other hand, studying the life of "small-town Jews and their neighbours in the United States," [46] declared that "it seems safe to say that the small-town Jew is similar to the city-dwelling Jew to the extent that he wants his children to remain Jews. He is firmly opposed to interfaith marriage." Yet it also appears that intermarriages involving Jews will take place in greater degree when the Jewish population is small and a large Jewish community is not within easy social contact.

Isolated Jewish families, in small towns where opportunities for social contacts with other Jewish families are not great, are generally worried about the problem of intermarriage insofar as their children are concerned. They mean no disrespect to their Gentile neighbors and friends when, after years of industry in the small town they move on to a larger city where they can become part of the Jewish community and provide their children with Jewish educational opportunities, hitherto lacking. One man explained:

> We lived in a small town in Minnesota for many years and we got along very well. My children were completely at home there. Everybody liked them and they liked everybody. My wife and I were very well accepted. But one thing was lacking—contact with other Jews. We had no synagogue; no Sunday school—nothing. With all of this, my wife and I realized that we were Jews and we wanted our children to remain Jews. The Jewish religion is still dear to us. So, finally we decided that we would have to move into Minneapolis where there is a fine Jewish community. We could send our children to the Hebrew School. We could belong to a Synagogue and our children would meet other Jewish children. We don't want intermarriage in our family. We believe that our chances of having the children marry Jews is so very much better than it could have been in that small town.

They are concerned not only with the survival of their religion and its values, but with the perpetuation and increasing solidarity of the Jewish people as well. A non-religious Jew may still be very much opposed to intermarriage because he wants Jews, qua Jews, to survive. Even though the ritual of Judaism may be dropped, synagogal attendance and worship completely ignored, there is the conviction that intermarriage must mean separation from the Jewish people. For this reason, intermarriage is regarded as a step leading to the ultimate end of Juda-

ism, in that it will undermine the structure of Judaism and hasten the final step toward assimilation.

The study of Jews[47] in Bayville to which we have referred corroborates other supporting evidence that even though contemporary Jews are not very observant of ancient Jewish rituals, they are strongly committed to a philosophy which includes positive identification with their fellow Jews. While only 47 per cent light Sabbath-eve candles in their homes and but 37 per cent purchase kosher meat; while only 27 per cent keep two sets of dishes (for milk and meat foods) and only 20 per cent attend Sabbath Services regularly, yet they oppose intermarriage, regarding marriage within the Jewish community as essential to being a good Jew.

So great, in fact, is this identification with the Jewish people that nine out of ten of these people would disapprove of their child's marrying a non-Jew. Of these, three-quarters "strongly disapprove." [48] Only one in ten persons in the Bayville survey, felt that it would make no difference who their child married.

The Riverton Study,[49] the first in the series of studies of the attitudes of Jews in various areas in the United States, helps us further to understand the views of Jewish parents with respect to their children.

When asked: "Do you think your child would ever marry a non-Jew?" the majority thought they would not; a good third simply didn't know; only 7 per cent thought they might do so.

The difference in attitudes of foreign-born and native-born parents to intermarriage is indicated by yet another report, "The Southville Survey," [50] which indicates that while 75 per cent of those young people with two foreign-born parents would disapprove, only 52 per cent of those with two American-born parents would respond in this manner. This is further supported by evidence from the same survey indicating that while 65 per cent of the American-born Southville Jews "strongly disapprove" of intermarriage, 80 per cent of the foreign-born hold to this view. Because of the reduction in the intensity of disapproval indicated by the above replies, we may assume that the farther removed American Jews are from their foreign-born ancestors, the greater will be the tendency to approve of intermarriage. The Southville study of 3,000 Jewish families reveals, however, that 68 per cent of the 200 respondents who have children would strongly disapprove of a child's intermarriage, 19 per cent would "mildly disapprove" while it "would make no difference to only 12 per cent." Only 1 per cent of the same would "mildly approve" and none would strongly approve. In this study 81 per cent or eight out of ten are American-born.

It is worthy of note, however, that in the Southville Survey[51] while

87 per cent of the "orthodox-affiliated" Jews said they would strongly disapprove of intermarriage, only 55 per cent of the reform-affiliated responded in like manner. Twenty per cent of the latter said that intermarriage would "make no difference," while less than 1 per cent of the Orthodox agree with this view.

In another survey of attitudes of the Jews in White Plains,[52] New York, an upper-middle-class community just outside of New York City, almost 6 out of 10 parents, consisting in the main of second-generation Americans (8 out of 10 persons interviewed were born in the United States), said that they would strongly disapprove if their child married a non-Jew, while 3 out of 10 said they would "mildly" disapprove, and 1 in 7 said "it would make no difference." Only 1 in 7 approved. Only 1 out of 20 Orthodox and Conservative Jews said that intermarriage would make no difference, while 5 out of 20 Reform Jews replied in this way.

The Riverton, Bayville, Southville studies make it appear that a majority of American Jews in these communities (and in all likelihood in all America), are gradually replacing traditional Jewish beliefs and practices with "a generalized set of secular humanistic moral and ethical principles and community responsibilities." The unfamiliarity of American Jews with their own culture and their failure to associate Judaism with principles that are distinctive or unique make it probable that the desire to remain identified with Judaism will decrease in the next decade. If the religious tie becomes less meaningful it seems likely that other forms of identification may also ultimately prove less significant.

Three other major studies that contain pertinent information on Jews and interfaith marriages are: the Greater Washington, D.C. study; the report on San Francisco, Marin County and Peninsula of Northern California; and the study on the Jewish population of Los Angeles.

The Washington survey[53] revealed not only an increase in intermarriage but further, that the increase is directly associated with the increased acculturation of the Jew. Evidence from this 1956 survey indicates that mixed marriages occur most frequently where the persons involved are born in the United States, have received *more* than a high-school education; and have high professional status.

The same study indicated that 12.2 per cent of the total number of households included in the study were "mixed," *i.e.,* some related members were Jewish while others were not. In the Virginia Metropolitan area of the District of Columbia 34.2 per cent of the households were "mixed"; in the northwest area, west of Rock Creek, 18.2 per cent of the households were "mixed" with 11.6 per cent of similar households in the Montgomery County area; 20.8 per cent in Prince George County in

Maryland (part of the Washington, D.C. Metropolitan area). The per cent of mixed families in the area of the nation's capital is obviously considerably larger than we had suspected.

Jewish education among Jewish native born, who are the children of native parents appears, in the Greater Washington Study, to be an important factor that reduces the likelihood of intermarriage. Rosenthal [54] analyzing that study reports that 16.4 per cent of the native-born men of native parents who intermarried, had some religious education while the rate of native born men who had no religious education was 30.3 per cent, or nearly twice as high.

Excepting for such constraining forces as religious education, the nature of one's employment and the relationship to one's immediate family, to name only the major forces, the rate of intermarriage would in all likelihood be far greater than it presently is.

Insofar as the general education of the intermarried is concerned, the Washington study indicates that 40.4 per cent of the males twenty-five years of age and over have received *more* than a high-school education. In fact, 23 per cent have received college or postgraduate training. In the case of the Jewish females, 8 per cent have had more than a high-school education.

The religious identification of these intermarried is of particular interest inasmuch as there is a greater degree of intermarriage among those persons who have no such identification. The Washington study reveals that nine-tenths of 1 per cent[55] of those who identify themselves as "Orthodox," 3.7 per cent of the "Conservative," and 14.6 per cent of the "Reform" are intermarried. It should be noted, further, that 21.5 per cent of those intermarried term themselves "undecided" as to their religion, while 39.4 per cent of the total number declare themselves to have "no religion." The contention that intermarriage is intimately bound up with nonidentification with the Jewish group is thus supported.

Forty-eight per cent[56] of these Jewish intermarried males and 42.5 per cent of the intermarried females reported that they never attended Jewish religious services. In fact, 44 per cent of these intermarried "have identified themselves with some religion other than Jewish or with no religion at all (28.7 per cent)." Of all Jewish intermarried males 80.9 per cent reported that they had never participated in the Passover "Seder." In those cases where the wife is the Jewish member of the mixed marriage, 41.3 per cent reported that they do not participate in this home service on the Passover.[57]

We learn further that, in those families in which intermarriage has taken place, when the husband is Jewish and the wife is non-Jewish, the children of the intermarried are much more likely to choose a non-Jew

in marriage (14.2 per cent) than when the wife is Jewish and the husband is not Jewish.[58] The influence of the mother is thus once again made clear.

The largest proportion of the males (28.5 per cent) and of the females (11.2 per cent) of the Jewish intermarried are, in terms of their occupations, "Professionals and technical workers, managers, officials, proprietors or clerical and sales workers." The "manual workers" provide the lowest proportion of intermarried [59] (1.6 per cent of the males and 0.3 per cent of the females).

In the Greater Washington study it is further reported that,[60] in 65.9 per cent of the total of 2,400 intermarried families who have children living at home, the children are being reared as Gentiles; in 8.7 per cent of these families, "at least one child is being reared as a Jew while another is being reared as a Gentile and that in but 25.4 per cent of all these families are the children being reared as Jews." The contention by religious leaders that the loss to this minority group is exceedingly great as the consequence of intermarriage is thus supported. There is reason to believe, too, that, in those families where the children are reared in different religions within the same household, the likelihood of marginality and personal insecurity for the children is further increased.

The rate of intermarriage among Jews in San Francisco proper in 1959 was 17.2 per cent; on the Peninsula it was 20 per cent while in Marin County, it was 37 per cent.[61]

We offer the following conjectures concerning the reasons for the high rate in the whole area:

Insofar as identification with the religious life of the Jewish community was concerned, 37 per cent[62] of those studied in San Francisco belonged to a synagogue or temple, while 44 per cent identified in this manner on the Peninsula and only 34 per cent were affiliated with a congregation in Marin County. This compared with a national average of approximately 60 per cent of Jews believed to be affiliated with synagogues or temples in 1960.

In San Francisco, the nonidentification of Jews with a religious orientation was 21.6 per cent; on the Peninsula, it was 27 per cent, while in Marin County the non-identification group dominated, being 43 per cent of the total Jewish population.[63] It is worthy of note that this group is almost 10 per cent greater than the number of Jews affiliated with any synagogue or temple in Marin County.

In San Francisco, 32.4 per cent[64] of its Jews *never* attended religious services and but 30.8 per cent attended on the High Holy Days alone. On the Peninsula 33 per cent "never attended" and 27 per cent

attended only on the High Holy Days. In Marin County, 49 per cent of its Jews *never* attended religious services and 27 per cent attended *only* on the High Holy Days, making a total of 76 per cent for these two factors combined.

Insofar as the observance of the dietary laws[65] is concerned, we find that 82.8 per cent of the Jews in San Francisco did not observe any of them. Their number increased to 84 per cent on the Peninsula and 89 per cent in Marin County.

Insofar as the lighting of the Sabbath candles by the housewife was concerned, but 20.4 per cent of the housewives did so regularly in San Francisco, 14 per cent performed this ritual on the Peninsula and a like number (14 per cent) did so in Marin County.[66]

There appears then, to be a positive correlation between the observance of Jewish ritual and practices, identification with the Synagogue and the degree of intermarriage that occurs within these communities. It must be noted, however, that 22.8 per cent[67] of those questioned in San Francisco had had "more than six years of Jewish education while but 10 per cent of the total number on the Peninsula and 11 per cent of those in Marin County had had more than six years of Jewish education. The degree of intensity of that education is, however, not recorded. Inasmuch as there is a vast difference between a Sunday-school education and an intensive three-to-five-afternoons-a-week Hebrew education, the exact significance of these figures is not too clear. We are informed, however, about the number of Jewish males who have been Bar Mitzvah. In San Francisco,[68] 51.6 per cent of those questioned were Bar Mitzvah; 52 per cent of those on the Peninsula and 47 per cent of those in Marin County had been Bar Mitzvah. The effectiveness of Bar Mitzvah as a means of supporting the desire for identification with the Jewish community or of opposing intermarriage may in this area of the country, at least, be seriously questioned. Whether this is related to the *kind* of Jewish education provided is not ascertainable on the basis of the information presently available.

The likelihood is that intermarriages involving Jews will increase. The evidence thus far presented, points in that direction.

It has been suggested that the only way by which the effects of intermarriage can be counteracted, is through a strong, concerted effort to convert the non-Jewish party in such a marriage to Judaism.

Although, Jews do not actively seek converts, Judaism certainly does not oppose conversion. The Talmud requires that the prospective convert be warned that, as a member of this minority people, he may be subjected to hardship, hatred and prejudice. He must be reminded that the lot of the Jew from the days of Haman to the days of Hitler has been difficult to bear. He must be asked whether, in view of these

facts, he would not prefer to follow the easier course of remaining within his own religious group. Judaism says that "the righteous of all nations will have a share in the world to come." Hence, the non-Jew need not look upon conversion to Judaism as his only means of salvation. In considering the would-be applicant for conversion, the Jew is urged to "push him away with one hand and draw him back with the other."

Conversion to Judaism, then, is possible if, in the view of the rabbi, the applicant is sincere in his desire; if he is also prepared to study Judaism, its history, theology, ritual practices and ideology; and if further, according to orthodox Jewish practice, the male candidate is willing to be circumcised and the female applicant will undergo the immersion (Tevillah) ceremony.

Often, even those persons who have prepared themselves satisfactorily for conversion to Judaism; whose motives are sincere and who have been vouched for by a rabbi, find themselves in the unenviable position of having been formally accepted into Judaism while Jews, *i.e.,* those born of Jewish parents, look often with suspicion and doubt upon their motives. In our interview-in-depth with one such a couple (see page 73), we noted the frustrations of one convert who faced exactly such a situation.

Orthodox, conservative and reform rabbis differ in degree as to the amount of training and indoctrination a proselyte should receive. Reform rabbis are less prone than the orthodox and conservative to insist upon a lengthy study of theological concepts, history, customs, ceremonies and the Hebrew language. They do not insist that the traditional ritual of conversion—immersion for the female and the circumcision of the male—be observed. Most conservative and orthodox rabbis tend to regard the reform rabbis as altogether too "lenient" in this matter.

Orthodox and conservative rabbis with but few exceptions insist that both parties to any marriage at which they officiate must be Jewish or have been formally converted to Judaism. Some reform rabbis do not agree with this view. Dr. Max Eichhorn,[69] a reform rabbi, and a careful observer, believes that as many as 20 per cent of the reform rabbis in the United States will officiate at marriages under conditions other than those laid down by the tradition.

Arguing that the traditional definition of a Jew as "a person having a Jewish mother or one who has been converted to Judaism in the traditional manner," no longer applies, Dr. Eichhorn says:

> My position is that, in the United States, a person is a Jew if (1) he says he is a Jew and (2) he lives as a Jew religiously.

Eichhorn believes that a rabbi ought, under certain circumstances, to officiate at a mixed marriage if certain commitments have been made

by the couple, concerned. He views the general refusal of rabbis to officiate as

> . . . doing incalculable harm to the Jewish group, first, because it is driving Jews away from Judaism, second, because it is making us appear before the non-Jewish world as bigots and third, because instead of making of mixed marriage something to be avoided wherever possible, and to be dealt with humanely and understandingly when it cannot be avoided, the prevailing rabbinate attitude of regarding mixed marriages as an unmitigated evil to be avoided and condemned at all costs, is probably serving to make mixed marriage more attractive to a certain kind of mentality than it would otherwise be.

The majority of all rabbis believe that formal conversion to Judaism prior to marriage is essential; that whatever unity can be acquired by the partners to the marriage by agreement on the matter of religion helps to stabilize the new family. However, they see other factors—in-law problems, general social acceptance, children—as likely to impede the success of the marriage.

When rabbis were asked about the value of formal conversion, all but three (and these were all reform rabbis) favored adherence to the rigors of traditional procedures. These three rabbis offer some interesting comments on the subject:

> We do *not* lose our children [through intermarriage] because the converts are always more devout than the average child. It also builds a bridge of good will to the Christian families of the community. I believe that inter-faith inter-marriages can, in the main, work out successfully.

> I conduct inter-marriages. I do not require a formal conversion. I am neither in favor of nor opposed to inter-marriage. I proceed in terms of each request that is made of me. A number of "cases" are referred to me by those who know my position on the matter (that it is better to assist the couple and their parents too by officiating than it is to refuse to do so because the details of formal conversion have not been complied with).

> I favor the officiating at mixed marriages even though I counsel the couple against such a marriage—unless it is too late. Under these circumstances, I want to salvage something (by having them realize that I, a Rabbi, officiated). I see no need for preventing an increase in such marriages if the couple are healthy, realistic and are going to rear their children as Jews. If they are immature and if the same factors that are generally responsible for couples getting divorced are operative then, the marriage will fail whether or not they are converted.

Eichhorn's[70] study on Conversion indicates that 14 out of 15 converts now being received by both reform and conservative rabbis

in the United States become converts because of "an impending or existing marriage."

The Conversion Service of Reform Judaism which is included in the *Rabbi's Manual*[1] follows:

CONVERSION SERVICE

Two persons representative of the Congregation should be witnesses of the ceremony. It is suggested that the service be conducted in the Synagogue, preferably before the open Ark.

Blessed be you who come in the name of the Lord: We Bless you from the house of the Lord.

Our God and Father, with grateful hearts we thank Thee for many blessings. We thank Thee that Thou dost reveal Thy truth to mankind. Above all, we praise Thee for the gift of the Torah, which has ever been a lamp unto our feet and a light unto our path. We recall with reverence and gratitude all those of the seed of Abraham who have been faithful unto Thee, and those who of their own choice have sought to serve Thee in the faith and fellowship of Israel.

Be near us in this solemn hour. Grant, O God, Thy loving favor to ————, as in this holy place we welcome him (her) into Jewish life. Help him (her) to live in fidelity to the decision he (she) has made, and to the promise he (she) is about to utter. May he (she) always find joy in the fulfillment of Thy Torah and enduring satisfaction in the practice of Judaism. Vouchsafe unto him (her) many years of strength and happiness as a worthy son (daughter) of the Synagogue. Blessed art Thou, O Lord, in Whose presence is fulness of joy. Amen.

The Rabbi delivers a brief charge to the convert, and then asks the following questions, to which the convert responds:

1. Do you of your own free will seek admittance into the Jewish faith?

2. Have you given up your former faith and severed all other religious affiliations?

3. Do you pledge your loyalty to Judaism and to the Jewish people amid all circumstances and conditions?

4. Do you promise to establish a Jewish home and to participate actively in the life of the Synagogue and of the Jewish community?

5. If you should be blessed with children, do you promise to rear them in the Jewish faith?

When the convert has answered "Yes" to each of the questions, the Rabbi says:

I summon you then to pronounce the affirmation by which the Jew lives, and which is on his lips even in his last moment on earth:

The convert recites the Sh'ma:

Hear O Israel: the Lord our God, the Lord is One. Praised be His name whose glorious kingdom is for ever and ever.

The Rabbi takes the convert's hand, saying:

May God strengthen you in the solemn commitment you have made. As a Rabbi in Israel, and with the consent of these witnesses, I welcome you warmly and joyously into our faith and fellowship; and I confer upon you the Hebrew name . . .   .

The Rabbi places his hand on the head of the convert and says:
May the Lord bless thee and keep thee.
May the Lord cause His countenance to shine upon thee and be gracious unto thee.
May the Lord lift up His countenance unto thee and give thee peace. Amen.

After the ceremony, the following certificate of conversion, properly signed by the Rabbi and countersigned by the witnesses and by the convert, should be read before it is handed to the convert. A duplicate of this certificate, properly signed and countersigned, should be put into the archives of the congregation represented by the officiating Rabbi:

CERTIFICATE OF CONVERSION

Hear O Israel: the Lord our God, the Lord is One.
This is to certify that . . . .
of . . . . came before me
. . . ., on the
. . . . day of . . . . , 19. . . .
corresponding to the Hebrew date . . . .
expressing . . . . desire for conversion to the Jewish religion and giving satisfactory evidence that . . . . knows and understands the principles and practices of Judaism. Therefore, with the sanction of the two associates whose names are signed below, I received the said . . . . into the fellowship of the Jewish people and faith, giving . . . . the additional Hebrew name . . . .

On . . . . part, ...
has solemnly declared . . . . intention to cast in . . . .
lot with the Jewish people, to live in accordance with the Jewish religion, and if blessed with children, to rear them as Jews.

. . . .
Rabbi of Congregation . . . .
City . . . .

. . . .
. . . .
Witnesses

. . . .
Convert

Thy people shall be my people and thy God my God.

Conservative Judaism, as officially represented by the Rabbinical Assembly of America, the National organization of Conservative Rabbis, has prepared a "Guide for the Admission of Proselytes" which is incorporated in the Rabbinical Assembly Manual (for Conservative Rabbis).

The number of intermarried families in most Jewish congregations is, at present, comparatively small. In some instances, Jewish males are married to non-Jewish females who have not been converted. Their

marriage is generally accepted *de facto,* but though the male may worship with the congregation and "work" with it, supporting it financially and otherwise, such persons seldom, if ever, occupy positions of leadership in the Synagogue. They may, however, be accepted as leaders in Jewish philanthropic and other Jewish community endeavors. Practices differ in different Jewish communities. In several Midwestern Jewish Temples, Jewish males and their non-Jewish wives (who have never formally been converted to Judaism) are welcomed into Temple membership. In many cases, however, in the event of death, the unconverted husband or wife may not be buried in the Jewish cemetery. Official traditional disapproval of intermarriage when there has been no formal conversion is thus indicated.

The rate of Jewish-Gentile intermarriages in the countries of Western Europe should be of great help to us in predicting the frequency of such marriages in the United States inasmuch as they suggest that Jews who have been settled in those countries for many generations tend to intermarry in ever-increasing numbers. That the present rate of marriages involving Jews for the United States *as a whole* is no more than 10 per cent does not assure us that within a generation or two, American Jews will not intermarry at a very much higher rate. The number of generations that have passed since the early immigrant generation of Jews first set foot on these shores and the consequent acculturation and assimilation appears to be directly related to the frequency of intermarriage. There is, indeed, cause for concern if not alarm.

Assuming interfaith marriages to be undesirable, and conversions infrequent, those rabbis who replied to our questionnaire have suggested that certain countermeasures could be undertaken. Among them are:

1. Indoctrinate your people so that they will "see" the implications of intermarriage.

2. Develop pamphlets and other literature for this purpose.

3. Place greater stress upon more wholesome family and community life.

4. Make Jewish life more meaningful. Judaism means little, if anything, to many young Jews. Link Judaism to an ideal for humanity as is the case with the Quakers and Peace.

5. Provide better and more intensive Jewish education in schools and more spiritually enriching Jewish life at home. Get children into our schools at an earlier age and keep them through their high-school years.

6. Intermarriage should be more severely condemned by the Jewish community so as to make it socially undesirable.

7. Provide more opportunities for Jewish young people to meet each other socially during their adolescent and college years.

8. Try to increase the self-consciousness of Jewish young people

so as to make them feel that they are deserting if they marry outside the fold.

9. Jewish parents should become greater disciplinarians of their children. There is no place for so high a degree of permissiveness. We need more dogmatic parents.

10. Discourage interdating among adolescents.

11. Begin planting the seeds of opposition to intermarriage in the children when they are very young.

12. Discourage the attendance of Jewish youth at small colleges where there are few Jewish students. Have them attend large co-educational universities where there is a Hillel Foundation.

13. Help young people to appreciate the importance of their religion and of group identification.

14. Insist upon stricter requirements for conversion thereby discouraging intermarriage.

15. Help young people to understand that democracy is in fact a symbol of self-determination of all groups. Conformity is not required by America in order to be acceptable.

16. Strengthen family ties. As strong as they are, they are still too weak.

And one rabbi stated: "The problem is essentially uncontrollable unless there is a large-scale religious revival."

There is no reason to believe that, despite an increase in interfaith marriages, the Jews will not survive in the United States as a distinctive minority group. Percentage-wise, the Jews can "afford" such an increase without the need to feel their existence threatened. Protestants and Catholics with seven to nine times their rate of intermarriage are managing to continue as separate minority groups. What is disturbing to the Jewish group is that, never before has it lived under conditions that are so favorable to a full democratic existence and also never before has the ritual practice of the Jewish people fallen to such a low point. Intermarriage is generally regarded by American Jewish leaders as a symptom of the weakening of Jewish religious ties and the lack of the empathy for their own people that has characterized Jews in the past.

GAIL AND ARTHUR

Gail is a pretty Catholic girl, an only child. In her teens she openly rebelled against the religious and social ideas of her mother and grandparents. Over a year ago, she married Arthur, a Jew, and the son of a highly respected, richly endowed attorney and his wife. Both of Arthur's parents are extremely unhappy about the marriage, but he seems not

to understand them or their points of view any more than Gail understands her mother. Both young people claim to have no ties to either Judaism or Catholicism and they are certain that they possess the strength to withstand the pressures that might otherwise weaken or destroy their marriage.

GAIL: Arthur and I have been married a little over a year. He is Jewish and I come from a Catholic family. We are both Americans, born and bred in New England. I used to live in Lexington, a suburb of Boston. There were no Jewish families there when I was going to school. There were, however, a considerable number of Catholics in what is certainly one of the wealthiest church parishes in the state. I am an only child, you know, and my parents looked out for me very carefully in every way. I imagine that it would never have entered my mother's mind that I, of all people, would be married to a Jew. But that's exactly what happened.

When I was at the junior-high-school stage of my life my parents sent me to a Catholic academy, but later I went to high school in Lexington. I don't think that my parents had any real religious motive in sending me to that Catholic school. It was just available and my mother, being a good Catholic, thought I should try it. (*Editor's note:* Subsequent events in Gail's life appear to support the idea that Gail's mother is a devout Catholic and that there was, in fact, a strong religious motivation for this act.)

I think that my mother is a rather medium-type Catholic. She goes to church on Sunday, but she isn't particularly religious. As for my father, he wasn't a Catholic and still isn't. He was never a church-goer at any time. I know that his family were not Catholics, although I've never met any of them. He had lived in Pennsylvania. His family originally came from Wales. They were miners. My grandfather on my father's side was Welsh, but his wife was Danish.

My mother would have liked my father to go to church with her, but he never went with her or with me. Of course, they were married in the Catholic Church by a priest. That means, I suppose, that he must have given his written promise to rear me as a Catholic.

Even though he wasn't a Catholic—and he certainly showed no special feeling for the religion at any time—my mother made sure, when he died, that he was given a Catholic funeral with all the rites of the Church. Actually, it would have been embarrassing otherwise because everyone thought he was a Catholic. He even had an Irish name, too—Mulcahy.

ARTHUR: Well, my parents are Jewish. *Both* are Jewish, that is. They were born in Boston and they were both reared in good Jewish homes, so there was never any difference between them on religious matters. The section they came from was predominantly Jewish. I always wanted to know about my parents' background and, as the result of just about a million questions from me, I know it pretty well. Neither my father nor my mother was completely orthodox in ritual observances, although I imagine

that they regarded themselves as orthodox. (*Editor's note:* Arthur's father discussed his family background with the author and indicated that he "came from a good Orthodox Jewish home, that my contacts had always been 'orthodox.' Even though I did not adhere to all Jewish ritual, mine was a real Jewish home." Identification with Jews and Jewish life was obviously marked.)

I went to grade school in Revere, then to Boston Latin School and from there I went on to Harvard University where I majored in American history. At the beginning I planned to be a lawyer, like my father. I took all the courses that would be required for such a career, but I never went through with it. An older brother had decided to become a lawyer, and as long as one of us was following in Dad's footsteps, I no longer felt bound to follow that career. That's why my major interest became American Literature.

I hadn't been too happy with the idea of becoming an attorney, but I had felt that I owed it to my father to do what he wanted me to do, although he never really insisted. I guess that it was just one of those things you sort of understand. My father has now retired. He hadn't been well and that hastened his retirement. He had been a very successful lawyer. He had a fine reputation and in addition he was financially very successful. He and my mother live in a very nice home, but they are "out of circulation," so to speak. Before retirement, however, Dad was really quite active in communal and Jewish affairs. Just recently he gave a very large gift to his Alma Mater here in the Boston area.

My parents weren't really very strict about Jewish ritual, but they observed Passover and all of the "Seder" business which we carried on in our family. We were a very relaxed family in terms of religious observance. We observed certain of the rituals not because it was the right thing to do, but rather because it served as an excuse to get the family together. At least that's the way it always seemed to me. But it should be very clear that my parents definitely identified with the Jewish people. Both of them did.

GAIL: In my case it was only my mother—not my father—who "identified" as you call it. And it was against my mother that I think I rebelled. My grandfather and my grandmother (my mother's parents) who lived with us, along with an unmarried aunt, were all good Catholics. They made their loyalties quite clear at all times.

Neither my mother nor my father had very much schooling. I think that my mother went through the second year in high school. My father had run away from home when he was about fifteen. He did a number of odd jobs for a while and then he took a few courses in hotel management. That was about all the education he had. My father worked in hotels in various capacities as long as I can remember. In fact, because of that, I started working in hotels, too, because if I was ever going to go to college, I had to earn my own money.

ARTHUR: I never had to worry about money. My folks were always well off and especially keen on education. My father would have done any-

thing to make it possible for me to go to school. But he didn't have to put himself out. Really, the money was there. Oh, I worked in the summers. I had camp-counselor jobs for several summers, but that was mostly for fun.

GAIL: In my case, my father had died when I was at high school, and although there was enough to take care of us, it seemed wiser for me to work. In fact, my mother still works as a hostess in a hotel dining room whenever she feels like earning something extra. But she really doesn't *have* to. After my father died, my mother never remarried.

It was while I was on one of my waitress jobs that I met Arthur. I was going to the university. I was a pretty good student, but to be sure of having money for school I took a job waiting on tables in the cocktail lounge at one of the nicer clubs in town. Arthur came there one night with one of his friends, and I guess we just took a fancy to each other.

ARTHUR: We started going together and in about a year we decided to get married. It was during that year, when things were getting serious between Gail and me, that I began to feel the pressure of my parents. I was really very close to both my parents—perhaps closer to my father. I sort of expected to do those things that he expected me to. It was very natural. Even when I decided not to go on to law school, I remember that my father was concerned about it. But he is always greatly concerned about his children. He worries for fear they may not be making the right decision. But he isn't a disciplinarian or a rigid or strict man at all. It's just that he has high standards. You want to meet them, that's all. At least, that's what I wanted to do. I have always felt his influence—which acts as a kind of self-discipline for me. It has guided me not because of his saying "do this" or "do that," but because I say it to myself.

My mother is quite a different type of person. She is very influential in the family. She is much more of a disciplinarian. She reacts from an emotional point of view while my father reacts most often from reason. But both definitely had influence with us children. We saw far less of my father because of his work than we did of my mother. She would get upset with us and my father would act as the buffer to try to smooth things over. He would say, "Now look, you have to conform and do what your mother is telling you to do. Make things easier."

GAIL: My mother is a fairly weak person. So was my father. There really wasn't any discipline in our home. Nor were her parents, who lived with us, very strong in their ways. I was a very withdrawn child, being an only child living in this adult family. I really never caused them any trouble. I did a lot of reading and I used to sit for hours on the porch and never bother anybody. That is, I never seemed to bother anyone until I was about sixteen years old and then I really caused a lot of trouble.

I sort of rebelled against any kind of pressures from them. For one thing, I was getting upset about their attitudes toward dating. My mother and my grandparents wanted me to date a certain kind of boy. He had to

be an Irish Catholic. If the boy happened to be an Italian Catholic, they didn't like that at all. There's a very marked difference between the two, of course. My mother was and still is very prejudiced about anybody who isn't Irish Catholic. I think it was this that sort of ticked me off. I rebelled by dating the very type of person she didn't want me to date. I did it quite deliberately. I didn't date any Jewish boys because there were none in my town—or at least none that I knew. There was only one Jewish girl in high school that I knew about.

My mother and I had some violent arguments. We disagreed about my dating, about the way things should be done by me, about life in general. It was at this time, too, that I started doubting my Catholic religion. Although I continued to go to church, mostly because of my mother, I had my say about the things I was doubting—and you should have heard the constant arguments. She would cause such ridiculous scenes if I said that I wasn't going to church that it was easier to go. But I wasn't very happy about it. She would get upset. She would cry, or she would not talk to me for hours. Sometimes she said that I wasn't a good daughter, that my behavior was going to kill her. I was getting more and more angry myself all this while. I think that my strong will began to manifest itself and I continued to do the very things—including interdating—that I know she didn't like. When she heard that I was going out with Arthur, she didn't seem to mind. Apparently she hadn't caught his last name, which is quite Jewish.

On Christmas Eve my family always had a big get together. Everyone went to Midnight Mass and then came home and drank all night long. It's a continuous, big party. I took Arthur there about a month after we had met. My mother and the whole family seemed to like him and everything was fine until it suddenly dawned on my mother to ask, "Is Arthur Jewish?" When I answered, "Yes," the roof kind of fell in on me.

ARTHUR: Gail was working late that evening. I met her about one o'clock in the morning, after her work, and we then went over to her family's house. There must have been forty or fifty people in that crowded apartment and they were all having a ball. We spent an hour there, and I must say that I enjoyed it. It was so different from anything I had ever known. I had the feeling that night of not really *belonging* to the group, so to speak. I was a little apprehensive about it, although these things don't really beat me down. But it certainly was different for me.

Now, Gail wasn't the first non-Jewish girl I had dated. When I had begun going out, I had dated Jewish girls most generally, but by the time I was getting through college, Jewish girls were in the minority. But it wasn't a matter of rebelling against my father or my mother.

Now, my parents knew about it and they certainly didn't like it. They never made a scene. They were disappointed though. That, I could tell. My parents felt strongly about it, though never with the intensity that characterized Gail's mother. But they certainly made their thoughts known and as a result, I would end up feeling quite guilty or upset about it. But still, I felt that *I* had to do what *I* had to do. It was my decision and no one

else's. I can still remember them saying, "It's all well and good that you go out with that girl, but if you play with fire, you'll get burned." I think that's the phrase they used. "Take a girl out to a prom or on a date, but let it go at that." Or, "I think that you should be interested in Jewish girls—and soon."

I've got my own ideas about why they talked this way. I don't think it was anything other than fear. They felt that the chances of a marriage success were far greater if intermarriage wasn't involved. I think, too, that they were afraid of being embarrassed if one of their children married out of their own background. They were afraid because of their friends, because of what they would say: that my parents didn't do a good job in bringing up the child, therefore the child married out of their background. And what was the matter with them? Wherein did *they* fail? And even that, somehow, by marrying out, the son had rejected them.

When other members of my family marry they are not, by any stretch of the imagination, marrying *religious* Jews. They are simply marrying Jews who are Jews by birth and nothing else.

GAIL: In my mother's case, I don't know what made her feel as she did about the Church. You see, my experience seems quite the opposite of Arthur's. When I stopped feeling that I should go to church, which happened during my freshman year at college, I just stopped. But the scenes between my mother and myself continued on and on until I got married. It was at the time of all those quarrels that I left home and moved into the city. I got an apartment and continued living in it through all my college years. I spoke to my mother and grandparents rather often. I phoned and all that. But I simply couldn't live with the family any more.

ARTHUR: When I was thirteen years old, I was Bar Mitzvah (confirmed) but even that I think was part of my parents' desire to maintain the conventions of the group. It wasn't out of deep religious conviction. I may be rationalizing. That's quite possible, but I don't think so. I think it was the thing to do. That's why we went to Hebrew School. That's why I was Bar Mitzvah.

GAIL: Anyhow, we were certain about ourselves and we wanted to get married.

ARTHUR: When I told my folks that I intended to marry Gail, they had trouble accepting the idea. They then asked that she be converted to Judaism, but Gail and I rejected it. I didn't even think twice about that nor did Gail.

GAIL: Even though neither of us felt at all close to the religions of our parents, the strongest objections came from my mother and not from Arthur's folks. They are very adjustable people. But I think the fact that

I was of Catholic parentage bothered them because Catholics usually are supposed to be more devout than Protestants.

ARTHUR: Although my folks tried gently but firmly to convince me not to go ahead as I was doing without conversion, they didn't succeed. Gail and I just decided we were going to be married. We had a feeling that some sort of a chapel wedding would be nice. I just walked into a Unitarian Church and had a talk with the minister. He is an awfully nice guy. We thought that it would be nice to be married in the chapel of that church. I told my parents about it and they saw I was determined, so they agreed to come to the wedding. One day I took them over to see the chapel. It was downtown. I hadn't noticed it, but there was a cross in the chapel and that ticked my mother off. She insisted that we *not* be married there, so we asked the minister what could be done about it. He said that the chapel at Harvard didn't have a cross hanging in it and he could officiate there. Frankly, I didn't object to it, one way or the other, but my mother and father seemed shocked. Well, the wedding took place on the date scheduled at the chapel. Gail invited her mother and the other members of her family to the ceremony. My parents showed up as they promised, but Gail's mother and all the other members of her family stayed away on religious grounds. That is all except one non-Catholic cousin who is a Protestant. My folks even threw a party in our honor about a week before the wedding. There were about two or three hundred people there.

GAIL: It was disappointing to me that my mother didn't attend. But I had rather expected that. Anyhow, about two months after the marriage, I phoned her and she didn't seem quite as angry. I think she is reaching out a little bit toward us now. She is lonesome, I guess.

ARTHUR: We have joined that Unitarian Church whose minister officiated at our wedding. That seemed like the real answer for us. And we attend services occasionally. But, really, insofar as religion is concerned there is, for us, mostly a vacuum. We don't seem to need it at all. I think my family has accepted our marriage all right. Gail and I see my mother and father. They like Gail, so everything is going to be fine.

GAIL: We'll have no problem about rearing our children because neither of us is religious. If you are strong enough, you can beat those who would like to break up marriages like ours—and *we* are strong.

INTERRACIAL MARRIAGE

Contrary to the prevailing attitude in the United States, interracial marriages are generally accepted, both legally and socially, among most peoples and nations. The nations of Europe, the Middle East, Mexico, Central and South America, Africa (excepting the Republic of South Africa) have never been race-conscious as has the United States. Indeed, racial mixture is "a very ancient phenomenon," as Shapiro[1] points out. It may very well be "as old as mankind itself." Certainly the Old Testament account of the marriage of Moses to Zipporah, the daughter of a Midianitish priest, and of King Solomon's marriages to women of many nations and colors, to mention but two, make it clear that the intermingling of peoples and races is nothing new in human affairs. Conquests of one people by another assured the conquest of the women of the vanquished nation as well. Greek and Roman expansions, as well as those of the Chinese, the Indian and Arabic peoples, their migrations and trade as well, all tended to produce widespread contact between nations and races.

The most marked movements of nations began during the fifteenth century, with the discovery of the New World in 1492. Explorations then began in earnest. Trade was begun with the East Indies and with China. New discoveries were made in unknown parts of the Old World. The Spaniards gained control of the Philippines; the Portuguese acquired a certain foothold in China, India and islands to the south, while the Dutch won the East Indies. The French and English fought for India. Africa became the spoil of numerous European nations. South Africa was settled by Europeans on a rather large scale.

Spain's influential settlements in the West Indies, California and portions of South America; Portugal's control of Brazil; Holland's colonization of South Africa and the effective colonization of other vast portions of the New World made the intermixture of races and populations throughout the world inevitable. "All this has meant a constant reshuffling and mingling of genetic elements and thus, the weaving of a biological inter-relationship far too complex for complete unravelling by any known method of analysis." [2]

The implication that there is a "pure" race in the sense of never having mixed with any other racial group is, on the basis of historical and biological evidence, not accurate. Some social scientists state unequivocally that "Race mixture has been going on during the whole of recorded history.[3] They contend further that on the basis of evidence

from the studies on fossil human remains, "even in pre-history, at the very dawn of humanity, mixing of different stocks, at least occasionally, took place." The "pure race" is, according to many noted geneticists and physical anthropologists, a mistaken idea. Twelve scholars,[4] writing under the sponsorship of the United Nations Educational, Scientific and Cultural Organization (UNESCO), released a Statement on the Nature of Race and Race Differences in September, 1952. In Article 7 of the Statement the matter of "pure races" is discussed:

> There is no evidence for the existence of so-called "pure races." Skeletal remains provide the basis of our limited knowledge about earlier races. In regard to race mixture, the evidence points to the fact that human hybridization has been going on for an indefinite but considerable time. Indeed, one of the processes of race formation and race extinction or absorption is by means of hybridization between races.

Nor is there scientific evidence to support the thesis that racial mixtures result in biologically inferior offspring. Article 7 in the UNESCO statement concludes:

> As there is no reliable evidence that disadvantageous effects are produced [by the mixture of races], no biological justification exists for prohibiting intermarriage between persons of different races.[5]

Sixty-nine additional noted scholars "contributed" to the final form of the whole statement.

Alpenfels' statement that . . . "every man and woman in the world today belongs to the same species, *homo sapiens,* because all men are alike in their body structure, all are closely related to one another, and all have a common ancestor" [6] is accepted by all reputable scholars. Nature dictates that only members of the same species may mate and produce offspring. On this important basis it is clear that biologically there is nothing to prevent interracial intermarriage.

The simple and all-important statement that must be made is that however "pure" mankind may have been at the beginning of time, races have long since ceased to be free from outside blood strains. We may have begun human life with an ancestral stock common to all humanity. However, as a result of natural selection and hybridization resulting from war, conquests, and many other factors, there is today no such thing as a pure race. We all are, no matter what our nation, people, religion or race, the product of the intermixture of blood and of culture that has been going on for thousands of years. The notion of a pure race is, then, little more than a myth.

Despite all the evidence disproving racial theories of superiority

or the inferiority of certain religions and racial groups, there are still vast numbers of persons who support them. Their attitudes can be explained only if we understand that such theories serve as a pretext. A racial theory is supported not because it has been proved, but rather because it helps to avoid a truth—that we are prejudiced—without reason or proof to support our thesis.

Although interracial marriages are not commonplace in the United States, they do occur, and with increasing frequency among the better-educated and socially elite of both white and non-white groups. The marriage of a New York post-debutante, a senior at Sarah Lawrence College, to an Asian Prince is of special interest because it points up the fact that, despite differences of religion and color, such marriages may prove socially acceptable, if the social or economic status of the persons directly involved is sufficiently high.

In 1957 there were thirty states in the United States that prohibited one or more forms of intermarriage. Since World War II the number of states that legally prohibit Negro-white marriages has been reduced to nineteen.[7] There is, however, no single plan or design indicated by these statutes. Weinberger[8] points out "While, in Utah, white-Mongolian marriages are illegal and void, in North Carolina they are permitted. In Arkansas, where white-Negro marriages are void, a Negro is defined as 'any person who has in his or her veins any Negro blood whatever.' In Florida, a person ceases to be a Negro when he has less than 'one-eighth of . . . African or Negro blood'; and in Oklahoma, anyone not of 'African descent' is regarded as a member of the white race."

These statutes apply not only to Negroes but specifically refer to American Indians, Cherokees, Ethiopians, Chinese, Japanese, Mongolians, Malays, Hindus, mestizos, halfbreeds, and "the brown race" as well. In all cases the Negro is directly affected by all of these statutes.

In December of 1959 the Arizona Superior Court held its statute on interracial marriage unconstitutional and void. In 1958, Nevada voided its miscegenation statute. Idaho, too, repealed its prohibitions in this respect, as did the State of California on April 20, 1958.

According to Myrdal the "white man's rank order of discrimination" places "intermarriage" at the very top of the list of practices against racial and ethnic groups such as Negroes, Mexicans and Indians, by prejudiced Americans.[9]

Despite these legal and social controls, interracial relationships have continued extra-legally throughout American history. However, no nation other than the United States has ever prohibited interracial marriage. In the year 1661, the General Assembly of the Colony of Maryland first "deplored the fact that there were many cases of intermarriage

between white female servants and Negro slaves." The law stated that if a free-born white woman married a Negro slave, she would be required to serve her husband's master throughout her slave husband's life and, further, that children born of such marriages would be regarded as slaves.

In 1691 the Virginia Act was legislated for "the prevention of that abominable and spurious mixture which hereafter may increase in this dominion as well by Negroes intermarrying with English or other white women as by their unlawful intercourse with one another."

In 1705 the State of Massachusetts passed legislation providing for a heavy fine and a period of servitude for any white person who married a Negro. The clergyman who officiated at an interracial marriage was also to be fined fifty pounds. Similar legislation was passed in North Carolina in 1715 and in Pennsylvania in 1725.

Despite prohibitive legislation, both interracial marriages and sexual unions continued without benefit of clergy, particularly in the south and southwestern portions of the United States. It was, after all, cheaper to breed slaves than to buy them. Negro slave women who were unwilling to submit to the sexual advances of their masters had no legal protection. A nineteenth-century decision of the North Carolina Supreme Court stated that a white man could not be convicted of fornication with a Negro slave woman because she had no standing in court.

As we have indicated, laws prohibiting interracial marriages or cohabitation between whites and Negroes as well as persons of other color are still on the statute books of over half of our states. Often, states differ with respect to the amount of Negro blood that would prevent a valid marriage with a white person. Mulattoes are specifically mentioned in the legislation of Arkansas, Colorado, Delaware, Idaho, Kentucky, Mississippi, South Carolina, Tennessee and Wyoming. Maryland, North Carolina and Tennessee prohibit marriage between whites and persons of Negro "blood" to the third generation inclusive,[10] while Florida prohibits such marriage to the fourth generation inclusive. Attempts have been made to define a "Negro" by declaring persons of one-sixteenth Negro ancestry, one-eighth or one-quarter Negro "blood" to be Negroes, and Florida legislates against persons who have "$\frac{1}{16}$th Negro blood."

While twenty-nine states legally prohibit the marriage of those who are defined as "Negro" to a white person, fifteen states prohibit the marriage of whites to Mongolians and ten states prohibit the marriage of Malays and whites, aiming their legislation specifically at Filipinos.[11] In addition, five states prohibit marriage between whites and Indians.[12] The intermarriage of Negroes and Indians is prohibited in Louisiana and Oklahoma. Negro-Malay unions are prohibited in Maryland. The States of Georgia and Virginia prohibit the marriage of whites with

Asiatic Indians; in Arizona, the marriage of whites to Hindus is prohibited.

Despite such laws, however, racial intermixtures do take place because those persons who desire legal unions go to states where there is no law prohibiting their intermarriage.

The number of racially intermixed persons in the United States is far greater than one would guess in view of these legal prohibitions. Aside from the descendants of the Negro slave women who bore children sired by the white master (and they are in the vast majority), there are many pockets of hybrids or racially intermixed peoples and their descendants in many sections of the United States. Some of the better-known interracial hybrids include the following:

1. *The Sabines.* Of mixed white, Indian and Negro ancestry, they inhabit "the marshy fringe of a Louisiana parish bordering on the Gulf of Mexico." [13]

2. *Brass Ankles.* Residing on the coastal plain area of South Carolina (5,000 to 10,000 in number).

3. *Cajans and Creoles.* In Washington, Mobile and Clarke counties in Alabama, as well as adjoining parts of Mississippi. The Creoles, who number several thousand, live in Mobile and Baldwin counties around Mobile Bay in Alabama. Their name is derived from Creole Colored and is said to mean "mixed."

4. *Croatans,* said to be Indian-Negro hybrids. Their center is in North Carolina (Robeson County), South Carolina (Marlboro, Dillon, Marion and Harry counties), and Virginia (Halifax County.)

5. *Guineas,* primarily of West Virginia (Barbour and Taylor counties) and Maryland. Also found in Ohio (Canton, Chillicothe, Zanesville, Akron, Sandusky), and in Detroit (Michigan). A mixture of whites, Indians and Negroes. They are also known as "West Hill" Indians, "Marleys," "Cecil" Indians, and "Z & B" Indians.

6. *Jackson Whites.* Numbering upward of 5,000, they reside in New Jersey (Bergen, Morris and Passaic counties) and New York (Orange and Rockland counties). They are a mixture of Negroes and whites.

7. *Issues of Virginia,* a mixture of whites, Indians and Negroes, living in Virginia (Amherst and Rockbridge counties). They numbered about 500 in 1926.

8. *Melungeons,* also known as "ramps." Their name is assumed to have been derived from the French word *"mélange"* meaning "mixed." They number about 10,000, and live in Tennessee, Southwest Virginia and Southeast Kentucky. They are of mixed Negro, Indian and white blood.

9. *Red Bones,* known by other names as well. They are called

"Houmas" along the coast of Louisiana, "Cane River Mulattoes," and "Sabines" (see #1 above). They number approximately 3,000 to 4,000. Their name is said to be derived from the French *"Os Rouge,"* the term used for persons of Indian blood.

10. *Wesorts.* They number about 3,000 to 5,000 and live principally in Charles and Prince George counties, Maryland. A few live in Pittsburgh, Philadelphia, Baltimore and Washington, D.C. They, too, are mixed—Indians, whites and Negroes.

Interracial intermarriage has seldom had a high incidence in the United States. Whatever intermarriage has occurred appears to have been due, in the main, to the disparity in the ratio between the sexes of some of these minorities, particularly the Filipinos who are almost entirely a male population. Certain of the marriages between Mexicans and Latin Americans or South Americans are the result of the cultural similarities that exist among them.

About 2,500,000 persons of Mexican descent (often the products of race mixture) now live in the United States. One-half of these persons reside in Texas while most of the others live in California, Arizona, New Mexico and Colorado. A few live in Illinois, Michigan, Ohio, Kansas and Pennsylvania.

Some 65,000 persons of Filipino origin live in the United States. Most of them are concentrated on the West Coast, with some living in Washington and Oregon, and a limited number in Chicago, New York City and other cities on the Eastern seaboard. The largest proportion of them are unmarried males.

Filipinos began coming into the United States in rather large numbers after 1920. Up to that time only a few students from upper-class families made their way to this country. However, when it appeared that Mexican as well as European immigration into the United States was going to be cut off, the California fruit-growers, anxious for a source of inexpensive labor, invited Filipinos to migrate to this country and provided them with very low-income jobs.

The Filipinos not only work in the fruit orchards but also follow the harvests or work in the fisheries. Some move on to other areas, do menial labor, find jobs in restaurants and cafeterias as bus boys, operate elevators and take other low-classification jobs. They have always constituted a mobile labor force.

The ratio of men to women among the Filipinos has been as high as 15 to 1.[14] In 1930, the total Filipino resident population was under thirty years of age. Since then, newer immigrants have also been young males. That the Filipinos have looked for the companionship of women of other races was to be expected. Bogardus[15] reported in 1930 that of 7,409 married male Filipinos in his sample, 1,775 were married to

women of other races. Although marriage with white females has been strongly disapproved by whites on the West Coast and disapproved, too, by Filipinos who plan to return to the Islands after they have accumulated some money, interracial marriages continue to take place.

Filipinos have intermarried with many different groups in the United States, including Mexicans, French, Indians, mulattos and American whites. Chiefly of Malayan stock even though their culture is only partly Malayan, the Filipinos have also mingled with Spanish, Chinese and other European groups. They now represent many different racial and cultural backgrounds, and in the main, may be regarded as a hybrid people.

Although the American Indian has been decimated and what few remain, are "controlled" by the federal government on reservations in the Far West, we would observe that contrary to the experience of the American Negro, the white American who can claim ancestry with an Indian now does so with a certain pride. However, the attitude toward intermarriage with the American Indian has not necessarily changed. What has changed is the general attitude toward having had a *deceased* Indian among one's progenitors.

The number of interracial marriages among members of the United States armed forces[16] during and immediately following World War II was comparatively small. There were 113,135 females who became brides of American soldiers. There were also 327 foreign men who married American women serving in some branch of the armed forces. Children of these couples (4,537 of them) were admitted into the United States from April, 1946 until 1949 when the "War Brides" Act expired. The number of Chinese war brides was 5,099 with another 752 coming from Japan. American soldiers married nationals of many countries during World War II. Almost one-half of all such aliens were from English-speaking countries. The U.S.S.R. provided 780. France's war brides numbered 8,531, while Italy provided 8,873 and Germany gave us 13,315. In addition, 8,312 alien fiancées of members of the armed forces were admitted from 1946 through 1949. In the early years of World War II, personnel on duty in a foreign country or possession of the United States were prohibited from marrying without the consent of the soldier's commanding officer.[17] Such marriages have, however, continued to this day. Troops stationed throughout the world do marry natives of the countries in which they are stationed.

Between June 30, 1947, and June 30, 1959, United States male citizens married 43,197 Japanese females. Since the latter date and up to June 30, 1961, United States males married 3,035 Japanese females in Tokyo alone. The presence of army personnel in Japan is obviously the primary cause of these postwar marriages.

The Chinese, first imported to the United States after 1845, were used as workers in the building of the crosscontinental railroads and in the Western agricultural and mining areas as well. Anti-Chinese attitudes, which developed very rapidly in this country during the 1870's, proved to be an important factor in increasing the social distance between the Chinese and the whites in the United States. The Chinese, too, were strong adherents of a family loyalty pattern which discouraged intermarriage. It was exceedingly difficult for them to defy parents who opposed intermarriage, and parental consent was, according to tradition, required for marriage.

Despite the high ratio of males to females, the number of Chinese intermarriages has not been large. Chinese interracial marriages in New York City in the period 1935-38 numbered 29 out of a total of 141 marriages or 20.7 per cent of the total number of marriages. In the four-year period preceding, 1930-34, there were 49 interracial marriages out of a total of 142 marriages involving Chinese or 33.8 per cent of the total.[18]

Hsu[19] believes that the Chinese objection to interracial marriages has nothing to do with the ideal of maintaining "racial purity." She suggests that such marriages are regarded as likely to be "socially inconvenient" in that Chinese and whites would find it difficult to communicate with each other. Lee[20] believes that there is a desire to maintain racial homogeneity and further that there is the wish to avoid marginality in any form.

Out of more than 700,000[21] Puerto Ricans, including children, now living in the United States, somewhat more than 600,000 reside in New York City. Attracted to this metropolis because it could, better than any other city, use their labor, vast movements of Puerto Ricans, "American citizens to whom the immigration laws did not apply," [22] have yet to make a really satisfactory adjustment to the metropolis or to be accepted as first-class citizens on the mainland. About 59 per cent of them read and write Spanish only. Racial and cultural differences have resulted in their being partly rejected by American Negroes and totally rejected by American whites. By the criteria of the mainland, two-thirds of the Puerto Ricans are regarded as "colored." There is no indication that Puerto Ricans are marrying "whites." The size of their population and its segregated character seems, for the present, to preclude that possibility.

Racial discrimination is no problem in Puerto Rico because a majority of the people comes from mixed, Indian, white and Negro stock. For well over four hundred years, since the first Negro slaves were introduced into the country, intermixing of these stocks has taken place. The traditional Hispano-Catholic attitude of acceptance of inter-

racial admixtures seems to have remained unchallenged through the centuries. There is no reason to believe that it will change now.

In 1940, prior to the engagement of the United States with Japan in World War II, there were 127,000 persons of Japanese descent in this country. Prior to Pearl Harbor and even following the conclusion of the war, Japanese in America, the Nisei, or American-born children of Issei, immigrant parents, were not among those peoples who generally intermarried with Caucasians. A study of the Japanese in the Los Angeles area, reported by Panunzio,[23] indicated that there had been scarcely any intermarriage. Whether this was due to the strictures of the state law forbidding their marriage to Caucasians or loyalty to Japan and its distinctive culture, which regarded intermarriage as an evil, remains uncertain.

At the conclusion of World War II about one-third of the Japanese-Americans who had lived on the West Coast prior to their evacuation during the war, moved to Midwestern and Eastern cities. We know that about half of the marriages of Issei males[24] have been with white or Eurasian women in New York City. The increase of contacts on college and university campuses promises to increase the number of such interracial marriages in the United States.

With such vast numbers of American soldiers on foreign soil and the absence of white females, it was inevitable that interracial marriages should take place between them and females of Korean, Chinese and Japanese origin. Not all such marriages are "accepted" by parents, friends and community. Differences in language and culture, in addition to the normal problems of marital adjustment, make these marriages difficult for both parties. As the image of the Japanese people has continued to change favorably since World War II, we may expect the number of such marriages to increase. In 1961, Gallup repeated a study, first conducted in 1942 for the Office of Public Opinion Research. The poll revealed that whereas, in 1942 (during the war years) the Japanese people were regarded as treacherous, cruel, sly, warlike and hardworking, they were, in 1961, regarded as hardworking, artistic, intelligent, progressive, but still sly.

Of all the fifty states in the Union, Hawaii, with its bewildering array of peoples has proven most fascinating for the study of racial admixtures. There one finds Polynesians, Europeans, Americans and Asiatics living and working together. Michener who spoke of the Hawaiians as "the Golden People" suggested that in Hawaii a new type of man was being developed—"men who see both the West and the East," who cherish "the glowing past and who apprehend the obscure future." A comparison of Michener's stories about Hawaii with Fuch's *Hawaii Pono* makes it clear that two good men can look at the

same people on the same scene and gain altogether different and even conflicting impressions therefrom. Fuchs, in his excellent social history of Hawaii reminds us of the bitterness and strife, the economic, political and social rivalries among these "Golden" men and the white men who have controlled the Islands' destiny for over a century. However, the admixture of races, characteristic of Hawaii, does not include the American white man in anywhere near the same proportions as the Polynesians, Europeans and Asiatics.

The Hawaiian Islands, often called "the show-case of American Democracy," is composed of people from many different races and cultures, who have come to these islands from all parts of the world. The Hawaiians are said to have been Polynesians who migrated to this area about two thousand years ago. Where they came from or why is still the subject of speculation.

Interracial contacts in Hawaii began with the coming of white settlers in 1778. Marriage between the first white settlers and the natives was possible because the Hawaiians were free from antagonism toward foreigners, as a consequence of which these whites were accepted in marriage by the royal families on the Islands. This standard of social acceptance played an all-important role then, as it does now, in the development of this polyracial region.

The great distance of Hawaii from home countries and their prejudices, the absence of white women and the rather loosely organized family system of the old Hawaiian families, encouraged the development of friendly contacts between whites and Hawaiians, and, in short order, between Chinese and other Asiatics who settled there. There was no tendency to regard the children of the intermarried as racially inferior or to associate them with an inferior caste. All evidence points to the fact that native wives and their children were not cast aside by the whites and Asiatics with whom they had married. In 1937, Adams[25] stated that, "at least one-third of the Asiatic Hawaiians have Caucasian and Asiatic blood as well as Hawaiian." Intermixtures of every kind have occurred there. Chinese, Japanese, Koreans, Filipinos, Portuguese and whites have all intermarried with the natives. Their descendants have continued the racial mixture process until this day, so that it is hardly possible to speak of a single racial or national group on the Islands that has not been racially mixed with Hawaiians.

The stamp of approval placed on such marriages by high-ranking Hawaiians with the coming of the first white settlers appears to have had a major affect in setting the standard for racial mixture. When, in 1778, King Kamehameha I gave two Hawaiian women of high social rank in marriage to two white seamen, and when it was observed that these white men treated their wives well, were good providers and gen-

erally comported themselves with dignity, the pattern came to be generally accepted. The respectful attitude shown by the Caucasians and others to the natives may, in part, have been due to the fact that the Hawaiians have never been a slave people. Hence, they were never regarded as inferior, nor did the natives themselves ever have reason to feel a sense of racial inferiority.

When, as late as 1900, "after a rather significant number of women had arrived from Portugal, China and Japan, the sex ratio of Hawaii's foreign colony was still 299.0 males to 100 females," [26] it is understandable why the number of marriages between Hawaiian women and men of other races should have continued to increase.

With each succeeding generation of part-Hawaiians, it becomes more apparent that this intermingling of the races—Caucasians, Asians, Polynesians, and Negroes, too—has decreased neither the vitality nor the abilities of this new people. Racial equality is basic to the code of the Hawaiian. The children of the intermarried have acquired social status equal in all respects to that of those not racially mixed. There are no superior or inferior races in Hawaii because so many people are, in fact, identified with more than one racial stock. This very fact has made it quite impossible for any racial group to direct a concerted attack upon any other.

Polynesians, Negroes, Europeans, Asiatics and Caucasians have intermarried freely with no social or economic impediments to their relationship ever since the earliest Portuguese sailors and some Negroes from the Cape Verde Islands, who had been in the service of whaling ships, found their way to these Islands. The Negro is not discriminated against, nor are other races the subjects of attack such as we have noted elsewhere in the United States.

Marriages with the native women occurred from the very beginning of their residence. The Hawaiians were never vanquished in battle nor enslaved. They represented the best society on the Islands. It was they who set the standards both social and economic. As a consequence, marriage with the natives improved the position of the Europeans both status-wise and economically. No racial caste system ever developed in this mixed-blood population because there had never been any opposition to intermarriage either by the native Hawaiians or by the Portuguese. The latter, in fact, were well aware of the importance of intermarriage as an indirect means of establishing themselves. Religiously, too, as Catholics, their tradition favored intermarriage as a means of making converts.

Historically considered, the economy of Hawaii centered around its plantations. The need to secure laborers for these plantations resulted in waves of many-colored, many-language peoples taking up

residence in Hawaii. These people never came as slaves but rather as free men, however low on the social and economic scale they may have been.

With the establishment of huge plantations in 1850, it became necessary to import laborers from foreign countries. The contacts established between the male plantation laborers and Hawaiian women increased as the number of immigrant workers became larger. When the number of immigrant women became larger the number of such marriages decreased. When the years of service for which they had contracted as plantation workers were concluded, these immigrants found other economic opportunities on the Islands and many established permanent homes there. Many of the Japanese who had worked on the plantations became small farmers; others became storekeepers in out-lying districts; still others engaged in various occupations in Honolulu. Chinese, too, established themselves all through Hawaii in different trades, in the professions and in gardening and agriculture.

There is little open opposition to interracial marriages. Whatever feeling exists, is expressed in small, unofficial groups. The plantation owners, white men and their families accept the racial admixture stand-ards of the Islands, even though they may not be part of it themselves. There are, in fact, three societal divisions to be reckoned with: (1) the white owners and managers of the major industries, pineapple-growing and sugar cane, (2) the majority of the people who are the descendants of the racially mixed peoples already referred to, and (3) those of the separate racial groups who maintain an endogamous way of life on the Islands.

Even in Hawaii, it has been noted that marriages between the races are more likely to end in failure than are those in which two persons of the same race are involved. During a three-year period (1952-54),[27] the rate of divorce for in-marriages in Hawaii was compared with the divorce rate for out-marriages. In that time, the divorce rate for *all* in-marriages in Hawaii was 20.4 divorces per 100 marriages, while the rate of divorce for all out-marriages was 29.8 divorce per 100 marriages. The divorce rate for the Japanese in-marriages in Hawaii during this same three-year period was 9.8 per 100 marriages as against a divorce rate of 24.1 per 100 Japanese out-marriages. For the Chinese, it was 12.6 per 100 in-marriages as compared with 28.3 per 100 out-marriages. Cultural factors obviously play an important role in the success or failure of marriage. Where the differences are few and there is a high degree of social acceptance we may expect more such marriages to succeed. When, however, there are great differences, more are likely to fail whether in Hawaii or elsewhere.

On the basis of the Hawaiian experience, it is clear that there need

be no strong feeling against racial admixture. If further proof is needed, Hawaii demonstrates that hybridization neither debilitates nor weakens a racial stock in any degree. We may learn from Hawaii that our attitudes on this subject result solely from the cultural values that are transmitted to us.

The likelihood of a marked increase in interracial marriage in the United States within the next decade does not seem bright. An increase will take place as higher-status non-whites (governmental officials, students, *etc.*) come to the United States to receive college and university training. Marriages between such persons and white females, in increasing numbers, seem likely. Visits to the campuses of America's most cosmopolitan universities will soon make it obvious that white female students are increasingly dating non-whites from overseas. Such dates are more acceptable on today's campus (certainly, they are not frowned upon) than they were less than a decade ago. Many of these non-whites are sent here by their governments to prepare themselves for political and economic leadership when they return to their native countries. They are most frequently scions of status-giving families. Intermarriage with them is often regarded as "marrying up" on the social scale and is, therefore, highly acceptable.

Up to this point I have discussed the general attitude of Americans toward intermarriage with persons of races and color other than their own. In the succeeding chapter specific attention will be given to the relations of Negroes and whites in the United States insofar as intermarriage is concerned.

THE LAMBKINS

Arthur Lambkin is a Negro. He was married to a white woman for twenty-four years, but was recently divorced. A civil-service employee of the federal government, Arthur, who is now over sixty, is "one step removed from the days of slavery." He knows that members of his family had been slaves. He recalls his own meager educational opportunities, his religious fundamentalism and how, by his own efforts, he broke away from that past. Arthur calls himself a "liberal." The white woman whom he married was also a liberal in her political and religious views. The parents of two children, a son and daughter, now grown to adulthood, Arthur and his wife lived together for almost a quarter of a century and then, by mutual consent, a divorce was agreed upon. Dif-

ference in color, according to Arthur L., played no role in this divorce. Whether this is so, in fact, is questionable. This interview with a lower-middle-class Negro provides insights into the realm of interracial relations.

ARTHUR LAMBKIN

My marriage to a white woman is, I know, of special interest to you. But in order that you may understand it better, I had better tell you about myself, a simple Negro living in Cambridge.

I can trace my ancestry back to five generations in America. My mother was born in Virginia at the very end of the Civil War. So you can see I'm really not very much removed from slavery. I have tried to trace my mother's family back over the years and I have been able to do so up to and including my great-great-grandmother. All of them were slaves, of course. As for my father, he came from North Carolina. He lived in a rural district about two hundred miles south of Richmond, Virginia, and he had been a slave. But his grandfather (my great-grandfather) was a white man. About that, I am quite certain. I was told that there was a mixture of Indian blood, too, on my father's side of the family. To get back to my mother's family for a moment, my maternal grandmother was a mulatto. So you see my family, like so many Southern families, was of mixed blood. The number of mixed bloods in the South was, especially during the days of slavery, very high. There were a goodly number of illegitimate births, too, in the old South, resulting from the white slave masters and their Negro slaves. I have some cousins living in New York City (on my father's side of the family) and another cousin living in Hawaii.

I was born in Virginia, where my parents lived in the little Negro section in our town, the equivalent of Tobacco Road. We lived by odd jobs that my father and mother managed to pick up. During my early years, I didn't really get very much of an education. Schools for Negroes in the South were largely a hit-and-miss proposition. Negro schools were practically neglected by the whites and *they* were in charge. Today, bad as the Negro schools may be, they are still very much better than they were at the turn of the century. In those days the money assigned for Negro schools could support the school for about four or five months. School began in September or October and continued until there was no more money to pay for a teacher. Then the school simply had to close. I would go to school as long as the school season lasted, then I went to work on a farm and did whatever farm work the owners wanted me to do. It was what we would call unskilled labor, of course.

I come from a very large family. I had six brothers and four sisters.

Six of us are still living. One of my brothers lives in Washington, D.C., and
two live in New Jersey. I don't see very much of them, but we do keep
in touch with one another through occasional letters.

Most of us lived in Virginia until our parents died, my father in 1910
and my mother in 1913. But after the death of my mother, several of the
children moved to Cambridge, Massachusetts, where one of my married
sisters already lived. A younger brother and I moved to Trenton, New
Jersey, where our married brother was living. I worked at very ordinary
jobs during the day—unskilled jobs—and went to night school for a couple
of years. In 1915, I came here to Cambridge, where my sister was living
and I decided that I was going to try to get as much education as possible
while here, so I went to high school for about two and a half years. That
is the only formal education I have ever had. I do a great deal of reading
and I belong to a few organizations like the NAACP. I quit high school to
go to work because I needed the money so badly. I worked on until I was
drafted for World War I. That was just before the war ended. When I
was released from service, I once again did odd jobs in and around Cambridge until 1923. I got to thinking a good deal about my future and decided
that this odd job business wasn't for me. So, after thinking some more
about it, I decided to take the civil-service exams in order to enter the
federal service. Well—I've been there ever since.

I want to talk a little about the racial discrimination that I have encountered through the years. A Negro doesn't have too easy a time of it—
even today. But when I was a child, I can only describe it as a traumatic
experience. A Negro feels it from the very beginning. It is part of the very
air we breathe and most of us, including myself, resent it very deeply, very
bitterly. There is a sense of frustration about it that is almost impossible to
describe. When a child sees no hope of ever getting away from racial discrimination, when he knows that it is just a very real part of the world he
has been born into, you can understand why it is a traumatic experience.
Today I see the most heartening development of my life in the sit-ins and
Freedom Riders down South. The young Negroes today who have not experienced those days of racial discrimination can hardly begin to understand
or appreciate the progress that is being made and the change in attitude on
the part of the Negro himself. There can be nothing worse than the raw
humiliation that I underwent as a child because I am a Negro.

I married late in life, when I was forty years old. As a consequence,
a couple of generations separate me from my own children. I have a boy of
eighteen and a girl twenty-two years old. Frankly, I do not believe that my
son has felt any real discrimination. My daughter is aware of racial feeling,
but in a way that is quite different from the way I experienced it. I think
that the attitude of Negroes themselves toward discrimination has changed.
It is certainly true of the younger generation, of the Negro young people I
meet. They are inclined to laugh at the pretensions of superiority on the
part of the whites. They have developed a belief that the white man is not
invulnerable. In my early days, most all of us Negroes believed that the
white man *was* invulnerable. The younger people probably wouldn't put it

in those words, but it is obvious to me that their attitude is different. It seems that all Negroes of the younger generation, including my own children, and others who were born in the North have not felt, could not possibly feel, the absolute stigma of racial discrimination and segregation the way the older generation, my generation, has felt it.

One of the reasons for this difference is the fact that Negro children, with all the problems they have getting a decent job or living in a comfortable home, *can* go on through high school at the very least. My boy, for example, doesn't intend to stop with high school. He is planning to work his way through college—and I'm quite certain he will do it. My daughter has gone through college and she took extra work and graduated as a schoolteacher. Now she is married. But she is continuing to work as a teacher while her husband goes to a technical school so that he can be a skilled mechanic. They will do all right. I'm certain about that.

My son-in-law is a Negro. I point this out because, as you know, I was married to a white woman for many years. My daughter never regarded herself as anything other than a Negro and that goes for my son, also.

My son doesn't always take life seriously. He isn't as easily upset as I was at his age about discrimination and things. He doesn't like these things. He will work to overcome them, pretty certain that some great gains will be made in the years ahead as they have been within the past five or more years. He is determined, but there will be no traumatic experience because of frustrations. He will go on to college, I am sure. Aside from that, he has two great loves these days—automobiles and girls. I'm having a bit of a time getting him to take life seriously, but I have confidence in him. He's got his feet on the ground. He will come through in fine shape.

My parents were Baptists. I grew up in an atmosphere of religious fundamentalism. I grew up in an environment where anyone who was not a Baptist was surely headed for Hell. The Negroes of the South where I was reared were all deeply religious. They believed the Bible literally. And I did, too. But as time passed and as I started really growing up in the North, it seemed to me that religious fundamentalism leaves a lot of questions unanswered. So, for that reason, I came to reject it. There was a long period of time when I just didn't go to any church. In fact, I rejected religious teachings of any sort whatsoever. But I found the Community Church in Boston. That is a liberal church and I go there. Today, I don't have any antagonism toward religion. It seems to me that my needs are best met by my Church. My daughter is not at all religious. My boy goes to church, though I don't think he has any real deep religious feeling. I know my girl hasn't. My boy went to the Community Church Sunday School. Then he became interested in the Congregational Church, so he's been going down there for the past three years and he has taken part in the activities down there.

Now, in both of those churches, there is absolutely no problem about the fact that we are Negroes. My boy is aware of racial feeling. My girl is certainly aware of it, but it has never been difficult for them to accept this feeling even though they do not like it.

I have not experienced anything like the racial feeling there was when I was a child down South. In my work as a federal employee for almost forty years, I must say that I just cannot think of racial discrimination as a real problem. I have been working hard side by side with white men for all these years and we get along very well.

Now, I'm going to tell you about my marriage and how it all happened. I first met the lady at public meetings where liberals are wont to gather. I was a Socialist. I became one after the First World War. She had pretty much the same views as I had. I don't think that we thought much, or at all, about trying to overcome the racial boundaries that separate Negroes and whites. I must say, too, that we both felt that we had a great deal in common. The color difference between us didn't really seem to be important. We became friends long before we thought of marriage.

Now, my wife, when I first got to know her, lived at home in this area with her parents, two sisters and a brother. Now, we didn't really get to know each other or to feel that we had anything in common right away, actually it took about two years before our friendship ripened into love. I must point out that it did not seem to be too difficult a decision for us to make—about our wanting to marry. But it certainly was difficult for my wife's family to take. In fact, when she told her parents that she was planning on marrying a Negro, they resented it deeply. They were deeply opposed to it and made it very clear to her and to me as well.

My wife came from a lower middle-class family. She had only a high-school education. Both her mother and father had lived in New Hampshire and their parents and grandparents before them. They were New England folk with a long history in this country. We were in the depression years then, and the "going" was difficult for everyone and it was certainly difficult for her and her parents. Of course, during those years, I really had no problem because I was doing quite well working in the civil-service job I had.

Even though her mother and other members of the family objected very strongly to the idea of our marriage, I recall that her father didn't, in the same way. At least, he wasn't outright determined to have us break up. Maybe it had to do with the fact that I was economically better off than many people, including him. Whether it was her father who made the difference, I do not know. I am sure, however, that my girl was of such a strong personality and character and her ideas and mine were so much alike—our liberalism, our way of looking at politics and economics—that the difference in skin color that existed between us just didn't seem to matter.

At this rather trying time, I had to make some important decisions myself. I did not consult with any members of my family. I never have about this or anything else. If I had, I was reasonably certain that no one in my family would object. After all, you will remember my own family history. We did not look at intermarriage in the same way that many whites do. As I thought about it, I felt that there were not any real impediments to our marriage. From the vantage point of years of experience and

careful observation, I had noted that there really are no special problems created by children in a family of a racially mixed couple. I mean that it is a common misconception that people have about racial intermarriage. Children know no barriers of race whatsoever. Their mother is their mother no matter what her color or race. The racial factor is removed. It's tangential to the whole issue. The racial factor, as I see it, has nothing to do with the relationship. The child of an interracial marriage knows that he belongs to the Negro group and there is no problem. They adjust to that fact and that's all there is to it. If a child of such a marriage doesn't try to be a white man and recognizes the fact that he is a Negro, there will be no unhappy reaction. It's psychological identification that is most important. If the child or children are psychologically adjusted to it, then there is no problem. Oh, I'll admit that there can be a serious problem if this kind of adjustment is lacking. It may be tragic for a child not to know to which race he belongs or to feel psychologically maladjusted to parents or to society, but most of my experience points to the fact that this need not happen.

Take the famous Walter White, for example. You will remember him as an executive of the National Association for the Advancement of Colored People. Now, he was as white as you are, ethnically and biologically. But he identified with the Negro race with no difficulty whatsoever. The whole problem then is psychological.

The problem is very much the same as with adults. Here, too, it is psychological. Will the white wife be accepted by the Negro community? Will the Negro husband of a white woman be accepted by the white community? Now, the latter question didn't bother me, because I did not care whether the white community accepted me or not. In my case, I felt that the Negro community would accept my white wife if she identified with the Negro group. That is the basic problem. If the white woman, married to a Negro, accepts the fact that she is really a part of the Negro group, as my wife did, then all suspicions and uncertainties are overcome. Oh, I will admit that at first, there is some suspicion naturally. Negroes have suspicions about motives, too. But they accepted my wife quickly because it was apparent that she *wanted* to be an integral part of the Negro community. I might say that, with reference to my own family, I had some problems to overcome. I was deeply attached to my sisters and brothers. I think that there was a stronger bond than exists in most average families. One of my sisters, a woman of very pronounced views, resented the idea of my wanting to marry a white girl. For most of the first year of our marriage she was still rather bitter about it all. But we just went along as though nothing happened. She lived about three miles from us and we would go to visit her as if we weren't aware of her feelings. This was also true of the attitude of another of my sisters. But gradually they came to accept us both.

I would say that the same feeling of uncertainty and insecurity that characterizes a white person under these circumstances characterizes a Negro, too, under the same conditions. There is a certain hesitancy, a fear that this person is not really part of the group—that is, that he or she may be play-acting and not real at all.

I think that the problem was even more difficult for me than it was for my wife, because she didn't seem to feel the need for family affection and regard the way I did. I don't feel that the family ties were as strong in my wife's family as they were in mine. Frankly, I was not at all concerned whether her family would accept me at all. It simply didn't cause me any discomfort in any way.

It's strange that I should feel this way about my wife's family ties when I know that her parents kept talking to her, urging her to break up with me. By the way, they never talked to me directly about the marriage. They had no contact with me whatsoever. They refused to recognize that I even existed.

Despite the fact that I am a sensitive person, I really wasn't bothered by her parents' attitude. I was content with the idea that if they wanted to play in their own back yard—if they wanted to ignore me—it didn't make any difference to me.

I feel that if two individuals want to marry, no matter who they are, family considerations must be brushed to one side. I think that marriage ought to be a bond between the individuals. Now, I'm not saying that families of these individuals may not, by their attitudes, affect the happiness of the individuals. I *am* saying that ideally, they shouldn't.

I know that we are not talking about the *ideal* society. We are talking about the society we have, of which we are a part. So, I will have to admit that families *do* play roles in the lives of individuals and that families can destroy marriages—about *that* I have no doubt.

You may be sure that we talked all of this over very carefully and many, many times, from the very beginning, that is, from the very time we contemplated marriage. Inasmuch as I was considerably older, I felt it my duty to explain the situation to her thoroughly. I explained what she would be up against—her parents—all her family and the whole white community would not accept her marriage to me as being legitimate. I made the point that they would regard her as an outcast. I told her what penalties she would have to pay if she went through with it. She was twenty-two years old at the time we met. She had had some friends, but she was a girl who had not been cultivated. She had lived a rather sheltered life. So for that matter had I, and I still do.

We were married twenty-four years ago in the Community Church, one very much concerned with social issues then, as it is now.

We lived here all the years of our married life. You may have noticed that we live in a neighborhood in which most of the families are Negroes. But there are a few white families and some that are mixed. In all cases but one, the wife is white and the husband is Negro. You see, the Negroes don't have the privilege of renting or buying where they may want to. It would be quite impossible for me to rent another place in a white neighborhood if I moved from this house. I would be up against it if I tried to move as would practically all of the Negroes here and elsewhere.

During all of our years together, my wife and I got along fairly well, I think. Although I must point out that we have been divorced for the

past two years. My son lives with me. My married daughter does not live in this community.

During all the years of our marriage I cannot say that I felt any special pressures being exerted on us by the community or by either of our families other than those I already told you about. We always went out together. You ask whether one of us felt it necessary to walk behind the other when we went out? Heavens, no! We simply took each other for granted. As a matter of fact, one of the stipulations we made was that we were going to try to live just like the average married couple in every way. So we went together among whites and among colored people. We just took each other for granted and in that way other people took us for granted as well.

My wife's father died about three years after we were married and shortly after our son was born. During all that time my mother-in-law had had nothing to do with us. My wife, independent person that she was, simply let it go at that. But when my son was born, my mother-in-law came to visit us and had dinner with us. She died about five years after that. I'm still not certain whether she got over her resentment or whether her visit had something to do with her being lonely. Her other children had moved away to other cities. So she was quite alone. But whatever the reason, the fact is that she *did* come to our home and we responded warmly to her. We saw her on occasion, thereafter.

Of course, I'm not certain that *all* Negro-white marriage relationships work out the same way. It so happens that I am the kind of person who doesn't require very many contacts with the outside world—Negro or white. I have my work and after work I come home and read the paper or my books (I have a fairly nice library) or I listen to music and I go to work again. I will go to the theater if I have the money or an inclination, but I really don't need people around me all the time, nor do I concern myself overly much about what other people think of me or my ways. I suppose that if I did, I might not respond in the same way to some of your questions, but each person is different.

Now, to get back to the subject of the reactions of Negroes and whites to a mixed marriage such as ours, I must say that there is always a certain suspicion about the person of different color that one feels at times. The Negro group accepts a person of a different color—but it doesn't completely accept. I think one has to keep proving one's identification with the group. But insofar as the white group is concerned, I rather doubt that most whites ever *completely* accept a Negro. I have seen some of the white wives of the Negro men who live on this street and I have the feeling that it may be more difficult for them than we sometimes think, simply because they are white folks. Whites accept us very readily during working hours, but after sundown, we do not see them. We are with Negroes. My wife was very active in various projects—P.T.A. and so forth, and she came to know the people in this neighborhood very well. With all the years I have lived here, I can't say that I do. But that may be because I work nights. My pay is higher when I work on the night shift.

Our divorce had nothing to do with the difference in our races. The

fact that she is white and I am Negro made it difficult for us at the outset, but during our years together *the* matter of skin color had nothing to do with our relationship. In fact, my former wife visits our children and they visit her. She calls on many of our Negro friends now, as she did before. The marriage broke up because of differences in our natures, I think. People use the word "incompatibility," which means that there are many little things that ultimately destroy the marriage. In our case, I do not think race had much, if anything, to do with it.

I think that, as time goes on, interracial marriage will increase in the United States as it has in other parts of the world. The educational level of the Negro is improving. There is increasing self-respect, increasing militancy on the part of the Negro groups. The rise of the new African nations, too, will cause a change in the attitude of the whites. I think that the whites are resenting Negroes more these days because, in my opinion, you resent your equal where in former years you could be patronizing to the Negro who was not the equal of the white. Legalism alone is inadequate to effect the new relationship that is bound to come between the races. I can't tell you how fascinating it is for me, an older Negro man, to see the marked changes that have taken place. To compare the world in which I was born —just one step removed from slavery—to this present day is like attempting to compare night and day. It is nothing short of a miracle. To see young Negro boys and girls risking their lives . . . ! Parochialism is being broken down. It is happening every day in greater degree in the North *and* in the South.

I remember some of the early schooling I had in Virginia. I remember the textbook we studied on the history of the Civil War. We studied about the five races of mankind. They were all beautifully arranged according to their degree of civilization. The whites were always at the very top. But at the bottom of the list came the Negro. We children resented that and teacher, who was Negro, of course, used to explain, "Now, children, *this* is the white man's view."

Today Negroes feel that America belongs to them, too. Or at least, that it should. The slave psychology no longer exists among Negroes. At any rate, it is very much reduced today. For all these reasons courageous people of different races will get together much more in the years ahead. It is a matter of indifference to me whether interracial marriages take place or not. There is no particular reason why they should nor is there any particular reason why they shouldn't. It all depends on the kind of individual who is involved. If the individual is in love and if he or she is strong, an interracial marriage *can* work out. The difference between individuals is, I think, enormously greater than the difference between groups or races.

If my son came to me today and said, "I want to marry a certain white girl," I would certainly tell him that the consequences might not be all he hoped for. There are attitudes of families to be considered. No one really wants to alienate himself from his own group or people, but that shouldn't really bear enough weight to prevent him from marrying. If one is religious and has a strong sense of identification with one's religion, then this would,

in my opinion, be a good reason for *not* intermarrying. But I do not have any particular religious feeling at all. Neither did my wife. So *that* was no problem for us. We had no religion in common. We did have political and social ideas in common. That is why we were able to make our marriage work, even though it finally ended in divorce. I don't think my former wife is happy now that we are divorced. I know *I'm* not. It takes a little bit of courage and very much wisdom to make a success of an interracial marriage.

THE SCOTTS

Helen Scott is a mature Negro woman. Her complexion is so fair that she can "pass" as a white person, yet, after numerous problems and inner conflict she has found her security and her strength in the colored group. She is married to a Negro, far more dark-skinned than she. She reared her sons as American Negroes. Both husband and wife have made possible the college education of one son and expect to do the same for the younger son.

"Marginality," the attempt to live in two cultures at one and the same time, is a serious problem likely to affect one's personality and philosophy. Helen had made her choice. She works with white persons, but she "belongs" to the Negro race.

HELEN

I look like any other white woman, my skin is so fair. But I am a Negro. All my life I have known I was a Negro. I could have "passed" as a white woman without any trouble, but, except for some rare instances, I have not done so. I remember that I "passed" when a job I was anxious to get simply wasn't open to a Negro and it was expedient to be white. So, I was white for a time on the job. But that's when it ended. I have never felt like some people I know who are tearing themselves apart to be white and are, despite their desire, having to be colored. Some people want so desperately to be white that they will pass and they often can do so easily if they are really fair-skinned. But there is, I think, a conflict within them that is much worse than living with being colored, which really isn't bad

at all. I could personally make any choice I like, but I chose to be exactly what I am. I am much more white than colored, but I belong to the colored group. I'm perfectly satisfied now.

There are special problems that a very fair person like myself has to face when she calls herself "colored," but they're really not insurmountable. You see, I know my parents and their background very well. If I were going to think only of myself that would be one thing, but if I remember my parents, then I know who I am ever so much better.

Now, my mother was as fair as I. She had a much more ruddy and darker complexion. Her hair was heavier. She was a large woman. She was of mixed parentage. She was a good deal white and some American Indian, too. Her father was of mixed blood, too, white and Negro. There isn't a pure-blooded Negro in the family for I can't say how many generations back. My father was Irish. He was white. His father's family came from England. His mother came from Ireland. My mother was born in the East. My father, too.

I am married to a Negro who, although he is far darker than I, is also of mixed-blood parentage. His mother's father was white and his mother's mother was colored. On his father's side, his grandmother was colored and his grandfather was white. In those days, during slavery and after, there was much interracial relationship. Although my husband's white grandfather couldn't marry the Negro woman he lived with, he always maintained a home for her and their children. All in all, I come from a family where mixed blood is the usual thing as it is with ever so many colored people.

I have two children, a boy and a girl. Although they are quite light, they are not absolutely white. They are Negroes and they know it. There's no uncertainty about it. When you are a fair-skinned Negro, you are mistaken for a white on occasion and you've got special problems, either explaining what you are or avoiding the issue altogether. When I was a little girl, I remember some unhappy experiences with that problem.

My mother and father happened to meet where they both worked. My father never spoke about his family. I certainly never met any of them, his parents or his brother and sister, and except for one occasion when, quite by accident, mother met her husband's brother, she did not know any of my father's family at all. He never took my mother to meet them. My parents fell in love and in about six months after they met, they were married.

Now it wasn't only their race which was different. It was also their religion. Father had been reared as a Roman Catholic and he remained a Roman Catholic all his life. He maintained his relationship with the Church throughout his days. My mother was a Baptist. When I was born, I was christened in the Catholic faith as my father wished. Except for that, my father never insisted on my mother becoming a convert or anything like that. He was quite a devout Catholic, too. He observed his Fast Days and went to church regularly.

I might have become a Roman Catholic had all things been equal because I had such a need, when I was growing up, for something more

than what I had at home. I did attend confirmation classes of my own accord when I was about ten years old, but I did not make my first Communion because of the idea of the Confessional. I really had no one with whom I could talk or from whom I could seek advice. I wasn't very close in those days to either my mother or my father. I had such guilt feelings and couldn't bring myself to confess them. So, I made the decision myself. I simply dropped out. Neither my father nor my mother ever asked why I did what I did.

When I was a youngster, I definitely had certain problems because of my background. It's something you live with from the time you are first aware of the fact that you are something which you do not appear to be. All my life I have looked and lived (I think) like a white and yet all my life I have known that I am a Negro. There is the temptation to "pass" and yet I somehow didn't choose to. I was brought up to regard myself as colored and it would have been an even greater conflict for me to think of myself as a white. Being colored is now natural to me. But I was a youngster. I hadn't found myself and I did have my problems. The problem would have been greatly aggravated had my parents not been divorced when I was quite a young child. They simply couldn't get along. I lived with my mother. She regarded herself as colored so that made it easier for me. She made her life among her people and I made my life with her and it was our life to be colored. Even though mother was much lighter than most colored people and I certainly was, the direct association and identification with Negroes helped to stabilize me. It helped in a measure to overcome my insecurities.

My being fair-skinned served to set me apart at first from the Negroes as well because they didn't know what I was. I had that problem especially in relation with other children in school. You can't go around with a sign printed and hanging on your back saying "I am a Negro." It takes a while for them to find out. When they do, there is a different attitude. They accept you where, before, they were polite and friendly, but certainly I knew that I didn't "belong."

I remember one time, my mother sending me to the hospital with a dark-complexioned Negro. The hospital authorities became quite indignant because a white child was there with this Negro. They asked all kinds of embarrassing questions and made many nasty remarks. When I finally got them to understand that I, too, was colored they were embarrassed, of course. But it was nothing like the feeling of hurt and resentment that I had.

There is sometimes a problem associated with darker Negroes. It's hard to define it. It's a kind of "Who do they think they are?" attitude expressed toward the fair-skin ones. I'm told that about a generation ago this attitude was much more pronounced. I think it is being overcome because there is more education and culture these days among the colored, and they don't feel the same way about identifying color with ideas of superiority. Many Negroes today marry foreign girls. Men who have been overseas or in the service have married Italian girls, French girls, and many of them have come back into this country.

When I was a child living in the South with my mother, it seemed important to colored people to lighten the race—at least this was the attitude around where I lived. Each Negro family expected their child to marry to improve the race, color-wise. I don't know what kind of "improvement" this was supposed to be, but I remember hearing over and over again such an expression as "white is right." This was a common axiom and the whiter you got the righter you were.

To be a fair-skin Negro meant, when I was young, that when you were with Negroes you were always more or less the object of curiosity. I was shy and terribly self-conscious about it even as I was about my parents' divorce. I felt that I was terribly different from other children.

To illustrate how a child like myself would get so hurt and so confused, let me tell you about what happened one day at school. The teacher was talking about the various countries in Europe from which American ancestors had come. She started naming all of the countries and asked the children who had parents who came from these countries to raise their hands. Now there were only a few Negro children in that school (this happened shortly after we came up North). When the teacher got to England and asked the children who had parents who came from England to raise their hands, I raised mine. After all, my father was from England and there was no reason I shouldn't. But there were several children who followed me all the way home from school and taunted me about the fact that I was a "nigger" and that I was "trying to be something that I wasn't."

You may be sure that my own personal insecurities, the attitude of Negroes toward me and then the attitude of whites toward me made me a very unhappy child.

During those days, I didn't have anyone to talk to about all this. My mother was working. The home situation generally wasn't good. Growing up was so difficult for me. I am grateful for the Power that has brought me through all these early years. My mother was completely unaware of what I was going through. She could never have imagined being anything other than a Negro.

I managed to graduate from junior high school and, in order to get along financially, I had to get a factory job. But I was unhappy about it all. So one day I boarded a bus and came to the town where my father lived. My mother knew I had planned to do something like this. When I got there, I located my father and he agreed to pay for my board and room so I could finish high school. Actually, I planned to go on to college. But that was when I met my future husband. As I said, he is a Negro—much darker than I. We met at a Baptist Church. I was still going to the Baptist Church at that time. It was a Negro church and I was living in a Negro neighborhood. The early question about what I was—white or Negro—no longer made any difference to me. I was quite satisfied to be a Negro and that is certainly why it was possible for me to marry a man who could immediately be identified as a Negro.

I have now been married twenty years. We live in a colored neighborhood. I work in an office with some fine white people. We have several

children. My oldest boy is away at college. The younger one, a daughter, is just finishing high school. When my older boy was very much younger, he attended a church conference. There was another colored boy in the group. All the others were white. There were girls in this group also. One of the white girls and my son seemed to take a shine to each other and she invited him to attend a Thanksgiving week-end party that was going to be held in her community. The girl's mother wrote and invited him. But suddenly I realized that these people, in all probability, did not know that my boy was colored. My husband and I talked about it and we felt that they should know. You see, my son, too, is so light-complexioned that he can be mistaken for a white boy if you aren't thinking about color. At that time, I had joined the Episcopalian Church. It is a mixed church. So I decided to talk it over with our priest. He agreed that I ought to write a letter explaining things. Well, I did that. I told the girl's mother, as one mother to another, that I thought that she might not know that my son is a Negro. And that even though we do not appear to be or at least are not obviously so, we are a colored family. I wrote that I realized that, in all probability this would not make any difference to her, but I realized that living in a small community there might be persons who would object to my son's presence. Well, this mother wrote back and thanked me for my letter and though she said it made no difference to her, some of her neighbors might take exception. Well, it was hard to take, for my son, especially. But it had to be done. Identity had to be clarified as quickly as possible. I want people to know, under all circumstances, that my children are colored. I always tell people "we are a colored family," so that everyone will know that we are *all* identified with the destiny and life of the colored people. I find that people accept that and understand this statement. I do not say "Johnny is colored," or "Ruth is colored." I say, "We are a colored family." That means all of us, including me! And they understand.

Being a Negro and so fair-skinned presents certain problems. People are always mistaking me for a white person and they make mean remarks about Negroes that hurt me very deeply. Sometimes they are highly offensive. But I know now what *I* am. I am a bit concerned that my son should get to feel that he has something to feel proud about as a Negro. He accepts his being a Negro, but he isn't proud about it and I think that a member of a minority group has to really feel proud about the people to which he belongs (he can't just take it for granted). Otherwise, he may be in for real heartaches when he has to suffer some kind of indignity because he is a member of a minority group. I have told him that the best way to have people know he is a Negro without having to tell them directly is to have in his wallet pictures of his family who are obviously colored. Show them the pictures and they will know soon enough. You will make yourself perfectly clear by this simple act. Show them your family and say, "This is my father, this is my mother, this is my grandmother." That's the way they can soon know.

If my son were to come to me one of these days and say, "I am planning to marry a white girl," I must say that I would not be happy about

it even though the choice is obviously his to make. There are so many problems involved. One of the two parties to the marriage has got to give up a great deal. One or the other has got to assume an identity with another group, and this may mean much unhappiness. Of course, it depends so much on the people involved, who they are, their background, education, religion, but certainly one of the two has to give up many things and he or she is not going to find satisfaction in that. It isn't just the two people who are getting married but their parents, brothers, sisters, and the whole relationship of two complete groups of people.

If I had a daughter who was very light-skinned and she wanted to marry a very dark-complexioned Negro, that too, might have certain problems, but they would be in no way like the other. I would in the latter case, be concerned about the youth's maturity, his sense of responsibility, his love for her, how he would take care of her and honor her. If those things were answered positively then he would look fine to me, no matter what his complexion. We have our white friends, but we also have our Negro friends. Our relationships are geared to our common interests more than they are to color or anything like that.

If a child of mine wanted to marry out of the faith I would hesitate to recommend such a marriage. When you have to give up something—anything—when you have to sacrifice your faith, this is a bad start to begin with. So, if my son were to want to marry a Roman Catholic—even though that was my father's religion, I would oppose it. To give up one's grand-children—and grandparents can be a great comfort to small children—is no simple matter. It would bring me a great deal of joy for my grandchild and me to be able to go to church together, for me to be able to give guidance to a child. This would be impossible under those circumstances. If a person's religion meant so little to him that he would give it up, I would question how that can be, since mine means so much to me. No, I don't favor a marriage that obliges any person to give up a faith. I do favor a marriage when both husband and wife have respect for each other's faith.

As a Negro, however white I may be—I know now the people to which I belong. My destiny is their destiny and their destiny is mine. Deliberately choosing to remain a Negro when I could have "passed" as a white means that I know where I belong and—why.

ARLENE AND BILL

Arlene is a Nisei, a Japanese girl who was born and reared in San Francisco, California. Her husband, Bill, was described by one of his friends as "a hill billy." Born and reared in Oklahoma, in a highly religious, fundamentalist environment, Bill has broken away from the

Church and religion. Both Arlene and Bill are gifted scientists. They met as students. Bill's marriage to Arlene is his second marriage. His first, to a girl from his own (and his mother's) church ended in divorce after ten years. Most of those years, Bill says, were unhappy. Now, with Arlene pregnant and with one child, a boy, by his previous marriage living with them, these two believe that there need be no special problems for them because of color difference because they live in a scholastic environment. Both teach at a large Eastern University.

ARLENE: I am a Nisei, a Japanese-American girl who was born in San Francisco. My parents were born in Japan, but they have lived in the United States for many years—about forty or more. At present, my parents live in Berkeley, California, which is just a very short distance from San Francisco. In the same neighborhood, you might say.

My father came to the United States from Japan as a young man. I don't know exactly how old he was at the time. He came with the thought of making his fortune and then returning to Japan. He did in fact return to Japan several times, but he returned to this country. He came originally to San Francisco, but in those early years he traveled around the country doing many different kinds of work. He worked in rice fields in Texas. Later he had a carpenter shop in Sacramento. He worked on farms and he was a delivery boy. Many different things, you see. But practically all of his years in this country were spent in California. I was told, too, that at one time he went to a kind of a business school in San Francisco, which seems to have been oriented to the Japanese people. He seems to have had many classmates who were from Japan. After some years, he went into the exporting-importing business on his own. About that time he went back to Japan to pick up his bride. You see, my father came from a very small village in Japan. His father, when he died, left him a piece of a farm. My father sold his share for passage money in order to come to the United States.

Although I would not say that my father was nonreligious, I do not remember that he was ever very much interested in religion. But, whatever his personal feelings, he did have a small shrine in our home. He was a Buddhist but mostly by tradition. He had those wooden plates on which were the names of his ancestors. My mother was always very careful to put out flowers and food on those special days. I don't remember now whether it was the birthdays or the anniversaries of their deaths that were specially observed.

You see, my mother was his second wife. His first marriage was arranged for him by his family in Japan. That was the practice. He was married to his first wife about six years when she died. They did not have any children. After that, he returned to Japan where his marriage to my mother had been arranged for. It was some time before he went back because he had to make some more money again to pay for his passage to and from Japan. My mother did not practice any religion. She and my

father had a strong belief in Destiny and Fate. My mother is very much of a fatalist. She does not go to church. I do not remember that she ever did.

We lived in what was an all-Japanese community on the outskirts of San Francisco. My mother never did learn to speak English. My father did because of his business, but he did not speak English at home. So, I spoke only Japanese. When it was time for me to begin going to public school, my mother worried a great deal about what would happen to me in school because I didn't know English. So she sent me and later, my younger brother, too, to a Japanese Catholic Mission school run by the Daughters of Mary and Joseph, an Order from Belgium. The school was called the Morning Star School and it was located in San Francisco. I remember that the kindergarten class was taught by a Japanese teacher from Japan in the Japanese language, and this, of course, was a great attraction. In the first grade we had a Japanese teacher part time and a nun who spoke English to us. So gradually we were "weaned" to the English language. Well, I just stayed on there and before I knew it I was converted to Catholicism. There really was no opposition to this from my parents. They were very permissive. Yet, I think they tried to dissuade me a little bit. They said, well, maybe I should wait until I was a little older. But I said "no." I was determined to be a saint and I certainly wanted to become a nun. I was highly impressionable, as you can gather. So my mother said, "Well, if that's what you want, fine. But it's not right for just one member of the family to join the church. We should make it a group then. So my brother, who had been attending the same school, was baptized and converted to Catholicism also. Neither my mother nor my father ever had anything to do with Catholicism themselves. It was all right for us children but not for them.

BILL: You see, not only are Arlene and I of different skin color, but we have utterly different religious orientation as well. I was born in Oklahoma in a very little town called Sulphur. That was a good name for it—it stinks. It wasn't too far from Oklahoma City. My father died when I was four years old. I don't know very much about him—only what my mother told me. My mother was my father's second wife. His first wife was an Indian. He had two children by her. But she died and a few years later he married my mother. There were six more children.

My father first came out to Oklahoma before it became a state. He had come from Tennessee. I really know so little about him except that he wasn't religious, according to my mother. She was a very religious woman and belonged to the Church of Christ. I was brought up in that church as were my brothers and sisters. In fact, I was supposed to become a preacher. I was selected for that because I was very religious, according to my mother.

By the way, it was not unusual for a white man to marry an Indian as my father had done. There were lots of Indians around. There wasn't a real prejudice against them as there was toward Negroes. As for Orientals, there were so very few in our area that we didn't have any opinions about

them. There was a Mexican family there when I was a kid. The boy was a good friend of mine, but people didn't think much of Mexicans either. My father was called "Mr. John" by all the Negroes. It was a kind of master-slave relationship, I think. My father had been in the cattle business and had some real-estate holdings also. He was rather well off compared with most people around there. Hardly anybody had anything they could call their own out there. But he lost a lot of money at the time of the depression in 1929.

ARLENE: Neither my father nor my mother were community organization people within the Japanese community or anywhere else. My mother was basically a housekeeper and a mother who looked out for her family. There were no club "doings" of any kind. Insofar as my father is concerned, he gave all of his time to the exporting and importing business. He shipped and received goods from Hawaii and from Japan. There were undoubtedly other places as well. He brought in things like shrimp and rice. Most of his business had, I think, to do with foodstuffs. All this while we were living in San Francisco, but in a separate Japanese community. Everything was going along fine until we got into war with Japan. We, along with practically all the other Japanese, were among the internees. They shipped us off to Utah. Before that, however, we lived at what had been a race track and in fact the building we lived in had been the stables. It had been repainted and it really was quite livable. The grandstand served as the mess hall for us all. There were about ten thousand Japanese out in the Utah internee's camp. Of course, there were a lot of other camps, too. These places were actually called "relocation centers." The ones where the families were separated were called internment camps. The camp we were at was for whole families. They used to separate families when they thought these Japanese were more dangerous to the government than the others. I think it had to do with the fact that some of these people had, at some time or other, signed a pledge of allegiance to Japan.

I was very young at the time and it was more fun to me than anything else. But it did play havoc with many families and particularly with whatever business such people as my father had built up. We were in this camp in Utah for three years. Although the loyalties of a lot of good Japanese-Americans were being questioned, I don't recall that there was much bitterness against the whites. You see, practically all of us regarded ourselves as Americans and actually we *were* Americans. We were born here. This is the only country we children really knew. It was, however, a traumatic experience for many! But there was a kind of majority-minority group relationship there. The whites, of course, were in the minority. The whites were such people as the head surgeon at the hospital in the camp, many of the teachers, the principal of the high school. And, of course, there were the bureaucratic people from Washington who were administering the camp program. These were in the minority.

Now, of course, I'm not sure as I look back on it that there was no feeling of anger with the whites. You see, the Japanese are very good at hiding

their feelings. But, I didn't get that feeling from them. As for the children in the camp, we were very, very friendly to those who liked us, and we were very, very unfriendly to those persons whom we thought disliked us. All my companions were Japanese. I'm sure that it was much harder on the grown people, my parents, for example, than it was for us. We didn't leave this camp until after the war—in September of 1945.

When the war ended, I was anxious to get away and enroll in a school somewhere. We were encouraged to leave camp after VE day. Things were gradually closed down there and we were told that the school in camp would not be reopened and that we must eventually leave. Some of the adults and their children left during that summer but my father, who, at that time, was over sixty years old, had no business left in San Francisco. He had absolutely nothing. He had a family and he wasn't exactly willing to volunteer to leave because he was a little frightened by his economic prospects back in San Francisco. So he more or less procrastinated. He was going to wait until he was forced to leave the camp site. But I felt that I wanted to go to school, so, with my mother's permission, I came to San Francisco. I was about fifteen years old—certainly not over that—when I left that camp.

I stayed at the home of some very good friends of my parents who had children around my age. I knew them and so we thought that this would be a good place for me. But it soon became obvious to me that I was really in the way. I could see that, what with their own family, their limited income and small house, I was really imposing. So I got a job like that many other Japanese-Americans were taking in those days. While I went to school I earned my room and board by living in, doing the dishes and as much other housework as I had time for. This was all in San Francisco. I continued that until I graduated from high school.

In the meanwhile, my parents had come back to San Francisco. They could not very easily find a place to live because the entire Japanese section had, during the war, been occupied by colored people. They had come to work in the shipyards and there was need for this whole area. Well, within short order, my parents found two rooms in Berkeley, just across the Bay, and they moved there. They soon decided that Berkeley was a lot nicer than San Francisco, so for the past fifteen years they have lived there.

My father had a very difficult time of it. He had lost his export-import business, so he turned gardener. He also did housework, but in time he came to do more gardening than housework. He is still pretty good at it, too.

Because we lived in Berkeley it was natural for me to think about attending the University of California which is situated there. All of my friends were beginning to go there. There were many people there whom I knew. I had little idea about courses, but these friends guided me. I found myself taking science courses and enjoying them very much. In fact, I really did quite well with them. I was graduated from there in 1951.

BILL: I sort of drifted into my field of science in much the same way. I just took everything that came along and found myself liking it much more

than other things. I guess so much of this curriculum business is a matter of luck. Some people find what they like very quickly. Others do not.

ARLENE: My friends were not all Japanese either during those days. I had many white good friends. I probably had more Japanese friends than any other kind simply because I had known more of them. There was a Japanese dormitory at the university. It had been difficult for Japanese students during the war to find housing. People just wouldn't take them in. So the dorm remained and the Japanese lived there even after the war. That dormitory had been purchased by some of the wealthier persons of the community and was rented out to Japanese girls who had come from various parts of California to the university.

BILL: There are more Orientals at "Cal" than at any other school in the country by far. People stay together with their own kind, I guess.

ARLENE: That's because they feel at home with them. They know that they won't be criticized for some superficial and unimportant reason. For example, once, when I was in Chicago, my girl friend (a Japanese) and I were talking rather loudly while we were walking about. Something must have happened that excited us. Anyway, some woman—white, of course— came up to us and made some unkind comment about the Japanese. On another occasion I was with two girls, one a white girl who had invited me to stay at her home. Well, one of the neighbors complained about there being a Japanese girl next door, meaning me.

BILL: I guess my early years weren't as exciting as Arlene's. I went to school in one of the many very small towns in southeastern Oklahoma until I was sixteen years old. Then I simply quit and went to work for the Civil Service as an airplane mechanic. The war had just started and this gave me an excuse to leave school. I was simply tired of it. Maybe, too, as I think about it, it was because I was tired of my home too. None of us children stayed around our home or the home town once they felt they were old enough to be on their own. It must have been the way mother pressed all of us to be religious. She was very insistent about religion and I took it better than anybody else in the family ever did. I took it, but I resented it. It's kind of hard to stick with anything as tight and rigid as a super-orthodox church. When I got to be about fifteen years old, I found it almost intolerable. It doesn't mix with the natural urges at all.

During the war I went overseas with that group of plane mechanics and I worked in England for a while. We were paid good money. I was there for about a year and a half. But I was getting kind of anxious to get back home. So, when I was about eighteen, I joined the Merchant Marine in order to come back home. Of course, during those years I had been with a lot of people who were of different colors and different religions. I met a lot of Mexicans, when I was working as a mechanic down in San Antonio before I went to England.

When I finally reached the States, about my eighteenth birthday, I joined the Air Force. I was stationed in Texas and California and a few other places when I was with the Aviation Cadets.

During all those years even though I was resentful about the Church and my mother's religious ways, I always communicated with her and with several of my sisters. In the meanwhile, my mother moved to California, because several of my brothers and sisters had moved there.

I got out of the service in November, 1946. Then somebody to whom I had been speaking about going to college and who knew my background, told me that I couldn't get into college and this made me mad. So I decided to go to college. You see, I had never graduated from high school. Well, I took a lot of tests during the war, sort of a serviceman's education, and as you know, they keep on giving you tests to see how competent you are. I was getting these tests—in fact, I had asked to take them. I got some good grades, so when the war ended, I took them back to my high school and said that I would like to get my diploma. Well, they looked the record over and then said, "No, you have to take some history," or something like that, so I just told them to go to hell and I applied to a school operated by my mother's church. The school is in Los Angeles. It is a fairly nice school. It's a highly religious school. They accepted me on condition that I would make up what I had missed in high school. I stayed on there for a couple of years and then I transferred to U.C.L.A. I graduated from there with a "major" in the physical sciences.

Now don't ask me how I happened to get into that. I started taking math and science courses and all of a sudden I was doing this. I'm a tinkerer at heart. So I just kinda drifted into it.

I didn't tell you about my marriage. While I was at that very first college, the highly religious one, I met a girl from Arizona, who was from the same church to which my mother belonged. (I guess that's another thing I resent about that church.) We stayed together for ten years. But I don't know how long the marriage actually lasted. Probably a couple of years. Insofar as I was concerned I wouldn't say we were terribly unhappy because I don't know. I could get buried in my school work and didn't pay much attention. But we did have three children.

When I finished my Bachelor's degree at U.C.L.A., I had done well and graduated with the highest honors. The faculty wanted me to pick out a good graduate school and go to it. But my first wife had not yet graduated from that little college, so I didn't want to leave. So I stayed on at U.C.L.A. and got my Ph.D. there. Well, the head of my department suggested that I go to Harvard University and work under one of the real "greats" in the field. I was quite excited about the idea, but my wife said that was "against the law"—the law of money. She told me that she wouldn't stand any more of our kind of living. Now, that I had my Ph.D. she wanted me to make money, so I went to work for one of the largest chemical companies, where I worked for about seven years. Most of the time I was working in California.

Even though things had not gone too well between us I don't think I

ever thought about the marriage breaking up. I was taught as a young man that you just don't do this. Our whole family was taught this by my mother. But I will say that our marriage was a pretty lousy thing.

ARLENE: You are wondering where we two met. It was at the chemical company where Bill was working. I worked there, too, after I had received my college degree. I decided to go on for graduate work to a large Midwestern University. In two years, I got my Master's degree there and then I came back to California and got a job in the same company.

BILL: Although I was still married, I used to go out with many different people. I had white friends and I had Japanese friends. You see, I had had Japanese friends at U.C.L.A. California schools have a lot of Japanese.

ARLENE: I had gone out with many different kinds of people, too. It has never made any difference to me. Except that there *are* certain racial characteristics. I remember that I tried very hard to find a colored boy whom I could like, but it was hard for me because I couldn't find any whose personality I liked. I always thought that it might be that they were treated badly when they were children, that they had had hurtful experiences and had scars on their souls as a result. As I stated before, my mother, unlike other Japanese mothers, was very permissive. My parents never raised any questions. Besides, I'm a rather strong person. I have my own likes and dislikes. I had been self-supporting since I was fifteen and I think that my mother felt that I was quite sensible. Once, I remember her saying to me when I was living in San Francisco that her friends asked why I wasn't living at home with the family because there might be some question about what I was doing in the Big City. She said that she had raised me and she thought that she knew the things I would do and the things I wouldn't do and she had confidence in me and my standards.

BILL: My wife and I had had an awful lot of fights. We couldn't agree on anything from major issues to the slightest, most trivial things. She was so much like her mother who was an extremely bigoted woman. She was so much like my mother, too. Only the kids in my family didn't give a damn. If she was going to be around them, then she was going to have to learn to be tolerant—or live by herself. It didn't occur to me that my going with Arlene here might have been a kind of revenge-taking on my wife *and* my mother for all their narrowness. I finally asked my wife to get the divorce. I guess what held it up so long was the children. I worried about them. She went ahead and got the divorce in 1958. I married Arlene the latter part of 1959. Even Tommy, my boy who is living with Arlene and me now, was with my former wife until last year. He got so out of hand with her that she shipped him to us. She said he was "intolerable." She must have kept on thinking that he acted so much like me, I should take him. I don't mind at all but Arlene, here, doesn't like Tommy.

ARLENE: I suppose that part of the reason is that I'm going to have one of my own soon and the other is that I'm not used to having children around. He irritates me. He has many built-in traits of living a certain way that don't appeal to me. Aside from Tommy, we—Bill and I—are really getting on very well. Of course, Harvard is a very special community. It's wonderful in many ways. People are quite cosmopolitan. They are never surprised at anything. Color differences make no difference to them. This is all to the good.

BILL: Maybe that is so, but I think our marriage will succeed wherever we are because neither one of us could ever find anyone else who would understand us better.

ARLENE: That's the way I feel, too. Bill is speaking for me also.

BILL: We're not going to have the problems I did in my first marriage because there is a basic understanding between us. It isn't only that Arlene and I are both scientists. It's something else—we are truly sympathetic to each other.

ARLENE: We're not going to have any problems about our difference in color because we realize that this is a problem only in the eyes of some rather limited people—not in ours.

BILL: We have solved the religious problem quite easily. She's a Catholic and I'm a Church of Christ.

ARLENE: I'm *not* a Catholic either. I'm really not. At first I was. Actually I stayed with the Catholics the whole time I was in the Midwest. When I got to the graduate house at school, practically everyone there was a Catholic, so I made myself into a Catholic again. It wasn't really a kind of social matter alone. I went to Mass and Communion because I was emotionally involved. But when I left school I stopped going to church. The first year was all right as a Catholic. But the second year, I knew that I didn't really have my heart in it. I was being a fake. I was emotionally involved because I was working for a difficult man at school. The Newman Club was a very congenial place. There were suppers and song fests and things like that. They helped me very much.

BILL: The way to solve the religious problem is to dump it.

ARLENE: It's strange that with all this talk we still felt that we wanted to be married by a clergyman. We started looking through the phone book and I got two Justices of the Peace. They were really terrible. Then I decided that the most reasonable person I could call would be a Unitarian. So I phoned several of them. Now, Bill and I didn't have much money. I

asked how much it would cost. Well, this nice one said that if we didn't have much money, he would be glad to marry us in his office without charge. He was the only one who would marry us without charge. So that's how we were married by a Unitarian minister.

BILL: I had a problem with Tommy after he came to live with us. He wanted to go to church. So I took him to a Catholic church, but they embarrassed him so badly that he gave that up. They asked him what church he went to and what church his parents went to. He was embarrassed because Arlene and I don't go to church. Well, then he decided not to go there any more because he was pretty hurt about the whole experience. Now he doesn't go at all to any church.

ARLENE: You see, we are of the same faith, Bill and I, because we are of the same philosophy. This means that we don't feel it necessary to go to listen to anyone preach or observe rituals of any kind. We read and we can get along without the church. That goes, too, for the baby I'm carrying now.

BILL: We aren't out of things. We have lots of friends. We enjoy folk singing and we often have people over who have an interest in the theater. Most of our friends are from our science department because we see them most often and we have a lot in common.

Soon, I will be moving on to another school and another teaching job. We hope to get out to California. I don't think there will be any problems about my being married to a Japanese girl. The real problem will be getting Arlene a job in her field of interest. I'm willing to wait for the right opening for myself. Arlene and I can't be on the same faculty according to the rules in most first-rate schools—but not because she's Japanese. Rather, it's because husband and wife are not supposed to be teaching in the same department.

ARLENE: Things will work out, I'm sure. My parents have given no sign whatsoever of being upset by my marriage to Bill. I thought my father would object, but he said absolutely nothing. My mother would have come to visit with us if she thought she were welcome. She really is welcome, but once when she wanted to come, there was some mix-up here and I haven't been able to make it clear to her that I would like her to come and that Bill would welcome her, too. I write to my mother every two weeks. If I didn't, I think she'd have a fit.

BILL: I keep in touch with my mother, but not so often. I'm just not a letter writer. We write to her about once a month. When I recall how, when I was about twelve or thirteen years old I was really the apple of her eye because I went to church with her, used to lead the singing and give speeches—all sorts of things—it's difficult to realize how different things are from the way she planned then. But, different or not, everything is fine

between Arlene and myself. We have each other and our work and that's all that matters. Whether a marriage such as ours would work out for other persons, I do not know. People are different. Their families are different. Their problems, their needs, and their expectations are different. We aren't troubled by in-laws on either side. We are strong people. We know what we want and we are, therefore, getting along fine.

FRANCES AND JACKSON

Frances and Jackson Starr are unusual people. Fran is white and Jackson is a Negro. They have been married for over twenty years and each is certain that theirs is a successful example of an interracial marriage. Their only child, a son in his teens, is attending an Eastern private school. Both parents have maintained high intellectual standards and both, too, are highly respected members of the small New England town in which they live. They have their own home in a pastoral setting. Whether the response of white neighbors and townspeople would be as friendly if there were many more Negroes in the community is anyone's guess. Whether the comparatively sheltered existence of their son has something to do with his freedom from insecurity and prejudice, it is difficult to know. One may merely guess concerning such matters. *This,* we do know. Both Fran—descendant of an old and honorable New England Yankee family and Jackson—brilliant, self-assured college professor—are quite convinced that their marriage is successful.

JACKSON: Although Fran and I are of different skin pigmentation, I really don't see why this should be of special interest to you or anyone else. We are individuals. We both have good backgrounds. Our educational and other standards are, I think, quite the same and, after all, marriage is a personal affair. But, inasmuch as we have gone this far, I will tell you all that you may want to know. As for me, I was born in Alabama, but I lived there only a few years—until I was in the third grade in elementary school. Then we moved to Boston.

FRAN: And I come from New England. My whole family and some of my ancestors came from this area. At least one of them is directly associated with the War of Independence. My father had been a clergyman in a Presbyterian church.

JACKSON: When we came to Boston, we all established our connection with the Baptist Church, the same church to which my family belonged

back in the 1880's. My family moved to Roslindale. There were a few Negro families there, but it was largely non-Negro. I would say, it was a white neighborhood. We, my family and I, got along very well with all the others in the neighborhood. There were, I suppose, the usual incidents— nothing serious, however. In fact, I remember clearly that the teachers used to take pride in me and show me off when the principal or some guest came through the school. All in all, I would say that the relationship was excellent. No real problems at all. (*Editor's comment:* At first, mention is made of "the usual incidents" and that is quickly erased from memory, so that the pleasant and happy experiences remain. "The relationship was excellent.")

During the period of fifteen years when we lived in Roslindale there were few Negro families there. I went through the elementary grades there and from there I went on to high school. It was one of the best schools, scholastically speaking, in the country. I never remember going to any functions of any kind when I was at school. The school simply didn't sponsor anything like that. At least, I can't recall any. From there, I went directly to Harvard, intending to study law, but I became interested in the social sciences and then I decided to go into teaching, which I did. Following my graduation from Harvard, I went to Graduate School out west. Then, I came back to Boston and taught at one of Boston's schools, but in a Negro neighborhood. I have, on several occasions changed my position, but each time there has been some advancement. Today I occupy an important teaching position in the Boston area.

FRAN: Jackson and I have been married for twenty-two years. We have one child, our son is away at a private school in Ohio. I think we are getting on just fine.

JACKSON: I suppose you are interested in knowing whether, since my elementary school days, I have run into anti-Negro prejudice. The answer is "Yes." You couldn't possibly be an intelligent person and not be aware of it, but it was nothing acute. People didn't talk about it very much twenty years ago. And it wasn't because they took it for granted. Rather, they just ignored it. They didn't feel that it was the thing you talked about. It was rather like a skeleton in the closet. You just never said anything about it. You knew it was there. You couldn't really ignore it completely, but you didn't talk about it.

I had very few problems because I was around Harvard and there wasn't any prejudice around the Square. There are so many different kinds of people around there, different colors, and different religions, that I had no problem of any kind. I lived at home, not in the dormitories. We were still living in Roslindale all this time. As I said, there were few Negroes in our neighborhood and we were no problem to anyone. We rented our place. It was owned by a Negro. Conditions, I would say, were good between the races. Of course, some Negro people regard Boston as a good place in which to live while others do not. It depends on who you're talking to. But

I regard it as a *very* good city in which to live. I never felt fenced in here. *Some of my best friends are white people.*

To get back to my graduate school days, I lived in a wonderful place where persons of many religions and races resided. People from just everywhere lived there. So I felt completely at home, of course. I don't think that I would have felt differently had I lived among whites exclusively. I received a Fellowship. (*Comment:* The intellectual prowess and leadership ability of the speaker is referred to at this and other occasions during the interview.)

FRAN: My early days were not so very much different from Jackson's, I think. I lived in a small town with my folks. I went through high school in that town and from there I went to a girls' junior college. It was really supposed to be a fine girls' school.

My mother had been born in Wales. She came to this country as a small child, six or seven years old. Her father was a merchant. He had come to the town here in the United States, to establish a business. Mother went through high school in that town and that's where she met my father.

JACKSON: Fran was a Unitarian. That's what her folks were, too.

FRAN: Even when I was at school, I attended Unitarian services. It was a very, very small organization that met in a house. In those days the college had to escort you everywhere. So, another girl and I were escorted every Sunday to this tiny Unitarian Church.

After my college years, two years in the South, I came back to my home town and then decided to enroll in a college in the Boston area. In those days the school was very small. After I was graduated, I went into teaching. I taught at one of the Boston schools and then I happened to get a teaching post at the college where Jackson taught.

JACKSON: The school we were interested in had some very important Bostonians on its Board—some of Boston's first families and very wealthy. After I started to teach there, I met Fran.

FRAN: We were in the same building most of the time and we became friendly in a superficial kind of way. It wasn't until well over a year later that we became serious.

Neither of our families knew that we were seeing each other or that we were getting serious during this period. Once, I invited Jackson to have dinner at our home, but my parents never gave it a second thought. They were very much interested in my work as a teacher. The folks were, in fact, very pleased to have Jackson come out to the house. Actually I had an apartment in Boston, so as to be close to the college. After the dinner, Jackson drove me back to Boston.

JACKSON: But it wasn't all so easy. Apparently Fran said something to her parents about me or someone else had, and the folks began to be unhappy about it. Her mother wanted to go visit some friends in England about that time. She was getting worried about us and she invited Fran to go with her on the trip. The principle being, "absence makes the heart grow fonder—*for another.*"

My father had died some time before all this happened. I was close to both my father and mother all through the years. My mother was rather surprised when I told her about Fran. I was living at home. My mother was more concerned about Fran than about me. She was concerned as to whether Fran could take it. She tried to talk me out of marrying Fran, but I wouldn't be dissuaded from my intentions and she took it all right. She had to because we had made up our minds. Of course, there were some people on the College Board who were upset. They weren't pleased because I think there was some hypocrisy about it. It may be that they were fearful that support would be withdrawn from the organization. You know, a Negro man and white girl getting married and they met in that college.

FRAN: We had talked over this question of color many, many times. You may be sure of that. We believed that we had many good friends who would accept our marriage without question. Of course, we realized that it was one thing to have friends and quite another to have friends who would accept an interracial marriage. But we really had wonderful friends. There was no question about it as far as they were concerned.

JACKSON: I think I was realistic. I knew that there are prejudices and there are attitudes, but it had no effect upon me. It had no deterrent effect at all.

FRAN: We discussed it very carefully and we decided that this was *our* problem and if we wanted to work it out *we* would have to work it out—no one else—not friends, parents, or family. Of course there were some friends who *did* put pressure on me. My brother really opposed the idea, but vehemently. And he still does after all these years. My mother was trying to discourage the idea of marriage. My father really didn't get into the situation at all. I suppose there was some gossip in the town.

JACKSON: But many of her townsfolk came to see us after we were married.

FRAN: Still some were horrified. I'm quite certain.

JACKSON: The newspapers really had a field day when we got married. At one time, I thought the papers were following us around because of our difference in color, but I'm inclined to believe that it was more associated

with the fact that a genuine New England Yankee was marrying a colored man.

FRAN: A minister in Washington officiated at our marriage—a Unitarian, and that is what I was.

JACKSON: When I got on the train to go to Washington to get married, a reporter followed me. He tried to get a story on the train and when I refused, he followed me up and down the streets of Washington until I finally got a little exasperated. I said, "Look, this is getting ridiculous. I'll give you a story back in Boston. But if you keep this up, you'll be the last one to know when I get married." Well, he agreed and even though our marriage got far more publicity than we suspected it would, there was nothing malicious about it. In fact, when the story of our marriage appeared in the papers around the country, we received a great many letters from strangers wishing us well.

FRAN: Through all these years we really haven't had any problem about our marriage. Nor has our son encountered any.

JACKSON: You ask whether the fact that we live in a very small town has anything to do with the manner in which people have accepted us. I wouldn't know. Perhaps it has, perhaps not. Our son went to the elementary school here in the town. He has some very close friends here with whom he keeps in touch even though he is away at the Friend School. Both boys and girls write to him. In the school he goes to, they admitted their first Negro about seven or eight years ago. At the school they tell us that he gets along very well. They seem to like him. I think that my son is completely free from any feeling of marginality although of course, I can't tell for certain. He knows that his father is a Negro. There is no difference, absolutely no difference, in his attitude toward either Fran or myself. He is, according to the school, "very sensitive" to my attitudes toward him and his work. He has never really showed any awareness of this race business, at all. (*Editor's comment:* Does the age of the boy, the kind of school he is in and the generally high position of the father affect the son's attitude?) He becomes indignant as do we when racial prejudice shows itself. But I think he has his feet on the ground and is quite all right.

FRAN: If our son were to fall in love with a Negro girl, there would not be any special reaction on our part. All I would want to know is whether or not the girl is a good person, suited to him. I would answer the same way if he were to fall in love with a white girl.

My answer has little to do with whether or not I think that our marriage has worked out successfully, although I am very certain that it has. I feel that my son is an individual, the same as you and I. He has to live his own life. I would try to offer guidance and counsel if I felt it were necessary, but *not* on the basis of the color of the girl. It would have to be on

the basis of the quality of the individual herself. There are certain things that we can't do for him. He has to do them himself.

JACKSON: I would react very much the same. I have the same feelings about that. If she were a person of character, of intelligence, and some ability and so forth . . . (laughing), in other words, a person much like myself . . . I could accept her.

FRAN: Why should color be such a major problem? It certainly wasn't to us even though it was a problem to my mother and certain of our friends. I've never noticed people staring at me when I'm with Jackson.

JACKSON: In fact, many people have been overly cordial to us. As I said, we always had a lot of close friends, *white* friends, with whom we mix socially. We get invited to their homes. There are lots of places to which we do not want to go. I will say that I have had no problems with the kind of people I have known. Most are college people and professional people. They are fine people. Over the years, I have retained my white friends and they come from some of the very finest families in the whole Boston area, some of the first families. I admit that I have had some unpleasant experiences, too, but I haven't permitted them to affect me. The good has more than compensated for the bad.

FRAN: Frankly, I don't feel any different from any other married woman and I never have. We always lived, I assume, as I would in any other marriage, only a little better. There is no question of my relationship to the people in the community. They accept me as a person, but they accept Jackson also.

JACKSON: They have voted me into a high elective office in this town.

FRAN: Some people say certain things in public and quite different things in private. There's always been a kind of dichotomy on this matter, as you know.

JACKSON: The thing that helped me tremendously was that these prominent people supported us and agreed with us. They were not afraid to stand up publicly if they felt it would do some good. As a result of their interest and support, others who, perhaps, were a little timid, fell in line.

FRAN: We've had good years together, and, as Jackson pointed out, we have the respect of the townspeople.

JACKSON: In a marriage such as ours, I would hesitate to generalize, because there are certain personal factors that enter into each situation. What, for example, are the circumstances at the time? Who are the persons involved? What is the estimate of their personal maturity? What kind of

families do they come from? What is their own sense of stability and security? All of these factors enter into it. As for us, we believe that there
simply is no problem between us. We do not believe that our son will face
any special problem—and we don't expect to solve his problems if they
should arise. We don't even believe that there need be a problem—any
more than one would expect in any other person's life, whatever their color,
religion, or ethnic background. *We* think that our marriage has succeeded!

NEGROES AND WHITES

My old man's a White old man,
And my old mother's black,
If I ever cursed my White old man,
I take my curses back.

If I ever cursed my black old ma
And wished she were in hell,
I'm sorry for that evil wish,
And now I wish her well.

My old man died in a fine White house,
My ma died in a shack,
I wonder where I'm gonna die,
Being neither White nor Black.[1]

LANGSTON HUGHES

Langston Hughes has put succinctly and accurately the problem which the children of interracial marriages so often face. The uncertainty about where and how one will live, "being neither White nor Black" is about as great as any problem a human being is likely to face. Most states in the Union insist that a person with one drop of Negro blood is a Negro. Nor does it not matter that one of the parents may be either white or a non-Negro. The child is officially declared to be a Negro, no matter what his inclinations or interests with respect to family, friends or even culture may be. That such persons may be faced with overwhelmingly serious problems, not easily resolved, should be obvious. That such persons, aware of their parentage, are part white does not solve the problem, for our society generally declares that they are also part Negro. The racial hybrid is thus faced with serious problems. Shall such a person try to "pass" as a white person? Is his skin color such that he could, assuming he would wish to do so? Should he rather identify with the Negro group and forget about his white ancestry? Whatever the decision, it is not easily made, and the problems likely to ensue for the product of an interracial marriage are many. There are major problems for the individual, involving personal insecurity and other psychological and emotional problems as well.

Despite these difficult personal and social problems miscegenation has taken place. Of the 18.8 million Negroes in the United States in April, 1960,[2] about four-fifths are racially mixed. Herskovits,[3] basing his estimates on anthropometric measurements made in Washington

D.C., New York City, West Virginia and other places, has concluded that 78 per cent of the American Negro population shows traces of mixed European or Indian descent; thus, according to him, only 22 per cent are of unmixed lineage. Interracial contacts have obviously played a major role in the development of the American Negro.

Davie[4] has stated that American Negroes constitute a "mixture of various African peoples, the Sudanese, Nilotic and Bantu peoples with traces of Hamitic and Semitic elements." They have mixed, too, with whites, American Indians and others, including West and East Indian, Chinese, Japanese and Filipino. Insofar as the American whites are concerned, a 'Negro' is a person who is known to have had a Negro ancestor and is regarded as a member of the Negro race.

Golden,[5] studying fifty interracially married couples in Philadelphia in 1949 and 1950, discovered that the courtship of most of these couples had been carried on *sub rosa* and further, that many of them were isolated from their families following their marriage. White families appeared most often to refuse to have "anything to do" with children who entered into interracial marriages. The Negro families were most often ready to meet with the white person who had married their son or daughter, but they were not too quick to welcome the white spouse until he or she had, in their opinion, demonstrated some feeling of understanding and even of appreciation for the Negro family.

In our "personal history" (pp. 271-278) of one Negro-white marriage in the Boston area it will be seen that the humiliation of the white parents some eight years after their son's marriage is still so great that they make every effort to avoid discussion of the matter on even the most objective and dispassionate basis. And yet, when this intermarried couple require temporary housing, the parents invite their son and his Negro wife as well as their children to live with them. After a brief period in the home, the boy's father speaks to his son about the "questions" his neighbors are asking and suggests, gently, to be sure, that the couple find their own residence as quickly as possible.

The condemnation by the white community is, of course, not unanimous. Otherwise, in smaller communities, it would be impossible for the interracially intermarried to find a place to live or work. Golden[6] found that several of the white spouses lost their jobs because of their intermarriage, while others felt obliged to conceal their marriage from their employers. The children born of such marriages identified themselves with and were, of course, accepted by the Negro community. Although such children were at least part-white (the Negro spouse may not be all-Negro) color arbitrarily decided the issue of identification.

Golden[7] has stated further that, among the fifty couples studied, "one is struck by the relatively large number of Roman Catholics among

Negro husbands, the white husbands and the white wives (19) . . .
Outstanding among the white brides are the Jewish women (19). He
notes, too, 26 Baptists, 19 Methodists, 9 Episcopalians, 6 Lutherans, 1
Congregationalist, and 1 Reformed, totaling one hundred persons or fifty
couples. The large number of Roman Catholics who are parties to these
marriages may, in addition to reasons of foreign derivation, improvement of economic condition through marriage, *etc.,* have some positive
relationship to the tendency to intermarry. He has further pointed out
that the *sub-rosa* pattern of concealment that existed before marriage is
continued after marriage. These interracial families lived in areas where
the Negroes formed but a small per cent of the total population. The
number of children born of these marriages was small. Golden has suggested that it may be because of the fact that these couples married at a
higher age than was generally true, but this seems doubtful. It may well
be that such marriages do not produce more children because the couple
is aware of the added burdens that such children may be obliged to bear.

Even though there are no legal prohibitions against interracial marriages in certain areas of this country, particularly the North and North-
east, there have been comparatively few such marriages. In New York
State, exclusive of New York City, from the year 1916 through 1937
the per cent of Negro-white marriages among all marriages involving
Negroes varied from 1.7 per cent to 4.8 per cent. In 1929 New York
State had only 2.7 per cent of Negro men marrying white women and
but 0.8 per cent of Negro women marrying white men. Only 11 out
of every 1,000 marriages in New York State, from 1924 through 1933
were interracial marriages. From 1916-1937 the per cent of Negro-
white marriages in New York State exclusive of New York City was
2.9 per cent. In Kennedy's[8] study of New Haven marriages from 1870
to 1940, racial intermarriages between Negroes and whites constituted
less than one-tenth of 1 per cent of all marriages.

In Boston, statistical evidence indicates that, from 1914 through
1938, Negro-white marriages constituted, at their peak, but 5.2 per cent
of all marriages involving Negroes and that was for the period 1914-
1918, the years of World War I. The average per cent of Negro-white
intermarriage for all these years was but 3.9 per cent. From the year
1919 through 1938, the per cent of such marriages never exceeded 3.7
per cent.

Interracial marriages, of all forms of intermarriage, even when state
laws do not forbid them, are at most, tolerated by most Americans. Difference in skin color is obvious for all persons to note. Even though
there is, in fact, no evidence to support the theory that pigmentation of
skin or, for that matter, any other factor about which we may have any
exact knowledge makes the Negro "different" from or inferior to a white

person biologically, physically or mentally, marriages between whites and Negroes remain comparatively rare in numbers. Warner's[9] observation that "custom, social usage and sanction make marriage between two people defined as Negro and white exceedingly difficult, painful for those involved and, more often than not, impossible" is substantiated in every way. Neither logically nor factually is there, to date, any evidence to support the hypothesis that such marriages are bad in themselves or produce inferior people. Allport's[10] comment concerning the contemporary Negro—that he "is as much a white man as he is a Negro"—reminds us of the vast numbers of race mixtures that have occurred in the relations between Negroes and whites throughout American history. Again, Allport's[11] scientifically supported observation deserves our attention: "Miscegenation between two healthy people has no weakening effect on the offspring."

Charles Smith,[12] in 1960, studied twenty-three Negro-white intermarriages in New York City. Fourteen of the husbands involved in these marriages were Negroes. He pointed out that 59 per cent of these marriages were *interreligious* as well as interracial and that 50 per cent of the whites involved in these marriages were of Jewish origin. Further, 57 per cent of the persons involved in those marriages had *no* religious affiliation. Smith reports that these couples, in discussing the reasons for the success of their marriage, believed that the external pressure of public opinion against them actually served as a unifying force for their marriage. They willingly bore the brunt of the unfriendly public opinion that manifested itself and which made life difficult for them, at times, because they hoped thereby, to keep their children from being hurt. However, they expected that when their children had grown to adolescence "things would change."

Despite official laws and public disapproval, such marriages *do* take place. For example, the rate of Negro-white intermarriage in New York State, exclusive of New York City, from 1914 to 1938, was 3.4 per cent. In Los Angeles, in the period from 1924 through 1933, only 11 out of 1,000 marriages involved a Negro and a person of another color. In other words, 989 out of 1,000 of the marriages involving Negroes were all-Negro marriages.[13]

In New York City for a period of five years, 1908-12, the rate of intermarriage for 100 marriages involving an American-born Negro was only 2.11 per cent. [14]

The number of Negro-white marriages in the city of Boston, Massachusetts, from the period 1914-38 was 276 or 3.9 per cent of all marriages involving a Negro. During this period the percentage of the Negro population to the total number of residents in Boston was practically

constant (about 2.1 per cent from 1900-1920. The rate rose to 2.6 per cent in 1930.)

The per cent of Negro men married to white women, in the city of Chicago, covering a thirteen-year period, 1925-38, was 2.1; in the same period the per cent of white men married to Negro women, 0.6.

In the state of Connecticut, for a seven-year period, from 1953 through 1959, there were 285 marriages between whites and Negroes out of a total of 124,746 marriages. This represents a rate of 2.3 per cent per 1,000 marriages.

The factors that tend to make Negro-white marriages possible are very much like those affecting interfaith marriages. Golden,[15] like Barron, lists them as demographic factors, factors of spatial and social propinquity, cultural factors, value factors and psychological factors.

Insofar as demographic factors are concerned any unbalance in the sex ratio of a given group causes the "numerically dominant" to seek mates outside their group. As these opportunities for contact in a greater number of areas of life increase, it is to be expected that Negro-white marriages will also increase. Industrial, economic and cultural contacts will surely play an important role in this associational increase.

Persons of different color with mutual interests in the arts and music, are likely to intermarry, as are those persons, Negro and white, whose educational and scholastic interests are similar. Eartha Kitt; Lena Horne; Sammy Davis, Jr.; Dean Dixon, conductor; and numerous others are noteworthy examples of the Negro-white marriages that have resulted from associational contacts in the "entertainment" field. The more numerous the Negroes who attend colleges and universities, the more likely is interracial marriage to occur. Similarity of cultural standards for Negroes and whites will remove another of the many existing blocks to social and cultural interrelationships that usually precede marriage. The marriage of Paul Robeson, Jr., to a white girl he met when both were freshmen at Cornell University is but one of many such marriages. Given equality of opportunity for Negroes to meet and work with whites, the intermarriage rate, as the result of such contacts, is bound to increase.

Religions that stress their universalism do not officially, at least, oppose interracial marriages. The Congregational Christian Church's[16] declaration: "Race is relevant to marriage only insofar as our un-Christian color distinctions make an interracial marriage more difficult than marriage within a given racial group," while recognizing the difficulties associated with interracial marriage also makes clear its conviction that racial difference ought really not to prevent otherwise good marriages.

Other church and synagogue groups while recognizing the many problems associated with interracial marriage, make clear their official

belief that the factor of difference in race is not an impediment to marriage.

The belief in the greater sexuality of both Negro women and Negro men is a psychological factor which may have influenced some whites in their choice of a marriage partner. Golden's view is that, for the Negro, the white person is the symbol of status and achievement and is therefore desirable as a marriage partner. Marriage with a white woman or even with a light-skinned Negro woman is thus viewed as "status giving," and is highly desirable to some Negroes.

There were 18,871,381 Negroes in the United States in 1960.[17] Of that number 1,417,511 Negroes live in New York State. Five other states have more than a million Negroes. In order, they are, Texas, Georgia, North Carolina, Louisiana, and Illinois. In California the Negro population is 883,861. In the District of Columbia there are 411,737 Negroes. In the highly industrial states of Michigan and Ohio and Pennsylvania there were 717,581, 786,097, and 852,750 Negroes, respectively.

Of the national population of Negroes 11 per cent have concentrated in the metropolitan areas of the United States. They number 25 per cent of the population of Philadelphia, 52 per cent in Washington, D.C., and 37 per cent in Newark, New Jersey. But, in the main, because middle- and upper-class white families have moved into suburban communities, the Negro remains isolated and segregated. Few Negroes have moved into suburban areas largely because whites have openly opposed it.

The growth of the Negro population in the North, despite all the forms of segregation that presently exist, is in no small measure, due to the better job and educational opportunities that generally prevail for the Negro.

Little wonder that Negro migration to the urban industrial center cities in the United States has increased both markedly and rapidly. In 1940, there were 458,000 Negroes in New York City but in 1960, according to the United States Census Bureau, the Negro population increased to 1,088,000. Such increases are recorded, too, for Chicago (278,000 in 1940; 813,000 in 1960); Los Angeles (64,000 to 335,-000); Philadelphia (251,000 to 529,000); Detroit (149,000 to 482,-000); Baltimore (166,000 to 327,000); Cleveland (85,000 to 251,-000); and Washington (214,000 to 412,000). The District of Columbia has increased its non-white population in the past decade (1950-1960) from 35.4 per cent of the total population to 53.9 per cent. Such increases may temporarily spell the curtailment of opportunities for integration but in my view they do, in fact, mean an ultimate increase in equal educational, housing and job opportunities.

Whether or not the Negro's exodus from the Southern states continues, as it has for the past several decades, there is little reason to expect a marked immediate upward trend in Negro-white marriages. The vast majority of Negroes still fare badly in the matter of securing better housing in white neighborhoods. They are still obliged to live within their own overcrowded, often decrepit "ghettos." The mores of the white men enforce this position. They will continue to marry other Negroes as they have hitherto. A few, by virtue of improved social, professional, cultural and economic status, will find a greater degree of social acceptance, but Negro-white marriages are certainly not likely to occur in significant numbers within the next decade. Our prejudices, particularly along color lines, are still very great.

Prejudice against the Negro takes many forms and tends to "keep the Negro in his place." The white man's suspicion that the Negro is seeking to escape from his own people through interracial marriage is nothing more than the rationalization of a prejudice. True, though it may be under particular conditions, it is certainly not "universally true." Dr. Martin Luther King, noted Negro leader in our day is said to have answered a white man who insisted that the ultimate objective of the Negro is interracial marriage with the words, "I want the white man to be my brother, *not* my brother-in-law."

Religion, although it is said to be color-blind, is not always so. Despite its insistence upon equality of all men and the Biblical doctrines of the brotherhood of man and the fatherhood of God, persons who call themselves "religious" are not always free from racial prejudice. In theory, all the great religions see no inherent objection to racial intermarriage. In practice, however, they act as if they see many.

Assuming the ultimate acceptance of the Supreme Court's decision of 1954 with respect to the educational and political rights of Negroes, there are, as yet, no visible indications that the American white man intends to accept him fully, as a human being, equal to the white man in all ways. Improvements in the educational, political, economic and even housing opportunities for the Negro do not, in themselves, assure his full psychological acceptance. The increase in the number of Negroes who are receiving a higher education has not yet eliminated the stereotype of the Negro as an unlearned, lazy and generally shiftless person.

Negroes, however capable they have generally proved to be as athletes, have by their prowess only added another element to the stereotype—which imagines that all Negroes are athletic supermen. The Negro is not yet regarded as a human being who is, in fact, very much like the white man in practically every respect. Until this occurs, the tendency to refrain from intermarrying with him will continue.

The number of Negroes who are enrolled as students in colleges and universities of the country is increasing. It is estimated [18] there are 80,000 students enrolled in predominantly Negro colleges and universities. This figure does not include those Negroes who are enrolled in predominantly white schools around the country. We must remember, however, that, because of a lack of federal statistics on this subject, we can only report the "educated guess" by an important Negro publication[19] that there are about 40,000 Negroes enrolled in interracial colleges. Altogether, then, about 120,000 Negro students are enrolled in our colleges and universities. As the barriers to fraternity affiliations are eliminated throughout the country, the number of Negroes accepted into fraternity membership will continue to increase. The attitude toward these favored Negroes will certainly continue to improve. Opportunities for higher education for the Negro mean improvement in their economic and occupational status as well. These, in turn, lead on to the desire for improved housing conditions for Negroes generally and for the Negro of higher status, in particular. Despite federal government, state and local legislation which prohibits discrimination in housing, it does not appear likely that these efforts alone will automatically assure the Negro of complete freedom to choose his place of residence for some time to come.

Yet, such changes as have already occurred and are likely to take place, offer no indication that the rate of Negro-white marriages will increase in any marked degree. Neither Negroes nor whites want it especially. Negroes are, supposedly, more "at home" with Negroes. Whites are generally more "at home" with whites. People of similar backgrounds, experiences, and hopes tend to remain together just as Catholics tend to create Catholic neighborhoods around a church and Jews like to live among their fellow Jews. Protestants, too, do very much the same thing and understandably so.

I believe that Negro-white marriages will increase slowly—but that they *will* increase. Such interracial marriages are likely to occur more frequently than hitherto among college-trained Negroes and whites, and in much the same way as our interviews-in-depth have indicated.

The marriage of Charlayne Hunter, first Negro girl to enter the University of Georgia in 1961 and first of her race to graduate from it, to Walter Stovall, a white student at that University, has confirmed the belief held by some persons that interracial contacts on the school level must inevitably lead to some degree of interracial marriage. The white community will have to come to terms with this fact. Contact—whether it be in school, housing or in employment will have its effect upon the rate of interracial marriage.

Negro-white marriages, however "reasonable" they may be, will,

in the foreseeable future at least, prove difficult and problem-laden because the parents, family and friends of the intermarried will continue to regard them with distress and anguish. They will, rightly or wrongly, be regarded as calamitous because the American people do not, to this date, accept them as proper. This has nothing whatever to do with their legal correctness. The mores of the American people are involved. Until they change—and I believe that ultimately they *will* change to a degree—interracial marriages will continue to be severely frowned upon.

Negro-white intermarriages are directly associated with the ultimate solutions that cities, states and national government will be able to work out insofar as social relationships are concerned. The greater the degree of integration, the more equal the economic returns, the greater the likelihood of social acceptance of Negroes by whites and, ultimately, of interracial marriage.

HENRY AND VIOLET

Henry, white and born of Jewish parents, has been married to Violet, a Panamanian Negro, an erstwhile Catholic, for some ten years. The parents of three children, they live in a modest home of their own, in a middle-class neighborhood. They make it clear that they do not regard themselves as a "problem" in any sense. "The difference in our skin color is obvious. People either accept us or not. Our problem is, we think, much more associated with our childrens' religion rather than their color." Somehow this vexing problem must be resolved. Yet, neither parent feels that he or she can identify with the religion of their parents.

Henry's parents are distraught. They are torn between love of their son and his children and their certainty that Henry has "ruined his life." Violet's parents are no problem whatsoever, for there is much mixed blood in their family. Violet knows herself to be a mulatto.

VIOLET: At first, we weren't too ready to see you for this interview because Henry and I think that our marriage, like all marriages, is a personal affair and ought not to be the object of prying eyes, but we have reconsidered. We believe that we have a story, perhaps different from what you may have expected.

HENRY: I see nothing strange or different in our lives than is true of other people, of whatever color.

VIOLET: You will understand us better if you know something about our backgrounds. Each is very much different from the other. Henry and I have been married nearly ten years. We have three children—two boys and a girl. The girl is the youngest. She is four. The boys are eight and six. Here are their pictures. You can see that they are bright-eyed happy children.

HENRY: Some people who don't know us might even regard them as white, but——

VIOLET: They are definitely Negro. We know it and they know it. The color of their skin is no problem at all. They are—that is the two boys who are in school are—accepted as are all other children.

Now, let me tell you about myself. I was born in Panama. Very recently my parents moved from Panama to California. There is a considerable admixture of races in Panama, very much like most of South America.

HENRY: I was born in New York City. I attended a public elementary and high school in New York. My parents live there now as they have for most of their lives. They came from Russia. My father is very much of an aesthete. He is a very liberal man in many ways. He isn't tied down by tradition as so many people are. My mother is very much interested in people and their problems. She and my father regard themselves as Jewish, although I often have wondered of what their Jewishness consists. There has never been any real religion or religious spirit in our home. The family is Jewish, though.

VIOLET: Actually, my father is dead. The man I call my father is really my natural father's brother. Now, my real father's family came from Jamaica in the West Indies to Panama when he was a young man. He acquired a job there and stayed on. My mother's family is rather mixed racially. My grandmother was a white French woman. Her father had been a landowner in one of the French possessions. She grew up there and married an African type. He was a mixture and he was dark. Of course, his background, too, was French.

HENRY: I have a brother and two sisters. My brother is married to a Catholic girl. One of my sisters is married to a Protestant. The other is married to a Jew. But none really has a religion that means anything to them. My brother who married a Catholic has not converted to Catholicism, and my sister hasn't converted to the religion of her Protestant husband. So, you see, there is quite an admixture of religious backgrounds in our family. In their cases, however, each is married to a white person.

VIOLET: I was a Catholic. All the members of my family were Catholics.

HENRY: My father didn't have too great a loyalty as far as the Jewish religion is concerned. I would say he is a "Judaist." I don't think he is a member of any Jewish Temple, but he belongs to one of the Temple Brotherhoods. He, also, attends a community nondenominational church. My grandfather, my mother's father, lives with them. He isn't really orthodox as I understand orthodoxy, yet, he claims to be orthodox. I guess that's because he insists on *kosher* meals. My mother prepares them for him and that is quite acceptable to him. I would say that, if there are gradations in such matters, my grandfather was certainly more religious, that is ritually observant, than either of my parents.

VIOLET: We maintain some contact with Henry's parents. We have telephone conversations and we see them about once a month. They come to see our children about once a month and, of course, we see them at that time.

HENRY: My parents opposed our marriage. But they do come. In fact, they attended our marriage at the community church.

VIOLET: My parents did also.

HENRY: We asked the minister, to tell my parents that we wanted them to come—that we wanted a relationship, but if they didn't, they would be making a choice. But they certainly *did* come.

(*Editor's Note:* Friends of Henry's parents report that the marriage of their son to Violet has proved to be a great shock—one from which they haven't really recovered in all these years. The mother, a sensitive person, when she finds the strength to discuss this marriage often asks, "Why did this happen to me?" The intermarriages of the other children do not disturb her in any degree comparable to Henry's marriage to a Negro (mulatto) girl. Friends have tried to reason with Henry's mother and father, but neither is inclined to listen.)

I feel that they would be inclined to come over to visit with the children much more often if it weren't for this kind of marriage.

VIOLET: Sometimes I think that I can understand what is disturbing them so. Their ego is involved more than anything else. Henry has acted on his own and has not listened to them. I'm not so certain that it is all a matter of religious feeling as people like to say. It may be some of that, but there is certainly a feeling about races—black and white. To some people, blacks are simply inferior.

I mentioned that I was brought up as a Catholic. The maternal side of my family was Roman Catholic. Now, my father's brother had been reared as a Catholic, the same as my own father. But he had converted to the Baptist Church. I was still allowed to go to the Roman Catholic Church in the early morning, but I could go to any other kind of church service I found interesting. So I had a wide religious background. But that kind of

background didn't help me to identify with any particular religion in any great degree. I came to this country from Panama in order to go to a university. I majored in psychology. At first I was an English major, but then I switched. During those years when I was getting acquainted with the United States and with the university, I affiliated myself with the Catholics. I even joined the Newman Club on the campus. Well, after three years with them, I drifted away because I found Roman Catholicism in this country is practiced a lot differently than in Panama and, frankly, I didn't like the attitude of the Church.

One of the first things that bothered me was that the church I attended had a coin box as you entered and a cashier's place to make change right at the entrance. None of this seemed to me to go with religion. It all seemed too commercial to me. And the sermons I heard were so often directed against non-Catholics that I didn't feel right about it. I didn't go to church one Sunday. In fact, I skipped two Sundays and then pretty soon I wasn't going at all.

Following my experience with Catholicism in the United States, I started to attend Buddhist lectures. I also attended different Protestant churches and even attended a synagogue once. I must say that in none of these places did I feel any racial discrimination. I am quite dark-skinned as you can see and I was rather uncertain, but everywhere, everything was fine. There was none of it in the Catholic Church either, but it is very much different from Protestant churches where everything is "How do you do, brother?" You go to the Catholic church, attend the service and then everyone leaves. There is no socializing. I went to an Episcopalian church on one occasion because an aunt of mine, my mother's sister, was a member of that church. This aunt and her family lived right at the very beginning of the Negro district in the city.

HENRY: The major difference in this respect between Violet and me was that she had a sense of belonging at one time, but I, even though I had gone to Hebrew School—not a very good one—and been Bar Mitzvah, didn't feel that I "belonged." Maybe it's because my parents never really made anything very much of religion. But what is more important than the difference is the fact that we two met at the university and found that we had much in common. There was certainly no discrimination at the university. The atmosphere was conducive to such relationships as ours. We got to know each other very well in the discussion groups and others to which we went. We were both quite liberal in our views about political and economic matters. We really were hoping for the day when there would be one world. We wanted equality for all people of whatever kind. All this drew us together. It was about that time, too, that we started to attend the Community Church. The ideas of the minister pleased us both. He was a true liberal. It was about then that we decided to become engaged.

You can just about imagine how my folks reacted. You already know something about it. But I wasn't very close to them. I don't know what it was—whether I was rebelling against them over a period of years. I don't

know what it was, but I simply would not listen to them and I have not listened to them on a great number of other subjects as well, and I have no regrets on that score. They can live *their* way. I will live mine.

VIOLET: I had lived away from my family for quite a while prior to the time of our engagement. I really had no problem because I was already very much separated from my family. I had no desire to make a permanent estrangement from them. That is why I told them about Henry and our engagement. I don't recall if we told them before we were engaged or after.

HENRY: I had been living out of my parents' home for quite some time. I really had gotten along very well. I didn't think about discussing my engagement with them.

VIOLET: Somebody told your mother about it and she asked you about it, Henry. When you told her that it was true, she invited us to their house. I remember that conversation.

HENRY: Well, they assured me that they had no prejudice and that they thought that Violet was a fine young lady, but they didn't think it was wise to have an interracial marriage. This is exactly what many eggheads would say, but I never have been completely confident that they were really free from prejudice.

VIOLET: You ask whether there are special problems that we have had because we are of different colors? Well, of course, there have been some, but I would say that things aren't really bad now.

HENRY: Well, there were more than we may wish to recall. In this neighborhood where we now live, for example, I would say that we don't notice much of a problem. There are still some professional people living here. Some white doctors, lawyers, etc. There used to be many more of that class and we were even freer of prejudice a couple of years ago. People bought their homes here and there really isn't much to discuss about our relationships here. The children have no special problem in school. . . . Oh, yes, one of our children was disturbed by the attitude of one little boy in the second grade. . . . But we are aware of the need to give our children as great a degree of security as we possibly can. This neighborhood is largely Jewish. That is the religious group that is in the majority in this community. Children keep asking each other, "What are you?" And they ask our children the same question and our youngsters turn to us and ask us what they are. We see that each one of these other children feels that he has a faith. We tell our boys that they are a mixture—half Catholic and half Jewish. At least they know what they are. Whether this kind of answer will always keep them happy, I can't say, but that is the truthful answer. When they grow up a bit, we will take them to many different churches and

synagogues to see the differences for themselves. Then they will be able to choose what satisfies them.

VIOLET: Henry has never had any trouble in employment. He gets work easily, and in fact, since he acquired specialized training as a physicist, is doing very well.

HENRY: My employer knows that I am married to Violet, but that makes no difference. We have participated socially with some of my colleagues at work—even with my employer. But still, I suppose it would be more correct to say that when it comes to renting a place to live and things like that, there has been trouble. Practically ever time we rented a house, I went around alone. That's because you can't go into some area and say "here we are" and then rent a house. So I have gone alone. About the time the landlord became aware that ours was an interracial marriage, we were already in the house, and he couldn't do anything about it. This sort of thing works out differently in different cases. At one time, we lived in a community which was just beginning to change from whites to Negroes. Now the white landlord was very sensitive to the racial situation, but he never overtly told us that he objected to us for this reason. He found other things that he said were wrong with us. Oh, we've had our difficulties.

Once we lived in a neighborhood, when we were out West, where there was absolutely no trouble because of color. But that was because it was near an army base and the army personnel lived in that area. They could not discriminate in renting to them, so this attitude affected the whole area in a good way.

When we came back to the East from the West Coast, we stayed temporarily with my folks. Yes—however, upset my parents may have been, they were still ready to help us. Well one day my father told me, after we were there a month or so—well, let me put it *this* way—he encouraged me to move a little faster in getting a place because his landlord was asking, "Who is the Negro woman in the house?" Another time, in Cambridge, we were evicted. That was, beyond question, a racial reason.

VIOLET: Our attitude at that time was if they don't want us then we, in turn, don't want to stay there. There are areas in Cambridge, however, that are definitely interracial. In our present community, whatever the people's real attitude may be at least they are cautious about it. As I said, only once did a little boy use the word "nigger" to one of my boys. We were quite angry about it and brought it up to the schoolteacher. Before long that family moved away from here. Oh, yes, there was another family, too, whose home my little six-year-old boy told me he could not visit to play with their little boy. That was because that boy's mother had told him that Negroes and whites must not associate. The white lady's little boy told my son later that he couldn't really understand it and they are still friends at school. So you see there have been and are problems both for us and the

children that have to be solved. It isn't always easy, I confess, but you have to be strong and above all else give the children as much security as possible.

HENRY: Our kind of family has its difficulties. There's no doubt about it. But we haven't had it too bad because we really don't associate much with the community. It seems not to be part of the general American culture to accept interracial marriages. We have always been conscious of this. We don't have any close friends who live nearby. As a result, we don't create any issues. We don't want to wear our marriage like a badge and we don't force ourselves on anyone. As a matter of fact, if we ever feel, even in my professional contacts, that someone may be inviting us as a matter of form—if we don't feel, in other words, that they would like us to be there, but are only extending the invitation in order to be "correct," we just don't attend.

In my professional work, I don't hesitate to invite "visiting firemen" from out of town to my home. I have never heard of any negative reaction to these invitations.

VIOLET: We have but one or two interracially married friends. The others are not. We have an interest in the arts and in music. We play instruments. Most of our friends do also. So we "make music" together as the saying goes.

HENRY: We get along very well, but we would be untrue if we didn't point out the difficulties, too, such as we have done. If my parents would be less upset about our marriage, I would be pleased, of course. If we could help to establish a milieu in which a marriage such as ours would be regarded as natural and reasonable, we would be happy, but that doesn't seem to be in the cards. But, I think that the major problem has to do with our children and frankly, Violet and I think that the matter of color is no problem at all to them. Color is something visible. You don't have to make choices. You don't have to decide anything. The children are Negro. They are that not only in the eyes of the world, but in their own eyes as well. We happen to think that the major problem has rather to do with religion than with color. When the other children ask, "What are you?" they mean "To what religion do you belong?" And our problem is that we cannot give our children anything positive along religious lines. If one of us were definitely positive in a religious sense, that would be good. Children would at least know what they are. But when neither of us really has any committment and when, as a consequence, we cannot give anything positive to our children, they are likely to be in for a difficult time. At least one parent ought to be religious and make a positive contribution thereby. To us, the question of faith is the most difficult of all and will certainly be more difficult for the chidren in the years ahead.

VIOLET: We have had people come to us, knowing of our intermarriage, to ask us whether they should go ahead and get married. Henry and I tell

them that it's a personal thing. They must make their own decision. We think that the problem is less one of race than it is an intercultural problem. We have exactly the same problems that other married people have. There is the clashing of personalities and sometimes of ideas, but not really of race. When we stop to think about our children and the difficulties they may run into, we know that we will have to train them very carefully. We try to make them see that they have the white and the black races in them and that there are good and bad characteristics to both races. Further, we want them to know that they must associate with both races. What we mean is that people must learn to avoid prejudices against any individual, regardless of the color of his skin or religion or anything else. But while we are teaching these lessons to our children, we know that it is going to take a lot to change the world.

PAUL AND DORIS

Paul is a Negro born of Fundamentalist Baptist parents. His wife Doris to whom he has been married for eighteen years is a Jewess. Both give evidence that theirs is a "successful" marriage. Roy and Peter, their sons, are sixteen and eight, respectively. *Café-au-lait* in complexion, well-built and happy, both youths appear to be well adjusted. The older son, an excellent Hebrew student, was graduated from the elementary department of a Congregational Hebrew School and is now attending the city's Hebrew high school. He regards himself as a devout, even orthodox, Jew. His younger brother also attends Hebrew School. Both identify with Judaism as does their mother. Their father, who is an agnostic, is proud of his sons and devoted to his wife.

PAUL

I can see that you are trying to figure me out. Here I am, a Negro, married to a Jewish girl and my two sons both regard themselves as Jews. Both go to Hebrew School and to *Shule* (Synagogue). I suppose you think either that I have been converted to Judaism or that I am closer to Judaism than any other religion. Actually I'm an agnostic. I'm not a religious-minded person at all. I believe that it is good for a person to believe in

something if he does so sincerely. I respect him. I believe in him. I have great respect for my wife and my children who have gone to Hebrew School. My older son, Roy, is in the high-school department of the city-wide school. You should know that he is a very good Hebrew student. He has been bringing home excellent marks, all "A's" and I'm very proud of him. Peter is just beginning Hebrew School. I only hope that he does as well as his brother. I have respect for learning, for education and I respect my boy's orthodoxy. You see he is wearing a *Yarmulke* (skull cap) in the house. He wears one all the time. He is really religious. He tries to be the best kind of Jew. He will not ride or turn on lights on the Sabbath. He even asked the rabbi whether he could eat with us because we don't keep *kosher*. The rabbi explained to him that I was not Jewish and that, as long as he doesn't eat pork products, he is doing as much as he can. He's a wonderful boy. Roy and Peter are both sources of great joy and pride to Doris and to me. I still cannot understand how all this should have happened to me, but I'm grateful, mighty grateful.

You have asked me about my background. Well, first of all, I'm a truck driver. I earn a fairly good living now, but I didn't always do so. My parents were Baptists. I can't tell you much about my father other than that he died when I was two years old. I had two brothers and three sisters. My mother was a devout Baptist. The Bible was the Living Word of God for her. She made us all go to church and to Sunday school.

It was a hell-fire-and-damnation kind of religion, but she believed in it. It was meaningful to her in every way. My folks had come up from Georgia to this town about fifty years go. First my father had come up here when he was working for a large company. He liked it so well that he brought my mother and the children up here. Most of my family is quite religious. I have one sister who is a very devout person. She does good for all people. The word of God means much to her. She is an unusual person.

My mother's mother was a full-blooded Indian. Her husband was a Negro. I still remember her as a little old lady who regarded herself as "different." She wasn't like so many Negroes who develop a Southern attitude that makes the Negro subservient. My grandmother could get around the bigotry more than any Negro. People *had to* respect her because that's the way she made people feel. She did it without fighting or quarreling. She was looked up to by everyone.

When I think of her, I remember that it was such persons as herself who really set the standard that in our day is represented by such people as Martin Luther King and his nonviolence policy. As far as I'm concerned that's the best policy for the Negro to follow. It's quite impossible for the Negro to fight back. The minute you do, you are committing a crime and that means the Negro gets thrown in jail. So what good is that policy?

I can't see the other policy that some Negroes are advocating, namely, let the Negro have some segregated place of his own where he can live among other Negroes. That's like what they did to the Indians when they put them on reservations.

The Black Muslims with all their hate of the white man and their

wrong ideas about a separate state for the Negro still have done a lot of good. They have taken Negroes out of prison and stopped people from committing crimes and made alcoholics give up drinking all in the name of the Black Muslims. They get those people to join them who feel most discriminated against by a white society. The people who have been hurt most by white "justice" or really injustice. They have helped such people. So I say, with all their weaknesses, there is still much good in them.

I never went beyond junior high school in my education because my folks needed to have some breadwinners and, as young as I was, I did anything I could to earn a few dollars. I have a respect, even a love for education, but I never got one for myself. I never shirked on any job. I took anything I could get, but it was always respectable. We had a good family life. My mother was a really strong and good person.

I worked, among other things, as a laborer. I had a government job for a while. I never could get very far though because Negroes can't get really good jobs, or well-paying ones. The white folks hold on to those. Even the unions do the same. White men look out for white men. I could hardly get into a union because I was a Negro, and even if I got in, I wasn't going to get very far because Negroes weren't supposed to be truck drivers earning good money.

I decided to be a truck driver if I could land a job because I figured that it was the best-paying of all the jobs that didn't require an education. But I wanted nice things in life and I was determined. Well, I found plenty of actual prejudice in the union. I have had all kinds of trouble upon trouble. I still wouldn't have gotten anywhere with this job if it hadn't been for a few Jewish men in this town who heard that my wife is Jewish. When they heard about my older son and heard that we wanted to give him a good Jewish education, these men really opened up a job for me and the union wasn't able to stop me. Negroes just don't find jobs through this union. I tell you, it's very hard; very hard, indeed.

I was only seventeen years old when I met Doris. We met through my sister. Doris knew someone who knew my sister. It was just a chance meeting, but we did have something in common at once—we both loved the Negro music played by such people as Cab Calloway and his band. Doris believed that their music was absolutely tops. She used to love to go to the local big theater where "name" bands, most of them Negro, used to play. I went with her to see and hear these musicians. Really, it wasn't anything serious at the beginning at all.

There never really was any feeling of strangeness between us because she was white and I was Negro. We were always at home with each other. She was a wonderful girl, a happy girl, and I enjoyed her very much. I guess that's because she always had Negro classmates and just was one of those people who do not think about color the way some people do.

But things began to grow more serious as time passed. In about six months after we met we knew that we were meant for each other. Doris will tell you her part of the story, but my part also has a few heartbreaks

in it because, when I told my mother that I was planning to marry Doris, she and my brothers and sisters almost exploded. It wasn't that they objected to Doris. They had seen her and liked her. What upset them was that they knew that Doris' father and mother were very much opposed to me or to any interracial marriage. They were worried about what Doris' folks might do to me if they got the police on my neck. You see, it isn't only a question of the law. (I couldn't get married without legal approval of my mother), but it was also a question of what white policemen were known to do to Negroes. Really, they have a reputation in this town of beating Negroes even if they have no good reason for doing so. My mother was most worried about this. She tried to break up our romance by shipping me off to my brother in Washington, D.C. He had a small business there. My family figured that once I got to Washington my brother would know how to deal with me. Well, he did, all right. He took away my suitcase with the little clothes I had in it and he also took away what money I had. That was to keep me from going back to my home town.

In the meantime Doris, who had been having her own troubles with her family, was searching frantically for me. Through a friend of my family she found out where I was and somehow placed a telephone call to me in Washington. Of course, when I heard her voice, I was very happy. I asked her to send me enough money to get back home and she did exactly that. So that's how I got back with my folks.

When my mother saw me and heard that I was still determined to marry Doris and that Doris was equally determined, she did a right smart thing. You see, she was still worried about what might happen if we eloped to some other state and got married, so she went over to the courthouse and asked to see a judge—a white man. She told him about Doris and me, how we were in love and that she was afraid of what might happen if we two couldn't get married as befits two decent people. Well, the judge agreed with my mother and signed the papers so that we could be legally married even though both Doris and I both were only seventeen years old.

How did I think of Doris? Believe me, I didn't think of her as a white person or anything like that. She was just a wonderful person with a big heart. I never term her a white person. She was and is just—a person. A real person, a decent person.

You know, when I was in Washington, and Doris went over to my mother and family to try to find out where I was, all they would say to her was, "Roy isn't going to return." They wanted her to give up on me and go away. But she just wouldn't do that. She had that confidence in me to know that I would never do such a thing. And she remained true to me. She trusted in me all the while.

We have been married for over eighteen years and I can't say that it has been easy. But our problems have not been because I'm Negro and Doris is white, or because Doris is a Jewess and I am an agnostic from a Protestant family. They have not had anything to do with how to raise our boys either. I'll tell you about them soon. Our problems have had to do with the

fact that we haven't always had enough money to meet our needs. It takes a lot of money to take care of a family and I haven't always had it. Doris works in a hospital and is well regarded there. Her money helps tremendously, but if we didn't have to rent and pay high prices for rather poor quarters, for example, if we would buy a place for ourselves, we would be better off. I think with all that I'm a lucky man—yes, a *very* lucky man. When a man has such a good wife and when his children are so good, then he's lucky. That's why I say, "I'm lucky."

Now, take Roy, for example. He is a Jew. He has been reared as a Jew like his mother. But there is something more. Roy wants knowledge. He wants it in high school and he wants more and more of it in the Hebrew high school. And, as I have already said, he is getting such good marks.

Roy understands that he is part Negro. But he has cast his lot with the Jewish people. He isn't against Negroes any more than I am. I am a paid-up member of the N.A.A.C.P. I *am* a Negro. But that doesn't mean that, in my view, all Negroes do the right thing. Now Roy doesn't know the Negroes in this area where we live. There are a few Negroes here. Mostly, it's a Jewish neighborhod. I see that most of the Negro boys think that the only sure way to break down the racial barriers between Negro and white is to become a star baseball player like Jackie Robinson or a football player like Jim Brown. So they work harder on athletics and not hard enough on their school studies. In fact, school still doesn't mean enough to them. What will happen if these Negro boys don't make the grade athletically? What will they fall back on? They will have no learning and they will hurt themselves and all Negroes because it's education that is going to make the difference. When both Negroes and whites have the same high caliber education, the chances are so much better of overcoming prejudice like you and I know it. Roy isn't interested in those kind of people. He is a scholar. He loves to learn and he loves Judaism. Even though I myself am not religious, I have respect for the person who *is* religious. I can see what it has done for my older boy and I hope it will do the same for the younger one.

I have to tell you something else that is important. The way the Jewish people in this neighborhood, in the synagogue and in the several Hebrew schools have responded to Roy and to us is just wonderful. They are all excited about Roy. They have given him scholarships in order to make it possible for him to continue with his Hebrew education. I have actually benefited very much from my marriage to Doris. Because of her being Jewish, I got the job that the union would not have given me. One of my bosses was so excited and pleased at the time of Roy's Bar Mitzvah that he wanted to take charge of everything and make it an especially nice occasion, but I wouldn't permit him to. Roy is my son and I was going to do things right for him. I was even called "the black Jew" by some of them. Of course, I'm not a Jew. I have no intention of converting to Judaism. I'm just proud of my boys and my wife and I'm glad to see such good Jews in my family. Maybe they all think of me as a freak; but, however they think of me, I'll be grateful to all of them.

Roy could pass for a white person, I guess, but he knows who he is.

Doris and I have talked everything over with him. We don't have any secrets from him.

Roy is growing up now. He's a big fellow as you can see. When he was in the elementary Hebrew school, he had absolutely no problems with other Jewish white boys or girls or their parents. (Right now, he's waiting for a boy whom he is helping to teach for his Bar Mitzvah.)

One day I had a talk with Roy and reminded him that he was likely to have problems about dating when he grew up. His mother and I tried to explain to him that the mothers of the Jewish white girls might not want him to date with them. And he has to be prepared to accept that. I drive Roy and four other children home from the Hebrew High School and up to the present I certainly haven't heard or seen anything that makes me feel that Roy has had the beginnings of a rough time because of the racial matter. He has gone to a few dances at the Hebrew High School and at the synagogue. There have been absolutely no problems to date. He dances. The other kids like him and he gets along very well. We just hope to prepare him so that if and when *it* happens he will not be disappointed.

Roy maintains contact with his Negro cousins. There is only one child in the family of his age, but there is a difference in interests. He had a "crush" on a little white girl in high school and would go over to her home just about every day. She was Jewish. There was no objection on the part of her parents. In fact they were all very friendly to him. The mother was especially friendly.

I've been thinking a great deal about Roy and I believe that he would have a brighter future if he went to live in Israel than anywhere else. He is a Jew and a good one. He knows the Torah. He knows Hebrew. He is certainly no darker than a lot of Jews who have come from all over the world to that land. I hope that someday he will do just that. At any rate that is my idea. (*Editor's note:* In this story we are dealing with two sons. The story and the problems might not be quite as easily dealt with had these parents had to deal with the problems of one or two daughters.)

Doris and I have gotten along very well, I think. We have never discussed religion, that is, my not going to church or not becoming a Jew. I respect Doris as a Jewess. I have tried to help the boys to be good Jews. I have encouraged them in every way. But that's for them and not for me.

I would say that our marriage has worked out very well despite the many hardships about which we both are concerned. Doris still has serious problems about her father's attitude that disturb and worry her. We still don't know how things will turn out with the children and, of course, we want them to be as free from heartaches as possible.

Intermarriages are not simple things. Interracial marriages here in America are the most difficult of them all. If someone came up to me and asked me whether or not I would recommend it, in view of all that I know about it, I would say, in order to make a success of it, you have to love your partner very much. You have to be better than an average person, too, because average people don't work hard enough at something to make it succeed where it might otherwise fail. If you have love and understanding

between yourselves then a marriage such as ours is a pretty wonderful thing. You also have to have a family that you appreciate. But if *you're* asking me, do I think that intermarriage is O.K. for an ordinary guy, the answer is "NO."

DORIS

People who know my parents say that they are both very good people. I think so, too. My mother is especially good. She has always been good to me. Now my father is a good man, too. But he has had his business to worry about. He has worked very hard all his life. Long hours and hard work! These two things have always gone together. My brother and I were born in a town not far from here. The two of us got along very well together. He is older than I. As I look back on my early years, I would say that I was a happy child. I enjoyed lots of fun and I had a goodly number of friends. But I was "spoiled." Everything I wanted I usually got if I stamped my feet hard enough or made a fuss about it. My mother would always give in to me.

But not my father. He was a different kind of person. If he said "no," he meant "no" and there were no two ways about it. Neither he nor my mother were religiously inclined. Oh, yes, they contributed to the Jewish Charities and gave to Israel, but they weren't active synagogue-goers. My parents' home was not *kosher*. (My grandparents' home was.) I remember that because once, I grabbed the wrong spoon or fork and my grandmother told me not to use it because it was the wrong one. Both of my parents were born in Europe. They spoke English very well and, as I say, my father's whole life seemed to be devoted to his business. Whenever he needed extra help, my mother would go down to the business too, so I was alone a good deal. Because my brother was older I didn't see too much of him. Still we were good friends.

We lived in one town all through my elementary-school days. I had friends. I kept busy. My best girl friend was a Catholic. My folks never raised any questions about that. And I certainly didn't think about it.

I never had any Jewish or Hebrew training. What little I saw in my home or elsewhere was about all I had. When we moved from that town, we moved into an all-Jewish neighborhood. My father's store was close by, so that's why it became necessary for us to move. I always thought of that move as being uprooted. Somehow, that made me very unhappy. Even though I had friends, I gradually lost contact with the family. Dad worked seven days a week. Mother was in the store most of the time, so I didn't really see them. We simply had no home life at all.

There were some colored people in my high-school classes, but I didn't

seem to notice them too much. Except that I do recall that if I was in a theater and if a colored person was sitting next to me I would say, to myself. "I'm not like all other white people," or something like that. I always wanted to make it clear that I saw no such distinctions between people because of their color, I knew some people made such a fuss about it. My brother also felt the same way.

I think that this attitude came about when I began to take a very special interest in the Negro music and the bands I used to hear on the radio. This was exciting music. I loved it. My folks weren't aware of this at all. They weren't aware of anything I did because we saw each other so seldom. I'm sure that if you asked my folks about that, they would really be surprised. They took it for granted that they knew where I was all the time. Actually that wasn't so.

My folks were certainly not aware of the fact that I was seeing Paul at the movie theater. There were many such things that they didn't know. That day when we were there to see Cab Calloway and his orchestra, an aunt of mine happened to see me. And she told my mother. And then—all hell broke loose! My mother and father were, first of all, very angry with me. Then when I told my mother that I saw nothing wrong in being with Paul at the theater, she began to cry and plead with me to stop seeing him. But that really made little difference to me, for I actually saw him quite regularly. My parents kept on talking about "marrying a Jew" and reminding me that I was a Jewess. But whether it was just my stubbornness (*Editor's note:* "Getting even with my parents for being left alone?") or whatever the reason, neither my mother nor my father got far with me. All the while I kept on seeing Paul. Then my mother hit on a different approach: to get to Paul and ask him to stop seeing me. Paul listened to her and between her pleadings and her tears he finally promised not to see me any more. He said that he couldn't bear to see my mother cry.

My father's approach was quite different. He took me to a psychiatrist. My father was sure that there was something really wrong with me. Later there was a woman social worker who discussed interracial marriage with me and assured me that such a marriage would be no bed of roses. Everybody was working on me, but none of it really seemed to matter to me very much. I guess the only one who influenced me in any degree was my mother. Her tears affected me, too. I still cannot understand why she and my father got so upset because Paul was a Negro or that he was not a Jew. But to please her I said that I would stop seeing Paul. Now it wasn't Paul who violated his promise to my mother. I was responsible. I would call him and ask him to see me. But this one time, when I gave my promise, I tried to keep it. I stayed home and I stopped eating and became very much upset.

While all this was going on Paul had been sent down to Washington to his brother's home. When he disappeared from the scene, I was quite frantic. When his family told me that he wasn't coming back, I refused to believe it. I kept on trying to find out where his brother lived and with the help of one member of his family, I was able to reach him on the phone

and help him to get back here with some of my money. When he came back, we two were very sure that we wanted to get married. Had I told my parents about that they would have put me away in a hospital, I'm reasonably certain. There was only one thing to do. I stole out of our home one night and the next day we were married, Paul and I, in his sister's home. A Baptist minister who had a room in Paul's sister's home officiated at the marriage.

I had left a letter for my folks telling them what I was doing. The morning following the marriage, I phoned my home and my father answered the phone. I tried to talk to him, but he didn't answer me. He just called my mother to the phone. I was all of seventeen years old at the time—the same age as Paul.

When mother came to the phone, she began to cry. She wanted to know just where I was, but I wouldn't tell her. If I had, she and my father would most certainly have come with the police and forcibly separated Paul and me. But that didn't end the matter because everybody including the police was looking for me. A cousin of mine actually found me. Then one day my mother came in a car and tearfully asked me to go riding with her while we talked. My father would have nothing to do with me from that time on to this very day. It's as if I don't exist. But my mother has softened up. As a matter of fact, I go to see her with an aunt of mine every Tuesday night. We go on Tuesday night because that's the night my father works in his store. If my two sons have no school session on Wednesday they come along with me.

My father will not talk to me. When my grandmother died and I went to the funeral and tried to talk to him, he told me to move away from him. That's how he is. But I still send him cards on Father's Day, on his birthday or on anniversaries. Nothing will move him. It's as if I didn't exist any longer.

My mother is devoted to me. She is wonderful. She comes here to my home sometimes. She is fond of Paul and the children—very fond of them.

What made me turn to Judaism the way I have? Why have I been giving my sons a Hebrew education? Well, you may notice that I am wearing a Magen David necklace (Star of David). I really feel more Jewish since I married Paul than I ever did in my life. (*Editor's note:* Was this need to identify with the Jewish religion and people a means of compensation for her marriage to Paul?) I never gave up being a Jew just like Paul never gave up his ideas about religion. I didn't expect that of him and he didn't expect that of me. When Roy was born, I was definite in my feeling that he should be reared as a Jew and Paul had no objections whatsoever. After all I am a Jewess and I had been told that, according to Jewish law, children born of a Jewish mother were Jewish. So, in every way, including circumcision, Roy and Peter were reared as Jews. I don't keep a kosher home. That would be too hard on us financially. Besides it wouldn't be fair to my husband. But when Roy was old enough to go to Hebrew School, I registered him. And, believe me, he has made us very happy and very

proud because he is such a good student and such a fine boy. Roy is a Jew. My husband has always helped me to get the children to respond well to Hebrew School. He has such a love for education.

When it came time for Peter to go to Hebrew School, we could see that it wouldn't be the same as it was in Roy's case, so Paul sat down with him one day and talked with him. The conversation went something like this: "Peter, do you know that I don't know any Hebrew?" Peter answered "Yes." Then Paul said, "I want to learn Hebrew so very much, so you will have to become my teacher. You go to Hebrew School and then you will teach me. O.K.?" And Peter smiled, understandingly, and replied, "O.K." So you see, this is how Paul has helped me. He is so grateful to all the Jewish people who have helped him with his job and who have been so nice to the boys. All our neighbors—and practically all of them are Jews, are good people. They treat us well. They seem to like us and we certainly like them.

One of the things that is especially hard is not having the kind of place to live in that we would like. That is one thing that happens to people of mixed racial marriages. We have had to work awfully hard to find a decent place to live. When landlords see one of us, show us an apartment and all seems about ready to sign a lease, I usually tell them that Paul is a Negro. Then it starts. You should hear the reactions: "I would gladly let you take the apartment. It's not me. It's the neighbors. They would object." Or "You wouldn't be happy here." Or, "We'll let you know tomorrow." There are a thousand different ways of saying the same thing: "No. We don't want you." But it all comes down to the same thing—people believe that interracial marriages are somehow a sign of decadence or something. Once we do get a place all usually goes well. But until we get in . . . ! When they talk to our children they like us. I can't say that I can blame them for staring. They just aren't accustomed to seeing Negroes and whites together. But they'll get used to it in the years ahead, what with the prestige the black nations in Africa and elsewhere are getting in the world. Things will change because people will discover what so many of them have not realized—that Negroes are also people.

Paul and I have friends. I work at a hospital where some of the Negro doctors are our friends. We visit back and forth. We have Jewish friends and there is, of course, the family. We see Paul's family and, as I already told you, we see my mother and aunt quite regularly.

I think that Paul and I have made a good marriage. Sure, we have our problems. Most of them have to do with finances. If we ever separated, it would be over a question of money. It would have nothing to do with race. Paul is a wonderful man, a good man.

You have already heard Paul's answer to your question about whether he would advise anyone to enter into an interracial marriage. I say it depends on the persons. They have to be good people, better than average people, with love and understanding in their hearts.

You may wonder what prompted me to remain so close to the Jewish

people since my marriage to Paul. As I look back over the years, I cannot think of a time when I thought of rearing my children as anything other than in the Jewish faith. I took that for granted.

Whether I was especially anxious to retain my ties to the Jews because I really wanted my parents, especially my father who has turned away from me, to know that I was very much a Jewess, I cannot really say. Maybe this was in my subconscious, but it certainly wasn't something that had come out in the open at any time.

When Roy was born, I wanted him to retain his ties to the Jewish people. My husband's not being religious didn't interfere with my ideas because he respected my wishes. Even though I knew so little about the Jewish religion, I have somehow felt that this was what I wanted.

As a child when I lived in a practically all-Christian neighborhood, I still felt that I was a Jew. This didn't mean that I didn't have many Christian friends. It's just that this certainly didn't make me less Jewish. Whether I was this way out of sheer stubbornness, or out of a determination to show my parents that, even though I married Paul, I was still a Jew and would bring up my family that way, whether it was because I remembered my grandparents who kept *kosher* or my grandfather who was a Jewish scholar, I don't know.

When Roy was about five years old and we were living in what was pretty much a Christian neighborhood, a Negro woman who lived near us became my good friend. She was a religious person, a Baptist. I remember that she asked me one day if she could take Roy to the Sunday school of her church. I didn't want to, but Paul said, "Why not? Why doesn't Roy learn *both* religions?" Although I wasn't quite sure about it, I let Roy go to church with this Negro lady. I was afraid that he would form opinions that would draw him away from being a Jew and the whole experience was an unhappy one for me. I wanted him to retain his ties to the Jews. So one day I decided that there would be no more of that, and I told the lady that Roy was a Jew and that I didn't want to confuse him any more.

You know, it's strange that you should think that you my father's attitude toward my marriage had something to do with my determination to have Roy reared as a Jew. You see, Roy was born on my dad's birthday. Do you suppose that this has always been in my mind?

When Roy no longer went to that church, I decided that it was time for him to really get to know something about being a Jew. I know that Paul had no feelings against it when I suggested that as soon as possible we should enroll Roy in a Hebrew School. He gave his consent when I took Roy to register him in the Hebrew School. The people there said that even though Roy was Jewish because I was Jewish, they wanted Paul to give his formal consent. And that he did very readily. In fact he said to Roy, "If you're going to go to Hebrew School, you've got to remember that you are going to learn and not to play," and Roy understood that his father was serious about it.

Paul is a good man. Sometimes I know he gets hurt, too, by something

that is done or said about Negroes. I remember, for example, that when Roy was about nine years old we were living in a predominantly white and Jewish neighborhood. But there were some Negro families and they had children about Roy's age. Well, Roy would more or less ignore them and would seem to be embarrassed about Negroes. My landlady was a Negro and she noticed it one day. Roy was with the whites and for no good reason made it obvious that he didn't want to be counted among the Negroes. Now this landlady knew what we were. She knew that we were racially intermarried and that neither Paul nor I were ashamed of it in any way. So she could talk with me about it. When this happened, I had a talk with Roy and I remember saying to him, "Life isn't worth anything if you can't be proud of what you are." I wanted him to be proud of both his Negro and his white heritage. My husband was hurt at that time because of what Roy was doing, but he didn't get angry with him. He knew how to handle the situation very well.

I have a question to ask you. Do you think Roy could "pass?" What do you think we should do about his future? Although Roy is of the Jewish faith, he still has to realize that he is a Negro. It's a difficult situation, I know, but we keep hoping that we'll find the right answer for both Roy and ourselves.

(*Editor's note:* Paul and Doris' marriage appears to be successful. Meeting them in their home makes this clear. Their sons appear to be getting along well, up to this point in their young lives.

Certain questions, however, may be raised. Would their marriage have worked out as well had Doris not sought identification for herself and her children within the religious Jewish community? Is not their very "success" the product of the friendship and empathetic concern bestowed upon them by the Jews? Might their marriage have succeeded had not Paul, quite accidentally, been aided by his Jewish employers in securing and holding a job? Let us suppose that their older son had been less of a Hebrew student and less concerned with Judaism, would the warm response they now receive, have been theirs? Had they failed to receive the community's support might not their marriage have taken a turn for the worse? Finally, it must be noted, too, that Doris and her children as well have paid a high price in their rejection by her parents.)

THE THOMPSONS

Ruth Thompson, rebelling against her parents, escaped from the unhappiness of her home situation and married a Negro. Within less

than two years they were divorced. With their daughter grown to womanhood and now married, Ruth looks back on her life and offers her reactions.

RUTH

I was eighteen years old when I married a Negro. In less than two years, I was divorced. I cannot say that Tom was a bad man. I can only say that he was a lazy man, not given to any program that might involve hard work. He had very little ambition, if any, and he was simply not very much of a breadwinner. In fact, most of the time we were married my husband was on "relief." We had just had a child and living in two very crowded rooms in a real slum area with the baby was more than I could take. I just up and left him. I took the baby and returned to my mother's home.

To get back to the beginning of my story, let me tell you a little about myself and about my parents. My mother was born in America. She came of European, quite orthodox, Jewish background. She was one of several children and none was religious, let alone orthodox. I remember that my grandmother, my mother's mother, was very orthodox. She spoke mostly Yiddish and very little English. The only place I ever heard Yiddish was at my grandmother's home. She lived in a real ghetto. However, she was a very fine woman. Even though I could hardly understand what she was saying to me—I spoke no Yiddish and simply could not understand it—I felt close to her. She was, in fact, about the only one to whom I really felt close outside of my father.

Now, of course, my father was a real character. He was a most unusual man. He had a warm personality and was one of the most interesting people I ever knew in my life. He, too, was born in America. He had little formal education, but he was a naturally smart man and he really made quite a success of his life in the business world. He wasn't a religious man at all. There was just no real religion in our home—certainly not anything that you could call Jewish. If you were to judge our Jewishness by the way we kept the Sabbath or the Holy Days, you would never know that there was any association between us and the Jewish people. I really don't think that my father or mother cared very much about such things. All that I really remember about them is that they were fighting all of the time. My father was a flashy dresser. He liked especially nice clothes. He always looked as if he had just stepped out of the barber shop. My mother looked older than my father, although she was really younger. But I think she was always jealous of my father and for very good reason. He was a really

passionate man. He loved women and I'm sure that he stepped out a great deal. Of course, my mother was jealous and angry and very much hurt.

But I'm not really telling you the whole story when I say that. It will be hard for you to believe what I am going to say, but, in the interest of truth, I'm going to tell you what has to be said.

My father always seemed to have had a violent "crush" on me. I can remember, from the time I was a very little girl, that he loved me very dearly, and showed his affection for me with gifts and many kindnesses all through the years I was growing up. My mother always thought that he was making too much of a fuss over me. I really think that I was very much in love with my father. As I look back at it all now, I realize that he really had no moral sense at all. He just made my mother angry and he caused me to daydream. I never really kept my mind on my school work, I was just a mixed-up kid. I just didn't know what to do about it. What with the violent quarrels I used to hear going on between my mother and my father, I was a very much upset person.

Even though I always suspected that my mother might have known about my father's behavior with other women, she always seemed determined that I should become a show girl, a dancer and singer. I was a very graceful and pretty person in my younger days. My mother was always trying hard to get me to study dancing, go to dancing school, take singing lessons, etc., and was even trying to get me into vaudeville acts. I think that my mother, who had herself always wanted to be an actress, was expressing her longings through me. Her ambitions for a stage career were, in a sense, realized through me when I got dancing jobs in various night clubs and shows.

All the while I was going to high school I can't say that I was a very good student. But, looking back, I think that I was really so much in a "dream world" of my own that I really didn't know how to react to the world. I was a quiet person. Some people used to say that I was shy. I think I was more scared of people than anything else. I belonged to a club or two and I had a boy friend, too. Between my mother and father, I was anxious to get away from them, to get married and live my own life. I was getting more and more afraid to be with either of my parents.

One thing my parents had always said and which impressed itself on me was, "All people are equal," and I really believed that. I still believe it, but not in the same way. I felt that it was wrong for some people to regard themselves as superior to others. I saw no real differences between people just because their skin color was different. During my high-school days I had friends of all kinds. I remember that two of my best friends were colored girls who were in my class. I used to drop over to their homes and nobody in my home ever objected or at any time said or did anything that indicated any prejudice against them. We took the equality of all races for granted, and, let me make it clear, despite my unhappy experiences, that I still do. The difference between my attitude then and now is that in my high-school days I felt like a crusader. I believed that it was important for

me to make this idea of equality clear to all persons. Today, it is enough for me to know how I believe without trying to change the world.

When I was about seventeen years old, I belonged to a group that used to talk a good deal against communism and against fascism. Those were the days of Franco and the Spanish Loyalists. We were all so much against Franco that we were ready to fight him and fascism wherever possible. Once, I was invited to attend a rally against fascism at someone's home. I remember it was at this rally that I first met Tom, the Negro boy whom I later married. He was a very nice boy. He had no special training or learning. He had been a day laborer and apparently we agreed that fascism should be fought. Before you know it, I was going with him regularly.

Now, one thing I cannot understand is why my parents, who had been preaching the equality of all peoples through all the years—who, as I have indicated, were not religious Jews at all—should have been so much opposed to our going together, but they were and what is more, they were both bitter about my going with Tom. As I look back at it now it seemed that by marrying this Negro boy I could do two important things at the same time: first, prove that I believed that all people are equal and that I was not a hypocrite; and second, get away from both my father and my mother by marrying. My friends all advised against the marriage, but I listened to no one. The boy's parents were good, simple, kind people. They accepted me and tried their best to make me feel completely at home with them. And I really felt at home with them. But this marriage didn't last. My husband proved to be such a poor provider and there were so many little things that irritated me. I never was upset when we found that we weren't accepted by most whites after our marriage by a Justice of the Peace. I didn't mind living, first in the Negro section of the city and later in a small town. I was still the crusader, you see. But when our baby daughter was born and he couldn't provide for us, I got more and more upset about it. When I got to thinking about what kind of a life my daughter might have if she were reared in the Negro community, I began to have certain regrets. My concern about my daughter had more to do with her being reared as a Negro than even the problem of Tom's inability to provide adequately for us. Suddenly it seemed as if I might have created special problems for my daughter because her father was a Negro. Yet, and I must say this, Tom was good to us in his way. He meant well. Of that I am certain.

Now all the while, my mother would come to see me and the baby. My father, although he didn't disown me, sort of kept away. Luckily, the baby was quite white in appearance, so I never had to go through the problem that some white mothers of colored babies face—a really traumatic experience. The baby looked more like me than like her father. My parents never threw me out. They never "sat *Shivah*" for me. They were just sad about it all, as were the various members of the family.

When things got so bad that there just was no money in the house, I finally decided to leave my husband and go back to my parents' home. My father was still a "chaser" and my mother was still angry with him. The same quarrels and fights were still going on. But I no longer minded it.

I returned home and let my mother take care of the baby while I sat in a rocker practically all the while, in a kind of a stupor.

I gradually collected my wits and decided to try to get myself a job dancing once again. Luckily, my parents were willing to help me over the rough spots until I got back to work and, I must say, I did rather well. I went on from small jobs to better jobs so that for some time I was dancing for pictures in Hollywood.

My daughter was growing up into a very nice person. She lived with my parents until she was grown up. She met a very nice young boy, just two years older than she and she married him about four years ago. I forgot to mention that he is a Protestant. His family are all religious people. He is an unskilled worker and he is very good to my daughter. She told him, long before their marriage, that her father is a Negro, but that didn't seem to make the slightest difference to him. I remember that it was difficult for her to tell that her father was a Negro.

During all this period I tried to find myself and I cannot say that it was easy. I didn't know anything about Judaism. I had never really gone into a synagogue or practiced any of the Jewish rituals, but I was sure that I would find greater security through religion than in any other way.

Because one of my friends urged me to come with her to a Christian Science Church, I started to go there, and I must say that I found my peace through that Church so that all through the years I have regarded myself as a Christian Scientist.

The strangest of all things in my life is that just a few years ago I met a fine Jewish man who is very much a Jew. We got married some time ago and somehow, with his kind help, I am beginning to feel that I am a Jew, for the first time in my life.

Do I think that I made a mistake in marrying the Negro? Well, yes and no. My answer is "yes" in that I didn't realize that he was a good person in *his* way and not in mine. His family thought he was doing all right. They didn't mind being on "relief," and I did. But that was not the most vital of all issues. I shudder to think what might have happened had my baby been born with a dark skin. She would then have been regarded by everyone as a Negro and would have had to live under the handicaps that confront all Negroes. Suppose that when I left my husband I had taken with me a dark-skinned child. What would have happened? Would my parents and friends have accepted her? Would they have accepted me? Frankly, I think not. Even having a light-skinned daughter whose father was Negro was often upsetting to me. I can't even tell you why.

Once upon a time I was a crusader. I said then and I still believe that there is no difference—no *real* difference between us on the basis of skin color. But there is a difference that comes about because of the environment in which we live. Negroes have to suffer more, put up with much more than do whites and things happen to them. In past years, I wanted to fight against it because I knew it was wrong. Now? Well, I have learned to take life as it comes, to stop rebelling against people and things I don't like, to sway with the punch as the prizefighters say. I'm just no longer a crusader. I

would not have wanted my daughter to marry a Negro because it would have meant too many problems and even hardships for her. I hope that her children will never marry a Negro for the same reason. If and when the battle for real equality between Negroes and whites is won—someday— you can come back to me and ask me *then* what I would do. I think that my answer would be quite different.

INTERETHNIC MARRIAGES

"The ethnic group is a human group bound together by ties of cultural homogeneity. Complete uniformity, of course, is not essential; but there does prevail in an ethnic group a high degree of loyalty and adherence to certain basic institutions, such as a family patterns, religion and language. The ethnic group often possesses distinctive folkways and mores, customs of dress, art and ornamentations, moral codes and value systems, and patterns of recreation. There is usually some sort of object to which the group manifests allegiance, such as a monarch, a religion, language, or a territory. About all, there is a consciousness of land, a we-feeling. . . . Ethnic groups, of course, are not all alike, and none would embody all the features enumerated above. . . ." [1]

Ware[2] adds to this definition when she states that "ethnics are groups bound together by common ties of race, nationality or culture living together with an alien civilization but remaining culturally distinct." If, then, the perpetuation of cultural distinctiveness is the desired goal, we are concerned with the ethnic group.

Each major religious group includes ethnic groups, as well. Protestants are divided not only on the basis of theology, creed or ritual practices but on the basis of national origin and cultural differences as well. The British, Germans, Scandinavians and Americans are primarily Protestant in religion, but each differs from the other on the basis of national and cultural differences, as well. This holds true of Catholics, also. There are obvious cultural differences between Polish Catholics, French Catholics, Italian and other Catholics. Insofar as Jews are concerned, they, too, differ in national origin as well as in practices and customs. Thus Jews, who are "ethnics," have their sub-ethnic groups. German Jews and Russian Jews are, culturally, poles apart from each other. And both are far removed from the Spanish-Portuguese Jew. Yet all are regarded as "Jews."

Ethno-centrism, however, the tendency of group members to give marked loyalty to their own group and to "judge other cultures by their own standards" [3] and values and to "intensify everything in their own folkways which is peculiar and which differentiates them from others" [4] appears to be less pronounced in all groups in the United States today than it was at the turn of the century, although it is still a significant and powerful influence among certain ethnic groups.

Identification with a religion through a Church or Synagogue is high

in the United States today. Sixty per cent of all Americans are affiliated with a religious institution.

There is evidence that the distinctive cultural ties of native-born Americans are not as strong as they were among their foreign-born ancestors. Mores and folkways are often ignored, national origins forgotten, and the desire to perpetuate distinctive languages, dress and value systems appears to be waning. The weakening of these ties in cultural and religious phases of life has affected the intermarriage rate among Italians, Irish, Poles, Slavs and other ethnics. It has, however, not yet significantly affected intermarriage along religious lines as Kennedy[5] and Barron[6] have pointed out. Kennedy has called the American tendency to marry within one's own religious group the "triple melting pot." It is her belief that even though ethnic and national characteristics have become less significant to an increasing number of Americans, there is, nevertheless, a strong desire to confine marriage to persons of the same religion. Thus, a Catholic, generally speaking, marries a Catholic, a Jew marries a Jew, while a Protestant marries a Protestant. Interethnic marriage, then, has not taken place indiscriminately.

Interviews with people in the major religious groups as well as those who claim no religious affiliation, make clear that ethnic consideration plays a minor or passive role in their lives, if they play any at all.

Among American Jews today, for example, little thought is given to family, national, European origins. Where Jews were once sharply divided between East Europeans and West Europeans and, in the main, each group moved within its own circles, such ideas no longer are significant. Jews, but two generations ago, established or became members of synagogues on the basis of ethnicity. There was the "Russian" Synagogue, the "Rumanian" Synagogue, the "Lithuanian" Synagogue, each representing a membership of Jews who had formerly lived (as children or adults) in Jewish communities in the above-mentioned countries. Marriages between Jews of East European and West European origin were regarded as "intermarriages." Such marriages had also been opposed for centuries in Holland, France and England by the Sephardic Jewish communities. It was their belief that their lines of descent had never mixed [7] with Jews of different origin. So strong was ethnocentricism among Jews that, as reported by Barron,[8] "if a Portuguese Jew in England or Holland married a German Jewess [about the end of the eighteenth century] he would, of course, lose all his prerogatives, be no longer reckoned a member of their Synagogue, forfeit all civil and ecclesiastical preferments, be absolutely divorced from the body of the nation and not even buried with his Portuguese brethren."

The relationship of the German-Jewish to the East European

Jewish community has ceased to be a major problem because East Europeans are so abundantly present in practically every community in the United States, and further, because, since World War II, the latter have become very much a part of the lower- and upper-middle economic classes in our society. Their homes, in suburbia and out, their active participation in the social, cultural and philanthropic interests of the total Jewish community have markedly reduced the areas of separation between these two ethnic subdivisions among Jews. Where, but a generation ago, Reform Judaism, its Temple members and leaders, were primarily Jews with German (West European ancestry), that is no longer true. Native-born American Jews of East European background constitute the majority in these and other areas of thought and action. Leaders of city-wide philanthropies and hospitals, many formerly of German descent are today, generally, the sons and grandsons of East Europeans. Marriage between the two occurs regularly. Whatever "feeling" may exist between parents and grandparents of both parties is of little or no concern to the couple itself. They feel secure in both their Americanism and their Jewishness. They have long ago ceased to be interested in or concerned with the national background of their ancestors. Children of the third and fourth generation have little interest in perpetuating the "national"—or even certain of the ethnic—interests of their grandparents. Yiddish with its many dialects once directly associated with ethnicity is no longer understood, let alone spoken, by the third- or fourth-generation American Jews. About all that remains of this ethnicity may be found occasionally in the culinary arts which mothers and grandmothers have taught to their daughters and granddaughters.

The same factors hold true as well for the Catholics of the third and fourth generations. Where the differences between Italian Catholics and Irish Catholics were pronounced and often, antithetical, they have ceased to be significant. Language barriers are down. The ethnic church differences continue to exist in some distinctly ghettoized neighborhoods, composed almost entirely of Italians, Poles or Irish, but, in large measure, according to informants among laymen and church officials, ethnicity is rapidly receding as a factor to be given serious consideration.

National and ethnic emphases among Catholics in the Church in America were roundly condemned by Irish and American bishops. They secured a condemnation by the Vatican of the tendency to establish churches consisting of Irish churches and Italian churches led by priests of these respective national and ethnic origins. Handlin[9] has reported that the condemnation was due to the fact that the Vatican "saw in it an implicit denial of the fundamental catholicity of the Catholic Church."

Poles, Lithuanians and Hungarians among Catholics established their churches on the basis of ethnicity. Handlin[10] reports that "in the 1890's, three independent and spontaneous controversies occurred between Polish parishes and their Irish bishops in Scranton, Buffalo and Chicago. The parishes cut loose from the Church and established the Polish National Catholic Church in America. They also established an independent American Lithuanian Church."

Marriages between Catholics of different national and ethnic origin are common today. Father Thomas,[11] has pointed out that such marriages have increased over the years, so that, it may be said, that ethnic differences are waning insofar as American Catholicism is concerned.

Although not generally as marked, American Protestants, too, were divided along ethnic and national lines until very recent days. This held true particularly of Lutherans on the American scene who, more frequently than other Protestant groups, established churches on the basis of country of origin of their congregants. There were (and still are) Swedish, Danish, Norwegian, Icelander, Finn and German Lutheran Churches. The pastors of these churches preached in their native tongues. The language of worship remained that of the church in the Old Country from which its members had come. The ethnic and national differences were thus perpetuated. Marriage between the members of these churches were often frowned upon. Not until June 27, 1962, did the four separate church organizations of which Lutheranism consisted in the United States, merge into the Lutheran Church in America. Until that day the United Lutheran Church, consisting chiefly of persons of German background; the Augustana Lutheran Church, predominantly of Swedish origin; the Finnish Evangelical Lutheran Church, and the American Evangelical Lutheran Church founded by Danish missionaries, went their separate ways, divided not only on the basis of theological distinctions but by ethnic differences as well. Here, too, the changing nature of the Church must be related to the fact that its members are now native Americans, who do not feel themselves directly related to or associated with the national or ethnic groups to which their parents and grandparents belonged. Immigration to this country has ceased for all practical purposes. Americans have become members of the great middle class on the economic scale and they regard themselves primarily as unhyphenated Americans.

In this sense, the melting pot described so vividly by Mary Antin and Israel Zangwell is really working. Even though most Americans marry within their own religious group, ethnic differences continue to fade.

Why has "ethnicity" lost so much of its early significance in the

United States? Certain factors distinguish the American of the 1960's from the American of the 1900's. Among them, is the important fact that today (1961) 94.6 per cent[12] of the American people are native-born. They do not know the old world from which their grandparents came. They have either never learned or have forgotten many of the distinctive practices, customs and even values of their ancestors. Today the vast majority of Americans use the American language because it is their native tongue. The foreign press has ceased to be much of an influence. In fact, it is rapidly disappearing from the American scene. Even the distinctive culinary arts of ethnic groups have been absorbed by American culture. Where, in a former generation, "foreign dishes" were looked upon as belonging particularly to a special ethnic or national group, today, Americans generally like to prepare and use these distinctive foods. Jewish, Italian, Chinese, Mexican foods, to mention but a few, have been accepted as part of the culturally pluralistic American pattern.

Handlin[13] has pointed out that "American society is pluralistic in its organization." He has further suggested that the tendencies toward uniformity in this country have been inhibited not only by the vastness of the country itself, but by the marked regional differences and diversity of antecedents. With but few exceptions—the Pennsylvania "Dutch," the Southern mountaineers and the farmers of Northern New England— Americans were never isolated, voluntarily or otherwise, from other Americans. Yet each group retained considerable of its own identity and distinction. The ethnic group, as a means of identifying people and, at the same time, of signifying certain positive qualities of character was early recognized in America as important not only for the individual but for America itself.

Religion, as I have already noted, remains a distinguishing characteristic of Americans today. But, religious differences appear to have less significance than was true but a generation ago.

However, the fact that ethnic differences are "fading" does not mean that they have already disappeared or are about to disappear from the American scene.

The French and Spanish people along the Gulf Coast and in the Southwest maintain their cultural differences through their "French Quarters" and Spanish settlements. The Louisiana French, an ethnic minority, have demonstrated their ability to withstand the pressures of assimilation by the native white population. Their success in this direction is associated with the fact that they number about 44 per cent of the population of Louisiana.

French-Canadians continue, too, to maintain their ethnic identity

in the New England States. They are to be found, also, in Michigan, Illinois and Wisconsin. They maintain their French-language parochial schools and a separate press as well as their own social associations.

Although ethnic loyalty is exceedingly strong among French-Canadians, Anderson's[14] study indicates that 41 per cent of the third generation, as compared with 25 per cent of the second and 18 per cent of the first, favored marriage with *any* white American. The emphasis upon endogamous marriages with persons of similar ethnic background is fading even though it is recognized that marriage to one, even of the same religious but of a different national and cultural background, may tend to weaken this French-speaking people as an ethnic entity.

The Pennsylvania "Dutch" still remain a people apart. Folkways, mores, many of the attitudes of these people are of common national and ethnic origin. They are, in fact, Germans who came into Pennsylvania long before the Revolutionary War. Living in comparative isolation, maintaining their own way of life, even a hybrid form of the German language interlarded with what purported to be English, they came to be regarded as a culturally mixed people. Marriage outside of their own group is still infrequent.

Mexicans, in large measure, a hybridized people, form the largest ethnic minority in Los Angeles County. They intermarry with native whites in large numbers. Panunzio,[15] studying intermarriage of Mexicans in Los Angeles in 1942, reported that of 11,016 marriages, 592 out of 1,000 were intramarriages in which *both* parties were Mexican and 408 out of 1,000 were intermarriages. Of these, 354 per 1,000 were with native-born whites; 40 were with foreign-born whites; 10 were with natives of Central and South America and 1 each with a Filipino, American Indian, Asiatic and Negro.

In San Antonio, Texas,[16] there are 142,000 Mexican-Americans. Although the Mexicans are, in the main, Catholics, they attend a different Catholic Church than do the "Anglo" Catholics. About 1940, the Archbishop of San Antonio, in an effort to bring together the Anglo and Mexican Catholics, abolished by decree the "national" or ethnic parishes into which the city was divided. But his effort has not succeeded because large ethnic residential concentrations still remain and because, too, neither of the two Catholic groups, "Anglo" or Mexican, have been inclined to worship together. There is "little home visiting between these two Catholic groups, little intimate friendship or cross-sex relations."

The ethnic church still exists and plays an important role in the lives of New York City's newest immigrants, the Puerto Ricans. Inasmuch as they are predominantly Roman Catholic (as of December 31, 1958, there were 849,000 [17] of them living on the mainland with about

650,000 living in New York City), it is natural that the Roman Catholic Church should be actively concerned with them, seeking to serve their religious and social needs.

The Puerto Ricans, despite their Roman Catholic Church propensities, are perhaps the most isolated of all ethnic groups, their position similar to that occupied by the Irish and the Italians of an earlier age. They are America's newest group of "foreigners."

The Puerto Rican is, however, legally, an American citizen. When he lives in Puerto Rico, he thinks of himself as an American. However, when he emigrates to the United States, he finds that there is a marked contrast between his rural and Spanish environment and the American milieu. He is, therefore, psychologically and culturally a "foreigner." Not only does he then so regard himself, but Americans generally think of him in these terms.

Marriage with a person who is not only a member of a "different" ethnic group but racially "mixed" as well is likely to occur but rarely. When these newcomers cease to be regarded as foreigners and, in time, acquire a higher economic, social and cultural status the present mood toward such marriages may change. Unless the American attitude toward interracial marriage changes markedly, it does not appear likely that marriage with Puerto Ricans will generally be regarded as socially acceptable.

Although remnants of ethnic solidarity continue in the United States, the acculturation process has, in large measure, reduced or even eliminated ethnic divisiveness among Americans. With the exception of some identification with religion and its institutions—excepting, too, the latest immigrants, the Puerto Ricans—ethnic differences do not appear to be either strong or meaningful to Americans. The concept of cultural pluralism, the right and duty of the American people to maintain the distinctive values associated with their respective ethnic group, is generally accepted—in theory. However, in fact, it appears to me that it is the melting-pot idea that increasingly seems to be the end toward which we are striving.

Interethnic marriages among the American people are becoming more common as the years pass. The preservation of racial and religious ties in that order, are definitely of much greater concern to us. There will always be those persons and sub-cultures who, for psychological and personal reasons as well as by reason of concern for the group itself, will insist upon maintaining a particular way of life. But their number is certainly being reduced as the decades continue to pass. The world has been reduced in size. Ethnic differences will persist, but I believe the number of such differences likely to be considerably reduced in the

United States and throughout the world with the passing of another generation. Interethnic marriages will increase whenever and wherever distinct cultures and ways of life fade into insignificance.

JOAN AND GEORGE

Joan and George are both Jewish. But Joan's family is of German origin while George's family comes from Russia. The differences between the Jews from Western European countries and those of Eastern Europe were, a generation ago, highly important. They implied social and cultural differences as well. The East European, it was generally conceded, had a greater knowledge of Talmudic Judaism, often a greater devotion to the ritual and ceremony of the Jewish tradition. Although the ethnic differences appear to have lost their importance, there are still overtones of these differences in such people as Joan and George. Their homes differed in certain attitudes, ritual and knowledge. The resolution of these differences, though slow, is apparent in their lives and particularly in their children who know nothing of the pride and sense of superiority that characterized some Jews of another generation, whose security lies in their love of an unhyphenated Judaism.

JOAN

I have been married for fifteen years to a truly fine man. We are both Jewish, so ours might not be called an intermarriage. And, yet, as I think about it, I suppose it really is. You see, our backgrounds are so different. Though both George and I were born in the United States, attended the elementary and high schools and went on to college—so that you would think that there really ought to be no actual differences between us—we are both aware of certain marked differences which we ascribe to our backgrounds. You see, George's family is East European and my mother is German.

George and I have three children, two boys and a girl. We're very proud of them and, I think, with reason.

I met George during World War II. He was attending a service dance and I, as a kind of patriotic service, I guess, acted as a hostess. We started going together at that time.

I'm going to tell you about my family background because you will soon see, I believe, why I say that with all that we have in common, there are still some ethnic differences between us that, on occasion, cause us some heartache.

My grandfather on my father's side came over from Poland when he was about fifteen years old. After the usual peddling chores that, I understand, characterized so many of these early arrivals, he started a little retail store in the Jewish section of Wooster and he became quite affluent. He married a woman whose background was similar to his own.

My father was born in New York City. He went to high school, of course, and then on to Harvard. One of the interesting things about him is the fact that the high school he went to didn't teach Latin, so in order to take the entrance exams for admission to Harvard, he taught himself Latin. He had apparently always wanted to be a lawyer and he worked away at it until he became one—and a good one, too. He was so good, in fact, that, when he was quite a young man, he was appointed a judge in one of the high State Courts. He was a highly respected citizen.

To get back to my grandfather, I must point out that he was a very active person in the Jewish community, highly respected by Jews and non-Jews. The Jewish community wasn't so very big. Everyone knew everyone else. You lived and worked more closely with people in those days. There was a very great integration of the Jewish community into the general community. I don't think that there was as much self-imposed ghettoism in those days as there is in ours, which may have been due to the fact that there were more non-Jewish immigrants then. Irish immigrants, Italians—ever so many people were immigrants. And Jews were also, so it wasn't strange or unusual. The Catholics and the Jews got on very well together.

My grandfather's family was quite orthodox, but they were very tolerant. And, I think, liberal. My mother's family, though they were reform, were very strict and intolerant. It's hard to explain, but that's the way it was. Jewish ritual was observed in my grandfather's home, but he certainly wasn't so observant outside his own home.

I spoke about the strictness of my maternal grandmother's home. Her family came from Germany and yet her Sabbath was observed very strictly. There was no deviating one inch from what was required according to Jewish ritual. My grandmother was a very strong and dominant person. She was very much a matriarch. Yet—and *this* will surprise you—she was born in New York City. I am then the third generation on her side of the family born in the United States.

I don't remember my maternal grandfather, but I don't think that he was as strict about things as my grandmother. I always recall her as living with my parents, so I know of her strictness at first hand. My mother was like her. She was always strong and strict and determined. She was the dominant one in our home, but my father was by far the greater person. At least, I always admired him more. He was devoted to people other than himself. He was not egocentric.

My mother had been an only child. Perhaps that is why she was so

self-willed. Yet, it seems to me that it was in part because her mother's family were all pretty much that way. When my maternal grandmother died, my mother discarded very much of the orthodox Jewish ritual that she had liked so much. She had really never agreed with my grandmother on the matter of ritual observance, but she had been terrified of her mother. She did inherit certain attitudes which she took over very completely. She was devoted to what was right. The difference between right and wrong always seemed clear-cut to her. But mother always used to say that one of the reasons she "flew the coop" so completely, once her mother died, was because she had been held down so much until that time.

My mother had an excellent scholastic background. She graduated from one of the best women's colleges in the country and she then went on to get her Master's degree in history. About a year or two after that, she married father.

Both mother and father had been interested in social-service work. My father especially in those years played a major role not only in the Jewish philanthropic and social-service agencies, but in those of the larger community as well. He was always so—humane! There was really a rather complete integration of these two into the community.

In my parents' home, religion really didn't matter so much. We knew we were Jewish. We took it for granted. But there was something else that mattered, especially to my mother, and that was a social-status kind of thing. I always heard that mother's family kind of "tolerated" my father's family. And, in fact, as a child, I remember getting that feeling from my mother's family whenever I visited them. You see, *they* were German Jews and that meant, so they thought, that they were somehow superior to these Polish Jews, my father and his parents' family. It didn't matter that my father was born in America. He was still a Polish Jew. And my grandmother, although born in the United States still thought of herself as a German Jewess, very superior to all East European Jews. The cultured people came from West Europe! It may also have had something to do with material wealth, because it was obvious that my mother's family was far more wealthy than my father's family. I'm not certain that I can say that the differences in family origin had very much to do with it, but I always felt that there was never complete acceptance of my father as an East European Jew (which he certainly was *not*) by my mother. Yet his high status as a judge was a source of pride to her. My parents were always so busy, so active in the community that I cannot think they would have had the time to quarrel over things like family origin.

I think that the difference in the two families can best be described by the kind of funeral that took place when my father's father died as against the one when my mother's mother passed away. I remember that my grandfather was placed in a plain casket and I remember the mobs and mobs of people, most of them who didn't even know him personally yet they seemed to be so very much moved by his death. I saw people lined up in the streets tearing their clothes when the funeral procession passed by. It was just like something from a different world. When my mother's mother

died, the funeral service took place in the house. My grandfather's had taken place in the largest synagogue where he had been so active. There had been no flowers. But at my grandmother's funeral there were so many flowers it smelled like a florist's shop. Everything was quiet and sedate and proper. There was quite a difference!

Now, to get back to my own story. I dated boys from all kinds of backgrounds. It didn't matter to me whether they were Russian or Polish or German or whatever other kind of background. And there was no opposition to this by my parents. Maybe this was due to my mother's deference to my father.

I really didn't know George too well when I married him. It was war time. People were on the move. George was going overseas in a short while. So we got married.

It was only then that I got to know George's family well. I always felt that I had a good relationship with them. Of course, they thought then that my mother ignored them, but then my mother ignores everybody. She's always so busy. I remember that George used to be bothered by that. He thought that she regarded herself as superior, but now we're quite used to it. As a matter of fact (and this has nothing to do with my mother), I think that George is the one who feels superior. We always resented the fact that he doesn't consider that I'm Jewish just because I come out of a reform environment and his family is of Russian-Jewish orthodox origin. I think that he is the one who is very definitely "high-hatting," feeling superior. And that goes in some degree for his family. You see, they think that my family is so un-Jewish because we go our own individual ways in our family whereas in George's family everybody is like one unit.

Then, take the matter of the kind of Hebrew education the children are to get. George insisted that the boys get a traditional Hebrew education. Well, I felt that my children should receive the kind of Sunday-school training I received in the reform Temple. I felt that I got so much out of it when I attended, I wanted my youngsters to benefit by the same experiences. But there have been changes made since I was there that change the nature of the schooling to a more traditional type and I am not used to that. I don't think that reform Judaism has stuck to what it was really doing when I was a child. Then, it was pioneering—trying to break through certain of the superstitions and things that didn't fit into the contemporary world. Instead of pioneering now, I feel that they are reverting to all the window dressings of traditional Judaism in order to win more people. It just doesn't seem natural or even honest to me.

I don't think that today there is really any issue involved any more on the question of whether one's family is from Eastern or Western Europe. People in the Jewish Community, as everywhere else these days, don't marry or make their friends on the basis of where they were born or where their families came from.

I think that the differences in ethnic background do make for some problems for married folk, still. They are not as marked in the Jewish community today because, as I understand it, over 80 per cent of us Jews are

native-born. We know the American tradition. We really care very little about this nonsense that our parents and especially our grandparents made so much of, the importance and relative superiority of Jews from Western Europe as against Eastern Europe. What is still very real with some of us is that the kind of Judaism we knew and were taught as children in our reform temples and Sunday schools seems to be on the way out. It is being forced out by the vast numbers of Jews from Eastern Europe with more traditional Jewish background, who are bringing their patterns of Jewish life and ritual into what were once liberal, pioneering temples. The interethnic conflict has gone out, but the conflict between the orthodox or traditional Jewish ritual and the trail-blazing reformers has yet to be resolved.

GEORGE

You have already heard from Joan as to how we met and a good number of other things about us, so I will tell you about my parents and my own background.

My father was born in Russia. He came to the United States as a grown man. But he didn't come directly. As a very young boy, he escaped from Russia to Germany. He did not want to be in the Czar's army. There were many reasons for this. Jews were often obliged to become converts when they got into the army. Jews just lost their identity. Besides, no Jew in Russia could have any love for the Czar or for Russia after the way that country treated its Jews.

While Dad was in Germany he learned to speak German fluently. After a good number of years there, he went to Holland and became a citizen. It was as a Dutch citizen that, after a period of years, he came to the United States.

Dad had no member of his family here. He came up to Philadelphia and from there he got a very excellent job in the West Indies—in Jamaica, to be exact. As the result of an earthquake there, he was injured. The company he worked for sent him back to the United States to convalesce. It was during this period that he met my mother.

She had come from Russia as an infant. My mother was very much more of an American in those early years than my father. They were quite an interesting team. Each was really so very different from the other.

Although, in his later years, my father became quite orthodox in his Jewish life, my mother was always far less so. It's strange about my father reverting to more orthodox ways because one of the reasons he gave for leaving Russia was the fact that his father and his whole family were fanatically religious and he wanted to dump it all.

My father's father was, I am told, a fine Hebrew scholar. He studied

Talmud in a Yeshiva (academy), while his mother operated a small business and supported the family. My grandfather expected my father to study the same as he did, but my father refused. He became a black sheep insofar as his father's attitude toward him was concerned. So when the opportunity presented itself, he ran away from home, from the Russian army service and from religion as he had seen it.

Because my mother didn't want my father to go back to the West Indies to work, he went into business on his own. Before very long he was doing exceedingly well as a contractor. He was well liked. He had a host of friends, both Jews and non-Jews. Most of his business, in fact, was done with non-Jews.

It wasn't until the 1920's that my father returned to Russia to see his only brother. When he saw that his brother had really become what he regarded as a holy man, he was amazed and there came about the most remarkable change in my father anyone can imagine. He was so impressed with the self-sacrificing religiosity of his brother that he, too, became quite religious. He began going to a synagogue. He began to pray and he introduced certain rituals into our home. My mother helped him by seeing to it that all the rituals of the home, including the traditional dietary laws, were adhered to. Even though his motives were very good, his knowledge of Judaism was really not very exact and he would do things, eat things, that I know are definitely not *kosher*. But to him that was fine. He used to be disappointed in me because I didn't have a good background in Judaism, but, I must say, he never provided me with an opportunity to get one.

Now, my father was no different from many other Jews whom I know. He was very, very strict about observances in his own home, but he led a life that was completely different outside the home. He felt that, out of his home, he was an American, a businessman and he entertained business people in a way utterly different, from point of view of traditional Judaism, than he would have done in his home. My father looked upon Hebrew as a holy language, the proper language in which a Jew should pray. He said that it made no difference if one understood Hebrew or not. Whatever there was in the prayer book was important and holy. Therefore, it should be said whether I understood it or not.

As far as my general education goes, my family and I, too, for that matter, wanted a good one. I was graduated from a Midwestern university and received a Master's degree in the social sciences. I was interested in study. My father sort of half liked the idea, but hoped that I would be more of a businessman than a scholar. But make no mistake about it, with all his strictness, he was a lovable person and I felt close to him.

My father was quite a traditionalist from point of view of Judaism. He had strong feelings for it, as I have explained, even though he really didn't understand its intricacies well at all. He was vastly different from Joan's father, who came from a family that had close association with the Synagogue, but not too close an adherence to traditional Judaism. Ritual didn't matter to my father-in-law in the same way as it did to my father. As for our mothers, they, too, were vastly different. My mother was pliable in her

Jewishness as in other things. She was lovable and kindly in everything she did, and ritual mattered to her primarily because it was important to my father. In my mother-in-law's case, she was very reform. Joan's mother's marriage to her father, even though he was already a successful lawyer, was quite a blow to her family pride because she was marrying out of her class into a family of Polish Jews. Had he and his father not been so highly regarded by so many people for intellectual attainments, and, in the case of his father, philanthropic endeavor, her family would not have allowed this marriage, I feel pretty sure. This was marrying beneath their social status.

But you are interested in knowing about how Joan was reared. I'm sure you know that she had an excellent college training and also got a Master's degree. But I am thinking *now* more especially about her Jewish training. When Joan was growing up, I would say that the reform Temple was more like a Unitarian Church than a synagogue. They observed the High Holy Days, but they didn't care too much about ceremony. I think they believed that Judaism was entirely a matter of ethics. All of this is fine from my point of view, but I think that Judaism is much more. It is ceremony *and* ritual *and* Hebrew *and* a lot of other things in *addition* to ethics. My father was a highly ethical and moral man. You may be sure that he wouldn't have won the friendship and regard of people in business had he not had high ethical standards. But his standards were different—and, so are mine!

When we married we knew, of course, that our family backgrounds were different—that I was from a Russian Jewish family and that Joan was a German Jew, but neither of us took it too seriously. We used to joke about ours being an intermarriage. In one sense, it was not a joke, for we both recognized that there was some element in our marriage—perhaps this feeling about superiority and inferiority—which was certainly obvious in Joan's family.

But really, I think that this business of ethnic difference was mainly our parents' generation's problem. Ours is a bit different. We are Jews, of course. But, Joan's and my attitude toward the traditional Synagogue and the reform Temple are very much different from each other's. I asked that our sons be trained in a conservative traditional way so that they would be Bar Mitzvah (confirmed) as I wanted them to be. But I did say that they should be allowed later to make up their own minds about whether they wanted to be reform, conservative or orthodox Jews. This difference in our background certainly made things more difficult for us. I have a certain feeling for the tradition and I try to stick by my guns and it isn't always easy. I think that my wife is changing her position because the reform Temple has changed. But she says that it isn't reform, or conservative, or orthodox, and that is what she objects to. She feels that it isn't anything, that it stands for nothing. She feels today that she can at least identify with the conservative Congregation because she likes what its rabbi stands for. To her, the temple of her youth is today a complete question mark. She wants something to lean on, to adhere to, and she hasn't found it in the temple of her youth.

It's sort of tragically funny to see my boy at home on Friday night just before dinner. He puts on his Yarmulke (skull cap) while we remain bareheaded and he recites the Kiddush (sanctification of the wine). Everything has to be just as he wants it, according to Jewish tradition. I really don't know how much he really knows because my Hebrew education is not so good, but my wife really gets a kick out of it, as do I. On Sabbath night he asks us if he can say the Havdalah prayers (the prayers recited just before the conclusion of the Sabbath day). He even tries to teach Joan, but he won't let her try to bless the Sabbath candles unless she is really serious about it. So far, he can't get her to be very serious about it. Still she lights them.

You see, we have a division in our home. My wife has her religion and I have mine, and the children are accepting my way. They are, in fact, much more religious than we are. They encourage us to be religious. We need not try to encourage them.

I have found out that where one's parents came from is of less importance than what attitudes they had toward traditional Jewish values. I know of many people who marry whose parents came from different backgrounds much as in our case. They have absolutely no religious problems because neither one has any loyalties to anything Jewish. But when there are two people such as Joan and myself—and we both have strong but quite different loyalties insofar as Judaism is concerned—*then* there are problems. But it's because we both have positive values and not because we are living in a kind of religious vacuum. If a child of mine were to come to us and tell us that he was in love, frankly, with all of my own experience, I wouldn't pay very much, if any, attention to whether the girl's parents came from East or West Europe or even whether she was orthodox or reform. I would be concerned with whether the girl came from a nice home with a good ethical and moral background, with an appreciation of Judaism on a high plane. I am certain Joan would feel the same way about it. The old ethnic distinctions mean nothing any more. It's the kind of character you have and the upbringing you have received that really matters. On that Joan and I are certainly in agreement.

CHAPTER 11.

WHAT OF THE CHILDREN?

My wife and I have a serious problem. We have come to you, hopeful that you can help us solve it. You see, we are intermarried. I am a Jew and my wife is a Catholic. She has always regarded herself as a good Catholic.

I met Charlotte about two years before we got married. We both knew that we were meant for each other almost immediately. Now I am not very much of a Jew. I know very little about Judaism. I was Bar Mitzvah. My parents belong to an orthodox Synagogue and my relationship with them has always been good. But whether I am a good Jew—a religious Jew—or not, I am a Jew and have never really felt that I was anything else.

When I first told my parents about Charlotte, my mother was almost hysterical. Even though she gradually calmed down, it has been difficult for her to accept Charlotte and only because she is a Catholic. She likes her because she is such a good person. She is a college graduate and is truly kind and lovely. But—she is a Catholic. To this day my mother has not gotten over the shock of knowing that I married Charlotte. My father took the idea of my marriage more philosophically, but I could see that he too was unhappy.

Charlotte also had quite a time of it, but not as hard a time as I did. Her parents didn't like the idea of her marrying a Jew. But when they were told that I had agreed to be married by the priest, which meant that I had agreed that any children born of our marriage would be reared as Catholics, the idea of our marriage was accepted.

We have been married for over two years and about six months ago, our child, a girl, was born. Insofar as the two of us are concerned, we are really happy. We are getting along very well. And our little daughter has been a real blessing. We love her so!

Almost from the day we were married I began to have regrets about the promise I had made to have any children of mine reared as Catholics. I have no feeling of opposition to Catholicism. It is rather that despite my ignorance of Judaism, I have felt that I am a Jew and I have been hoping that my children would be Jewish. I can't explain how it happened, but you may be certain that I am describing a genuine emotion. I seem to have developed a very strong feeling about having our children reared as Jews, pledges previously given notwithstanding. I feel that I didn't think too seriously about the pledge I was making because I was much more concerned with marrying Charlotte. Everything else seemed so unreal, so distant!

We are both very much concerned about how our daughter will be reared. I am so anxious for her to be raised as a Jewess. Charlotte reminds me about my promise, but is herself less inclined toward Catholicism as each day passes. We feel that we must not have a home that is divided in its religious affiliation. We believe that this would be

bad for our daughter developing insecurities in her and that it may be equally bad for Charlotte and me.

What shall we do? Should Charlotte permit our child to be reared as a Jew? If she herself is not a Jewess, how can she do a good job for our daughter's religious security? Should I permit our daughter to be reared as a Catholic when I feel that, however I may have felt when we were married, today it is more right that she be reared as a Jewess? I have no intention of giving up being a Jew, nor will I convert to Catholicism. Charlotte is less sure about her religion today than ever before. We both want to do what is good and right for our little girl. What shall we do?

This true story, told to me by the persons directly involved, presents some of the basic problems with which well-intentioned young people who have entered into a mixed marriage, each retaining his or her own religious affiliation, are confronted and with which they, in turn, confront their children.

The solution is obviously not simple. Is it enough to advise the husband who has signed away the lives of his unborn children to the Church, with all good intention and in all sincerity, that he has no right to change his mind no matter what the circumstances? Is it sufficient to ask the wife, in this case, a Catholic, to resolve the problem by renouncing her faith and Church and convert to her husband's religion? If the parents continue to retain their respective religious affiliations, what is likely to happen to the ultimate sense of security of their young daughter? Is it possible for a child to avoid instability within such a home? What religious heritage, if any, is any child entitled to?

Similar to the problem already presented, is the following:

I have been married two years, and am expecting my first child in a few weeks. My husband and I are of different faiths, but up to now religion has never been a source of conflict in our marriage. We had our parents' approval before we married, which I think was a point in our favor.

Although we have gotten along beautifully up to now by respecting each other's beliefs, we have started to argue over what religion we should bring up our child in. As this is the first grandchild, my parents are eager that the child be brought up in my faith, and I would so like to please them. On the other hand, my husband feels that it is better for children to follow in the religious footsteps of their father. He says they bear the father's name and should also have his religion. How can we settle this amicably?

Ella

Ella and her husband face a grave situation in their lives. However, compared with the problems that may confront their child because of the differences in religion between husband and wife, the problems of these parents are simple, indeed.

Is it proper for such parents to oblige their children to confront more than the usual problems that normal human beings are obliged to face in the process of growing up? Is a child who requires both love and security likely to have either when he discovers that his parents are poles apart in their religious beliefs? If religion has meaning for either parent, is it correct to ask either parent to give up what has been treasured, in order to create a formally "united" family?

As I view the matter, I believe that when a child is born, we parents become transformed human beings. However much we may have imagined ourselves in the role of a parent prior to marriage; however many and detailed our plans, hopes and aspirations may have been up to that moment, the realization that we have, in fact, become a parent has a direct and startling effect upon our emotions and our ultimate behavior. It is one thing to talk about parenthood in the abstract. It is quite another matter to become a parent! Any parent will testify to the correctness of this observation.

Because of this "before and after" difference in us, it is often difficult if not almost impossible for even the best-intentioned young people to abide by decisions they may have made about their unborn children prior to their marriage. What seems superficial, insignificant and unimportant at one stage in our lives may assume utterly different meaning with the arrival of children. Religion to which we may have paid but little attention now becomes important—"for the children."

I still do not care for religion for myself. But I think that my children ought to be brought up in some religion and I can see no reason why it shouldn't be the religion I was brought up in. Yes, it's true, I'm not very religious, but I know that I am a Jew and I want my children to know that they are Jews. They ought to know Jewish history and Hebrew and be able to pray and—whether or not I believe in it—I want my son to be Bar Mitzvah the same way I was. I want him to feel at home with my parents and my whole family. It will be impossible unless he goes to Hebrew School.

Of course my wife is right about what I said before we got married. I did say that we would "settle" for some neutral religion like the Community Church or Unitarianism or one of the others, but now that my first child has been born, I just can't go through with it. Now my wife who was a Congregationalist wants our child to belong to her parents' religion while I suddenly find it important for my son to be a Jew. To try to satisfy both of us is impossible. We'll only create problems for our son. To ignore both religions is equally impossible because I, for one, have changed my mind since our marriage. I can't help it. It isn't a question of who's right and who's wrong. Nor is it a question of compromise. How can I compromise when I have come to feel that this would only serve to break my parents' heart and provide no security whatsoever for the child? My wife and I were married by a

Justice of the Peace so as to avoid a religious conflict. But now, with the birth of my son, we both realize that we haven't escaped the problem at all. It is still very much with us!

The experience of this parent may be duplicated many-fold among people of all religious denominations, sects, churches and synagogues. However anxious we may be to avoid such problems, we can hardly escape them nor can we readily escape our past. These problems are real and ever-present. It should be obvious that we owe an obligation to our children to come to terms with ourselves and to provide for their spiritual security as well.

In the case of mixed marriages, where husband and wife retain their own respective religious affiliations, various suggestions have been made by which to resolve the problems of religious affiliation of their children. "Let the children choose for themselves," is one answer. This solution suggests that each parent has, in fact, by word, deed, or even by inaction, maintained an absolutely neutral position with respect to religion. The likelihood that, however much the parents may desire it, they can maintain their home in an absolute spiritual vacuum, utterly free from any minutia of religious rite or values is, I think, not to be taken seriously. What people *say* they believe and what they *do* are very often utterly different. A mother, born of Christian parents, may not consciously seek to influence her children along religious lines, yet, the introduction by her of the Christmas tree at the Yuletide season, the distribution of Christmas gifts, Santa Claus, are all obviously associated with Christianity and the Christian way of life. The fact is that Christmas has its uniquely Christian significance and importance. Christmas, then, becomes her children's holiday, with its religious connotations. The father who, born of Jewish parents, insists that he is not a religious Jew, but seeks, nevertheless, to introduce the Hanukkah festival and the story of the Maccabean heroes into his household is establishing certain values for his children. He may insist that he does so with nonreligious, purely secular motivation. Whatever his motive, the fact is that Hanukkah is Jewish and is associated with the Jewish way of life.

Even if not a single ceremony, rite, or observance is introduced into such a home, it is still unrealistic to assume that grandparents, family and all friends, not to speak of school and other societal influences will not operate and influence the child in *one way or another*. It is folly to assume that parents, however slight their own religious interests at the time of marriage, are ever completely free from the emotional and intellectual values associated with their parents, family, friends, or their heritage.

Let us assume for the moment that father and mother can, some-how, remain completely free of religious ties themselves. At just what age should the child of a mixed marriage make the proper choice of religion? And on what does this choice depend? Shall the child make his decision on the elaborateness of Hanukkah, or Christmas, or upon the church or synagogue rites alone? Is the ultimate decision to be made on the basis of the oratorical or other personal qualities and talents of priest, minister, or rabbi? Shall it be made on the basis of the quality of church or synagogue music and liturgy? In such situations, the child has not had the benefit of serious intensive training in any religious school. Should parents who take pride in their own emancipation, whose responsibility for the emotional, intellectual, and religious well-being of their children is clear, permit the ultimate choice of religious identification by the child to be based on factors that may be purely superficial? If the careful study of religious values, theological and social concepts is contemplated, just how many or how few religious cults and sects should the child study before he is certain that the proper choice of a religion has been made? And we may ask, parenthetically at what age should the search for the "right religion" begin and end, or positive religious identification begin?

Another suggested means of dealing with the problem is: "Have the male children of a mixed marriage reared in the religion of the father and the female children reared in the mother's religion." This pseudo-Solomonesque approach may appear to offer an equitable solution to a vexing problem but it literally divides the offspring of a family from each other. The solution, therefore appears to me to serve as a means of division of the home and the family. When all the evidence that has thus far been gathered on the factors making for a successful marriage indicates that divisiveness in religion is obviously important, it is reasonable to suppose that further segmentation of the family will ultimately prove harmful to the children, the parents and their hopes and efforts for maintaining a unified home, as well as to society.

It is, I think, unfair to any child to create situations that may place additional stresses and strains upon him. The home that cannot provide emotional stability is not really the best kind of home, in that it does not provide a high degree of emotional security for the child.

Leiffer,[1] speaking about the problem of mixed marriages, says, "If religious attachments are taken seriously, they constitute a basis of conflict especially after the advent of children." Mixed marriages that remain "mixed" because one or both of the parties have a strong feeling for their particular religion may become especially difficult when, upon the birth of children, such a parent suddenly feels the necessity of making a choice of religion for them.

In this connection, we may point out that Baber[2] has reported that in his sample the difficulty of training children was foremost in interfaith intermarriages. He indicated that one-half of the conflicts in Protestant-Catholic marriages were over matters of religion, involving questions of how to train the children. So great is the problem for both parents and their children!

If either or both partners to a mixed marriage has any unexpressed reservation whatsoever with respect to the religious upbringing of children, I believe that it is not honest or moral to ask a priest or rabbi to officiate at such a marriage and yet not to accept the terms which Church or Synagogue have set as the basis for the marriage. One man stated his position as follows:

> I had no intention of abiding by any premarital agreement regarding the rearing of any children born of my marriage to a Catholic girl. The Church's demand that I agree to their terms in order to have a priest officiate, is itself immoral. I figured that the Church was making demands on me it had no moral right to make, so I refused to abide by them. Sure, I never told my wife how I felt, but she knew that I really had no intention of ever becoming a Catholic. If she is angry with me now, I am sorry, but I don't intend to permit any child of mine to be reared as a Catholic. And if the Church tries to force me by legal means to rear my child as a Catholic, I believe that it will lose because such an agreement, I have been told, is actually unenforceable.

Assuming that there is justification for fighting what one regards as an "immoral" act (by the Church) with yet another "immoral" act (by the young man), was the husband justified in the first act of withholding from this Catholic bride the information that he had no intention of living up to his written or unwritten agreement with her?

Over three decades in the ministry have taught me that young people, prior to their marriage, are not likely to consider the special problems that may result for their children, yet unborn. However, such considerations often come to the fore when children are born. They bring marked changes in the attitudes of many parents who hitherto have been indifferent or even belligerent toward religion. More parents of mixed religions seem suddenly to become aware that they are facing a problem that involves their child directly. How shall the child be reared? Shall he (or she) be reared in two religions with two sets of Holy Days (Easter-Passover, Christmas-Hanukkah) and their attendant differences in philosophies and emphasis? Shall he or she be reared without any religious influence in the home, in a kind of vacuum? Shall he be introduced to a third religion or way of life far removed from the religions of either parent? Persons of mixed religions, neither of whom intends to give up his religion and accept the religion of the other are

faced not only with the ordinary problems of human adjustment, but with the additional problems that have to do with the rearing of healthy, secure children who have the need to identify with some way of life they can call their own.

Persons of different religions who contemplate marriage have an obligation to their unborn children that dare not be ignored. That responsibility is related not only to the physical nurture of the child, but to its social and psychological adjustment as well. Failure to recognize this latter responsibility may ultimately lead to difficulties for both child and parents.

In the case of a mixed marriage, as in all marriages, there is always a confrontation at some time or other. There is a moment when "identification" becomes important to either one or both parents. A Jew may marry a Protestant, a Catholic, a nonaffiliated person or one of another religious or nonaffiliated group, yet, when a male child is born, I have found that the non-religious Jewish father often asks, "Shall this child of mine be circumcised according to Jewish ritual or shall he not?" Such questions are real and they require unequivocal answers. Confrontation at some point in time cannot be avoided. The same principle applies to a Protestant-Catholic marriage or to any marriage involving persons of different religious groups.

Each of us needs to identify in some degree with parents, family and other clearly recognizable groups, nations and religions. It is not enough that we identify with the human race. We wish to know who we are among humans, wherein we are alike and wherein we differ. And the differences, I have discovered, are, at least, as important as are the similarities. When asked, "Who are you?" we may answer, "I am an American," or "I am a Catholic," or "I am a Protestant." Whatever national or ethnic identity we have, we also identify with some religion. That is why so many of us "belong" to churches or synagogues without ever stepping into them. They help others to identify us, even as they help us to identify ourselves. We seek identification for ourselves through identification with some group or groups. Without these we tend to become tension-laden.

I believe that a child who is deprived of identification by the most well-meaning of parents has been done a disservice. Nor is it advisable for parents of different religions to expect a child to wait until he or she reaches adolescence "to make up his mind" which religion satisfies him. This, too, according to the psychiatrists whom I have interviewed constitutes a disservice to the child simply because children cannot be expected to make wise comparisons and judgments without any basis therefor. To do so is to create added stresses and strains that can be dealt with only with great difficulty.

At the very most, never informing a child of his parents' religious affiliation or nonaffiliation commits the child to nothing and *that too* is a commitment. It is, therefore, a mistake to believe that one can rear a child to age twelve, thirteen or fourteen with absolutely no commitment. Rebellion by a parent or parents against religion is a commitment that communicates itself to the child. How, under such circumstances, can it be reasonably expected that such a child will be able to choose a religion when all he has hitherto received is rebellion and antipathy?

Children, more often than their parents, are the victims of intermarriage because of their uncertainty concerning their identity. Well-intentioned intermarried parents find it difficult to provide their children with the security that comes from "knowing *who* I am and *what* I am." The story of one parent, repeated many times in the experience of the author, deserves mention:

> You know, children are brutal. I had my son going to a Jewish Sunday School. I was trying to get him to feel that we were Jewish (his mother was never converted, you know). One day, the kid comes home and says that he's never going to a Jewish Sunday School again. Well, you can imagine how I felt. My wife, too, was unhappy about it because she was really trying to bring up the children as Jews even though she was a Protestant. At first I couldn't get him to tell us what happened. Even when I threatened him, it did no good. He wouldn't go back there. Some rotten little bugger in that Sunday school had told him that he didn't belong there because his mother wasn't Jewish. I don't know how the kid found out, but there was nothing we could do. I went up to the school and had an argument, but that didn't help. The damage had been done.

The Protestant mother who does not intend that her children shall be reared in the religion of her Catholic spouse regardless of premarital pledges or promises may have difficulty in obeying the dictates of her conscience. But her problem is less complex than that of her children whose religious training is being done secretly and often knowingly against the wishes of the father. One mother reports:

> I shall not soon forget my embarrassment when, one day while my husband was talking about getting the children ready to go to church with him, my little boy spoke up and said, "Mommie says we're Protestant. Why should we go to your Church, Daddy?" My husband was more hurt than you can imagine. He looked at me reproachfully. I couldn't have felt worse myself. But my little boy spoke up again and in all innocence asked, "What are we, anyhow?" The poor child was obviously confused and I, with every good intention in the world, had helped to make him so.

A child's growth is associated not only with physical but also with emotional factors. Growth is inhibited when insecurity concerning one's identity creeps into the picture. The child who "doesn't know who or what he is" because his parents, however happy their mixed marriage may be, are identified with different religions, may become emotionally insecure, unhappy and even on occasion develop neuroses. One such parent discussed her bewilderment as follows:

> I cannot understand Johnny. They say that children can become disturbed and unhappy if their parents are unhappy with each other. But *we* are *really* happy people. We get along fine. I am a Congregationalist. My husband is Jewish. John knows that he has the two great traditions. Why should he be unhappy? Is the fact that he has two rather than one religion more difficult for him to accept? Is that possible?

John may be affected not only by his inability to identify with one religion but also by his desire to please both of his parents. And this is far more difficult than it would appear. Stress and strain may affect this, or any other child, negatively, even adversely. A "happy" marriage does not necessarily produce a happy, well-adjusted, emotionally secure child. "Happy" mixed marriages may even serve to increase the chances for maladjustment in the children of such a marriage.

A psychiatrist reports on his experiences in this connection:

> Theodore is the son of a Protestant man and a Catholic woman. Neither the mother nor the father are really interested in Protestantism or Catholicism. They are definitely not religious people. When the two married, they gave up their old friends, moved into a new community and seemingly got along very well. However, neither of the parents has any really close friends other than those who are business associates of the father.
>
> Theodore has no religious affiliation. He sees no religious life within his home, but is troubled because his friends [adolescents] keep on asking, "What are you?" [meaning "What's your religion?"] and he has no answer. When he approached his mother to talk about the matter, he was told that she had given up her religious affiliation in order to marry her husband and that his father, too, had given up what little affiliation he had in order to maintain a home and family life that was free from conflict.
>
> The fact remains, however, that even though the parents are getting along well because, literally, they have no religion in common, their son is now quite unhappy with both his parents and is secretly visiting both churches and synagogues as well as reading what little he can find on religion in order to identify himself with some religion. Whether Theodore will pull away from his parents or acquiesce in their program remains problematical.

Consider also the case of Tom, the product of a mixed marriage:

Tom's father is a Jew in name only. His mother had been a devout Catholic. Yet Tom has been reared completely away from religion. He is aware that his mother attends church regularly. Tom, who exhibited many signs of emotional instability, finally came to the attention of a psychiatrist who gained from him the admission that he regarded himself as a "nothing." With him, the fact that he had never identified either with his mother's church or his father's made him a "nothing." He was simply not a real person. He was a "nobody" with no respect for himself as a person. He was always tense, anxious, ill-at-ease and had no desire to acquire any learning or take any courses that would ultimately lead to a degree. "What was the use?" he asked. "I'm a nothing. Everybody should be something and I'm just a plain big nothing."

Another psychiatrist's file offers the following:

Harlan Levy's father was a lawyer (Jewish). His mother is an Episcopalian. Through all of Harlan's early years he never dated a Jewish girl. Despite his first (given) name, he not only looks Jewish, but his last name is definitely Jewish. He has never had any religious or other contacts with the Jewish people. He knows that his father who was most successful as an attorney committed suicide; that he had no association with Jews and did everything he could to make it clear that he did not regard himself as a Jew. Once, when Harlan was a little boy, he met his grandfather [father's father] and recognized him as a Jew. He has had many problems that involve identification. He wants to have nothing whatsoever to do with his father's family. Yet he is uncertain as to whether he takes after his mother or his father. He is like a little child who keeps asking "Am I a boy or a girl?" "Am I like mommy or am I like daddy?" He is sorely troubled, ill-at-ease and anxious. He wants desperately to be like his mother and her family but his surname (Levy) prevents him from making that kind of identification. Should he adopt another surname he feels that, much as he is repelled by his father and the Jewishness he represented [in name only] this would be unfair to his father's memory. He is trying to escape and cannot do so.

From the files of a psychoanalyst comes the following:

Tim is the son of a Christian (Protestant) father and Jewish mother. During his early and adolescent years his relations with both father and mother seemed to be excellent. During his later adolescent years he developed tensions which seemed difficult for his parents to understand. After a series of medical [physical] studies it was concluded that he was not physically ill in any sense. His physician believed that his emotional outbursts and demonstrations of malaise would be outgrown in later years. It was suggested that perhaps he was working too hard in school. Another physician suggested that, in view of a series of

disappointing romances, he was undoubtedly troublesome, moody and emotionally unstable at times. The tensions and insecurity persisted. It was finally agreed by Tim and his parents that a psychiatrist ought to "see" Tim. After a series of sessions it developed that Tim felt that he lacked identity as either a Protestant-Christian or as a Jew. Although he was devoted to both parents, he regarded himself as more like his mother. But he had not been reared as a Jew and he would not identify either with the Jewish people or with Judaism. The closest approach to identification was with his mother. This form of identification caused him to identify with her as a female, rather than as a Jewess. As a consequence he believed that he had homosexual feelings. There had been no incident or series of incidents to support Tim's feeling.

The psychoanalyst believes that Tim is seeking identification with his mother. Inasmuch as he cannot do so on the basis of religious affiliation without feeling that he may thereby offend his father, his insecurities express themselves in this strange manner.

An example of both a racial and religious mixed marriage is represented by the following excerpt from a case history:

Arthur is the product of an interracial marriage. His father is Negro. His mother is Jewish. They live in Harlem. Through all his years he has been aware of the fact that his mother's family has turned its back on her because she married a Negro. Even though she acknowledges that she is a Jewess, she does not attend a synagogue or perform any of the rites and rituals associated with Judaism. Arthur, who looks like a Negro, is deeply resentful of his father. He feels that the lot of a Negro is quite unbearable and that his father must bear the blame for this marriage. Even though his mother declares that she loves her husband and Arthur recognizes that his father has been "good" to his mother, he is nevertheless deeply resentful of him.

Although less deeply hurt by his mother, he wishes to identify as a Jew. Accordingly from time to time, he enters a synagogue on the Sabbath and claims that he feels a greater sense of identification with the Jewish people even though he believes that they would not acknowledge him as a Jew or permit him to identify with them socially. He is also aware that by attending a synagogue he is expressing his resentment against his mother's parents who refuse to accept her. But Arthur knows that he will not identify with his father's family because it is Negro and he cannot identify with his mother's family because they will not regard him as Jewish.

Intermarried couples who have had their child come home and repeat some canard about a minority to which one of the parents happens to belong are often painfully hurt by the experience. Yet there is very little that such a parent can do under these circumstances inasmuch as his response must appear to be a form of self-explanation or *apologia pro sua vita*.

My experience with the children of mixed marriages has led me to believe that, more often than their well-intentioned parents may realize, such children are faced with problems which tend to produce within them reactions of guilt, insecurity and emotional instability. For instance:

> Joe, the son of a Jewish father and a Catholic mother, who had been married by a Justice of the Peace many years before was, in accordance with his father's wishes, being reared as a Jew. That is, he was being sent to Hebrew School. Joe was seemingly getting along well. One day we received a report from another student at the Hebrew School that when, toward dusk, he had left Hebrew School and was about a block or two from the school, he was accosted by a youth who barred his way and, in an aggressive manner, asked him, "Are you a Jew?" When the youngster replied in the affirmative he was immediately pounced upon and given such a beating as to require the care of a physician. The police, too, were notified. Later a detective happened to come across Joe a few evenings later lurking in the darker areas near where the attack had occurred. Upon questioning Joe, he discovered that it was Joe who had been responsible for the dreadful beating given to the youth.
>
> When I invited Joe's parents to sit down with me and talk the whole matter over, I discovered that Joe was the product of a mixed marriage, that Joe's father was preoccupied with a new business venture while his mother, sincerely desirous of pleasing her husband had enrolled Joe in the Hebrew School even though she maintained her own Catholic religion and she had informed her son that she was a Catholic.
>
> "Consultations with a psychiatrist made it clear that, Joe, although a good student in Hebrew School, did not regard himself as a Jew even though he wanted to please his father. Actually his aggressiveness toward a schoolmate was his way of expressing his opposition to his father's religion and to his mother, for she had forced him into a Jewish School when he resented being Jewish. Actually, Joe was neither a Jew nor a Catholic. He came from a divided home and was utterly uncertain about his loyalties. It is my belief that Joe's parents were his worst enemies. They had done him a great disservice. When these matters were discussed with the parents, it took some time to convince them of their responsibility for Joe's behavior. I tried to get the father to realize that he needed to be much more of a Jew himself and give much more time to Joe's training and education than he had. The psychiatrist sought to have the mother understand that Joe was unlikely ever "to know who he was" unless she and her husband were formally of the same religion and the home ceased to be divided religiously against itself.
>
> Joe now appears to be getting along well. His mother was formally converted to Judaism. His father is making a greater effort to give his son the time and attention he needs. The family appears more united.

Children of mixed marriages may express their insecurity in many different ways. They may be highly irritable, overly sensitive, hostile

either directly or indirectly, negative in their response to other persons, suspicious of others verbally or even express guilt feelings in one of many different ways. Parents may not always recognize any of these symptoms yet psychiatrists have informed me that they believe that they exist more frequently in the children of mixed marriages than in others.

In another case, involving a mixed marriage, a rabbi reports:

> The wife was a Protestant and the husband, a Jew. The children of this mixed marriage had been sent to Hebrew School. Not only were the two children fine students, but the mother saw to it that the children attended Sabbath service each week—and she accompanied them. Although the mother had never given up her religion, her loyalty to her husband was so great that she participated as wholly as she could in the religious life of the Synagogue. Her husband was a Jew in name only. On rare occasions he would come with his wife to some Synagogue function. I do not believe that he would be regarded as an exemplary Jew in any respect.
>
> I was pleased because it seemed to me that these children were well-adjusted, happy youngsters. I do not believe that either of the two youngsters knew that his mother was not Jewish.
>
> One day it became known throughout the community that the father was involved in some illegal act. The mother was shocked when she heard about it and utterly ashamed of her husband's acts. How did she express her righteous indignation? She packed her bag and the bags of her children and moved to California, telling her sons that their father—the Jew—had done some great disservice to them through his illegal acts. The children suddenly discovered in the midst of what must have been a traumatic experience that the mother really regarded them as Protestants. What has happened to these children? What religious affiliation, if any, do they now have?
>
> The guilt of the father is clear. But what has the mother gained by creating an uncertainty within her children as to their affiliation? Are they Jews or are they Gentiles? I suspect that they do not know nor are they ever likely to know who or what they are.

Inability to identify with both parents often tends to create problems of anxiety and guilt on the part of young people. Differences in religious identification between the parents, no matter how well they may "get along" tend to affect a child. One says:

> What am I anyhow? A Jew or a Roman Catholic? All the other kids on the block keep asking me, "What are you?" and all I can say is that my mother is a Catholic and my father is a Jew. But that doesn't seem to satisfy them or me because I want to be something and there is no name for it. When I grow up I'm going to make my own choice of a religion. I don't know what it will be. Maybe Catholic, maybe Jewish, or maybe, some other religion. I want to be able to answer the question, "What are you?" for myself and to myself. And yet I feel bad about the whole thing. I love my mother and my father, but they've

kind of let me down in this matter of religion. It makes me very unhappy at times. I try to tell myself that I'm better off because I have two great religions as part of my heritage, but that doesn't do any good. I know that I don't really belong to either. I wasn't ever in a synagogue because that would have made my mother unhappy and my father didn't want to do that. So just what can I do? Frankly, I feel guilty as anything about talking this way but I'm really more unhappy about it than my parents or anyone can imagine.

Mixed marriage may tend also to produce an attitude of resentment against either one or both parents. Children who would like to identify with both parents find themselves torn between the loyalty they feel they owe to each parent. As a consequence of their inability to identify with *both* parents, a feeling of resentment develops against one or both parents.

If a child cannot come to terms with the social values of his parents and his environment his chances of unhappiness and insecurity are increased. Mixed marriage where each parent represents a distinctive way of life is likely to induce problems involving the ego of the child, who may react in a variety of ways that both the parents and society may regard as negative. In spite of that, parents may insist that, insofar as they are concerned, their marriage is both happy and successful. When the individual's relationship to his environment is disrupted as Hartman[3] puts it, we may expect problems in greater numbers and with greater intensity than are considered "normal."

Landis and Landis[4] report:

> College students, looking at the mixed marriages of their parents, were inclined to believe that, in general, it had been a serious handicap in their home lives.

The religious experience is primarily an emotional one. Children who are torn between two sets of emotional experiences—each parent relating to different ways—become the victims of these parents, who, however well-intentioned they may be, seek to arouse the child's emotions through different religious values and rituals.

The inner conflict, often maladjustment, that results from attempting to live in two worlds, cultures or religions at one and the same time is often too great to bear. Certainly an unfair burden is placed upon a child whose parents expect to rear him in two (to them) equally good cultures or religions.

Stonequist's[5] definition of the "marginal man" is sufficiently exact (whatever the arguments that have been advanced against it) to be worthy of our careful attention at this juncture:

A marginal man is one who lives in or has ties of kinship with two or more interacting societies between which there exists sufficient incompatibility to render his new adjustment to them difficult or impossible.

Such marginal people are, as Lewin[6] explains "on the boundary between groups or being in both groups but really in neither."

A marginal person may not only be insecure in his feelings toward others, but is very likely to indulge in self-pity that may prove ruinous to his own personality development. The belief that one has been deprived of an "identification," that parents have not been "fair" and that opportunities were not offered for a close relationship to a culture or way of life, of which religion is an integral part, tend to create a mood of self-pity that may be harmful to one's wholesome development.

Rosten[7] surveyed the lives of fifteen "mischlings" (children born of cross-marriages, in this case, Jewish-Gentile marriages) who were students at Harvard University and Radcliffe College. Of these, nine were male and six were female. Of the former, seven had a Jewish father and a Protestant mother. One had a Jewish father and a Catholic mother. One had a Protestant father and a Jewish mother. Of the six females, two had a Jewish father and a Protestant mother, two had a Jewish father and a Catholic mother and two others had a Protestant father and a Jewish mother. This study was based on questionnaires and personal interviews with the sons and daughters of these intermarrieds.

Rosten's interpretation of the replies he obtained is interesting, not only because of the persons studied, but because the author describes himself as a "mischling." He concludes that, "Fate has been both kind and cruel to the mischling; kind, because it offers him an opportunity to move within two cultures, unshackled by the predetermined customs of an anonymous past; *cruel, because it has not given him a secure ethnic place in life,* but has left him in a limbo between two larger cultures which will never completely accept him as one of their own. If a 'mischling' accepts the gift of free mobility and can overcome the pangs of ethnic insecurity, his life may become exceptionally rich and meaningful. But if he cannot liberate himself from the frustrations of an existence without a firm, ethnic ground, or if he does not want free mobility, he may well feel that he has been 'condemned' to a totally unwelcomed position in society." [8] It is his view that the child of the intermarried is "ethnically isolated from most of mankind,[9] because he does not have a clear sense of where he belongs inasmuch as "he is a living battleground for the interplay between the two cultures." This sad situation, he believes, results from the fact that "both societies have

erected barriers which will prevent the mischling from being totally accepted." [10]

The conviction attested by Rosten's thesis that children of cross-marriages are more likely to lack security than the children of endogamous marriages is also supported by the personal histories in the present study.

Donne's[11] oft-repeated words: "No man is an island, entire of itself: each man is a piece of the continent, a part of the main" is accepted as a truism, yet we have the tendency to believe that none of us really requires membership in a family, ethnic or religious group for our personal well-being, a notion which, I believe, is wholly unsupported by the facts.

The background, the memories and the loyalties generally associated with the group cannot so easily be rooted out of our minds and hearts or those of our children. Even though some persons may succeed in such an endeavor, most of us do not and cannot, precisely because an important part of our security is bound up with the religious and cultural group with which we have been associated. Difficult as it may be for adults to cut themselves off from their past, the problems for the children of such persons are even more difficult. The children of the intermarried can very easily be psychologically regarded as "marginal" should they lack clear-cut religious identity, living as they do, on the margins of two religious and cultural worlds. Because humans seem to require both self and group approval, any act that tends to prevent us from acquiring either tends to make us insecure, uncertain of ourselves and of our identity in varying degrees.

Rosten declares:

A mischling may be buffeted between the two cultures unable to form a firm attachment to either. . . . When a Jew and a Gentile marry, both bring with them remnants of their upbringings permeated with these different traditions, remnants which, unless one side is completely repressed, will undoubtedly affect the couple's children.

Just as children in a family do not necessarily respond individually to the very same physical factors, they may likewise not respond in exactly the same manner to emotional or psychological factors. J. S. Plant,[12] a psychiatrist who had wide experience with children, has pointed out that, among other psychological needs, they require "belongingness or security" in their personal lives. Emotional security, so important to each of us, is not necessarily the lot of all children even though their parents may seek to provide it for them. Uncertainty concerning themselves may develop when each parent represents, or claims

affiliation with, a different religion. A child may feel emotionally insecure despite the parents' love of each other. Nor does the love of each parent for the child assure the child's own emotional security. As long as the child senses any difference between the attitudes or affiliations of the parents there is the likelihood (not the certainty) that the child may question his "belongingness" and his own security.

Parents who either avoid the subject of religion altogether and have none of it in their home or those who sometimes, through mixed marriages, have two religious ways of life represented in their home, make life more complex and more insecure for their children. The security which children acquire because their parents feel secure as a result of Church or Synagogue affiliation is likely to be lost when each parent maintains a different affiliation. Children, because they are insecure, may acquire a fear about what the future holds in store for them. Insecurity really means that a child feels that he is not protected from dangers real or imagined that, for him, lurk around the corner. Mixed marriages may add to the problems faced by children. They will seldom, if ever, reduce them, as society is presently constituted.

Not all children, of course, respond to a given situation in exactly the same manner. It cannot therefore, be declared that *all* children of mixed marriages will demonstrate emotional insecurity at one time or other, but case histories and personal experience provide evidence that such insecurity occurs in these cases more frequently than when both parents are of the same religion.

The nature of the problems that may be faced by the children of marriages in which each partner maintains his or her own religious affiliation, is well illustrated by the following report:[13]

> Charles is a boy in the religious school. He is twelve years old and in the sixth grade. He also attends a special Hebrew class during the week and engages in some activities in the temple. However, despite his activity, he is not popular and has few friends among the other students. He has shown strangely disruptive behavior in all his classes, and as a result, his classes have been a problem to the teachers who are in charge of them; while the students do not appreciate his nonsense, they see in it a challenge to the teacher so they do nothing about it.
>
> I [the case worker] called Charles' mother regarding the problem. She promised to come to see me regarding the situation. When she first came in, she seemed agitated and annoyed, but her behavior calmed down as we talked. She said that Charles liked to come to religious school and enjoyed all its activities. Then she calmly announced that she was not Jewish, but a practicing Catholic, and that she was doing this for Charles' father who is Jewish. Also in the interview she revealed that Charles had been expelled from another temple last year because of the same situation. His mother did not want that to happen again, as she was very desirous of having Charles Bar Mitzvah next year.

Afterward I spoke with Charles and I realized that the situation is far more confused than before. It seems that the parents have a pact that one year the child will celebrate Christian holidays and the next year the Jewish holidays. He said that this year he is celebrating only Christmas because he is to be with his maternal grandmother, and that at Passover he will be with his father's family. He also asked me at the same time to teach him the four questions, as he wanted to take part in the Seder and have a spot that he covets from a cousin.

He sees his mother acting one way, yet telling him to follow another example. Added to this is the father's complete apathy toward the method of the boy's education other than the fact that he wants his son to be a Jew. The father takes no active part in the boy's life, religious or secular.

"Cross-faith marriages make it easier for challenging values to get through and confuse the child" is Zimmerman's[14] way of stating the case.

When contrasting and even conflicting values are made readily available to the children of mixed marriages, they do not find it easy to make a choice between the two or even to accept both (as some persons suggest). As a consequence "a crack in the psychological armor about the child tends to widen." The victim of this situation is often the child of the mixed marriage.

In another case which has come to my attention the following reaction was indicated:

My mother is Jewish and my father is a Protestant Christian. It had been agreed that I would be brought up as a Jew. My father never really cared about religion and he knew that it meant a good deal to my mother. So I was a Jew, and that's the way I thought of myself. That is, I did until one day when, quite by accident, I happened to come into the kitchen and soon realized that my father had been drinking. For some reason I still cannot understand, he caught hold of me and shook me hard while he said, "You little Jew!" I'll never forget the look on his face and my sudden fear of him. All of a sudden I realized that he was a Christian and my mother was a Jew. I tried to say something to him. I can't even remember what it was except that I was trying to protest that I was only half a Jew. But my father wouldn't listen. And I ran out of the room crying bitterly. Since then I've been trying to make up my mind whether I am a Christian or a Jew. Just because my mother is a Jew—does *that* make *me* a Jew? I'm caught between them. What am I anyhow?

A Jewish educator reports:

One day a husband and wife came to see me about the poor record their son, who was approaching confirmation age, was achieving in Sunday school. Both parents, good people in their own right, didn't seem to understand that there was any association between the son's

poor public-school record in both deportment and subject matter and his many emotional outbreaks in his Sunday school. They assured me that "he's growing up and he'll get over all this." When I probed as deeply as circumstances permitted, I discovered that the mother was a Catholic and the father a Jew; that they had been married outside of the church and that neither really intended to be associated with any formal religion. When their son was born they began to rethink the matter and finally decided to rear him as a Jew "to please my husband." But the mother's parents and friends reminded the child often and in various ways that he was really a Catholic. I know that both parents meant well, but they have really created serious problems for their son. I advised them to see a psychiatrist not only because I believed that this was important for their son, but for themselves as well.

The difficulties that confront the children of mixed marriages, and their parents as well, are called to our attention through the following story:

Benson, a Yale Law School graduate and a successful lawyer, is the son of an outstanding Jewish religious liberal leader who has never renounced Judaism or accepted any other religious affiliation. He is a member of the reform Temple. He fell in love and married Rachel, a brilliant New England Congregationalist. They have been married for approximately thirty years. Benson has few Jewish community contacts other than formal affiliation with the Temple. Both have many Jewish friends. Rachel has continued to attend the Congregationalist Church although she attends a few Temple services (High Holy Days) with her husband. They are the parents of two sons, Eldon and Daniel, both graduates of Eastern universities. Eldon, long before the fraternities at his school became "nonsectarian," accepting Jews as well as Christians, Negroes as well as whites, was a leading member of his fraternity. When one Jewish youth was being considered for membership, Eldon voted against him, it is reported, "because he didn't want Jews in his fraternity." Both sons regard themselves as Christians and both have married non-Jewesses.

Benson is unaware of the fraternity incident. He is unaware, too, of the fact that Rachel, who both before and after her marriage has taught mathematics at a university, was bluntly informed by another faculty member that he would not accept an invitation to have dinner at her home because "I don't associate with Jews."

The older son, Eldon, received his religious training in the Congregational Church, with which his wife is also affiliated.

Daniel is studying for his Master's Degree in Business Administration. His wife, whom he met while on a summer (vacation) job, has had a particularly turbulent time of it. They were married in the Lutheran Church (his wife's church). Daniel has been under psycho-

analysis for some time. Persons who have known him believe that indecision associated with his parents' religion has had much to do with his "inability to decide who he is." If Eldon's attitude with respect to the admission of Jews into his fraternity may be taken as evidence, his relations with his father's people are not good. Daniel seems to have had a difficult relationship with his mother—not because of religion because Daniel regards himself as a non-Jew. When but a child, and despite his association with his mother's religion, his classmates called another child "a dirty Jew." His mother reported that Daniel referred to this one day and added, "if he had called me that, it would have been true." Later, when Daniel was attending college and appeared to be having "troubles," a counselor told Rachel that he believed Daniel's troubles were his way of reacting to his mixed parentage. Rachel, however, has never accepted this reaction as having any validity.

Rachel has her problems, too. According to one friend "she [Rachel] is the only partner in a Jewish or mixed-Jewish marriage who ever asked me, a Christian, if my husband and I would mind coming to their home."

It would seem that the parents as well as the children have had special problems resulting from the mixed marriage.

Benson, the father, adamantly denies that he has been faced with problems resulting from his intermarriage. "I parted from the idea of an insulated Jewish 'community' when I married Rachel. By nature or temperament I lack a conventionally religious view toward life's problems. I am not aware that, in order to be a righteous Jew, one has to subscribe to any prescribed order of belief. My grandfather who devoted himself to Jewish scholarship all his life, never entered a synagogue." Benson has never voiced any objection to his sons' marriages. Nor has he expressed any attitude toward the fact that they have regarded themselves (been reared, in fact) as Christians. He regards himself as a Jew and has never wavered from that position. His wife, too, regards him as a Jew. A judge officiated at their marriage. In the thirty years that have elapsed since then, Benson has always regarded his marriage as successful. He has stated that there are no psychological difficulties resulting from such a marriage of which he is aware. Rachel appears to be much more sensitive to the problems that have resulted therefrom.

The sons, Eldon and Daniel, are not quite alike in their views on this intricate theme. Eldon has no interest in religious observance. He saw no Jewish observances in his parents' home although he knows that his father and mother "belong" to the temple in their home community. Daniel does not attend religious service either in church or synagogue. What their attitudes will be as the result of the marriages to Christian girls is still uncertain.

Benson's Jewish mother has always responded warmly to Rachel. They have remained good friends through the years. Rachel's parents, upon hearing that these two planned to be married were skeptical at first. They passed away shortly after her marriage. Benson's father died many years before his son's marriage. Both Rachel and Benson believe that if "they had to do it over again," they would marry each other.

Benson's sons have no relationship to the Jewish tradition. Rachel, their mother, has certainly not set her sons against their father or the Jewishness of the family. And yet—Eldon and Daniel have, by their marriage to Christian girls, made it clear that they wish to regard themselves as Christians. The obvious end result of this mixed marriage is that, whether planned or not, the sons, insofar as religion is concerned, are related to their mother and have no relationship whatsoever with the father's tradition.

To insist that the children of mixed marriages are uniformly faced with problems relating to their religious or racial identity is, of course, untrue. There are undoubtedly many children, the products of such marriages, who clearly and unequivocally identify themselves both religiously or racially. But my experience indicates that such children are more often confused and uncertain about their identity.

Elsewhere we have noted (*see* page 111) that father and mother record the fact that, of two children, their son of college age, even though Bar Mitzvah (as insisted upon by his Jewish father) wrote a carefully worded letter to one of the colleges into which he sought admission, pointing out that although his father was Jewish, his mother was a Christian. He stated, according to his mother's account, that he hoped thereby to improve his chances of admission into the college. In this case, also, the non-Jewish mother was disturbed and even unhappy because of what this act signified. The Jewish father who listened to the episode, as related by his wife, was astounded. Apparently even a Bar Mitzvah ceremony, or the love one feels for Jewish grandparents and family, however much attested, can, in a crucial moment, be less important than we realize or expect.

In another case of mixed marriage, the parents, a Jewish father and a Christian mother had agreed to rear their children as Jews. The mother saw to it that her sons were given Hebrew training. The traditional Bar Mitzvah ceremony took place. When this marriage ended in divorce, for a very good reason, the mother insisted that the children leave the Synagogue and join the Church. This method, by which this mother demonstrated her justifiable contempt for the father, may bring a sense of satisfaction to her. But what did such behavior do to her two sons whose early years had been lived as Jews and who now are obliged

to live their lives as Christians? And what will be the quality of their Christianity? Will it prove as nominal and vague as was the mother's concern for the Jewish training of her sons?

The case of the Protestant mother who is married to a Catholic man affords another interesting and important example of the manner in which the lives of children can be disrupted. Both parents are fine and good people, well-intentioned, highly educated, seemingly understanding folk. Yet, even though the mother had agreed to rear the children as Catholic and was, as a consequence married by a Catholic priest, she, according to her own testimony, now has her regrets and uncertainties. Although her own identification with the Protestant Church was never clear, there appears to be a drawing away from the Catholic husband and a return, in degree, to her Protestant parents.

Because she is a highly principled young woman, who has given her solemn pledge concerning the religious training of her children, it may reasonably be assumed that they will be reared as Catholics. Yet the mother now finds "Catholicism less attractive" than it appeared to be prior to her marriage. She is obviously resentful of her Catholic husband. In what ways will she demonstrate her unhappiness and dissatisfactions to her children? Despite their formal relationship to the Church, how "good" are they likely to be as Catholics?

When the authority of parents is divided, we may expect that children's loyalties, too, will be divided and that their insecurity will become more marked than we would normally expect. My observation has led me to believe that parents who represent different religions are less likely to be able to provide the total security that children require, no matter how sincere and devoted each parent may be.

As the future becomes less certain because of the many overwhelming changes that have already occurred within the world, with morality generally undergoing certain basic changes because, in our complex age, it is not always clear what is the right path that any man or woman should take, it becomes increasingly important that religion serve as a stabilizing influence for both the parent and the child. The emotional need filled by religion is still very great. The child who has not gained this kind of security in any degree is, I feel, impoverished.

Nor does formal conversion of one person to the faith of another always guarantee the solidarity of the home, or the certainty that children will feel secure.

When Jacob and Priscilla married, Priscilla, a Catholic, was converted to the religion of her husband, a Jew. But all through the years she was unable to accept her conversion without a certain regret. She felt that she had betrayed her parents and she was unhappy and even in conflict with herself. Her husband sensed the changes that occurred

in her attitude, not only toward Judaism, but toward him as well. Even though Jacob had not been very much of a religious Jew, he was aware that his marriage to Priscilla had been accepted by his parents only because she formally converted to Judaism. The desire to maintain his identity with his parents obliged him (so he felt) to be more of a Jew, to observe more of its ritual and recite the Kiddush on the Sabbath. These observances, for him, were synonymous with his identification as a Jew.

When Joe, their first son was born, the father insisted on the ritual of circumcision, while the mother opposed it because this meant identification of Joe as a Jew.

Joe was always a problem child at school and at home. His parents could not understand that there was any relationship between their problems and those of their son. Joe's father was certainly solicitous for his welfare as was his mother. But only when Joe approached his mother one day and asked, "What am I?" did the parents realize that despite his love for both father and mother and a desire to please them both, Joe was uncertain in his own mind whether he was Catholic or a Jew—even though he had not been baptized or reared as a Catholic. He was aware of his mother's unhappiness about her conversion as he was deeply disturbed by his father's insistence that Joe was a Jew. His problems in the primary grades in school appeared to stem from his uncertainty about himself. His desire to please both of his parents resulted in his inability to please himself.

Even formal conversions then, are no assurance that identification of all the members of the family with one religion or people will result. Children may become the victims of their well-intentioned but unhappy parents.

The parents of young people who intend to retain their separate religions may be satisfied momentarily by inviting clergymen representing these faiths to officiate at one or separate ceremonies. Notices of such marriages appear, on occasion, in newspapers throughout the country. They may be noted particularly in the Sunday edition of the New York *Times* where the following[15] appeared:

> Miss Ann DeVincente, daughter of Dr. and Mrs. William DeVincente, of New York City, and Abram L. Goldberg were married yesterday afternoon in two ceremonies.
> The Rev. Thomas Wilson performed the first ceremony at the _____ Church. The second, a Jewish ceremony, was performed by Rabbi Charles Goldleaf. . . .

Inasmuch as each set of parents is able to invite their relatives and friends to a ceremony performed in accordance with their own religious persuasion, initial embarrassments are eliminated and the problems attendant upon such a mixed marriage are temporarily avoided. But the major problem related to such a marriage has really not been resolved. In which of these two faiths will children born of such a marriage be reared? Which of the two sets of grandparents will ultimately feel "re-

lated" to the children? And what price will such children be obliged to pay in terms of their own security and identification with a religious group because of such a hollow victory?

Formal conversion to the faith of the *dominant* marriage partner is often the price that must be paid for a happier marriage, but it must be remembered, this does not guarantee a successful marriage. One such example has come to my attention:

> I received a phone call from one of my congregational members. She was anxious to talk with me so we arranged an appointment. When she came in to see me, she was obviously quite upset. Much to my surprise she revealed that she was a non-Jew who had been married to a fine Jewish man for well over fourteen years. She had never converted to Judaism because her husband had never asked her to and because she did not think it important. But, she pointed out, her son was to be Bar Mitzvah within the next three months. Further, this boy and a brother and sister were attending our Hebrew School and were fine students. She noted that she had insisted that her children be reared as Jews. Her husband was not very much interested in religion but he considered himself to be a Jew and "he was proud of it."
>
> During all the years, she had never revealed to anyone that she was not Jewish or that she had never been converted to Judaism. Through all the years she had kindled the Sabbath candles on Friday evening and had tried to maintain a Jewish household. Her mother-in-law had always been kind and considerate and had taught her all that she wanted to know about Judaism. She had attended Synagogue services on the Sabbath and especially on the High Holy Days. But now—with the approaching Bar Mitzvah of her son she felt that "she could no longer live a lie" and have her children believe that she was Jewish when she knew very well that she was not. Should her children ever discover the truth, she was sure that they would be distressed and that problems would develop for them. She felt that she wanted to be formally converted to Judaism, and, later to be remarried to her husband in accordance with Hebrew ritual. This fine woman spent six months in study. She was converted according to orthodox Jewish ritual and, after the proper interval, remarried by me, a rabbi, to her husband. When her son's Bar Mitzvah took place, I knew how proud she was that she was now a Jewess and that her children's Jewishness need never be questioned henceforth. She felt that what she had done was "to provide her children with security they might otherwise have missed."

The children born of Negro-white marriages in the United States are, I believe, among the most socially unfortunate persons in all the world if they seek or expect acceptance by the white community in America. To date there is no evidence that persons with even one drop of Negro blood will, knowingly, be accepted as whites. To the white person the amount or per cent of Negro blood is of no importance. If there is any Negro blood, the person is generally (almost always) re-

garded as a Negro. He must find his roots within the Negro community or remain unaccepted and unacceptable to the white community. It will do no good to argue whether whites are correct in taking such an attitude. It is far more important to know that, realistically speaking, this unfortunately is their attitude.

The Negro-white families interviewed by the author were unanimous in their belief that their children were likely to find their teen-age period (when partying and socials were being emphasized) the most trying period of their lives. Refusal on the part of whites to permit such interdating is quite general in the United States. Permission on the part of some white parents to allow interdating is sometimes given only because the Negro-white youth is a rarity in a particular neighborhood or community. The subsequent resentment built up by children of interracial marriages against these attitudes must be regarded as unhealthy and even dangerous.

The children of the racially intermarried are likely to be faced with the same discriminatory practices as are their parents. Unless a miracle occurs that will eliminate discrimination from our society—and that does not seem probable—we may expect such children to suffer the same indignities as do their parents.

Whether people, however much they may love each other, have the moral right to create such a problem for a child is, of course, debatable. It is my belief that interracially intermarried parents are committing a grave offense against their children that is far more serious and even dangerous to their welfare than they realize. The Negro in the United States suffers greatly. He is most often provided with the poorest housing available, the least desirable job and faces the unwillingness of people to accept him socially. The children of Negro-white marriages are thus easily hurt, even by their well-intentioned parents.

The ultimate attitudes of children of all marriages, including mixed marriages, depends in large measure upon the way in which their parents introduce them to the outside world. If parents, however happy they may be themselves, are disturbed or unhappy about the manner in which they have been received by other persons, this attitude is more than likely to manifest itself in their relation to their own children. They, in turn, respond to the world of men in accordance with the attitudes and beliefs that have become part of their natures.

Jacobson[16] has pointed out that in 1955 "about 343,000 minor children were involved in the 377,000 final decrees of divorce and annulment . . . or roughly nine children for every ten marriages." He has also indicated that "about two-thirds of the children affected by divorce are under the age of 10."

Inasmuch as we have already noted the higher rate of divorce

among the intermarried, is it not proper to ask, "Shall we then add to the number of children who become the victims of their intermarried parents?" If there is any possibility that this is likely to occur—and the evidence certainly points in that direction—it would seem that our obligation to children should tend to reduce the number of such marriages.

It is my contention that a home in which the religions of the parents differ is more likely than not to confuse their children and make for their insecurity. That this does not occur in each and every case of mixed marriage does not, in itself, support the argument that it never happens. If it occurs *at all,* if a single child is either confused or insecure because he does not know "what he is," or "who he is," this is sufficient reason for raising serious questions and even objection to this kind of mixed marriage. It requires no statistical tables to support the position that this situation occurs frequently. For that reason, if for no other, such mixed marriages are to be discouraged. They are unfair to children, the innocent victims of often well-intentioned parents.

THE WYMANS

Professor Samuel Wyman, Jewish and a native of New York City, is a social scientist. A teacher in the Department of Sociology of one of New York City's well-known universities, he has written extensively in his special field of interest and is well regarded, both personally and professionally.

Dr. Wyman's wife Leota, is from Trinidad, in the West Indies. She is brown in color—of Indian descent. She is a graduate of an American university. These two, married seven years, and the parents of two children, have recently become aware of the fact that their marriage has created for their children problems that beg for solution. Are they Jews or Christians? Will they be regarded as members of the white community or will they be looked upon as non-whites? What effect will these decisions have upon these children?

SAMUEL

I teach sociology at one of America's great universities and I hope to make that my life's work. My interest in the social sciences began when I

was an undergraduate student at a college in New York City, the city in which I was born, my hometown.

I have been teaching for the past ten years. I have a special interest in problems relating to racial, religious and cultural minorities. I met my wife, Leota, when I was still at college. She was born in Trinidad, in the British West Indies. She came from her native country to study in the United States. Her major interest was English Literature. Ours is what you would speak of as an interracial and interfaith marriage. She is brown and I am white. She is a Presbyterian and I am of Jewish descent. She is not a Negro. She is Indian, that is, of Indian ancestry. Her parents, as well as her grandparents and all of her forebears were born in India.

We met at a university in New York City where we were both studying for our Bachelor's degree. I continued on for my M.A. and then went on for the Ph.D. degree.

After she received her A.B. degree, she returned to Trinidad and taught there for a while. She had, in fact, been teaching before she came to New York City.

We were married in Boston almost ten years ago, a justice of the peace officiating. That seemed like the best way to handle the situation. We are the parents of two children, both of whom are brown-skinned like their mother.

Originally, my wife's family was Hindu. Her mother's mother was converted to Christianity, so Leota's mother was born into a Christian family. And because they were Presbyterians, I suppose one can say that her mother, too, was a Presbyterian. Her father was a Hindu who was interested in getting into Teachers Training College. In order to do so, it was necessary to be a Presbyterian—so he converted. It was as simple as that. My father-in-law had three brothers. One, converted to Christianity. He, too, is a Presbyterian. The other two are still Hindu.

The family never really knew any Jews. There are very few Jews in all of Trinidad and about 750,000 people in all. So, neither my wife nor her family ever really got to know Jews personally even though they, too, like so many others, had formed stereotypes of what Jews were like. They use such expressions as "Jew somebody down" for example. But my wife commented to me that, aside from the Bible, the only other Jews she knew anything about were to be found in "The Merchant of Venice" or *Ivanhoe*. But "Jew" has very little meaning to her people in actual fact. They are not aware of having had any contact with Jews at any time.

Still, when she returned to Trinidad after her first year at school, the idea of her going out with someone who was Jewish didn't seem to please her parents too well. Not because of what they actually knew about Jews, but just because of the stereotype. But it appeared to be a temporary state of mind with them because when Leota came back to New York, she was very much interested in a marriage developing. This meant, I suppose, that the original reaction of her parents was somehow changed.

You see, the Presbyterians had done much missionary work in Trinidad. They were fundamentalists, highly orthodox in their Christianity and literal-

ists insofar as the Bible is concerned. At least that was my impression. The Canadian Presbyterians concentrated upon the Indians in Trinidad and made a considerable number of conversions. In this group there was no drinking, no dancing, no smoking. They were really quite strict. My wife's father became an Elder of the Church in Trinidad in which her mother had always been very active. And both of them, as principals and teachers, were very influential, at least in their own community. They are both British subjects. In fact, my wife, too, has a British passport. I'm telling all this about my wife's background and about her parents so that you may know that she did come from what must be termed a "religious" home. And I think it always meant a good deal to her.

While we were still undergraduates, I recall that a young Indian student, a very popular young fellow who was friendly with my girl's sister, raised some questions about her dating, not only me, but other Jewish boys as well. She reported that he reacted negatively to the idea and especially to the thought of a possible intermarriage. His remark was, "Well, why doesn't your sister marry an Indian boy and, if not an Indian, why not, at least, someone who is a Christian?" So, you see, the pressures came not only from the parents but from "friends" and society in general. The fact that we did marry means that the vague kind of stereotype that was operating had no real emotional meaning for Leota.

There is, generally speaking, a feeling of uncertainty and even prejudice on the part of some people against Jews, but I can't say that it really affected me very much. Insofar as my wife's sisters are concerned, both those who are married and those who are not, I have really not been able to detect any prejudice. I would say that my relationship with them is generally very good. This may be due, in part, to the fact that we see each other only on rather brief visits, but we appear to have a very wholesome regard and respect for each other.

You ask whether this may be due in part to the fact that all of us are teachers. I think that may have something to do with it, and it helps to explain why I would want to marry a daughter from this kind of a family. At least in terms of our intellectual interests, we were on the same level.

Now I will tell you something about my own family background. I'm sure you want to know. I was born on the East Side in New York City, in the heart of an all-Jewish neighborhood. My parents were Orthodox Jews. Both my mother and father had come from Russia. Neither of them spoke English very well. Both had a pronounced accent. My father died some years ago. I have a brother and a sister, both of whom are considerably older than I.

I spoke Yiddish to my parents, and I can still speak it fairly well. But I spoke English to my brother and sister. I never felt that my parents were "foreigners" in the unpleasant sense in which some people use the word. There were so many other people just like them in the neighborhood that they were in no way unusual. And I certainly do not recall ever thinking that I wanted to get away from them or their kind of life. My friends were all Jewish while I was going to elementary school and high school. In the

main, I lived exactly the same kind of life that the thousands of other children in the area lived. There was nothing strange or unusual about it.

My father didn't have very much Hebraic knowledge. He certainly was no Hebrew scholar, but he and my mother wanted to be sure that I went to Talmud Torah (Hebrew School) every day after school hours. My father was a sewing-machine operator in a garment factory working on vests. Both parents would go to *Shule* on Holy Days. My father attended occasionally on the Sabbath. For years I recall that he "davened" (prayed) every day and put on his "T'fillin" (phylacteries) fairly regularly up to the time he died. He was about sixty-one years old at the time.

Now my mother wasn't as devout as my father was. Although her house was always *kosher,* there were many things done that led me to believe that she was not as observant as my father. They lived a very simple life, worked hard and tried to give us an education and that was it.

I guess that somewhere around my twelfth birthday I made it clear that I was anxious to stop going to Talmud Torah and there was quite a fight about it. I think there were several different factors that caused me to react as I did. The first is that the educational system was certainly not of the best. We spent a lot of time sitting and reading from the prayer book. The teacher would just go around the class and each of us would read so that eventually we became fairly fluent in reading fast, but it didn't mean anything to me. I didn't understand the meaning of the prayers and nobody ever bothered to explain. It was a boring and wasteful process. The other reason for my reacting as I did was the fact that many of the kids in my friendship group were not going. Once we got involved with the principal of the Talmud Torah. Something we did. Anyhow, it was finally settled that I would continue for an additional year, have my Bar Mitzvah and then I would stop. If I may say so, as I look back upon the whole Talmud Torah experience, it was a damn lousy education they gave us. I should be able to read and speak Hebrew, but aside from a few words, I just don't know any Hebrew. I can read it a bit, but I certainly don't understand it at this point. I have no emotional attachment to Hebrew, the Synagogue, or the Talmud Torah.

My contacts with my brother and sister were not very important either because I didn't know them very well nor did they know me. They were so much older than I.

Now to get back to the story of my marriage. It seems strange that two people from such different backgrounds, color-wise, religion-wise, nationality-wise, could have fallen in love and decided to get married. But our common ground was college and education. We met at school and we made new friends there. It wasn't unusual for me to date Christian girls. I never bothered to ask, or even to think, about it because just about everyone was doing it. Jewish boys and girls—Christian boys and girls—and here, you have an Indian girl, whose family had been Hindu and was now Christian—Presbyterian—interdating without its being regarded by any of us as any kind of a problem.

It's especially interesting about my wife and her reactions to persons of

other colors or religion because, in Trinidad, the Christian Indians feel very much superior to the Hindus, in terms of economic and social class distinctions as well as in terms of religion. Occasionally it gets verbalized in simple class terms like, "You know, the Hindus are crude," or something like that. But the American schools particularly are breaking down such barriers, I believe.

When I first started dating non-Jewish girls I didn't say anything to my mother about it. But she heard about it. I forget just how it happened. She objected strenuously, but frankly I just did what I wanted to in this respect. When I began going out with the girl I was going to marry, I certainly didn't talk about it to my mother. Yet word got back to her through one of my friends, I guess, and she made her attitude very clear. She kept asking how could I do this sort of thing to her? And "Why go out with somebody who isn't Jewish?" She really became very emotional and she cried. She hoped all along that nothing would really happen between us. It was hard for me to take because I have a warm feeling for my mother, but I just had to decide whether I was going to live my own life or someone else's.

We had talked things over as much as one can, I suppose. I felt that I was on my own and responsible only to myself. And as for my girl, she really didn't have a problem because I had not asked her to convert to Judaism. I certainly wouldn't!! She had a religion in which she felt at home. We had arrived at certain decisions as to how we would conduct ourselves—so we got married by a Justice of the Peace. We figured that we would not involve any rabbi or Protestant clergyman. This seemed like the proper and easier way to meet the problem.

A few days before we got married, I decided to write to a few people and tell them about our plans. I wrote to my brother and sister, a few others who were close friends and I sent a very carefully worded letter to my mother.

When my sister received her letter and the one to my mother that had been sent in her care, she intercepted my mother's letter for a number of weeks in the hope that she would save her some anguish. I'm sure that she did it with every desire to keep my mother from being hurt. After our marriage, I phoned my sister to get her reaction and to find out how my mother had taken it. It was then that I found out that she didn't even know about it. By this time some of my friends had heard from me and I felt that it would be most unfortunate if my mother heard about my marriage from someone other than me. So I flew to New York with the purpose of telling her about my marriage.

Well, I spent a couple of hours that were really difficult. There were copious tears and much emotion generally. She cried hysterically for a long period of time. Some of the things she said made sense, some did not, but she was certainly the most distressed human being I had ever seen. I guess I spent a couple of days trying to talk with her, to make her understand that this was a good marriage and to get her to see that the world had not come to an end. By the second day, she had calmed down somewhat—

not that she was really calm, but she was considerably changed from the way she had been, and then, suddenly she went to a trunk, opened it, and pulled out a white tablecloth which, she tearfully told me, I should take back home as a present to my wife and myself. And then she gave me some advice: "She's your wife; treat her well. Don't run around. Be a good husband" and words of counsel like that. She seemed to be coming around at least to the point of recognizing that we were really married.

I had some very negative reactions to my marriage, too, from my sister, and strangely, I thought, from my wife's sister. But there was not too much emotion and it wasn't excessively maudlin. There were other negative reactions from some friends, but not too bad.

Now my mother was always "the strong one" in our family. She was certainly the dominant person. Between her and my late father, the discipline had been quite strict. I just had taken it for granted that it had to be that way. It was only when I went to college that it began to dawn on me that I could make my own decisions and really be on my own. I didn't have any formal dues-paying affiliation with the Hillel Foundation, the Jewish organization on our campus. I would drop in every once in a while, but certainly for no religious reason. During a four-year period, I went there only about a half-dozen times. As I explained, Judaism—what I knew of it —really didn't mean very much to me. I never belonged to any Jewish fraternity or to any other fraternity for that matter. I don't believe that during my college days I ever went into a synagogue. I had friends, a few very close friends, and I retain some of them to this day. In fact, one of these friends is intermarried, too.

In these years, my mother visits us for about a week during the summer. She loves our two brown children very much. Although everything on the surface seems satisfactory in the relationship between my mother and my wife, I would say that there is still an undercurrent of feeling on my mother's part and a feeling of resentment on the part of my wife. No, I can't say that the problems in our family relationship have really been solved.

We two get along very well. There are differences of opinion and ideas, but they are not really basic. What I am concerned about much more is our children. They aren't old enough now to receive formal religious training, but I can see that this is going to lead to various questions and perhaps problems, too, of one sort or another. I rather suspect that they will simply follow in their parents' footsteps. I mean—I don't go to any synagogue and my wife doesn't go to any church at all. But that in itself will not solve the problems. For example, although I wouldn't say that we observe Christmas, we do have a tree at the Christmas season. We observe Hanukkah, too, in the sense that we talk about giving Hanukkah presents at that season.

The children know that I am Jewish. Occasionally we talk about these things and about their being half Jewish or their being half Indian. But, at this age, it makes no kind of an impression upon them. Now this is one of the problems I'm thinking about. We decided a long time ago that

nominally we would say that our children were Jewish if they have to fill out a form at school or anything like that. *But my wife isn't happy about this decision and every now and then complains about it.* Originally, we had decided that if there were a male child, he would be circumcised ritually and that he would also be christened. You see we didn't care too much about these things ourselves. We thought we would satisfy both our families in this way. But my mother's reaction, which I have described, was so great that I was prompted to eliminate the christening and this is something my wife still has some concern about. Well, not the christening itself, maybe, but what it might symbolize later on. I guess that she will want our children to identify with Christianity while I, only out of regard for my mother, would want some form of identification with the Jewish people. It isn't because I am such a devoted Jew, you understand. Well, maybe, what I am trying to say is that I would rather they would not be identified with any other faith. *This* is our immediate problem and just how we will resolve it, I don't know. But it *is* a problem. Wherever the fault, the difference in religious background does seem to create a problem.

Whether or not the color problem will ever become a serious one for our children, I do not know. I do not think that it ought to be. They are Caucasians, you know. Indians are included in the Caucasian race. Yet, many people unfamiliar with this anthropological classification of races, may raise questions, for after all, Caucasians or not, there *is* a difference in skin color. We shall leave that problem for our children to resolve simply because we cannot do anything about it. But I am beginning to worry about it.

You ask what my response would be if my children, when grown to adulthood, were to come to their mother and me and say "We would like to marry persons of a different color and a different faith from ours." I think that my wife and I would both respond by asking *"Which* other color? *What* other faith?" For it would depend upon the particular circumstances and the particular individuals involved. What's right in one case is not necessarily right in another. Therefore, I think that it would have to be completely up to them.

Now you may gather from this that I, for one, have no emotional attachment whatsoever, either to Judaism or to the matter of being a Jew. But that isn't altogether correct. Personally, I find that I do have attachments, indicated for example, by my wanting to talk to my children about Hanukkah while my wife talks to them about Christmas. I find that on occasion I will sing a Yiddish song for them, or use certain Hebrew words so that they will learn the sounds, but it's very difficult for me to do much more than that. I would like them at least to be aware of the fact that I am Jewish and at least to have a little knowledge of Judaism. Unfortunately I'm really not the best one to give them the kind of Jewish content they should have because I don't know enough.

As for my wife, I'm certain that she hopes that they will eventually decide on their own to become Presbyterians. Once we talked about switching to Unitarianism or something like that, in the hope of finding a middle

ground. There may be some possibility of the children wanting to nod in some such direction, but it's really pretty hard to say now.

It has always puzzled me that persons who are born into Jewish families, yet practice or observe almost nothing of Judaism, seem to be unable to accept the idea of mixed marriage. They simply get emotional about it. It is, to many of them, as if the bottom had dropped right out of their lives. I suppose that to a large extent intermarriage signifies giving up the very core of identification with one's group. Identity is not only a religious matter. It is a social one as well. The final and last step, so people seem to think, is to give up that identification by intermarrying. Perhaps they are right. I'm beginning to see what they mean.

To conclude, let me say that, insofar as my wife and I are concerned, I think we would agree that we are personally getting along nicely. But the problems associated with the lives of our children have yet to be resolved. I keep hoping that in time we can resolve them.

ANN AND IRWIN

Irwin, a Jew, was married to Ann, a Protestant. Prior to their marriage, it was agreed that children born to them would be reared as Jews. Irwin, whose parents were orthodox, regards himself as "reform." Ann always thought of herself as a "liberal" Christian. When, following their marriage, Irwin protested the use of Christmas symbols in their home, he was informed that he was cruel. When he tried to introduce any Jewish symbol or rite into their home, Ann frowned upon it. Their daughter, who has been reared as a Christian, is an unhappy and even sick person. Whether or not the open conflict within the home prior to the parents' divorce is the direct cause of the child's illness is not clear.

Irwin is married again, this time to a Jewish girl. He is now clearly opposed to mixed marriages. Ann has been married twice since her divorce from Irwin, in both instances, to Protestants. These marriages, too, have ended in divorce.

IRWIN

After eight years of married life, our interfaith marriage ended in divorce. Neither Ann nor I ever imagined that this would happen, but it

has happened and, unfortunate as it is for us, it is still worse for our young daughter.

I am a Jew. Ann is a Protestant. Actually she had always been a church-going liberal Protestant. When we married, she retained her religious affiliation and I retained mine. We were quite certain that no force or series of forces, family, friends, Church, or Synagogue, would ever break our marriage. And we were right. It wasn't any of these. It was ourselves —what was inherent in each of us—that finally did it. [*Editor's note:* Whether or not Irwin is correct is questionable.]

I come from an orthodox Jewish family. At least my parents were orthodox even if my brothers and sisters were not. I have two brothers and two sisters. We are all deeply devoted to one another and since our early years have been close. My father was a learned Jew. He was a highly respected member of the community in which we lived, not only because of his knowledge of the Talmud and other Hebrew texts or even because of his active participation in the Jewish community, but also because he was a very successful businessman. My mother was as sweet and kind a person as one could ever meet. She was a devoted wife and mother and a genuinely religious soul. We, her children, loved her very much. We were close to her as she was to us.

Each of the children was given every opportunity to develop according to his or her interests. My brothers were quite different. One became a businessman, the other became a physician. It was assumed that I, too, would go into my father's very successful business when I grew up. One of my sisters became a teacher, the other a medical technician. All of us children got along very well together. We went to elementary school, high school, and on to the state university. We all did well in our school work. I had hopes that someday I might become a lawyer, even though my father was heading me in the direction of a business career.

We had a Hebrew teacher who came to our home every day to teach us. There was no really good Hebrew School in the city when I was a youngster. My father was concerned about our Hebrew education, so he engaged a teacher for us and we studied in organized fashion at home. One room of our home was set aside as a classroom for this specific purpose. This will give you some idea of how important Hebrew learning was to my folks. Of course, we children took it all for granted.

We lived in a Jewish neighborhood, not far from the synagogue. We boys attended the synagogue on the Sabbath with my father regularly. It wasn't regarded as obligatory for my sisters to attend, but they did study Hebrew and the Chumosh (Five Books of Moses) at home.

As I look back upon those days, I cannot think of anything that ultimately caused me to rebel against either of my parents. I do not believe I rebelled against anyone or any idea in those days or that this "rebellion" ultimately led me to intermarriage. I wasn't fighting anyone. [*Editor's note:* Irwin's family disagrees.]

It is true that my father's business went bad and my brother and I were no longer going to be able to go right into the business as had been

contemplated. This meant that there had to be a reconsideration of our future plans. One of my brothers decided to continue with his university career so that he might ultimately become a physician. The other decided that he was cut out for business even if my father's business had failed. I was disappointed because my first taste of business had shown me that it was fairly easy to be in business and after one has had the satisfaction of having one's own bank account and feeling well off, it isn't easy to adjust to something else. But I *did* come back to my first love. I decided to go back to the university and get my law degree.

Those were dark days for me. They were difficult, too, for my parents, who had lost practically everything they ever owned. But somehow, getting back to school soon revived my spirits and I began to feel good about being "on my own." My sisters, too, took odd jobs and helped to finance their way through the university. But hard as it was, we remained together as a family and tried to maintain a home, with each of us children contributing toward its maintenance.

It was about that time that my father and mother decided to move to another city where, it was hoped, better business opportunities would present themselves. Of course, my brother who was in medical school remained at the university. My older brother had begun some business venture that made it next to impossible for him to move. But my sisters who had their degrees from the university found jobs in the same city with my parents, lived with them and helped, as did the boys, to support the home. I had graduated law school and I decided to try my luck in the new city, as well. So there we were, away from the friends we had made, away from our old environment and part of "the lonely crowd." We were in a big city to be sure, but we were very much alone.

It was during that period in my life that I met Ann. I had gotten a legal position in the city with a good firm. Ann was a secretary. She came from a lower-middle-class working family. Her father had died about ten years before, so through all of her teens Ann had been cared for by her mother. Ann had graduated from high school, and the pressing financial needs of the family had obliged her to go to a secretarial school and take a job thereafter. Both parents had regarded themselves as Protestant although her mother was now affiliated with a very liberal church that had no formal creed. Ann had always regarded herself as a religious Protestant.

Ann and her mother had lived in Peoria for about five years. Prior to that, they had lived in a small town in Missouri. I can only guess that the opportunities for work were greater in the big city and Ann and her mother both needed to work in order to live, that the move to Peoria was prompted by this consideration. I am quite certain that during all the time I knew her, Ann's relationship with her mother was excellent and I remember Ann telling me that they had always been good.

We met on a double date. One of my friends had a date and he asked his girl friend to bring along someone for me. This was not one of those "quickie" affairs. We actually went together off and on for about two and one-half years before the affair became serious. All this while I was at the

law office and enjoying my work, but I was lonesome. I didn't go out very much. Of course, there was my own family for part of the time, but due to another change in fortune, my parents decided to move back to their first home town. So, really, I was pretty much alone. I didn't see the family very often. I wasn't earning too much and things were generally quite tight. My office associations did not bring me in contact with Jewish girls. I hardly knew any Jewish people socially. Then, too, one man in the office had intermarried and he was getting along fine. Ann and I were invited over to their home rather often and I saw that intermarried people could get on very well together. The few people I knew who saw us together all seemed to think of her as a sweet girl. The office in which she worked was just around the corner from my law office, and all of these factors sort of drew us together more and more.

I knew, of course, that the members of my family would not approve of an intermarriage. I knew that they would try to dissuade me by every possible means, but I also knew that my mother would eventually accept whatever I did. I felt certain about that all the time. Yet it was a difficult decision to make because, even though I had drifted far from my parents' orthodoxy, I still had some strong feelings about being a Jew and I had no real intention of giving up that identification. I guess that the strongest point was the fact that I knew of at least one successful intermarriage and this helped to convince me that, regardless of what others in the family might say, I knew what I wanted to do.

I shall never forget the way in which my mother pleaded with me not to marry Ann. She cried bitterly. She talked and pleaded with me, but somehow I didn't feel that she understood me or Ann. When the other members of the family, including my father, talked with me, they were just as anxious as my mother to dissuade me, but, even though I knew that it would hurt them, I felt that they would get over it. I thought that all they needed was to really get to know Ann. But it obviously required more than that.

I cannot today look upon their pleadings, discussions, and arguments as improper or as wrong in any sense. They were, I think, wiser than I was at that time.

I think that our marriage ended in divorce not because of my family or Ann's, but because of us. We were really very much different from each other and religion did play an important role in our break-up. But it wasn't the Church or the Synagogue that did it. It's the way we responded to our own religion after we were married.

We were married by the liberal minister of the Community church Ann used to attend. Ann's mother had attended this church, too. In fact she had worked hard for this particular church.

But, however liberal I thought I was with respect to religion, I knew that I was a Jew and I did not want to have my home become a Christian home. Of course, I felt this way much more after our marriage than I had ever realized I would.

For example, at Christmas time, I would not permit a tree in the

house, nor would I allow anything resembling a Yuletide celebration. To Ann and her mother that was cruel and inhuman treatment, for it shattered the traditions of her childhood. (I forgot to mention that Ann's mother lived with us in our apartment.) Whatever Jewish symbols I tried to introduce into the home after my daughter was born were made fun of by Ann. Now, lest you think that I was taking advantage of Ann by acting as I did, I want to make it clear that prior to our marriage, we had agreed that any children born to us would be reared in the Jewish religion. But Ann changed her mind about all that. She was disillusioned, I guess.

I know that my family invited Ann and my daughter up to their home for vacations, *etc.* She came, mostly because I insisted, but it wasn't very successful for any of us. Ann was quite aloof from the family and I felt that she looked down upon their very Jewish way of life, the ritual observance, the Sabbath meal, with the candles kindled. Where, to me, this was lovely and warm, to Ann it was quite meaningless. Whether or not she thought the family were barbarians, I do not know.

I spoke before about our differences, but they were not just religious differences. I think they were cultural, educational and social differences, as well. That came to the fore as time went on. When you marry, you actually bring your entire past—religious and cultural—with you and it remains with you.

It was obvious after four difficult years that we could not remain together. We were separated for about three years, and it was my hope that somehow we would be able to reconcile our differences, but that was not to be. We finally got a divorce.

Some people think that if things don't work out, you simply get a divorce, but I can tell you that there is much more to it than that. In our case, we had a daughter. Ann wanted the child to remain with her, and I have been supporting her for the past ten years. But it isn't a question of dollars and cents that is important. It is rather what we have done to a child. I feel reasonably certain that my daughter, who is a very unhappy person, would not have been that way had we, her parents, remained together and had she known what she really was—Jew or Christian. She has been seeing a psychiatrist and has been quite ill for a time, but though neither Ann nor I feel entirely responsible, we cannot help but feel that our unsuccessful marriage was certainly a contributing cause to her unhappiness and illness. I am convinced today that interfaith intermarriage can work out only for people who either do not want or cannot have children. The arrival of a child into a mixed marriage changes the entire scope of the original intention, no matter how emotionally strong the professed love was before marriage.

I do not believe that the unhappiness that came about in our marriage was the result of the fact that I came from an orthodox Jewish family while Ann came from a so-called liberal Christian family. Unfortunately the prejudice and deep-rooted intolerant attitudes that one finds in non-Jewish families must be considered, too. These attitudes are often such that nothing can overcome the outside pressure upon the non-Jewish girl. It may be argued

that a highly intelligent girl, perhaps one who has a higher university degree or someone like that, can withstand all these pressures quite normally. But I would even challenge that postulate.

I believe now that the only possible route for a Jewish man who marries a non-Jewish girl, and is determined to make his marriage last, is to gradually give up contact with his Jewish circle of friends. This happens sometimes and I know of such people. While I can recall a few mixed-marriage families who apparently seem happy and who have children, I feel quite certain that they are the exception to the rule.

I would do everything within my power to convince a child of mine that he was violating every principle of his faith and every standard of his family and more important, what was best for his own future welfare, if he considered getting married to a person belonging to a different religious group. I have discovered that, if one has any feelings at all about one's own faith and one's family, it is the height of folly to undertake such a marriage.

In our case both Ann and I had strong feelings about our own religion even though we did not realize it before we were married. But we found that out soon enough.

I have remarried. My wife this time is a fine Jewish girl and we have two lovely daughters. I know now what it means to be happily married.

CHAPTER 12.

CONCLUSIONS: A PERSONAL VIEW

Thirty-five years in the active Rabbinate in large urban congregations have afforded me innumerable opportunities to meet a multitude of young people of all faiths contemplating marriage or intermarriage. I have met, too, with the parents of these youung people. I have listened carefully and as dispassionately as possible to the tales they have told me about their romances and their hopes for marital happiness. During these many years I have attempted to counsel and advise these youth and their parents as well with respect to their plans for intermarriage.

These highly personal and intimate contacts in which I have shared experiences sometimes joyous and, at others, sad have provided me with some insight into the nature of the problems intermarrieds face.

During most of these years I have been fortunate in that I have been able to call upon my knowledge of the social sciences and of the growing literature and studies in the field of intermarriage and the family to assist me in the ultimate words of counsel I was able to offer. This concluding chapter, then, like the chapter that has preceded it, represents something more than a mere survey of sociological data presently available on an ofttimes vexing and intricate theme. It represents, in addition, a personal credo and a firm conviction. I believe that there is evidence to support the thesis that interfaith marriages are far less likely to succeed than are those in which both parties have a religion in common. The evidence on this score seems clear and unequivocal. My experience, together with a knowledge of the studies that have been made on this subject, as well as my own research, causes me to believe that intermarried persons, however capable and intelligent they may be, require far more courage and strength of spirit to make a go of their marriage than is true of partners in all other marriages. (And even they obviously require far more fortitude and determination than many humans possess. Otherwise the ratio of one divorce to three marriages would not be so startlingly high.) Marriage out of one's own faith is, according to the evidence I have examined, almost three times less likely to succeed than ordinary marriages. Whether or not religious difference in these cases is only one of the factors that has resulted in the ultimate dissolution of the marriage, the fact is that interfaith marriages fail in far greater numbers than intrafaith marriages. If I were a betting man, I would certainly not wager against such odds.

The chances for the success of an interracial marriage are, according to my research, even less than for that of an interfaith marriage. In

the latter case, parents, the family, the Church and Synagogue play significant roles in militating against marital happiness. In the former case, obvious difference in skin color makes for an unfavorable societal attitude toward the intermarried. Public opinion generally opposes such marriages. Persons who entertain the thought of entering into an interracial marriage should know that they and any children born to them will suffer many hardships and disadvantages as the result of such a marriage. If interfaith marriages require great courage, then interracial marriages may be said, under present conditions in our society, to require even greater fortitude. I believe that the institution of marriage certainly does not require that we make martyrs of ourselves and of our children. Marriages in which the husband and wife have more (rather than less) in common are, according to all the evidence, far more likely to succeed. And, inasmuch as "success" in marriage is the desired goal, the information we have acquired about interfaith and interracial marriages ought to be heeded.

If the college youth we have studied continue to hold to the ideas that are presently theirs, as indicated in this study, we may expect that intermarriages will continue to increase in our society. The number and the significance of the factors that will continue to affect the rate of intermarriage in the decade ahead make this prognostication quite clear. In a democracy such as ours, where the opportunities are provided for men and women to move both horizontally, from neighborhood to neighborhood, city to city or state to state, and vertically from a lower to a higher rung on the economic or social ladder, we must expect the number of intermarriages to increase. Our democracy would soon be defeated if any group on the American scene was required to cut itself off from contacts with persons of other religions or races. The segregation of any group, religious or racial, either voluntarily or involuntarily, that creates walls of separation between some Americans and their fellows is, as I see it, unthinkable and even dangerous to the body politic.

This is not to deny every man's right to maintain and preserve his particular religious heritage. Constitutionally guaranteed, there ought, at this point in American history, to be no question concerning such a right. Judaism, Catholicism, Protestantism, or any other religion or body of religious beliefs and practices need not offer apologies for their existence here in America. We have neither the legal nor moral right to insist that any religious body give up its particularistic and distinctive way of believing or acting unless such ways interfere with the welfare of American people, or the democratic way of life.

In our diversities, we Americans are often compared to the members of a symphony orchestra. We like to point out that the varied in-

struments when played together in consonance are the factors that "produce" the richest symphonic orchestral qualities. However, the orchestra ceases to exist when each musician, however much of a virtuoso he may be, produces even the richest of instrumental tones within the privacy of his own studio, utterly independent of the other musicians who, together with him, would comprise the symphony orchestra.

The privilege of being part of an open society—which is America—entails certain responsibilities and risks as well. The voluntary or forced isolation and insulation of any minority group behind ghettolike walls is not only undesirable but spells danger, as well, to the social and political philosophy of America. I believe that our culture is enriched by contact with other cultures. Our neighbors' culture may broaden our vista and add depth and understanding to our own views. I believe that the contact with varied cultures and religions characteristic of America is both profitable and spiritually enriching to us all.

Such contacts as we have discussed, however, undoubtedly create added problems, because examination of another religion or culture may ultimately lead some to believe that this religion or culture more closely represents his philosophy than does his own. We may, as a consequence, be tempted to discard some phase—or all—of our heritage.

In the fear of mixed marriages, for example, there are those who, concerned lest their heritage be discarded or in some way betrayed, counsel a return to ghetto-like existence. "Give up your contacts with the outside world," they command. Such insulation is no longer acceptable to most Americans. It is rather frowned upon and discouraged.

What, then, is likely to reduce the likelihood of intermarriage while contact with other Americans of different religious and cultural heritage is maintained?

I believe that the only counteractions under these circumstances are the development of better, more effective religious schools that will, with increasing intensity help to create in the growing child a genuine love of his heritage, and the creation of better homes and families by parents who will also provide rich and meaningful religious experiences for their children within the home and through the example of their personal lives as well. The child who respects and honors both the moral and ethical values *and* practices of his parents and has been helped to see that they stem from the parental religious heritage, is, I believe, unlikely to disregard the significance of that heritage when he chooses a mate. This is not to say that all children will respond in this way to good parents, good homes and good schools. Rather, it is suggested that a positive response to one's own heritage may result from such a program.

A child who sees his parents superficially concerned with reli-

gious observance, who senses that whatever the parents' acts, their hearts are devoid of any feeling for the significance of the ritual acts they perform, is not likely to respect their ways. Nor is he likely to feel the warmth and comfort of such a "religion." It is more likely that children will feel repelled and offended by its emptiness and hypocrisy. Respect and love of one's religion cannot be achieved by fiat. It is more likely to result from a series of impressions created over a period of many years by sincere devout parents and teachers.

The impressions a child acquires from his early years to adulthood, remain. Let the reader look back upon his own childhood and recall those moments that have meant most to him through the years; those acts that helped to give meaning to life itself; that helped to assure loyalty to parents and to their way of life, and he will discover that a religious heritage is often transmitted by direction, not by indirection.

I believe that the parent who teaches religion to his child by personal example is not likely to lose that child to another religion at a later date. I cannot prove that this is invariably so, but I believe that the number of factors that lead to intermarriage may be significantly reduced thereby.

As we have already noted, it is difficult to understand why a contemplated interfaith marriage becomes a major issue in families that are often indifferent to religion and do not maintain any formal identification with Church or Synagogue. Such persons usually fall back upon such an argument as: "People should marry their own kind," a statement largely tribal in its implications. Others, objecting to interfaith marriages, speak of the alleged "inferiority" of some religions or racial groups in contrast to their own. It would be difficult, indeed, to convince such persons that they are the victims of religious or racial prejudices, yet that is, nevertheless, the case. For neither logic nor statistical evidence supports their views.

Whether or not all persons look upon religion as essential to a well-rounded, meaningful life is less important than the fact that society, through the past centuries up to and including our own age, has agreed that the proper kind of religion can influence men and nations for good. To deprive a child of his right to obtain a religious upbringing, which can be a source of security and inner strength is, I believe, to commit a grave offense against the child and the future adult. It is equally unfortunate to confront a child with two different religions within the same household for this substitutes insecurity and uncertainty for security and a sense of identification. To fail to provide a child with a religion because parents of different religions have, in the interest of compromise, forfeited their own individual heritage, is wrong. A child reared in a religious vacuum is, I believe, the poorer because of it.

It is important to recognize the fact that no greater abilities—physical, mental or metaphysical—have ever emanated from peoples who have assimilated and given up their own identity, than from those who have maintained their separateness and distinctiveness. Diversity in color, race, or religion, is, then, neither a blessing nor a curse in itself. It may become one or the other, depending entirely upon how diverse peoples use their diversity.

In this connection, a word about interdating is important. Interdating among teen-agers and college youth, must be recognized for what it is—a form of courtship which may ultimately lead to marriage. If we accept this fact and approve of interdating, we must, in turn, be prepared to face the consequences of interfaith marriages. Those persons who cling steadfastly to their own religion have much more at stake as a consequence of interdating than do those who are indifferent to their Church or Synagogue and its values. Those persons who interdate stand every chance of falling in love whether they wish to or not. Romantic love is little concerned with other considerations. "Let the interdater beware!" is the kindliest advice that I can give to those who would interdate, but who think that somehow the possibility of love and marriage is not involved. I advise against private interdating if you wish to preserve your own faith. I believe in group activities, inter-denominational, intercultural, and international because they have social and educational value. Parents, with the co-operation of schools, churches and synagogues, can through these media develop their young peoples' respect for those who differ from themselves as well as for the group to which they belong. But to permit the close personal relationship encouraged by interdating is, in fact, to encourage intermarriage.

Young people, contemplating marriage with a person of another faith, owe it to themselves and to the children that may be born to them to consider carefully the implications of such a marriage. Young people who have never regarded themselves as religious, coming into direct contact with a potential marriage partner of another faith, frequently feel compelled to identify themselves in various ways with the religion of their parents. Having taken their own religion for granted when they were not faced with a direct challenge, they suddenly become positive with respect to their own religion.

To those who contemplate the possibility of intermarriage, I suggest that if your religion is, at present, of little or no significance to you, it is obviously difficult for you to imagine that the time will ever come when it *may* assume a far greater meaning in your life. Yet such situations do occur far more frequently than we may believe and they must be reckoned with. There is simply no way of knowing if or when a change of heart or mind will ultimately occur This possibility must,

however, be carefully considered. For, if it does occur, it may create a difficult if not an intolerable situation in marital life.

If religion plays an important role in the life of the proposed marriage partner and is of no significance to you, then it would seem best to accept the religion of your partner by formal conversion. Such a conversion, resulting from the love of one's mate, is both honest and right. It is well, however, to recognize the difficulties that may be encountered in such a supposed acceptance and in the frequent change of mind and heart of the converted partner.

Although similarity of religions will certainly not assure or guarantee marital happiness, it is likely, on the basis of the statistical evidence presently available, to reduce the number of factors that may obstruct successful marital adjustment and affect the personal happiness of parties to the marriage.

Marriages that commence as *mixed* marriages, where one of the partners has not formally accepted the religion of the other, are definitely less likely to "work out." Although formal conversion, based upon a sincere and thorough knowledge of the religion to which conversion takes place, is to be preferred, there are cases where conversion, motivated by love alone, may prove to be sufficiently strong to make it possible for the marriage to succeed. Yet my own experience with intermarried couples for well over three decades causes me to refuse to officiate at a marriage in which no effort has been made by one party to undertake the serious and solemn study of the other's religion.

Parents who face such a problem should insist, *for the young peoples' own ultimate happiness,* that a formal period of study of the new religion be undertaken in all sincerity and truth, and that there be a formal conversion to the religion of the dominant member of the couple. The fact that, at a certain fixed time, such a conversion ceremony occurred, serves as a reminder to both parties to the marriage that the marriage was entered into in terms of the all-embracing emotion of love and of knowledge and reason, as well. Such a marriage, I have found, appears to be more likely to succeed. Further, it eliminates from discussion and argument the questions that must otherwise, inevitably, arise concerning what the religion of the children who may be born to them will be. Children have a right to know who they are. They have a right to know with which religious group they identify—and why. They may, as a consequence, be saved at some future date from utterly unnecessary and thoroughly vexing situations in which others (perhaps their own intended in-laws) may question their familial and religious antecedents. All other approaches to the problem of intermarriage are, in my opinion, compromises that may fail. Inasmuch as ultimate happiness is the goal of all married couples, everything that may help to

assure such happiness should be complied with. Formal conversion is, therefore, all important.

Of even greater consequence, as we have discovered in our interviews, is that even in those instances where intermarrieds have had the strength to withstand onslaughts of organized religion and family they have not necessarily solved the problems their children may ultimately face. It is noteworthy that even those parents in our interviews who term themselves "liberal" and who claim no allegiance to any single religious group, denomination, Church or Synagogue, seem to have a difficult time of it when it comes to their children. Although it is possible to "live in two worlds," as marginality implies, such a condition is apparently not a happy or healthy arrangement. Children will ask and parents must ultimately answer the question, "What are we?" As one of our intermarrieds pointed out:

> It is far easier to deal with the question of the differences in our races. All our children have to do is to look at themselves in a mirror and, *from point of view* of color, they know exactly what they are— they are Negroes. But inasmuch as neither of us has any religious affiliation now, even though in his youth my husband was Jewish and I was Presbyterian, our children are utterly without a specific religious identity and *this* seems to disturb them very much.

It is *their* lot with which we must be primarily concerned. Persons anticipating cross-marriages, however much in love they may be, have an important obligation to unborn children. It is not enough to say that such children will have to solve their own problems "when the time comes." Intermarriage frequently produces major psychological problems that are not readily solvable for the children of the intermarried. Living as we do in a world that emphasizes the importance of family and religious affiliations, it is not likely that the child will come through the maize of road blocks without doing some damage to himself.

I believe that parents who attempt to dissuade their children from intermarrying are not selfish, intolerant people, as their children and others are wont to say. They know, by their own experience, the experiences of others, and even intuitively as well, that opposites in color or religion are far less likely to be as successful in their marriage as are persons of the same color and religion. Ethnic differences were greater sources of friction in an earlier day than they are today because the memories associated with life in other countries were far greater when there were comparatively few native-born Americans. Today, when the native-born constitute about 84 per cent of our total population, ethnic differences fade into the background. They are far less significant, though they remain sources of potential disturbance to a marriage.

Parents, I think, to the very best of their ability, ought to attempt to dissuade their children from intermarrying. They should do so lovingly and as persuasively as possible, but always realizing that their most important "possession" is their child. Parents who threaten their children, or who insist that they will disinherit them, or refuse to acknowledge them as their children, are guilty of the greatest of all crimes.

I believe that religion is often associated with the problems that arise among persons of mixed marriages. It is much more of a problem than many persons realize precisely because it is so intangible. Religion is something more than a matter of ritual. That persons of mixed marriages observe different rituals is obvious. But different religions also teach different values and standards. The Catholic who refrains from reading certain books because of obedience to the dictates of the Church, whose views on such matters as birth control and contraception are acquired from his Church, does not see life in quite the same way as does a Protestant or a Jew. The Protestant who believes in the autonomy of his Church, who may be a teetotaler or have serious objection to dancing, is living by values that would be utterly foreign to the Catholic or Jew.

The Jew who does not bow down to any graven image, who does not believe that the Messiah has yet come, whose Torah tells him what he shall *do* to attain human brotherhood rather than what he should *believe,* is concerned about values that are not likely to be fully comprehended by either Protestant or Catholic. These are but a few of the values that affect one's outlook upon life. And each is definitely associated with a particular religion. Hence, it is, I think, correct to say that our religious philosophy and practices often provide the basis for differences and misunderstanding between people of different religions. It is one thing to recognize the fact that differences do exist on this level. It is, however, quite another thing to be required to live with these differences day in and day out as must persons of "mixed marriages." Religious differences are less easily dealt with than are budgetary problems within the home. Because of their mercuric nature, differences in religious values persist even when it is believed that the problems arising out of such differences have been resolved. The roots of religion are planted deep. They are not easily uprooted or neutralized.

Whether or not we agree that religion plays an important role in the lives of most people, we must agree that we are all conditioned, from the moment of birth by the attitudes, examples and values set for us particularly by our parents and other members of our immediate family. Even in those families that do not regard themselves as "religious" in terms of their observance of ritual and ceremony of the faith of their parents or grandparents there are, nevertheless, certain values and atti-

tudes toward life that have been offered to the ever-learning child, and have become fixed in the character and personality of the youth. Neither the parent nor the child may regard them as being a matter of religion. Often, in fact, such persons vehemently deny that they are religious— and in a strict sense this is undoubtedly true. Yet the values or way of life adopted by the parents come to be fixed in the child's life as well.

For example, regular church or synagogue attendance, the saying of Mass, observance of the dietary laws may be regarded as "religious" acts, while the setting of a special table, the lighting of Sabbath candles —yes, even a chicken dinner on the Sabbath eve—may be regarded by the Jewish family as a means of bringing the family together rather than a religious act. The decoration of the Christmas tree and distribution of Christmas presents may be regarded by the nonreligious Christian as a social (in contrast to a religious) act, and the practice of birth control may be regarded as irreligious by Catholics. Yet, in each instance we are dealing with a way of thinking and acting that is derived from religious sources. And so many other attitudes and values in our lives that are, in themselves, nonreligious owe their origin to religion. The love of the study of Torah (Divine Law) which has been translated into love of learning, philanthropic endeavor, so much associated with the religious idea of "Zedakah" (the practice of righteousness and charity). Family solidarity, so characteristic of the Jewish group through these many centuries; teetotalism, emphasized by certain Protestant sects and frowned upon by both Catholics and Jews, are in themselves nonreligious acts that directly or indirectly call attention to certain values. These values may still have special meaning for those who declare that they are far removed from the religious way of life of their parents or grandparents. That meaning becomes evident only when, married to someone of another and different set of values, the attitudes implanted in one's youth suddenly become important, if only because one does not relish the prospect of giving up all the standards acquired from one's parents.

It appears to me that the reason certain sociologists cannot find definite proof that interfaith marriage has any direct effect upon the divorce rate (while acknowledging the obvious fact that intermarriages end in either divorce or separation much more frequently than do other marriages) is because they define "religion" too narrowly. They ignore or minimize the degree of "religious" conditioning that occurs within Catholic, Protestant and Jewish families. Viewed in this way, the obviously greater number of intermarriages that fail can be better understood.

Lenski's[1] observation that, whereas the Jewish associational or religious bond is weak, the communal bond is extremely strong is in my experience correct. The ties of the Jew to the family and the Jewish

community are, in fact, so strong that, in my opinion, they compensate for the "weakness" of the religious ties. The "commitment" of Jews appears to be far greater in the direction of a strong feeling of relationship, or "belongingness" to the Jewish community and the kin group than it is toward belief in a personal God, the value of prayer, or the observance of distinctive ritual and ceremony. To be a "good Jew" is seemingly much more associated with one's relationship to the Jewish people and one's own family and their values than with theological or even ritualistic concepts and values. We may well explain the present low rate of interfaith marriage among Jews as the result of the value which they place upon family and people rather than upon ritual or theology.

Elsewhere,[2] I have noted that the religious practices that remain among Jews involve the family and the community very directly. The Passover Festival Seder commemorating the Exodus of the Jews from Egyptian slavery is centered around the family. Those rituals and ceremonies that are associated with the family as a unit—Hanukkah (the Feast of Lights), the Sabbath meal, Bar or Bat Mitzvah, confirmation—these and other observances that relate to the family and its individual members, tend to be preserved, even though orthodox theology, prayer, and synagogue attendance show no signs of increasing among Jews.

The emphasis upon the preservation of the Jewish community is in part, a reaction to prejudice and anti-Semitism, but it is certainly not *wholly* that. The preservation of the Jewish community, the sense of one's relationship to fellow Jews may more correctly be termed a socio-religious response than anything else. The concern of Jews for the physical and psychological well-being of their fellow Jews may also be regarded as a socio-religious act. Thus, the view that Jews are not as "religious" as Catholics or Protestants, is, I think, incorrect. It is more correct to say that, whereas, Protestants and Catholics interpret religiosity in terms of belief, ritual and prayer, religion for the Jew implies a far greater emphasis upon the community and the family.

Inasmuch as Jews have traditionally been close to persons within their own group, family and community—and this relationship is due not solely to external pressure against the Jews but to an inner and purely voluntary and positive choice on their part as well—the fact that Jews have hitherto not intermarried as frequently as have Catholics and Protestants becomes more understandable.

The argument that persons who oppose intermarriage—religious or racial—are per se "prejudiced," may be true of some persons; true, in degree, about others; and yet be completely untrue about still others. The desire to perpetuate one's own religion or to prevent its assimilation is understandable and reasonable. If it were necessary to "prove" that

each of us is entitled to life only because we possess some demonstrably unique or special talent or gift of mind or body, our society would be decimated in short order. Just as no individual needs to explain his desire to live, so it would seem to me that neither races of man nor religious or ethnic groups need offer apologies for their desire to perpetuate themselves. I believe that the tendency to classify all persons who oppose intermarriage as "prejudiced" is, in itself, a prejudice.

Those persons who indicate a favorable attitude toward intermarriage may look upon such a course as one important means for the attainment of human brotherhood. They may be impelled by high motivations. In fact, they may be convinced that the quickest and surest way to conquer prejudice between peoples and groups is through such a practical means as intermarriage.

Such an argument appears to me to be weak, utterly impracticable and even fallacious. Assuming that prejudices could, in fact, be utterly eliminated by the act of intermarriage, on what day, at what hour, at what minute, would all mankind be of one mind concerning acceptance of such a course of action? Obviously, from a practical point of view, it is not likely to happen. A comparatively few individuals here and there will intermarry with persons of other ethnic, national, religious or color groups. The time seems far distant, however, when the American people will accept the idea of interracial marriage, if the attitude of our student sample is at all representative of the general attitude.

Serious questions may also be raised against interfaith marriages because, even though not all persons may see the relevance or uniqueness of the values of Catholic, Protestant, Jew, or any other of the religious groups extant, many of the adherents of these groups *do* see such values and *do* regard them as worth perpetuating. To such persons, intermarriage means the ultimate loss of the values by which they live.

Even if there were nothing unique or valuable about the contribution of each religious group to the development of humankind (though I believe they have made and can continue to make valuable contributions), it is hardly likely that any sectarian group of which I am aware would deliberately seek to destroy itself or even to weaken itself to the point of complete and utter noneffectiveness. On the basis of group self-pride and self-respect, it does not appear likely that intermarriage will ever be regarded as a basic or major solution for the ills of our age. Universal brotherhood, freedom from prejudice, intolerance and hatred of the unlike will hardly be purchased at the price of the giving up of all group personalities. None of the great prophetic voices out of the past ever proposed that national or religious groups, however different from their own, should cease to exist in order to achieve universal brotherhood.

Viewed in terms of the short-time situation with which we are generally confronted, intermarriage appears to the major religious bodies, as well as to national ethnic and racial groups, to constitute a betrayal of the ideals and values which each professes. It appears, also, to constitute a betrayal of family and group values. A deep hurt is often created in family and friends whose values are spurned. Pride is affected. Families, friends, religions and races, knowing that their "values" differ from those of others, believe that their unique way of life is somehow endangered when mixed marriage occurs. To minority groups—racial, cultural or religious—the possible extinction of the group as the result of intermarriage looms as a very serious threat.

Some proponents of human brotherhood insist that the biological, cultural and religious intermixtures of humankind would not only improve the human race, but would inevitably assure the ideal state in which brotherhood would become a fact rather than merely a desirable goal. Whether human society as a whole would be physically improved by such admixtures remains to be proved. At most, all that can be stated with any degree of accuracy is that no one has yet provided any scientific evidence that the human race is physically despoiled by the intermingling of the blood of various races of mankind. Nor is there evidence to support the contention that because of these admixtures, society actually suffers a severe cultural loss. The evidence is not available because no society has wholly given up its own culture and substituted therefor the culture of another people. Proponents of human brotherhood may believe that "it would be a good thing" if we were not divided, in many cases arbitrarily, into races, nations, cultures or religion, but there is not a single shred of evidence to support such a view.

There is, on the other hand, evidence available that we *are,* in fact, separated by color, language, national, cultural, religious and ethnic differences. Those who support the premise that human brotherhood can come about only through the breaking down of racial, national, cultural and religious walls that now separate people from each other, tend to assume (a) that the fact that men are not biologically different from each other implies that cultures and religions, too, do not differ; (b) that there are no higher or lower cultures, no higher or lower religions. There are, in fact, cultures, civilizations and religions obviously more advanced or less primitive than others. Belief in the distinctiveness of a certain culture or religion and the desire on the part of some individual or group of individuals to perpetuate that distinctiveness because of its demonstrable superiority does not, of itself, make any person less a proponent of human brotherhood. It is rather a question of which road to take to reach the desired goal without destroying all other goals

that have been or are in the process of being achieved by a particular society.

When the prophet Isaiah envisaged the day when swords would be beaten into plowshares, spears into pruning-hooks, there was no indication that he believed that peace would result only from the elimination of nations. None of the Hebrew prophets implied that "internationalism" meant the elimination of the nations. They believed, rather, that it was the duty of each nation to learn how to live in peace and harmony with other nations.

The goal of brotherhood similarly does not assume that there is no room in the world for different races, cultures or religions. Insistence that only through the admixture of races, cultures and religions can such a desirable end be attained is therefore unrealistic. It fails to evaluate the many factors that divide men from each other while assuming that brotherhood can be achieved if, by some magic, we persuade some nations, or cultures or religions to give up their identity wholly and completely and identify with some other culture or religion, larger perhaps, but not necessarily superior or more advanced.

Proponents of intermarriage have declared, too, that mixed marriages tend to reduce prejudice, that inasmuch as prejudice and intolerance are certainly among the greatest enemies of human brotherhood, an increase in such marriages is highly desirable. The desirability of attaining this goal is unquestioned. Whether or not intermarriage is the one and *only* way to reach this goal is questionable. There are those persons who insist that the elimination of the many languages that men speak and the substitution therefor of one common language would bring about a new and better order in human society. Others suggest that all national lines that separate people from their neighbors should be eliminated. This, they declare, is the solution to our basic problem of lack of human understanding and tolerance. What we are attempting to point out is that there is no single or agreed upon solution for the problem of prejudice and intolerance. The breaking down of barriers that separate men from their fellows is certainly desirable. Perhaps all lines of divisiveness that separate families from other families (to begin with the basic social unit) might be desirable. In their early years the Russian Revolutionists attempted this only to discover that although certain ills in society were seemingly overcome, other ills cropped up to take their place; the latter were regarded as far more dangerous than the former.

Further, what may prove desirable for the individual may prove wholly undesirable for a group. An individual here or there may find the answer to his or her particular problem through intermarriage, but this seldom, if ever, is true of a group of any large segment of society.

It is jokingly related that a few Jewish families sought conversion to Christianity—the Episcopalian Church—in order to break with their Jewish past. And, as the story goes, they succeeded very well in their efforts to assimilate. When other Jewish families, hearing of the "success" of their friends, sought conversion and membership in the same church, the Vestry called a hurried meeting and decided that they would accept the Jewish converts and open a new church for them adjacent to the old building. The moral is clear. Individuals may find solutions that are not available to the group.

Those well-intentioned students of psychology and related subjects who suggest that intermarriage is the solution to the problem of prejudice, appear to place little faith in their own fields of study. They are, by indirection, suggesting that it does not really matter how much we get to know about ourselves and our fellow men because we shall never know quite enough to conquer the evil of bigotry and prejudice.

Human brotherhood cannot be assured by intermarriage. One physician put it well when I asked him if the goal of human brotherhood was not worth the means—mixed marriage. He replied:

> Those who argue as if Human Brotherhood is worth any price might just as well argue that the way to avoid having to darn sox is to cut off the heel and the toe of the sock. In that way you are assured that you will no longer have to darn the sox. But you are also assured that you have eliminated the sox. If its warmth and comfort means so little, if you want to go around barefoot that's O.K., but you still aren't solving the matter of how to meet the problem of the hole in the sock. So, the argument that intermarriage will bring about human brotherhood is just a myth. It assumes that you erase all differences. Actually, you create other differences that are just as bad. Differences between people must be respected. You cannot eliminate them by pretending that they don't exist. Intermarriage may resolve one kind of problem, but it creates a host of others, equally bad.

The elimination of racial, national and ethnic differences appears, at first glance, to be justified. There can be no argument with those who point out the prejudice, intolerance and hatred that exist, and wars that have been fought because of these differences. It is, however, merely an assumption that the elimination of such elements of difference will eliminate the causes of societal disharmony. That is guess work, pure and simple. There is no clear evidence to support this theory, nor is there any support for the premise that prejudice, intolerance and hatred are the inevitable results of such differences. Even if this hypothesis were, in fact, true, there is still no reason to assume that there is any practical means by which elimination of these differences could be attained. Nor is there any certainty that the elimination of present

differences would not result in other societal and personal differences that would produce prejudice and hatred. What these good souls are really saying is that *all* differences except those of sex are harmful and even destructive to society. They are advocating conformism as the solution of society's basic ills. Aside from the question already raised concerning the practicability of such a move, we may well raise the important question of its desirability.

I believe that basic differences will not be eliminated. I believe further that the most we can hope and work for with any degree of moderate success is that we will grow more accustomed to the idea that it is possible for persons of different colors, races, nations and religions to work together in many areas even while retaining their distinctiveness.

Mixed marriages, in my view, need not necessarily prove harmful to and destructive of our society. They may, however, dull the impact of that distinctiveness and uniqueness that often give races and religions meaning and actually contribute to the improvement of our society.

America makes no demands upon its minorities other than that they be good citizens, whatever their religion. There are, however, powerful psychological forces that react upon them. Many members of minority groups believe that they are expected to be like all other Americans and to some this implies conformism in all things, cultural and religious and political. Conformism ultimately means nothing less than assimilation. It was Zangwill's dream[3] that the Republic of Man and the Kingdom of God "would be built in America where 'the great alchemist' would melt and fuse Celt and Latin, Slav and Teuton, Greek and Syrian, black and yellow, Jew and Gentile. Yes, East and West, North and South, the palm and the pine, the pole and the equator, the crescent and the cross through the great Melting Pot, into one People." This has not ceased to be the great American hope for the future, as envisaged by many Americans.

The right to religious distinctiveness is generally accepted today by Americans even though they expect ethnic assimilation. Religious differences within America are regarded as quite normal.

Parents are often ineffective in preventing a son or daughter from intermarriage because the lateness of their strictures tends only to induce a little more "rebellion" on the part of their child. They create a sense of resentment rather than understanding.

They are often ineffective, too, even though their arguments against intermarriage are logical, because, in the light of their personal behavior patterns their expressed views are palpably false and meaningless to their children. A youth who listens to a well-reasoned argument against

intermarriage is not likely to be impressed if he is aware that the sincere religiosity of the parent is open to question. He will ask:

> Why does it suddenly become important for me to marry a Jewish girl when I know that my mother hasn't set foot in a temple in a year, that the Sabbath is never observed in our home, that we don't "keep" the dietary laws, that we give a few dollars to charity but hardly in accordance with our means? And to top it all off, I've been hearing my parents talk about how all people are created equal—so what's the fuss all about?

The same argument holds true for Protestants and Catholics as well. Those who are "nominal" Protestants or Catholics are as likely to discover that the theoretical arguments which they advance to children contemplating intermarriage have little significance. As the daughter of one Protestant family said:

> My father used to talk about how unprejudiced he was, that he had real and good friends among Catholics and Jews. But when he heard that I was dating a Catholic boy, he simply went wild with anger. "What did I mean by going out with a "Catholic?" he asked. And all I could do was to look at him and wonder how sane he really was. I didn't remember the last time he went to church on a Sunday. On every nice Sunday he was on the golf course. There was nothing about our home that distinguished it as a Protestant family home. The fact is that I knew that my father—and my mother, too—really were indifferent to religion. Some persons would say that they had no religion.

Parents cannot hope to meet the challenge of mixed marriage successfully if they begin to think seriously about it during their children's adolescence or later. To make this a major issue in the life of children at this age serves only to antagonize children and creates an unwholesome spirit within the home. Such tactics only hasten the desire of a child to get away from such parents. Tensions are created that cannot easily be resolved.

Parents who from the earliest moments in the life of the child are themselves kind and loving, and who in that spirit equip the child with a positive attitude toward religion may be more effective by their indirect approach than are the others. A home in which the child from his earliest years associates gentleness, love, compassion and understanding with the religious way of life is more likely to reduce the possibility of mixed marriage than will all the preaching in the world.

Young people tend to believe that their parents "do not understand" them; they are under the impression that parental opposition to their proposed intermarriage stems from this fact. It may well be that

parents understand their children only too well, that they know their weaknesses—their unstable natures and immature judgment, among other things—even as they know their strength. Parents may know their children sufficiently well to realize that they have neither the strength of character nor courage to be able to meet the problems often created through intermarriage. In defense of parents, let me say that they are generally much more concerned with the welfare and happiness of their sons or daughters than their offspring believe.

Some persons approve an increase of marriage between Negroes and whites on the ground that the "race problem" will only be overcome if, through intermarriage, all external marks of distinction between peoples are to be eliminated. Such reasoning assumes that the rational and emotional responses of Americans have already been prepared for this solution. Despite the number of years in which Negroes have lived in America, little, if anything, has transpired until very recent times to indicate that it was ever seriously assumed that Negroes would be accorded social as well as political equality. Inasmuch as political equality has not yet been accorded to the Negro, *de facto,* it appears likely that a considerable time will elapse before social equality is actually accorded him. Interracial marriages will, of course, continue to take place sporadically. They will tend to increase among Negro and white college youth since, as time goes on, more Negro and white students will meet. There may be an increasing tendency in this direction as more kinds of employment are open to Negroes and whites *alike.* However, based upon signs presently available, it is likely to take a quarter of a century (a little over one generation) to note a psychologically more friendly receptive and emotional response of the white man to the Negro.

Even though we may decry the unreasoning and highly emotional basis for opposition to Negro-white marriages, we must, nevertheless, in all truth, remind those who are contemplating such a marriage, that, in the present state of American society, they will be placing an unwarranted burden upon their children as well as upon themselves. Opportunities for cultural, economic, political and social advancement may, for some time to come, remain closed to these children because of their color alone. Should prospective parents readily take such a responsibility upon themselves without careful consideration of the implications of their mixed marriage for children yet unborn? I believe that young people definitely have this grave responsibility and that they must meet it.

However much in love young people may be, they must be made aware of the special problems with which racially intermarried folk must deal. The reports that have come to us of interracially married

couples where the white husband (or wife) would rent the home in which they planned to reside because of fear that the house would somehow not be available if the landlord knew that he was renting to a Negro-white couple (*see* p. 276) are typical of the embarrassments that occur in the case of such marriages. The Negro may take this situation for granted, but neither of the intermarried can be pleased by it. Awareness that, out of concern for what "people will say," the white husband walks ahead of his wife and children in public so as not to attract attention to themselves is another source of embarrassment. If the intermarrieds walk together in public, they must expect untoward stares and hostile glances. The fact is that, some couples are not given "credit" in some stores. They know, too, that they must never see their parents, family and old friends, for fear of distressing or embarrassing them. Unless such families manage to find a place of residence where they are socially acceptable or where they can live quite independent of other people, including their own parents and families, they are not likely to find complete happiness. These and many other situations place heavy burdens upon the interracially married.

American society is definitely hostile to Negro-white marriages. Generally speaking, it rejects such an idea. That this attitude is without biological support, is clear. However, there is still reason to use cultural differences between Negroes and whites as an argument because the number of Negroes who receive a higher education is still proportionably much smaller than that of the white population. That whites, by their control and even denial of job and schooling opportunities, are responsible for this situation hardly needs to be pointed out. The vicious circle must somewhere be broken. Equality of educational, job and housing opportunities appears to offer the best means to attain this end. Interracial marriages will become acceptable when the equality of the Negro—politically, culturally, socially as well as biologically—is generally accepted by whites. In the meantime, the rate of interracial marriage will remain far behind that of interfaith marriages.

Catholics as well as Protestants and Jews will be increasingly affected by intermarriage. The son of a chief rabbi in one of the Scandinavian countries is intermarried as are the sons of several noted American rabbis. A well-known clergyman in the Boston area is the son of an intermarriage between a Jew and a non-Jew. Among Catholics, there is evidence that intermarriage occurs not only in the families of the laity, but among the relatives of the clergy as well.

A Catholic "sister" in charge of a Catholic girls' school reported in an interview with me that her eldest sister had been married to a Protestant whose conversion to Catholicism occurred only three years before he died. The children of this marriage were all baptized in the

Catholic faith, yet one son married a Lutheran, and a daughter married a non-Catholic, who converted to Catholicism several years after his marriage. Another daughter of this same marriage became a devout Catholic and is presently a nun, teaching in a Catholic college.

Another of this (Catholic) informant's sisters married a member of the Church of England, who later converted to Catholicism. During most of his married life, however, he practiced no religion at all. Their children, reared in the Catholic faith, remained loyal to Catholicism, though their mother, reared as a "good" Catholic, "became less strong in her convictions and practices during the years of her marriage to her non-Catholic husband."

The third sister of our informant married a Catholic, but her eldest son married a Protestant girl and now attends the Protestant Church in his community. The latter couple had three children, only one of whom was baptized as a Catholic at the instance of the husband's Catholic mother. The other children were not baptized as Catholics and were, in fact, reared as Protestants. One of these, a daughter, married a Protestant and her father (born into a Catholic family) "never protested."

Our informant, discussing these and other interfaith marriages in her family, commented that on the basis of her experience with the intermarriages in her own family she is convinced that intermarriages tend to weaken the "Catholic religionist" of the mixed marriage, a fact verified by social scientists, the world over.

Marriage outside the religious or racial group represents a threat to the survival of that group. This is particularly true of minority groups. When the problem of survival as a group appears to be particularly great, emphasis upon the importance of in-group marriages is magnified.

Jewish, Catholic and Protestant religious groups wish to survive not only because the desire for life is characteristic of normal, healthy people and groups, but because each religion believes that the elimination of the values by which it lives would be a disservice to the total society of which it is a part. It believes further that its unique "way" represents the path that God has directed man to take. Identification with the group then is tantamount to identification with its values as well. However much one may argue about the real worth of these values, the fact remains that to each group they have significance, and no religious group will wittingly give them up.

All the evidence we have been able to gather points to an increase in intermarriage within another generation. The factors that make for intermarriage, religious, ethnic and racial continue to increase. The likelihood that controls will be strong enough to counteract this tend-

ency does not appear to be marked. Unless a wave of anti-Semitism or anti-Catholicism sweeps over these United States, or unless an increased antipathy to persons of other races and colors expresses itself, we certainly have no reason to assume that intermarriage will remain at its present level.

Will a given intermarriage work out? The truth is that no one really knows whether it will or not. There are so many factors, personal, interpersonal, hereditary, environmental, psychological and cultural that must be considered in great detail if we are really to attempt to answer this question for each particular case. Inasmuch as few, if any, can really know the detailed answers to each of these questions, we must rely upon statistical probabilities relating to success or failure in marriage. This much we know—marriages in which there are, or were, differences of religion between the contracting parties prior to or after the formal marriage, appear two to three times less likely to work out than do those in which both parties were of the same religious affiliation before marriage and remain so. Because the statistical studies were made under different circumstances and the conditions under which they were made quite naturally vary, all sociologists are not agreed even on the matter of statistical probability. There are those who say that marriages involving partners who were or are of different faiths are *twice* as likely to fail as are those marriages involving persons of the same faith. Others insist that interfaith marriages are likely to fail *four* to *six* times more frequently than those in which both parties were and still are of the same religious faith.

Because differences between Americans are being reduced does not mean that they do not exist or have no effect upon us. Nor are we assured that, with the passing of time, all the present differences that exist among us are likely to vanish and that, as a consequence, all lines of distinction and differences between Americans of differing religious or cultural backgrounds are bound to disappear.

Kennedy's[4] conclusion that "intermarriage does not relentlessly increase in the dimension of time in a smooth, unbroken pattern" serves as a significant reminder to those who assert that the assimilation of religious minority groups into majority groups is inevitable, or that the three major religious denominations will certainly merge into one amalgam—whatever its name or content will be. That "no mystical force pushes any aspect of intergroup relations in a single pattern," is an important reminder to those who wish to retain their identity as a member of a distinctive religious group that identification with one's present group, religion or culture is quite possible.

It is my conviction that intermarriage is definitely inadvisable. It places a greater stress and strain upon marriage than is ordinarily true

when persons of similar religious views are married. We need not guess about this. In every case of interfaith marriage that we have examined, the facts about the greater strains involved have come to the fore. The fact that divorce and separation rates are higher in these interfaith marriages serves also to support this view. No two people are so alike in their views as to make some adjustment and accommodation to each other unnecessary. How much more true this is of persons whose religious heritage differs from another's. Marriage, under these conditions, becomes much more difficult. It may prove successful only if *both* of the parties are themselves strong and if, further, they accept one philosophy —not two philosophies—of religion for the family that may someday include children.

It is unfair to a child to rear him in a religious vacuum. It is not possible for anyone who has had no experience with organized religion to "choose" a Church or Synagogue "when he or she is old enough." Just when will that be? When is a person old enough to make such a choice when his parents either differ in their religious views or have no view whatsoever?

Intermarriages are wrong, too, because they are often based on the mistaken premise that, in this way, universalism and human brotherhood is assured. Not only has this theory not been proved—it has, rather, been exploded. Two nothings are still nothing. A plus and a minus simply cancel each other out. Nothing of any significance is gained by such a marriage. If all humans on a given day gave up all their differences (an utterly fantastic idea) we might have half a chance. But in the world as we know it such an idea is impracticable if not absurd.

It is the duty of men and women of different faiths, colors and nations to learn to live together in peace and amity while maintaining their differences. Our duty is clear. We must learn how to live together despite differences that almost inevitably exist. It is our duty, further, to perpetuate those values and ideals that we know to be significant in our religious philosophy. Our obligation as humans is to learn to have respect for each other without regard to differences that may separate us in degree from each other. Conformity is not to be mistaken for an unmixed blessing. Blandness is not a virtue. The elimination of all differences in religion or color could only lead to blandness and is, therefore, not to be mistaken for a blessing to mankind but rather as a serious threat to the welfare of individuals and the society of which they are a part.

As I view it, intermarriage constitutes a threat to society and is not necessarily a promise of a brighter day to come.

On the basis of the evidence presently available it is clear, too, that

the chances of happiness in marriage are greatest for those who are culturally, socially, educationally, temperamentally, ethnically, nationally, racially, and religiously more alike than they are different from each other. Opposites may attract, but that does not guarantee that they will stay together. If one out of every three marriages are known to fail, and if we know that the percentage of these failures increases when differences in race and religion are considered as separate factors in these marriages, we must conclude that intermarriage is unwise for most individuals and must, therefore, be regarded as a threat to both personal and group happiness.

Our personal histories reveal the fact that no parent in a mixed marriage, however intelligent and capable he or she may otherwise be, can assure his children of the security in family and society they both want and need. Psychologically the children of mixed marriages are faced with more numerous emotional problems than we have a right to bequeath to them. It does not seem reasonable, therefore, to intensify the nature and quantity of the difficulties that mixed marriages and the children thereof are likely to face!

Even though young people, viewing the statistics concerning the failure of such marriages, are generally certain that by some special ability, talent or quality of character of their own they can deal successfully with these problems, there is no reason to believe that they can. Alert and intelligent though they may be, marriage involves not only the man and woman who are the primary parties to the marriage but their parents, kindred and society as well. Their views are generally opposed to such marriages, and the pressures that result have their effect upon the married couple. Let no one contemplating intermarriage be so certain that he or she can withstand all these opposing forces. While some succeed, let it be noted many others try and fail!

The fact that intermarriages do not succeed in the same proportion as other (non-mixed) marriages is, in large measure, due to the fact that the number and degree of differences between the parties to such marriages are likely to be greater than the normal differences that exist in marriage. It takes great skill and much effort to resolve intermarriage differences. It also takes families that will not by word or action, direct or indirect, add to the problems of the intermarried. Although most couples contemplating such a marriage are quite certain that they possess these advantages, the statistical evidence at hand makes it clear that, unfortunately for them and their children, they are less likely than they think to have them.

A rereading of the factual material contained in this study of intermarriage in its various forms, and of its effects on those who intermarry, leads me to the conclusion that intermarriage is actually a threat to

ultimate happiness, that the problems that result from the major differences in religion and race are so weighty as to require that those who would intermarry be persons of far greater strength and courage than is ordinarily required in marriage. If, in the average marriage, there are differences that must be resolved and adjustments that must be made, and if, even then, the divorce rate is about one in every three marriages, we may expect that the divorce rate for the intermarried will be much greater. We have offered the evidence to support this thesis in that the rate of divorce in cases of intermarriage is two to four times as heavy as the "normal" rate.

I believe that intermarriage is also a threat to the children of such a marriage, in that it may tend to make them marginal in their relationships to parents, their faiths or their races. When we make it difficult and sometimes quite impossible for children to identify with us and our way of life, or our people, we have created a threat to their welfare and to the welfare of society as well because highly charged emotional experiences often leave such children disturbed, frustrated and unable to believe that they can live normal, happy lives.

There is a threat, also, to the religious way of life with which one has formerly identified. Its strength is reduced numerically, and its ability to survive is reduced as well. Interfaith marriage may result from indifference to one's religion, but there is always the chance that religious interest will be revived. If one believes, as I do, that organized religion benefits human beings and helps to keep a distinct set of values alive and meaningful, then the loss of a single adherent to any faith is a loss to religion. We have already noted that intermarriage tends to reduce religiosity. Protestants who marry Catholics are frequently less loyal to the Church, Jews who marry non-Jews are less loyal to the Synagogue, than persons who marry a partner of the same faith.

In the case of interracial marriages, I have found that the white partner often imagines that his or her child born of such a marriage is really white and the hope appears to be present that such a child though dark in color can "pass." Difficult as is the problem of the parent in such a situation, the problems which confront the children of Negro-white marriages appear to be even more complex and emotionally frustrating.

Intermarriage, as I view it, holds no promise for a bright and happy future for individuals or for mankind. The evidence, as I view it, is clear on this point. The facts speak for themselves.

Intermarriages will continue to take place in America because there are so many factors at work that lead inevitably to such marriage. In our open society they cannot be completely avoided. When parents seek my counsel on this subject, I remind them that there are not many

choices open to them if they seek to avoid the marriage of their child to a person of another faith. (1) Parents should provide their child with the best possible training in their home, as well as in the religious school. There is no substitute for the education (some would call it orientation) of children along lines that will cause them to understand, appreciate and love their own spiritual heritage to such a degree that no other set of religious standards or values will prove to be as satisfying. Such an education need not create a false standard of superiority in the child. Just as the love of one's own family does not necessarily imply that we need look down upon all other families, so the love of one's religious heritage need not produce a sense of disdain for the religious heritage of others. (2) This education must begin as early as possible in the life of the child, under conditions that will not cause the child to feel that he or she is being surfeited with a complex of religious values. (3) Parents must be aware, too, that a child who sees numerous inconsistencies (often, hypocrisies) on the part of parents is not easily fooled into believing that they really have positive religious convictions. To speak in glowing terms about one's religious tradition and, at the same time, to ignore its implications is to give the child reason to feel a sense of disgust not only with parents but with the tradition as well. Parents must, therefore, be ready to teach and practice the highest religious standards at all times for the child soon learns to distinguish between "talkers" and "doers."

Some parents believe that they can segregate themselves and their children from people and ideas they do not countenance, but this is, in my opinion, an illusion. A child who attends the public schools is inevitably exposed to ways of life that must differ from those he has seen in his home environment. Sooner or later values and standards other than those he has known within his home or religious school will, more than likely, have their effect and the result is apt to prove unhappy to those who cannot cope with differences. The child who has had a certain religious self-consciousness implanted within him through the media of religious practice, values and beliefs, is however, less likely to lose his religious identity than one who has not, even if he ultimately falls in love with a person of another set of religious practices and values. (4) Loyalty to parents and their standards can be acquired when the child regards the parents' way of life as rich and rewarding. The love of parents and a sincere appreciation of the values by which they live can produce the desire within the child to identify with them. Such identification generally includes the parents' religion as well. If parents strive to attain this goal, it must be their aim to inculcate their values, both directly and indirectly, within their child. Generally, children with this kind of a relationship to parents and family may be

relied on to follow in the path of their heritage. (5) An increase in the number and quality of those institutions that are directly related to our sub-cultures, will help also to increase the desire to maintain a particular way of life, religious, racial or ethnic.

The survival of a group depends in degree upon the quantity and quality of the institutions which it has established. If these organizations and institutions provide their members, even indirectly, with the desire to maintain their sub-cultures, they serve a valuable purpose as means of counteracting the forces that make for complete assimilation. They may be termed "positive" insofar as the group is concerned.

By following such a program there is more than a likelihood that interfaith marriage can be avoided. However, there can be no guarantee to that effect because children and parents differ so markedly and further because the circumstances under which young people of differing faiths meet vary so greatly. The young people may have received excellent religious training in school and home, their parents may have set near-perfect examples of personal integrity and high purpose, and yet intermarriages *do* take place, not because parents or schools have failed or even because of certain psychological factors that affect the attitude of the young people but simply because, by sheer accident, as it were, young people of different faiths have met and fallen in love with each other.

What should parents who are opposed to intermarriage do?

They ought to remember that young people in love, living in our free society, generally free from religious prejudice are naturally likely to intermarry. What matters most is that parents, however emotional and upset they may be because of a contemplated intermarriage, should attempt to keep their wits about them and meet the situation with as high a degree of calmness and logic as possible. They should try, lovingly and persuasively, to dissuade the young people from intermarrying. To do more—to coerce, to threaten, or to use force—only hastens the likelihood of intermarriage. Further, there is every chance that, by this approach, we may drive our children from us forever.

I believe that parents ought, without rancor and bitterness (and this is highly important), to point out to son or daughter the implications of the contemplated intermarriage for (a) the intermarried themselves; (b) the perpetuation of the particular way of life associated with a given religion and (c) the people whose way of life it is. The statistical evidence incorporated in this study makes it clear that the "odds" do not favor intermarriages, in that almost two to four times as many intermarriages as intramarriages end in divorce, separation or annulment. This is a highly significant fact. It is objective and utterly free from emotion-inducing factors. It ought, therefore, to be considered

and weighed most carefully. I have pointed also to evidence which indicates that a particular religious way of life, hitherto adhered to, may not be perpetuated in an intermarriage; that the family is weakened and that the people who live by a particular religion may not survive as an entity because intermarriage gradually gnaws away at these values and standards and children of the intermarried are, as a consequence, unlikely to live by them.

Parents should, also, discuss the problem with their minister, rabbi or priest, who may be able to assist the youth by explaining the difficulties that intermarrieds may encounter and why the hazards of intermarriage are so much greater than an ordinary marriage. If the couple insists upon the marriage, then every effort ought to be made to get both young people to agree to the formal conversion of the less dominant to the religion of the other.

In the event that the opinions of the parents and clergy are ignored and the intermarriage takes place, how should parents respond? Of course, circumstances vary in these situations and that variance must always be taken into consideration. Parental responses differ as well because parents are people and people differ in their natures.

Even though I frown upon intermarriage, I could not myself—nor could I urge others to—break every tie that binds parents to the son or daughter who would intermarry. Perhaps the manner in which I live and the values by which I live will ultimately impress these young people. Perhaps my religious philosophy will yet appeal even though my words have failed.

I lay no claim to omniscience or infallibility; hence, I can not claim that the views expressed here are correct in every detail and meet every situation. Both years of study of intermarriage as a concern of the social scientist, and years of intimate personal contact with people who have come to me asking for counsel and assistance with marital problems, make me feel that I may be of assistance to others who contemplate intermarriage. Perhaps our society will change so radically in its views and attitudes within the next decade that my views, too, will change. However, I doubt that such a condition is likely to occur. So for the present these views are, I think, worthy of careful consideration and study.

APPENDIX

A NOTE ON METHOD

Fifty professors in forty-four colleges and universities responded favorably to my request that their students be asked to complete a questionnaire on the subject of their attitudes toward several forms of intermarriage. The choice was given in each case either (1) to use class time and have the questionnaire completed in the class and returned to the instructor or (2) to give it to each student with the request that it be completed and returned at the next class session. In all of the schools represented in this sample several classes were asked to complete the questionnaire. Instructors were urged to secure approximately one hundred or more replies per school. In some cases, however, the number of returns fell short of this number.

Upon return of the questionnaires, I.B.M. cards were punched according to a pre-arranged code. Because 231 items of information were ultimately required, it was deemed advisable to use an I.B.M. 7090 Computer. The programming was painstakingly carried out so as to avoid possible errors in the results obtained. I am pleased to report that the program for this operation proved both interesting and successful so that the Littauer Computation Center asked for and has in its files a record of it. After many months devoted to the elimination of errors that crept into the operation, the task was completed. I then discovered that, although I had secured whole numbers in the replies from each of the schools, it would be necessary to convert all this information into percentages based on the total number of replies received from each school, in order for the results from all schools to be compared.

Not all of the answers and correlations which I have obtained have been used for the purpose of this study. It is my hope that at a future date, additional relevant material will be published.

The colleges and universities from which the information was obtained were chosen with great care. Schools of all types are represented. There are state universities as well as privately endowed colleges and universities. There are co-educational as well as all-male and all-female student bodies. There are schools whose student body is Negro and there are those where the student body is exclusively white. There are eight Catholic universities and colleges in the sample. Finally, these schools are located in the nine census areas of the United States. This is not a representative or random sample of all student opinion in each of the schools. About one-third of the students "major" in the social sciences. It is interesting to note, however, that the opinions and attitudes of these students appear to be quite similar to those held in (1) Northeastern University, where most of the students in our sample were other than social science majors and (2) the University of Hawaii where 72 per cent of those students who replied indicated that they are other than white or Negro. In our total sample, the liberality of students in the social sciences did not prove to be very much different from that of students whose "major" was not social science and those who were "other than" white or Negro. The title of the chapter dealing primarily with student opinion should be carefully noted. It is "What *Some* College Students Think About Intermarriage."

TABLE 20 SURVEY ON ATTITUDES OF COLLEGE AND UNIVERSITY STUDENTS

General Directions

1. Please, do <u>not</u> put your name on this questionnaire.
2. Be frank in your answers. We all have our own beliefs and opinions. <u>Your reactions</u> and attitudes are most important.
3. Please answer each question. Use (√) or circle O wherever possible.
4. Please return the completed questionnaire to your instructor.

1. Name of your College or University _____

2. Your class (circle) Fr. Soph. Jr. Sr. Grad. 3. Your "major" _____
                                                      4. Your "minor" _____

5. Your Age _____ 6. Sex _____ 7. Color: White _____ Negro _____ Other _____

8. Your religion _____ 9. Specify denomination _____

10. Your "hometown" _____ 11. How long have you lived there? _____

12. Give city, state, country of your birth _____

13. Are you single? _____ Engaged? _____ Married? _____

14. Father's occupation _____ 15. Father's place of birth _____

16. Your father's father's country of birth _____

17. Your father's mother's country of birth _____

18. Your father's education: Formal schooling? Yes _____ No _____

19. If "Yes," give last grade completed _____

20. Father's religious affiliation: Protestant? _____ Catholic? _____ Jew? _____

Eastern Orthodox? _____ Other (?) Please specify _____

21. Mother's occupation (including "housewife") _____

22. Mother's place of birth _____ City _____ Country

23. Your mother's father's country of birth _____

24. Your mother's mother's country of birth _____

25. Your mother's education: Formal schooling? Yes _____ No _____

26. If "Yes," give last grade completed _____

27. Mother's religious affiliation: Protestant? _____ Catholic? _____ Jew? _____

    Eastern Orthodox? _____ Other (?) Please specify _____

28. (Check one)
    Are your parents living together? _____ Separated? _____ Divorced? _____ Widowed? _____

29. How many brothers _____ and/or sisters _____ do you have?

30. Ages of brothers _____, _____, _____   31. Ages of sisters _____, _____, _____

32. (Check one)
    Would your total annual family income be: a) Below $5,000? _____
       b) Between $5,000 and $10,000? _____   d) Between $15,000 and $20,000? _____
       c) Between $10,000 and $15,000? _____ e) $20,000 or more? _____

33. From which High School did you graduate: Public? _____ Parochial? _____ Private? _____

34. List High School activities (athletics, literary or other) in which you actively participated

_____

_____

_____

35. If any member of your family (including yourself) is married to a person of a different religion from your own, please check which: Brother _____ Uncle _____ Aunt _____ Sister _____ Niece _____ Nephew _____ Yourself _____

36. It has been said that, at some period, young people tend to react partially or wholly against religion. Has this been true in your case? Yes _____ No _____

37. If "Yes," at about what age? _____

38. Have you ever travelled abroad? Yes _____ No _____

39. Were you ever in the armed services? Yes _____ No _____

40. About how often do you now attend religious services?

   a) Once a week? _____   b) Once a month? _____

   c) 2 or 3 times a year? _____   d) Never? _____

41. (Check) Were you ever: Confirmed? _____ Bar Mitzvah? _____
    Baptized? _____ Bas Mitzvah? _____

42. How many years did you attend: Sunday School? _____ Hebrew School? _____
    Never attended? _____

43. Were you brought up under a religious influence that was: Moderate? _____
    Strong? _____
    Weak? _____

44. Which of your parents is (was) most dominant? Mother? _____ Father? _____

45. (Check one)
    If your sister or brother married outside of your own religion, would you – Approve? _____
    Mildly disapprove? _____ Strongly disapprove? _____ Be unconcerned? _____

46. (Check one)
    If you found the girl (boy) for you and it developed that she (he) was of a different religion
    from yours, would you:

    a) Continue to date her (him)? _____
    b) Break off at once? _____
    c) Be undecided as to what to do? _____
    d) Ask her (him) to convert to your religion? _____
    e) Offer to convert to the other religion? _____

47. Do your parents object to your dating a person of a different religion? Yes _____ No _____

48. Do you date persons of a different religion? Rarely _____ Sometimes _____
    Frequently _____ Almost Always _____ Never _____

49. If your father objected to "mixed dating" would you be inclined to follow his decision?
    Yes _____ No _____

50. If your mother objected to "mixed dating" would you be inclined to follow her decision?
    Yes _____ No _____

51. Can you imagine yourself marrying a person of a color or nationality other than your own?
    As for color: Yes _____ No _____
    As for nationality: Yes _____ No _____

52. So far as your private views are concerned, under what circumstances would you give up
    your religion? Under no circumstances _____
    Under the following circumstances _____
    _____
    _____

53. In the order of their rank, which of the following would be the hardest (1); next hardest
    (2); not quite so hard (3); fairly easy (4); easiest (5) for you to do —
    (Use numbers)   To marry outside your own

    _____ Economic class?   _____ Religious group?
    _____ Educational group?   _____ Nationality?
                      _____ Color group?

54. Please check (✓) those categories with which you are in _personal agreement_, notwithstanding general public sentiment.

A person who is	Italian	Negro	Jewish	Japanese	Catholic	Filipino	Protestant	Mexican	Greek	Irish	Polish
I would have as an intimate friend											
I would work beside on a job											
I would live in the same neighborhood block											
I would marry											
I would bar from my block											
I would bar from my social, recreational or fraternity, lodge or society											
I would date or allow a son or daughter to date											

Please record your agreement or disagreement with a ($\checkmark$) to the following statements?

55. <u>For Catholics only</u>

A. "Protestants, as a group, believe that this country really belongs to them."

I agree _____ disagree _____

B. "Being born a Catholic means having two strikes against you."

I agree _____ disagree _____

C. "I can hardly imagine myself marrying

a Jew." I agree _____ disagree _____

a Protestant." I agree _____ disagree _____

D. "Although Catholics may be well treated, people really don't mean it."

I agree _____ disagree _____

56. <u>For Jews only</u>

A. "If I could somehow conceal my Jewish background, I would certainly do so."

I agree _____ disagree _____

B. "Being born a Jew means having two strikes against you."

I agree _____ disagree _____

C. "No matter how nicely people treat a Jew, they really don't mean it."

I agree _____ disagree _____

D. "I can hardly imagine myself marrying

a Catholic." I agree _____ disagree _____

a Protestant." I agree _____ disagree _____

57. For Protestants only

A. "I can hardly imagine myself marrying

a Jew." I agree _____ disagree _____

a Catholic." I agree _____ disagree _____

B. "This is really a Protestant country and Protestants ought to run it."

I agree _____ disagree _____

C. "As long as Jews and Catholics are so clannish, they have no right to expect to be treated the same as other people."

I agree _____ disagree _____

D. "The sooner we all forget our religious differences the better off we will all be."

I agree _____ disagree _____

58. For Eastern Orthodox only

A. "Protestants, as a group, believe that this country really belongs to them."
    I agree _____ disagree _____

B. "Roman Catholics give the impression that this country really belongs to them."
    I agree _____ disagree _____

C. "I can hardly imagine myself marrying
    a Jew."   I agree _____ disagree _____
    a Roman Catholic." I agree _____ disagree _____
    A Protestant."   I agree _____ disagree _____

D. "No matter how nicely people treat an Eastern Orthodox person, they really
    don't mean it."
    I agree _____ disagree _____

59. For Non-Religionists only

A. "I can hardly imagine myself marrying
    a religious Jew."   I agree _____ disagree _____
    a religious Catholic."   I agree _____ disagree _____
    a religious Protestant." I agree _____ disagree _____

B. "This country is a great melting pot. The sooner we all forget our religious differences, the better off we will all be."

I agree _____ disagree _____

C. "As long as people stick to their churches and synagogues, intolerance and bigotry will continue."

I agree _____ disagree _____

D. "Most people lose their religion when their parents are too strict and too hard on them."

I agree _____ disagree _____

TABLE 21 COLLEGES AND UNIVERSITIES USED IN THIS STUDY. SIZE OF SAMPLE FROM EACH SCHOOL AND NUMBER OF STUDENTS IN SAMPLE FROM EACH CLASS

College	Size of sample	No inform.	Freshman	Sophomore	Junior	Senior	Graduate student
Annhurst College	162	0	75	38	34	15	0
Atlanta U.	116	3	0	24	14	0	75
Boston College	118	7	1	14	44	33	19
Boston U.	150	0	30	45	50	22	3
Bowdoin College	95	4	0	27	42	22	0
Brown U.	177	0	67	55	32	18	5
U. of Calif. (Berk.)	315	0	61	104	71	78	1
U. of Colorado	95	0	6	10	37	39	3
U. of Denver	93	1	63	18	8	3	0
Emmanuel College	73	0	0	0	1	72	0
Emory U.	100	0	13	35	28	22	2
Fisk U.	85	3	0	31	23	28	0
Florida State U.	93	1	2	26	33	29	2
Grinnell College	95	1	7	62	16	9	0
Harvard U.	48	0	0	18	12	10	8
U. of Hawaii	225	2	77	95	34	15	2
Holy Cross College	55	0	0	31	13	11	0
Indiana U.	163	3	89	53	14	4	0
U. of Iowa	147	0	2	86	40	15	4
U. of Kentucky	141	1	27	28	45	38	2
U. of Minnesota	280	2	112	86	44	32	4
Newton College of Sacred Heart	99	0	50	14	23	12	0
Northeastern U.	167	5	0	23	114	25	0
NE U. Control Group	150	1	0	35	68	43	3
Notre Dame U.	99	0	15	19	23	37	5
Oberlin College	193	0	79	62	37	15	0
Ohio U.	166	1	0	49	66	48	2
Ohio Wesleyan U.	161	1	31	80	21	28	0
Queens College	53	0	0	4	30	19	0
Santa Monica City C.	196	3	105	88	0	0	0
St. Louis U.	239	1	2	32	108	96	0
Stonehill College	154	0	2	71	9	72	0
Texas Southern U.	96	5	1	26	34	30	0
Tulane U.	96	0	33	38	15	8	2
Washington State U.	174	0	100	36	20	18	0
Wesleyan U.	60	0	3	33	10	14	0
Western Reserve U.	85	0	9	17	33	24	2
U. of Wisconsin	76	1	1	12	34	28	0
Women's College A	118	1	0	39	62	16	0
Women's College B	71	1	1	40	20	9	0
Women's College C	128	0	41	41	36	10	0
TOTAL	5407	48	1105	1645	1398	1067	144

TABLE 22 "MAJORS" OF STUDENTS IN 40 COLLEGES COMPARED WITH THOSE AT U. OF HAWAII AND NORTHEASTERN U. CONTROL GROUP

Subject	Per cent at 40 schools	Northeastern U. control	U. of Hawaii
Social Sciences	34	2	35
Business	6	11	10
Humanities	15	0	7
Engineering	2	67	5
Physical Sciences	2	1	2
Education	14	1	13
Nursing	3	1	5
Mathematics	2	1	4
Medicine	2	0	0
Creative Sciences	3	0	3
Physical Education	1	0	1
Home Economics	0	0	1
Social work	2	0	1
"Other"	11	12	10
No information	3	4	3
TOTAL	100	100	100

TABLE 23 PERCENTAGE OF STUDENTS IN EACH OF 40 AMERICAN COLLEGES AND
UNIVERSITIES WHO DATE OUTSIDE THEIR RELIGION AND FREQUENCY OF
SUCH DATING

Name of School	Rarely	Sometimes	Frequently	Almost always	Never
Annhurst College	35%	37%	7%	3%	18%
Atlanta U.	16	53	18	1	3
Boston College	34	37	8	1	20
Boston U.	18	41	20	7	15
Bowdoin College	16	46	26	5	7
Brown U.	19	39	23	9	8
U. of Calif. (Berk.)	18	35	26	12	5
U. of Colorado	12	44	24	17	5
U. of Denver	9	45	29	13	6
Emmanuel College	30	38	8	1	23
Emory U.	26	32	16	5	21
Fisk U.	5	37	34	17	7
Florida State U.	32	31	19	12	6
Grinnell College	16	54	16	9	7
Harvard U.	19	28	30	16	2
U. of Hawaii	8	42	31	11	6
Holy Cross College	49	38	9	2	0
Indiana U.	21	40	25	8	6
U. of Iowa	13	45	26	7	9
U. of Kentucky	19	29	34	17	11
U. of Minnesota	15	40	19	8	7
Newton Sacred Heart	28	41	18	10	9
Northeastern U.	20	24	17	7	9
NE U. Control Group	7	33	30	17	6
Notre Dame U.	28	36	17	8	9
Oberlin College	17	17	25	13	6
Ohio U.	17	40	25	9	7
Ohio Wesleyan U.	25	51	13	5	6
Queens College	31	18	8	4	38
St. Louis U.	42	30	5	1	22
Santa Monica City C.	14	40	26	12	8
Stonehill College	33	36	5	1	25
Texas Southern U.	26	51	10	12	0
Tulane U.	15	39	25	11	8
Washington State U.	18	39	20	9	10
Wesleyan U.	18	39	28	5	5
Western Reserve U.	21	35	14	10	18
U. of Wisconsin	19	38	27	6	10
Women's College A	17	55	14	5	11
Women's College B	16	52	14	14	0
Women's College C	16	50	21	9	4
40 SCHOOLS AVERAGE	21%	39%	20%	9%	10%

TABLE 24 PERCENTAGE OF STUDENTS IN 40 AMERICAN COLLEGES AND UNIVERSITIES WHO AGREE WITH STATEMENTS IN MODIFIED SOCIAL DISTANCE SCALE WITH RESPECT TO ITALIANS

Name of School	Have as intimate friend	Work beside on job	Live on same block	Marry	Bar from block	Bar from social club	Date or allow child to date
Annhurst College	94%	98%	94%	90%	1%	1%	88%
Atlanta U.	60	76	66	40	6	5	64
Boston College	84	93	81	86	1	3	85
Boston U.	73	95	79	46	6	8	57
Bowdoin College	82	86	80	67	3	3	74
Brown U.	92	97	85	64	6	6	77
U. of Calif. (Berk.)	87	94	87	65	0	1	80
U. of Colorado	93	95	83	76	1	1	74
U. of Denver	90	96	67	66	4	5	74
Emmanuel College	97	97	95	88	1	1	92
Emory U.	69	81	64	28	12	16	41
Fisk U.	78	85	80	48	2	7	69
Florida State U.	83	93	75	48	1	5	70
Grinnell College	82	93	86	66	3	3	80
Harvard	92	100	94	81	4	2	90
U. of Hawaii	62	79	69	40	4	5	57
Holy Cross College	98	100	93	89	2	2	95
Indiana U.	77	89	74	53	5	9	66
U. of Iowa	88	95	80	66	8	5	78
U. of Kentucky	67	90	67	55	4	8	57
U. of Minnesota	84	93	89	70	1	1	42
Newton Sacred Heart	84	87	81	72	2	2	79
Northeastern U.	92	93	86	77	1	1	83
NE U. Control Group	89	89	83	70	3	2	77
Notre Dame U.	97	99	93	89	5	7	97
Oberlin College	94	100	96	77	6	6	93
Ohio U.	89	93	85	66	3	4	84
Ohio Wesleyan U.	88	97	84	83	5	5	78
Queens College	85	98	89	34	6	4	53
St. Louis U.	94	100	93	84	0	0	90
Santa Monica City C.	78	90	75	54	4	5	68
Stonehill College	89	88	86	80	1	0	85
Texas Southern U.	49	66	50	22	7	5	43
Tulane University	82	89	80	53	7	11	67
Washington State U.	77	93	81	59	3	3	75
Wesleyan U.	78	92	83	60	5	3	82
Western Reserve U.	82	81	76	60	1	4	66
U. of Wisconsin	86	88	84	64	3	1	83
Women's College A	87	95	81	52	3	5	70
Women's College B	83	99	86	66	3	3	79
Women's College C	91	95	88	70	2	2	84
40 SCHOOLS AVERAGE	84%	92%	84%	65%	4%	4%	76%

TABLE 25 PERCENTAGE OF STUDENTS IN 40 AMERICAN COLLEGES AND UNIVERSITIES WHO AGREE WITH STATEMENTS IN MODIFIED SOCIAL DISTANCE SCALE WITH RESPECT TO NEGROES

Name of School	Have as intimate friend	Work beside on job	Live on same block	Marry	Bar from block	Bar from social club	Date or allow child to date
Annhurst College	56%	93%	56%	6%	17%	12%	6%
Atlanta U.	89	84	84	91	2	2	85
Boston College	54	92	58	8	18	16	8
Boston U.	65	89	64	8	14	15	15
Bowdoin College	71	87	66	6	17	12	16
Brown U.	76	94	69	10	15	17	10
U. of Calif. (Berk.)	61	90	61	23	17	18	39
U. of Colorado	45	85	42	16	29	34	24
U. of Denver	57	74	54	2	31	34	11
Emmanuel College	55	95	66	5	12	11	7
Emory U.	31	62	23	1	72	77	5
Fisk U.	91	88	91	92	0	1	88
Florida State U.	36	67	31	2	5	56	4
Grinnell College	78	90	75	17	22	19	43
Harvard U.	85	96	88	31	13	13	58
U. of Hawaii	43	71	59	6	13	15	32
Holy Cross College	62	87	49	5	29	31	36
Indiana U.	47	81	34	3	51	54	7
U. of Iowa	67	91	59	6	21	28	12
U. of Kentucky	38	77	34	5	45	52	9
U. of Minnesota	60	92	65	7	7	18	19
Newton Sacred Heart	49	80	29	3	31	22	6
Northeastern U.	71	87	52	8	20	14	15
NE U. Control Group	63	84	50	5	34	21	13
Notre Dame U.	67	91	53	11	29	34	17
Oberlin College	93	100	90	30	9	7	66
Ohio U.	59	88	57	22	25	29	20
Ohio Wesleyan U.	61	92	55	9	32	32	17
Queens College	48	92	13	2	30	8	9
St. Louis U.	56	88	44	5	33	34	10
Santa Monica City C.	37	86	40	8	38	28	13
Stonehill College	62	88	55	5	23	19	6
Texas Southern U.	83	76	76	96	1	1	83
Tulane U.	48	77	39	7	47	51	9
Washington State U.	46	79	53	17	30	26	9
Wesleyan U.	80	92	67	12	18	15	30
Western Reserve U.	52	89	47	15	39	29	16
U. of Wisconsin	53	83	53	8	32	28	12
Women's College A	64	94	63	4	18	17	17
Women's College B	69	97	68	8	17	17	27
Women's College C	83	100	80	18	13	6	37
40 SCHOOLS AVERAGE	63%	89%	58%	29%	26%	24%	24%

TABLE 26 PERCENTAGE OF STUDENTS IN 40 AMERICAN COLLEGES AND UNIVERSITIES WHO AGREE WITH STATEMENTS IN MODIFIED SOCIAL DISTANCE SCALE WITH RESPECT TO JEWS

Name of School	Have as intimate friend	Work beside on job	Live on same block	Marry	Bar from block	Bar from social club	Date or allow child to date
Annhurst College	79%	92%	88%	2%	2%	4%	42%
Atlanta U.	59	78	67	35	3	4	58
Boston College	67	93	78	18	8	9	9
Boston U.	84	89	83	56	4	5	68
Bowdoin College	82	90	83	58	1	3	75
Brown U.	90	94	86	62	5	9	78
U. of Calif. (Berk.)	87	97	87	44	3	10	70
U. of Colorado	86	92	82	35	6	13	75
U. of Denver	86	95	86	38	9	15	79
Emmanuel College	81	96	86	19	3	4	40
Emory U.	70	82	78	16	10	43	38
Fisk U.	77	87	86	42	0	6	67
Florida State U.	81	93	80	16	4	18	52
Grinnell College	90	91	90	41	0	2	79
Harvard U.	94	98	92	67	4	6	90
U. of Hawaii	57	72	65	24	9	5	45
Holy Cross College	76	96	84	38	5	31	55
Indiana U.	77	90	80	26	7	23	53
U. of Iowa	86	96	88	35	3	12	61
U. of Kentucky	67	79	78	24	7	23	52
U. of Minnesota	77	92	85	29	4	7	53
Newton Sacred Heart	69	83	74	20	6	28	23
Northeastern U.	86	92	84	44	6	6	67
NE U. Control Group	77	87	77	38	11	7	59
Notre Dame U.	83	97	73	13	13	17	54
Oberlin College	97	99	97	63	5	5	91
Ohio U.	81	94	86	41	6	13	70
Ohio Wesleyan U.	87	96	87	40	6	11	72
Queens College	91	94	96	72	4	6	83
St. Louis University	77	94	84	20	3	24	18
Santa Monica City C.	83	93	88	56	4	6	75
Stonehill College	55	71	58	5	11	10	13
Texas Southern U.	55	70	63	19	6	7	39
Tulane U.	90	92	92	61	2	13	82
Washington State U.	68	90	77	6	10	17	17
Wesleyan U.	88	95	85	23	3	8	35
Western Reserve U.	89	95	87	54	2	6	66
U. of Wisconsin	83	95	80	33	38	17	37
Women's College A	88	97	86	48	3	8	76
Women's College B	99	99	89	56	1	8	80
Women's College C	92	97	92	66	2	4	91
40 SCHOOLS AVERAGE	85%	93%	84%	37%	6%	12%	60%

TABLE 27 PERCENTAGE OF STUDENTS IN 40 AMERICAN COLLEGES AND UNIVERSITIES WHO AGREE WITH STATEMENTS IN MODIFIED SOCIAL DISTANCE SCALE WITH RESPECT TO JAPANESE

Name of School	Have as intimate friend	Work beside on job	Live on same block	Marry	Bar from block	Bar from social club	Date or allow child to date
Annhurst College	68%	86%	68%	13%	7%	6%	22%
Atlanta U.	54	75	63	6	3	9	55
Boston College	55	90	66	15	10	10	21
Boston U.	68	87	67	13	7	13	27
Bowdoin College	72	84	76	38	7	5	45
Brown U.	84	95	81	33	5	7	48
U. of Calif. (Berk.)	81	95	85	25	8	15	37
U. of Colorado	68	95	68	24	9	12	39
U. of Denver	73	93	77	23	11	17	45
Emmanuel College	60	97	67	12	8	8	19
Emory U.	52	80	57	15	15	38	23
Fisk U.	75	84	80	42	2	8	56
Florida State U.	62	86	63	10	4	17	29
Grinnell College	85	93	87	36	8	9	68
Harvard U.	92	98	96	60	4	4	79
U. of Hawaii	90	93	87	73	4	4	83
Holy Cross College	67	82	69	29	11	15	56
Indiana U.	57	87	61	16	16	36	27
U. of Iowa	75	91	72	17	10	14	17
U. of Kentucky	55	83	50	22	12	24	4
U. of Minnesota	69	90	79	21	6	9	35
Newton Sacred Heart	61	82	62	22	8	8	21
Northeastern U.	71	90	69	23	7	7	39
NE U. Control Group	70	84	64	23	11	5	36
Notre Dame U.	72	78	74	25	14	18	40
Oberlin College	95	100	96	57	6	6	84
Ohio U.	75	92	63	25	11	14	41
Ohio Wesleyan U.	75	95	78	21	9	11	39
Queens College	74	100	77	2	6	13	19
St. Louis U.	65	88	71	27	5	8	41
Santa Monica City C.	61	79	56	18	16	12	28
Stonehill College	63	85	69	18	9	8	27
Texas Southern U.	49	66	53	16	7	9	35
Tulane U.	69	89	71	26	6	16	3
Washington State U.	63	89	70	13	16	17	23
Wesleyan U.	83	93	83	50	7	3	18
Western Reserve U.	64	91	72	22	7	6	15
U. of Wisconsin	79	91	70	21	4	7	32
Women's College A	77	97	79	19	4	7	40
Women's College B	79	100	79	13	11	11	41
Women's College C	90	95	89	30	3	2	59
40 SCHOOLS AVERAGE	72%	90%	74%	24%	8%	11%	46%

TABLE 28 PERCENTAGE OF STUDENTS IN 40 AMERICAN COLLEGES AND UNIVERSITIES
WHO AGREE WITH STATEMENTS IN MODIFIED SOCIAL DISTANCE SCALE
WITH RESPECT TO CATHOLICS

Name of School	Have as intimate friend	Work beside on job	Live on same block	Marry	Bar from block	Bar from social club	Date or allow child to date
Annhurst College	97%	98%	98%	98%	1%	1%	94%
Atlanta U.	74	80	73	55	0	3	74
Boston College	97	94	94	95	1	2	96
Boston U.	88	91	87	38	1	4	59
Bowdoin College	86	86	84	53	1	4	42
Brown U.	95	97	95	51	1	3	7
U. of Calif. (Berk.)	94	97	96	50	0	48	3
U. of Colorado	99	96	99	55	1	1	88
U. of Denver	91	96	94	51	2	4	81
Emmanuel College	99	97	96	96	1	1	95
Emory U.	97	96	97	39	0	2	73
Fisk U.	85	89	88	66	0	1	81
Florida State U.	95	96	84	26	1	1	14
Grinnell College	92	96	95	34	4	5	79
Harvard U.	98	100	100	58	2	2	92
U. of Hawaii	73	85	84	42	2	2	68
Holy Cross College	98	100	100	98	4	4	98
Indiana U.	90	93	94	50	1	3	75
U. of Iowa	97	97	95	53	1	2	74
U. of Kentucky	91	94	94	48	1	1	75
U. of Minnesota	91	95	94	47	1	2	75
Newton Sacred Heart	91	88	89	98	2	1	84
Northeastern U.	94	95	93	72	1	1	84
NE U. Control Group	91	93	91	68	2	1	81
Notre Dame U.	100	100	95	100	4	3	96
Oberlin College	98	100	99	52	5	5	93
Ohio U.	96	99	98	62	1	1	84
Ohio Wesleyan U.	92	97	97	47	3	3	87
Queens College	87	96	92	34	2	4	55
St. Louis U.	99	100	99	100	3	2	100
Santa Monica City C.	86	96	87	50	3	6	78
Stonehill College	95	90	90	95	1	0	92
Texas Southern U.	67	72	70	39	2	2	60
Tulane U.	95	96	95	7	1	2	81
Washington State U.	93	99	98	51	2	3	80
Wesleyan U.	95	95	95	48	0	3	87
Western Reserve U.	88	95	94	53	0	5	69
U. of Wisconsin	93	99	99	50	0	1	79
Women's College A	96	98	98	47	1	3	76
Women's College B	21	17	13	1	0	0	3
Women's College C	97	99	98	49	1	1	86
40 SCHOOLS AVERAGE	92%	95%	83%	56%	1%	3%	73%

394

TABLE 29 PERCENTAGE OF STUDENTS IN 40 AMERICAN COLLEGES AND UNIVERSITIES WHO AGREE WITH STATEMENTS IN MODIFIED SOCIAL DISTANCE SCALE WITH RESPECT TO FILIPINOS

Name of School	Have as intimate friend	Work beside on job	Live on same block	Marry	Bar from block	Bar from social club	Date or allow child to date
Annhurst College	63%	93%	66%	15%	10%	9%	9%
Atlanta U.	53	74	64	31	3	5	53
Boston College	58	92	73	17	13	12	24
Boston U.	65	87	65	13	12	14	27
Bowdoin College	72	85	74	38	6	6	45
Brown U.	83	94	78	33	8	7	49
U. of Calif. (Berk.)	70	94	70	19	10	17	36
U. of Colorado	65	88	66	35	16	1	39
U. of Denver	69	91	86	18	8	16	43
Emmanuel College	60	92	69	14	10	4	25
Emory U.	54	78	56	14	17	33	25
Fisk U.	75	82	79	44	4	8	67
Florida State U.	55	82	57	8	12	22	25
Grinnell College	85	62	85	46	7	7	66
Harvard U.	50	98	96	60	4	4	73
U. of Hawaii	59	56	71	37	12	9	44
Holy Cross College	67	80	64	27	15	13	49
Indiana U.	53	79	55	15	23	19	18
U. of Iowa	75	90	72	22	12	14	35
U. of Kentucky	55	89	72	16	10	22	36
U. of Minnesota	68	90	78	24	6	6	36
Newton Sacred Heart	57	79	53	17	23	19	27
Northeastern U.	69	90	70	23	8	7	40
NE U. Control Group	69	84	65	3	10	7	38
Notre Dame U.	73	97	74	2	38	16	41
Oberlin College	94	100	95	54	6	6	86
Ohio U.	77	94	78	26	11	15	42
Ohio Wesleyan U.	73	95	74	24	9	16	45
Queens College	68	100	66	8	8	8	24
St. Louis U.	72	41	76	32	6	7	45
Santa Monica City C.	57	88	55	17	14	11	25
Stonehill College	66	86	70	22	8	25	34
Texas Southern U.	47	64	53	5	7	6	48
Tulane U.	70	85	64	24	8	23	40
Washington State U.	55	85	64	9	17	20	18
Wesleyan U.	80	92	83	43	5	3	68
Western Reserve U.	54	86	76	26	11	12	45
U. of Wisconsin	79	88	66	26	9	9	30
Women's College A	75	96	72	18	6	8	38
Women's College B	72	97	76	15	10	8	42
Women's College C	87	93	93	38	3	1	62
40 SCHOOLS AVERAGE	69%	89%	73%	24%	11%	12%	42%

TABLE 30   PERCENTAGE OF STUDENTS IN 40 AMERICAN COLLEGES AND UNIVERSITIES
WHO AGREE WITH STATEMENTS IN MODIFIED SOCIAL DISTANCE SCALE WITH
RESPECT TO PROTESTANTS

Name of School	Have as intimate friend	Work beside on job	Live on same block	Marry	Bar from block	Bar from social club	Date or allow child to date
Annhurst College	89%	97%	97%	50%	1%	2%	72%
Atlanta U.	80	81	83	72	0	0	77
Boston College	85	96	95	46	2	3	70
Boston U.	92	91	91	59	1	3	72
Bowdoin College	91	90	88	81	0	1	82
Brown U.	97	97	96	80	0	1	89
U. of Calif. (Berk.)	96	98	97	84	0	0	93
U. of Colorado	98	95	97	90	3	0	92
U. of Denver	96	96	95	87	1	1	88
Emmanuel College	93	96	95	38	3	1	59
Emory U.	78	96	98	90	0	0	90
Fisk U.	86	87	88	80	0	2	84
Florida State U.	96	97	96	96	1	1	93
Grinnell College	94	94	93	9	0	1	91
Harvard U.	100	100	100	96	0	0	96
U. of Hawaii	85	81	87	77	4	4	83
Holy Cross College	91	98	96	49	4	5	81
Indiana U.	96	96	94	86	1	1	92
U. of Iowa	98	97	95	83	1	1	89
U. of Kentucky	97	96	94	92	1	1	91
U. of Minnesota	91	93	96	79	1	1	87
Newton Sacred Heart	83	89	87	53	2	1	75
Northeastern U.	94	95	92	71	0	0	85
NE U. Control Group	93	93	91	71	3	0	81
Notre Dame U.	98	100	97	53	4	4	67
Oberlin College	99	100	100	96	5	5	10
Ohio U.	99	99	100	96	1	1	96
Ohio Wesleyan U.	98	37	99	97	1	1	99
Queens College	85	98	98	42	2	4	53
St. Louis U.	87	97	95	36	1	2	53
Santa Monica City C.	92	93	92	80	0	1	84
Stonehill College	82	91	90	37	2	3	55
Texas Southern U.	69	73	68	51	4	4	65
Tulane U.	96	94	94	65	2	2	84
Washington State U.	97	98	97	95	1	2	95
Wesleyan U.	98	95	98	92	0	3	95
Western Reserve U.	89	96	94	60	0	1	71
U. of Wisconsin	100	100	100	91	0	0	93
Women's College A	99	98	98	87	0	3	92
Women's College B	89	93	92	87	0	0	99
Women's College C	97	98	97	91	0	0	94
40 SCHOOLS AVERAGE	92%	95%	96%	74%	1%	1%	83%

TABLE 31   PERCENTAGE OF STUDENTS IN 40 AMERICAN COLLEGES AND UNIVERSITIES WHO AGREE WITH STATEMENTS IN MODIFIED SOCIAL DISTANCE SCALE WITH RESPECT TO MEXICANS

Name of School	Have as intimate friend	Work beside on job	Live on same block	Marry	Bar from block	Bar from social club	Date or allow child to date
Annhurst College	69%	90%	65%	21%	6%	7%	27%
Atlanta U.	58	73	62	36	7	8	66
Boston College	56	91	63	44	12	13	35
Boston U.	66	81	64	17	13	15	31
Bowdoin College	71	89	73	40	8	5	49
Brown U.	81	93	63	41	8	11	54
U. of Calif. (Berk.)	71	92	66	28	12	16	45
U. of Colorado	68	81	56	31	15	22	38
U. of Denver	61	84	57	19	29	26	36
Emmanuel College	70	89	71	29	10	7	38
Emory U.	56	76	44	11	31	43	21
Fisk U.	77	84	77	53	4	8	73
Florida State U.	57	79	49	12	17	27	29
Grinnell College	81	90	80	38	12	8	62
Harvard U.	88	98	92	71	6	6	77
U. of Hawaii	51	71	61	24	8	8	43
Holy Cross College	69	85	58	27	25	20	44
Indiana U.	55	82	45	14	32	37	23
U. of Iowa	73	88	63	20	17	18	35
U. of Kentucky	57	83	55	22	14	26	30
U. of Minnesota	66	89	73	24	10	11	35
Newton Sacred Heart	61	80	55	25	13	17	49
Northeastern U.	69	89	67	37	10	7	51
NE U. Control Group	67	83	65	35	15	10	46
Notre Dame U.	72	97	64	34	25	21	45
Oberlin College	95	100	95	63	8	6	27
Ohio U.	75	92	70	29	14	20	48
Ohio Wesleyan U.	71	93	69	29	13	15	45
Queens College	74	96	64	13	11	13	57
St. Louis U.	70	76	69	42	11	10	16
Santa Monica City C.	58	84	50	18	19	15	31
Stonehill College	69	84	68	34	12	5	41
Texas Southern U.	53	67	47	13	19	16	48
Tulane U.	69	82	61	27	19	22	44
Washington State U.	52	79	58	12	25	24	30
Wesleyan U.	73	88	73	43	0	8	62
Western Reserve U.	54	85	55	22	13	12	32
U. of Wisconsin	72	89	61	34	22	17	62
Women's College A	73	95	70	88	8	8	49
Women's College B	72	96	70	25	10	14	66
Women's College C	84	91	82	47	4	3	71
40 SCHOOLS AVERAGE	68%	88%	66%	31%	14%	15%	45%

TABLE 32 PERCENTAGE OF STUDENTS IN 40 AMERICAN COLLEGES AND UNIVERSITIES WHO AGREE WITH STATEMENTS IN MODIFIED SOCIAL DISTANCE SCALE WITH RESPECT TO GREEKS

Name of School	Have as intimate friend	Work beside on job	Live on same block	Marry	Bar from block	Bar from social club	Date or allow child to date
Annhurst College	80%	95%	80%	46%	2%	2%	59%
Atlanta U.	58	74	62	32	3	3	52
Boston College	72	95	80	40	4	7	56
Boston U.	75	89	76	33	6	7	49
Bowdoin College	81	87	81	61	3	3	68
Brown U.	88	96	84	60	2	3	72
U. of Calif. (Berk.)	89	96	88	56	2	3	76
U. of Colorado	88	95	80	59	1	2	68
U. of Denver	81	93	85	47	1	4	62
Emmanuel College	85	96	88	52	3	3	66
Emory U.	64	84	65	21	11	22	39
Fisk U.	75	73	80	46	1	6	68
Florida State U.	75	88	71	4	2	51	13
Grinnell College	84	93	86	54	5	4	78
Harvard U.	90	98	94	77	6	4	85
U. of Hawaii	55	75	68	31	4	5	56
Holy Cross College	93	96	96	91	4	4	93
Indiana U.	70	86	69	42	9	10	56
U. of Iowa	81	87	76	52	3	1	64
U. of Kentucky	71	88	74	42	4	6	57
U. of Minnesota	76	91	51	54	2	2	63
Newton Sacred Heart	65	87	70	42	4	4	59
Northeastern U.	74	92	84	55	2	2	69
NE U. Control Group	81	87	76	52	3	1	64
Notre Dame U.	83	97	84	60	7	9	72
Oberlin College	96	100	96	97	6	5	18
Ohio U.	84	94	83	51	3	5	67
Ohio Wesleyan U.	81	96	82	48	7	6	70
Queens College	81	98	87	32	2	4	47
St. Louis U.	80	93	89	59	2	2	72
Santa Monica City C.	73	92	78	50	6	6	61
Stonehill College	73	94	86	55	5	9	58
Texas Southern U.	55	70	64	24	4	4	45
Tulane U.	78	86	75	43	5	9	65
Washington State U.	71	89	79	35	5	7	48
Wesleyan U.	78	85	82	12	2	5	75
Western Reserve U.	75	91	83	49	1	5	55
U. of Wisconsin	91	95	84	51	5	7	67
Women's College A	89	97	82	45	1	2	72
Women's College B	94	100	99	87	1	0	93
Women's College C	91	95	88	67	1	1	84
40 SCHOOLS AVERAGE	80%	93%	82%	50%	4%	6%	64%

TABLE 33 PERCENTAGE OF STUDENTS IN 40 AMERICAN COLLEGES AND UNIVERSITIES
WHO AGREE WITH STATEMENTS IN MODIFIED SOCIAL DISTANCE SCALE WITH
RESPECT TO IRISH

Name of School	Have as intimate friend	Work beside on job	Live on same block	Marry	Bar from block	Bar from social club	Date or allow child to date
Annhurst College	80%	95%	80%	46%	2%	2%	59%
Atlanta U.	58	74	62	32	3	3	52
Boston College	72	95	80	40	4	7	56
Boston U.	75	89	76	33	6	7	49
Bowdoin College	81	87	81	61	3	2	68
Brown U.	88	96	84	60	2	3	72
U. of Calif. (Berk.)	89	96	88	56	2	3	76
U. of Colorado	88	95	80	59	1	2	68
U. of Denver	81	93	85	47	1	4	62
Emmanuel College	97	97	93	90	3	1	89
Emory U.	91	92	86	55	3	3	74
Fisk U.	77	82	81	48	0	5	68
Florida State U.	87	90	87	62	1	3	76
Grinnell College	87	92	90	72	2	3	79
Harvard U.	96	96	94	83	4	2	92
U. of Hawaii	65	82	64	54	4	4	58
Holy Cross College	98	100	98	95	5	4	96
Indiana U.	81	91	87	65	1	4	75
U. of Iowa	94	97	92	80	11	1	84
U. of Kentucky	81	91	80	60	2	3	64
U. of Minnesota	89	94	84	76	1	1	81
Newton Sacred Heart	89	89	87	88	1	1	87
Northeastern U.	91	95	90	78	0	0	84
NE U. Control Group	86	91	87	73	3	0	79
Notre Dame U.	99	99	98	96	4	3	99
Oberlin College	95	100	99	88	6	5	94
Ohio U.	93	98	93	73	1	1	87
Ohio Wesleyan U.	93	97	89	75	4	2	89
Queens College	83	98	87	36	2	4	51
St. Louis U.	95	98	97	35	1	0	86
Santa Monica City C.	83	93	85	63	1	2	74
Stonehill College	89	88	95	84	1	1	84
Texas Southern U.	51	66	55	16	7	7	35
Tulane U.	84	88	85	55	3	3	70
Washington State U.	91	97	94	76	2	2	85
Wesleyan U.	87	92	92	75	0	3	87
Western Reserve U.	81	94	91	62	1	4	67
U. of Wisconsin	95	99	95	79	0	0	88
Women's College A	89	97	82	45	1	5	72
Women's College B	94	100	94	72	0	1	92
Women's College C	93	96	91	3	1	0	88
40 SCHOOLS AVERAGE	87%	95%	88%	64%	2%	3%	77%

TABLE 34 PERCENTAGE OF STUDENTS IN 40 AMERICAN COLLEGES AND UNIVERSITIES WHO AGREE WITH STATEMENTS IN MODIFIED SOCIAL DISTANCE SCALE WITH RESPECT TO POLISH

Name of School	Have as intimate friend	Work beside on job	Live on same block	Marry	Bar from block	Bar from social club	Date or allow child to date
Annhurst College	90%	96%	94%	78%	1%	1%	88%
Atlanta U.	53	73	60	30	4	5	50
Boston College	86	92	86	75	1	2	86
Boston U.	77	86	76	42	7	9	54
Bowdoin College	80	85	80	68	2	3	73
Brown U.	91	95	86	61	3	5	74
U. of Calif. (Berk.)	87	97	89	65	2	2	82
U. of Colorado	88	95	79	63	3	6	73
U. of Denver	85	85	76	59	1	3	67
Emmanuel College	93	96	93	79	1	1	90
Emory U.	63	81	63	27	8	13	39
Fisk U.	74	80	79	40	4	6	66
Florida State U.	74	87	73	37	2	5	58
Grinnell College	85	94	87	61	6	6	79
Harvard U.	92	96	94	81	4	2	90
U. of Hawaii	56	75	67	33	4	5	25
Holy Cross College	89	96	89	85	5	4	85
Indiana U.	77	88	74	44	6	11	60
U. of Iowa	88	95	82	66	3	3	75
U. of Kentucky	67	82	67	50	4	6	62
U. of Minnesota	84	94	89	67	2	2	77
Newton Sacred Heart	85	87	77	68	2	2	73
Northeastern U.	86	93	87	71	1	0	79
NE U. Control Group	84	88	82	67	3	0	73
Notre Dame U.	93	99	94	83	5	6	89
Oberlin College	96	100	97	81	7	5	92
Ohio U.	91	96	89	63	2	4	78
Ohio Wesleyan U.	88	99	82	51	3	4	75
Queens College	81	96	87	45	4	6	55
St. Louis U.	88	94	90	75	1	0	86
Santa Monica City C.	74	90	77	53	4	4	65
Stonehill College	82	88	83	76	3	3	77
Texas Southern U.	45	63	47	11	7	8	61
Tulane U.	74	86	76	49	3	11	61
Washington State U.	73	92	81	53	2	3	66
Wesleyan U.	80	92	85	65	2	5	28
Western Reserve U.	82	93	89	61	2	4	69
U. of Wisconsin	89	96	91	67	1	3	82
Women's College A	85	96	80	56	3	6	71
Women's College B	86	99	97	69	3	4	86
Women's College C	87	93	85	69	2	2	82
40 SCHOOLS AVERAGE	83%	93%	83%	61%	3%	4%	72%

TABLE 35 ATTITUDES OF STUDENTS IN 40 AMERICAN COLLEGES AND UNIVERSITIES TOWARD MARRIAGE TO A PERSON OF ANOTHER RELIGION IN TERMS OF PERCENTAGES

Name of School	Hardest	Next hardest	Not quite so hard	Fairly easy	Easiest	No inform.
Annhurst College	12%	65%	9%	10%	4%	0%
Atlanta U.	6	14	22	19	38	1
Boston College	24	57	9	6	4	0
Boston U.	9	46	21	12	12	0
Bowdoin College	3	54	30	9	4	0
Brown U.	3	42	25	18	12	0
U. of Calif. (Berk.)	5	32	25	16	22	0
U. of Colorado	4	26	29	19	21	1
U. of Denver	5	32	30	14	19	0
Emmanuel College	14	59	17	8	2	0
Emory U.	2	24	39	15	19	0
Fisk U.	8	18	15	22	37	0
Florida State U.	1	35	38	16	10	0
Grinnell College	5	43	26	10	16	0
Harvard U.	9	31	22	16	22	0
U. of Hawaii	17	16	27	16	20	4
Holy Cross College	15	59	13	7	5	1
Indiana U.	3	35	33	15	13	1
U. of Iowa	6	41	18	18	17	0
U. of Kentucky	6	28	30	19	17	0
U. of Minnesota	13	49	18	10	10	0
Newton Sacred Heart	10	60	15	11	4	0
Northeastern U.	9	53	16	10	7	5
NE U. Control Group	6	57	19	12	5	1
Notre Dame U.	18	65	3	10	4	0
Oberlin College	6	25	22	25	18	4
Ohio U.	3	42	25	14	6	0
Ohio Wesleyan U.	5	34	31	17	13	0
Queens College	4	61	22	9	4	0
St. Louis U.	21	56	13	6	4	0
Santa Monica City C.	5	32	30	15	18	0
Stonehill College	23	60	12	4	1	0
Texas Southern U.	8	14	29	20	29	0
Tulane U.	2	37	27	22	11	1
Washington State U.	4	36	39	13	8	0
Wesleyan U.	12	40	20	21	7	0
Western Reserve U.	6	42	32	8	10	2
U. of Wisconsin	4	52	27	9	8	0
Women's College A	1	33	28	25	13	0
Women's College B	4	27	29	13	27	0
Women's College C	6	22	32	23	17	0
40 SCHOOLS AVERAGE	9%	41%	24%	14%	13%	1%

TABLE 36 ATTITUDES OF STUDENTS IN 40 AMERICAN COLLEGES AND UNIVERSITIES TOWARD MARRIAGE TO A PERSON OF ANOTHER NATION IN TERMS OF PERCENTAGES

Name of School	Hardest	Next hardest	Not quite so hard	Fairly easy	Easiest	No inform.
Annhurst College	1%	4%	10%	13%	72%	0%
Atlanta U.	31	24	16	22	7	0
Boston College	1	5	20	22	51	1
Boston U.	1	14	28	25	32	0
Bowdoin College	1	10	25	43	21	0
Brown U.	2	11	20	28	37	2
U. of Calif. (Berk.)	2	27	18	25	28	0
U. of Colorado	1	16	23	27	33	0
U. of Denver	1	23	23	24	28	0
Emmanuel College	0	0	5	20	75	0
Emory U.	0	45	24	22	9	0
Fisk U.	14	21	28	21	16	0
Florida State U.	3	44	31	6	16	0
Grinnell College	0	8	20	30	42	0
Harvard U.	0	10	25	20	45	0
U. of Hawaii	10	24	25	21	20	0
Holy Cross College	2	9	22	22	45	0
Indiana U.	2	35	35	17	11	0
U. of Iowa	2	20	30	22	26	0
U. of Kentucky	4	38	21	19	17	1
U. of Minnesota	1	17	24	23	35	0
Newton Sacred Heart	0	5	8	20	67	0
Northeastern U.	2	12	24	21	40	1
NE U. Control Group	2	9	25	33	31	0
Notre Dame U.	2	8	29	23	38	0
Oberlin College	4	13	23	24	36	0
Ohio U.	2	22	27	21	28	0
Ohio Wesleyan U.	1	23	25	21	30	0
Queens College	2	12	30	24	30	0
St. Louis U.	1	9	20	19	50	1
Santa Monica City C.	1	23	26	22	28	0
Stonehill College	0	1	17	15	67	0
Texas Southern U.	32	21	23	7	17	0
Tulane U.	1	25	26	19	29	0
Washington State U.	2	35	25	18	20	0
Wesleyan U.	0	12	25	28	33	0
Western Reserve U.	2	10	23	28	36	1
U. of Wisconsin	3	17	20	20	40	0
Women's College A	1	8	20	28	43	0
Women's College B	12	0	16	33	39	0
Women's College C	2	20	31	21	26	0
40 SCHOOLS AVERAGE	4%	12%	23%	23%	35%	0%

TABLE 37   ATTITUDES OF STUDENTS IN 40 AMERICAN COLLEGES AND UNIVERSITIES
TOWARD MARRIAGE TO A PERSON OF ANOTHER ECONOMIC GROUP IN
TERMS OF PERCENTAGES

Name of School	Hardest	Next hardest	Not quite so hard	Fairly easy	Easiest	No inform.
Annhurst College	1%	6%	35%	43%	15%	0%
Atlanta U.	12	19	27	21	31	0
Boston College	3	8	22	41	26	0
Boston U.	3	8	22	24	41	2
Bowdoin College	0	8	9	27	56	0
Brown U.	2	8	21	30	39	0
U. of Calif. (Berk.)	2	13	22	27	36	0
U. of Colorado	2	8	27	27	36	0
U. of Denver	1	12	22	35	30	0
Emmanuel College	0	6	23	51	20	0
Emory U.	1	12	16	26	45	0
Fisk U.	17	27	20	16	19	1
Florida State U.	2	8	17	33	40	0
Grinnell College	2	9	21	38	30	0
Harvard U.	4	7	26	38	25	0
U. of Hawaii	6	16	21	26	31	0
Holy Cross College	5	5	25	36	29	0
Indiana U.	1	8	23	34	34	0
U. of Iowa	2	12	22	28	36	0
U. of Kentucky	3	10	22	33	32	0
U. of Minnesota	3	3	19	43	32	0
Newton Sacred Heart	0	4	30	46	20	0
Northeastern U.	2	9	22	36	31	0
NE U. Control Group	4	11	18	33	31	4
Notre Dame U.	0	3	17	43	37	0
Oberlin College	1	7	24	33	33	2
Ohio U.	1	8	24	33	34	0
Ohio Wesleyan U.	2	5	20	33	40	0
Queens College	2	8	14	32	44	0
St. Louis U.	0	5	23	42	30	0
Santa Monica City C.	2	12	26	30	30	0
Stonehill College	1	3	21	52	23	0
Texas Southern U.	20	4	25	28	21	2
Tulane U.	1	9	18	37	35	0
Washington State U.	2	11	18	37	32	0
Wesleyan U.	2	6	18	30	44	0
Western Reserve U.	2	10	19	43	26	0
U. of Wisconsin	1	11	16	42	30	0
Women's College A	0	8	30	28	34	0
Women's College B	0	12	39	35	14	0
Women's College C	0	7	31	26	36	0
40 SCHOOLS AVERAGE	3%	10%	23%	31%	33%	0%

TABLE 38 ATTITUDES OF STUDENTS IN 40 AMERICAN COLLEGES AND UNIVERSITIES
TOWARD MARRIAGE TO A PERSON OF ANOTHER EDUCATIONAL GROUP
IN TERMS OF PERCENTAGES

Name of School	Hardest	Next hardest	Not quite so hard	Fairly easy	Easiest	No inform.
Annhurst College	4%	14%	45%	31%	6%	0%
Atlanta U.	18	22	19	25	16	0
Boston College	2	13	46	27	12	0
Boston U.	9	23	25	31	12	0
Bowdoin College	3	27	30	28	12	0
Brown U.	11	28	31	22	7	1
U. of Calif. (Berk.)	12	24	26	25	13	0
U. of Colorado	11	41	21	21	6	0
U. of Denver	3	28	24	27	18	0
Emmanuel College	4	25	48	19	4	0
Emory U.	4	22	17	33	24	0
Fisk U.	34	18	20	20	8	0
Florida State U.	2	16	19	43	20	0
Grinnell College	15	30	25	19	11	0
Harvard U.	18	40	19	15	8	0
U. of Hawaii	17	20	20	26	13	4
Holy Cross College	5	18	44	22	9	2
Indiana U.	7	19	10	32	32	0
U. of Iowa	11	21	28	25	15	0
U. of Kentucky	3	21	25	28	23	0
U. of Minnesota	6	22	9	30	33	0
Newton Sacred Heart	2	27	40	27	4	0
Northeastern U.	3	14	33	30	20	0
NE U. Control Group	4	16	30	26	23	1
Notre Dame U.	1	6	50	28	15	0
Oberlin College	24	31	24	12	9	0
Ohio U.	6	26	24	26	18	0
Ohio Wesleyan U.	7	31	22	27	13	0
Queens College	6	7	46	28	13	0
St. Louis U.	1	13	41	30	15	0
Santa Monica City C.	5	26	24	28	17	0
Stonehill College	4	12	48	27	9	0
Texas Southern U.	19	27	16	30	8	0
Tulane U.	14	16	30	23	17	0
Washington State U.	5	12	22	32	29	0
Wesleyan U.	7	26	32	20	15	0
Western Reserve U.	6	26	34	18	16	0
U. of Wisconsin	7	11	34	27	21	0
Women's College A	7	47	22	14	10	0
Women's College B	9	41	25	13	12	0
Women's College C	14	45	19	17	5	0
40 SCHOOLS AVERAGE	8%	24%	29%	26%	15%	0%

TABLE 39 ATTITUDES OF STUDENTS IN 40 AMERICAN COLLEGES AND UNIVERSITIES TOWARD MARRIAGE TO A PERSON OF ANOTHER COLOR IN TERMS OF PERCENTAGES

Name of School	Hardest	Next hardest	Not quite so hard	Fairly easy	Easiest	No inform.
Annhurst College	86%	9%	4%	1%	0%	0%
Atlanta U.	36	20	15	16	11	2
Boston College	75	15	4	1	3	2
Boston U.	81	8	4	3	2	2
Bowdoin College	90	4	3	1	1	1
Brown U.	81	9	4	1	5	0
U. of Calif. (Berk.)	81	8	6	1	4	0
U. of Colorado	80	11	3	2	4	0
U. of Denver	88	4	3	3	2	0
Emmanuel College	79	11	8	2	0	0
Emory U.	93	5	0	0	2	0
Fisk U.	27	20	16	20	17	0
Florida State U.	88	7	2	0	3	0
Grinnell College	77	9	12	0	2	0
Harvard U.	61	14	17	6	2	0
U. of Hawaii	44	31	10	10	5	0
Holy Cross College	77	11	5	5	0	2
Indiana U.	84	6	5	1	4	0
U. of Iowa	81	8	7	1	3	0
U. of Kentucky	85	8	5	0	2	0
U. of Minnesota	79	11	4	4	2	0
Newton Sacred Heart	90	6	3	1	0	0
Northeastern U.	81	7	4	2	6	0
NE U. Control Group	84	4	4	2	3	3
Notre Dame U.	79	18	1	1	1	0
Oberlin College	62	19	6	3	5	5
Ohio U.	86	6	4	3	1	0
Ohio Wesleyan U.	88	7	1	1	3	0
Queens College	85	8	0	0	6	1
St. Louis U.	76	17	5	1	1	0
Santa Monica City C.	86	6	2	3	3	0
Stonehill College	76	20	1	3	0	0
Texas Southern U.	24	22	16	23	15	0
Tulane U.	86	9	3	0	2	0
Washington State U.	91	3	1	2	3	0
Wesleyan U.	78	13	6	0	2	1
Western Reserve U.	87	8	1	2	2	0
U. of Wisconsin	82	7	1	1	9	0
Women's College A	91	6	1	1	1	0
Women's College B	91	2	3	1	3	0
Women's College C	76	12	5	2	5	0
40 SCHOOLS AVERAGE	80%	11%	3%	3%	3%	0%

NOTES

CHAPTER 1

1. Paul H. Jacobson, *American Marriage and Divorce* (New York: Holt, Rinehart and Winston, Inc., 1959), p. 62.
2. George E. Simpson and J. Milton Yinger, *Racial and Cultural Minorities* (New York: Harper & Row, Publishers, 1953), p. 493.
3. Biennial Survey of Education in the United States, *Statistical Summary of 1955-56*, U.S. Government Printing Office, Washington, D.C., pp. 64-5.
4. From an address delivered on November 19, 1961, by Rabbi Benjamin Kahn, National Director of Hillel Foundation, B'nai B'rith.
5. J. H. S. Bossard and E. S. Boll, *Why Marriages Go Wrong* (New York: The Ronald Press Company, 1958), pp. 11-12.
6. Figure reported by Public Health Service, U.S. Department of Health, Education and Welfare, Washington, D.C., 1959.

CHAPTER 2

1. The material contained in this chapter is the result of my own research. See tables in Appendix.
2. Emory S. Bogardus, *Immigration and Race Attitudes* (Boston: D. C. Heath & Co., 1928).

CHAPTER 3

1. Oscar Handlin, *The Uprooted* (Boston: Little, Brown & Co., 1951), p. 227.
2. *New York Times,* November 12, 1961, p. 48.
3. Stanley R. Brav, *Jewish Family Solidarity* (Vicksburg, Mississippi: 1940), pp. 39-73.
4. Aaron Antonovsky, "Aspects of New Haven Jewry," in *Yivo Annual of Social Science* (New York: 1951), p. 143.

5. Max Lerner, *America as a Civilization* (New York: Simon & Schuster, Inc., 1957), p. 689.
6. Nahum Goldmann, excerpt of address delivered at the opening session of the World Conference on Jewish Education, convened in Jerusalem, August 12, 1962. Dr. Goldmann is the President of the World Zionist Organization and the World Jewish Congress.
7. Reported in the *New York Times,* March 19, 1962, p. 66, from article by Gerhard Lenski, Jr., in *The Lutheran.*
8. Joseph Maier and William Spinrad in *The Phylon Quarterly,* Atlanta University, Atlanta, Ga., fourth quarter, 1958, pp. 355-60.
9. The Harvard *Crimson,* Cambridge, Mass., June 11, 1959. See particularly pp. 5, 7, and 8.
10. The Harvard *Crimson.* See article by John B. Radner, "Agnosticism at University Challenges Catholic Faith," *ibid.,* pp. 3-5.
11. Richard N. Levy, "The Increase and the Sin," *Mosaic,* published by the Harvard-Radcliffe Hillel Societies, Vol. 1 (Spring, 1960), pp. 3-12.
12. Rose K. Goldsen, Morris Rosenberg, Robin Williams, Jr., and Edward A. Suchman, *What College Students Think* (Princeton, N.J.: D. Van Nostrand Co., Inc., 1960), p. 154.
13. *Ibid.,* p. 157.
14. *Ibid.,* p. 160.
15. *Ibid.,* pp. 153-68.
16. *Ibid.,* p. 161.
17. The *New York Times,* January 8, 1961, p. 76.
18. Dr. Yoshio Fukuyama's survey was financed by the Congregational Mission Board and was carried out in conjunction with an urban church project conducted by the Bureau of Research and Survey of the National Council of Churches,

475 Riverside Drive, New York, N.Y.

19. George Simpson, *People in Families* (New York: Thomas Y. Crowell Co., 1960), p. 4.

20. Jacobson, *op. cit.* (Ch. 1, n. 1), p. 153.

21. Will Herberg, *Protestant—Catholic —Jew* (New York: Doubleday & Company, Inc., 1955).

22. Bossard and Boll, *op. cit.* (Ch. 1, n. 5), p. 153.

23. Paul Popenoe, "Meetings That Lead to Marriage," *Ecumenical News,* Vol. 17 (1932), p. 86.

24. William Haber, "Changing Patterns in Jewish Life on the Campus," pamphlet published by B'nai B'rith Hillel Foundation (Washington, D.C.: 1961), p. 5.

25. *U.S. Census of Population, 1960,* U.S. Government Printing Office, Washington, D.C., p. xiv.

26. See Ruby Jo Reeves Kennedy, "Single or Triple Melting Pot? Intermarriage Trends in New Haven, 1870-1940," *American Journal of Sociology,* Vol. 49 (January, 1944), pp. 331-39. See also Marvin R. Koller, study of Columbus, Ohio, in 1936 and 1938, in *American Sociological Review,* Vol. 13 (October, 1948), pp. 613-18. Also Alfred C. Clarke, "Residential Propinquity as a Factor in Mate Selection," *American Sociological Review,* Vol. 17 (February, 1952), pp. 17-22.

27. Carle C. Zimmerman and Lucius F. Cervantes, *Successful American Families* (New York: Pageant Press, Inc., 1960), p. 37.

28. John L. Thomas, *The American Catholic Family* (New York: Prentice-Hall, Inc., 1956).

29. J. H. S. Bossard and E. S. Boll, *One Marriage, Two Faiths* (New York: The Ronald Press Company, 1957), p. 59.

30. August B. Hollingshead, "Cultural Factors in the Selection of Marriage Mates," *American Sociological Review,* Vol. 15 (October, 1950), pp. 619-27.

31. Marvin R. Koller, "Residential and Occupational Propinquity," *Ameri-*

can Sociological Review, Vol. 13 (October, 1948), pp. 613-18.

32. Maurice R. Davie and Ruby Jo Reeves, "Propinquity of Residence Before Marriage," *American Journal of Sociology,* Vol. 44 (January, 1939), pp. 510-17.

33. W. I. Thomas and F. Znaniecki, *The Polish Peasant,* Vol. 2 (New York: Dover Publications, Inc., 1958), p. 1128.

34. Willard Waller and Reuben Hill, *The Family: A Dynamic Interpretation,* (New York: Holt, Rinehart and Winston, Inc., 1951), p. 114.

35. Reuben B. Resnick, "Some Sociological Aspects of Intermarriage of Jews and Non-Jews," *Social Forces,* Vol. 12 (October, 1933), pp. 94-102.

36. J. S. Slotkin, "Jewish-Gentile Intermarriages in Chicago," *American Sociological Review,* Vol. 7 (February, 1942), pp. 34-39.

37. W. I. Thomas, *Source Book for Social Origins* (Chicago: University of Chicago Press, 1909).

38. Maria H. Levinson and Daniel J. Levinson, "Jews Who Intermarry: Socio-psychological Bases of Ethnic Identity and Change," *Yivo Annual of Jewish Social Science,* Vol. 12 (1958-59), pp. 103-30.

39. St. Clair Drake and Horace R. Cayton, *Black Metropolis* (New York: Harcourt, Brace & World, Inc., 1945), p. 148.

40. Levinson and Levinson, *op. cit.*

41. *Ibid.*

42. *Ibid.*

43. Jerrold S. Heiss, "Premarital Characteristics of Religiously Intermarried," *American Sociological Review,* Vol. 25 (February, 1960), pp. 47-55.

44. Joseph H. Fichter, *Social Relations in the Urban Parish* (Chicago: University of Chicago Press, 1953), p. 17.

45. Kurt Lewin, *Resolving Social Conflicts* (New York: Harper & Row, Publishers, 1948).

46. Gordon W. Allport, *The Nature of Prejudice* (Reading, Mass.: Addison-Wesley Publishing Co., Inc., 1954), p. 37.

47. Herberg, *op. cit.* (n. 21).
48. Evelyn Millis Duvall, "Saving Your Marriage," Public Affairs Pamphlet No. 213 (1954). See also Duvall and R. Hill, "When You Marry," Public Affairs Pamphlet No. 113 (1952).
49. Franz Boas, *Anthropology and Modern Life* (New York: W. W. Norton & Company, Inc., 1928), pp. 73-4.
50. Gerhard Lenski, *The Religious Factor* (New York: Doubleday & Company, Inc., 1961), p. 196.
51. *Ibid.,* p. 38.
52. *Ibid.,* pp. 33-40.
53. Marshall Sklare and Marc Vosk, "The Riverton Study: How Jews Look at Themselves and Their Neighbors," pamphlet published by the American Jewish Committee, New York: May, 1957.
54. Antonovsky, *op. cit.* (n. 4), pp. 129-164.
55. Sidney E. Goldstein, *The Meaning of Marriage and Foundations of the Family* (New York, Bloch Publishing Co., Inc., 1942), p. 161.

CHAPTER 4

1. "Religion Reported by the Civilian Population of the United States, March, 1957," Table 1 in *Current Population Reports,* Series P-20, No. 79 (U.S. Bureau of the Census, February, 1958), reported by Donald J. Bogue in *The Population of the United States* (Glencoe, Ill.: The Free Press, 1959), p. 689.
2. Heiss, *op. cit.* (Ch. 3, n. 43).
3. See the *Official Catholic Directory, 1962* (New York: P. J. Kenedy & Sons), pp. 1-2.
4. Thomas, *op. cit.,* p. 156. See also by Thomas "The Factor of Religion in the Selection of Marriage Mates," *American Sociological Review,* Vol. 16 (August, 1951), p. 487.
5. William J. Goode, *After Divorce* (Glencoe, Ill.: The Free Press, 1936), p. 36.
6. Lenski, *op. cit.,* p. 267.
7. Judson T. Landis, "Religiousness, Family Relationships and Family

Values in Protestant, Catholic and Jewish Families," *Marriage and Family Living,* Vol. 22 (November, 1960), pp. 341-347.
8. *Ibid.,* p. 343.
9. *Ibid.,* p. 344.
10. *Ibid.,* p. 345.
11. *Ibid.,* p. 345.
12. M. C. Elmer in a personal letter to the author, dated October 31, 1960.
13. Zimmerman and Cervantes, *op. cit.,* p. 7.
14. *Ibid.,* p. 23.
15. *Ibid.,* p. 151.
16. *Ibid.,* pp. 153-4; 158-60.
17. *Ibid.,* pp. 147-62.
18. See information service published by the Bureau of Research and Survey, National Council of the Church of Christ in the United States of America, 475 Riverside Drive, New York 27, N.Y.
19. Harvey J. Locke, *Predicting Adjustment in Marriage* (New York: Holt, Rinehart and Winston, Inc., 1951), pp. 68-9.
20. Judson T. Landis and Mary G. Landis, *Building a Successful Marriage* (New York: Prentice-Hall, Inc., 1948), p. 139.
21. H. Ashley Weeks, "Differential Divorce Rates by Occupation," *Social Forces,* Vol. 21 (March, 1943), p. 336.
22. Howard M. Bell, *Youth Tell Their Story,* American Council on Education, Washington, D.C., 1938, p. 21.
23. *Ibid.*
24. Weeks, *op. cit.,* p. 336.
25. Judson T. Landis, "Marriages of Mixed and Non-Mixed Religious Faiths," *American Sociological Review,* Vol. 14 (June, 1949), pp. 401-7.
26. Landis, "Religiousness, Family Relationships and Family Values," *op. cit.* (n. 7), p. 342.
27. Landis, "Marriages of Mixed and Non-Mixed Religious Faiths," *op. cit.*
28. Landis, "Religiousness, Family Relationships and Family Values," *op. cit.* (n. 7), p. 345.
29. *Ibid.*
30. Heiss, *op. cit.* (Ch. 3, n. 43).
31. Locke, *op. cit.* (n. 19), p. 68.

32. *Ibid.*, p. 240.
33. Emily H. Mudd in the *Woman's Home Companion* (March, 1953), p. 30.
34. Clifford Kirkpatrick, *The Family: A Process and Institution* (New York: The Ronald Press Company, 1955), pp. 346-354; 599-620.
35. E. W. Burgess and L. S. Cottrell, Jr., *Predicting Success or Failure in Marriage* (New York: Prentice-Hall, Inc., 1939), Ch. 5.
36. John E. Mayer, *Jewish-Gentile Courtships* (Glencoe, Ill.: The Free Press, 1961), p. 20.
37. *Ibid.*, p. 152.

CHAPTER 5

1. Leland Foster Wood, "If I Marry a Roman Catholic," pamphlet published by Department of Family Life, National Council of Churches of Christ, New York, 1945.
2. *Ibid.*
3. *The Christian Century* (March 14, 1962), p. 318.
4. Murray H. Leiffer, "Mixed Marriage and Church Loyalties," *The Christian Century* (January 19, 1949), p. 401.
5. "Interfaith Marriage," a statement adopted by the General Synod of the Evangelical and Reformed Church, meeting at Tiffin, Ohio, June 17-24, 1953, published by the Commission on Christian Social Action, Cleveland, Ohio.
6. Excerpt from a letter written by the Rev. Myron Fowell to the author, dated November 22, 1961.
7. J. H. S. Bossard and Harold C. Letts, "Mixed Marriages Involving Lutherans," *Marriage and Family Living*, Vol. 18 (November, 1956), pp. 308-310.
8. Prepared by the Family Life Committee of the Board of Parish Education, 210 N. Broadway, St. Louis 2, Mo., June, 1959.
9. Bossard and Boll, *One Marriage, Two Faiths, op. cit.* (Ch. 3, n. 29), p. 81.
10. *Ibid.*, p. 59.
11. "Christian Guidance on Marriage and Family Life," pamphlet published by the Board of Social Mis-sions of the United Lutheran Church in America, 231 Madison Avenue, N.Y. 16, N.Y., October 16, 1956.
12. Preliminary draft of statement by the Committee on Research and Social Action of the American Lutheran Church, 422 S. Fifth Avenue, Minneapolis 15, Minn.
13. See James A. Pike, *If You Marry Outside Your Faith* (New York: Harper & Row, Publishers, 1954), pp. 98-9.
14. The author is indebted to Bishop James K. Mathews of the Boston area of the Methodist Church for this information. This resolution of the General Conference of the Methodist Church was passed in Minneapolis April 25-May 7, 1956.
15. Resolution of the General Convention of the Protestant Episcopal Church, San Francisco, Calif., 1949.
16. Quoted from mimeographed material prepared for the North American Conference on the Church and Family Life by the National Council of Churches, New York, 1961.
17. From a letter to the author from Dr. Donald S. Harrington, minister of the Community Church of New York, dated August 1, 1961.
18. Excerpt from a letter to the author by the Rev. John Ogden Fisher, then minister of the First Unitarian Church in Newton, Mass., February 27, 1961.
19. Algernon D. Black, "If I Marry Outside My Religion," Public Affairs Pamphlet No. 204 (1954).
20. The colleges and universities served by these clergymen are: Harvard University, Radcliffe College, Amherst College, Boston University, University of Massachusetts, Mt. Holyoke College, University of Connecticut, Brandeis University, Massachusetts Institute of Technology, Simmons College, Wellesley College, and Wesleyan University.

CHAPTER 6

1. Gerald J. Schnepp, *Leakage from a Catholic Parish*, Catholic University, 1953, p. 88.

2. *Official Catholic Directory, 1962,* p. 2.
3. *Ibid.*
4. *Ibid.*
5. Thomas, *The American Catholic Family, loc. cit.* (Ch. 3, n. 28), p. 160.
6. Thomas, "The Factor of Religion in the Selection of Marriage Mates," *loc. cit.* (Ch. 4, n. 4), p. 488.
7. Thomas, *The American Catholic Family, loc. cit.,* p. 160.
8. *New York Times,* March 15, 1956, p. L-35.
9. Lucius P. Cervantes in *The Tablet* (Brooklyn, N.Y.), January 11, 1958.
10. John J. Kane, in *The Voice of St. Jude* (Chicago, Ill.), June, 1957.
11. Information Service published by the National Council of Churches, 475 Riverside Drive, N.Y., N.Y., February, 1954, p. 34.
12. Schnepp, *op. cit.*
13. Fichter, *op. cit.* (Ch. 3, n. 44), pp. 76-7, 192.
14. M. C. Elmer, *The Sociology of the Family* (Boston: Ginn & Company, 1945), p. 191.
15. *Ibid.,* pp. 191-2.
16. Landis, "Marriages of Mixed and Non-Mixed Religious Faiths," *op. cit.* (Ch. 4, n. 25), pp. 401-07.
17. Bishops' Committee on Mixed Marriage, "A Factual Study of Mixed Marriage (Washington, D.C.: National Catholic Welfare Conference, 1943), p. 5.
18. Francis J. Connell in the *American Ecclesiastic Review* (January, 1946).
19. John Walsh, *This Is Catholicism* (New York: Doubleday & Company, Inc., Image Books, 1959), p. 281.
20. *Ibid.,* p. 283.
21. *Ibid.,* p. 287.
22. I Cor. 7:39.
23. J. D. Conway, *Facts of the Faith* (New York: Doubleday & Company, 1959), pp. 251-3.
24. From Petition for Dispensation used by the Archdiocese of Boston, Massachusetts.
25. *New York Times,* June 6, 1961, p. 33.
26. Walsh, *op. cit.,* pp. 290-1.

27. Sister Frances Jerome Woods, *Cultural Values of American Ethnic Groups* (New York: Harper & Row, Publishers, 1956), p. 214.
28. *Ibid.,* p. 214.
29. Fichter, *op. cit.* (Ch. 3, n. 44), pp. 76-7.
30. Francis Tei Haar, *Mixed Marriages and Their Remedies* (New York: Frederick Pustet, 1933), p. 13.
31. Charles Bruehl, "Pastoralia Ways of Approach," *Homiletic and Pastoral Review,* Vol. 30 (May, 1930), pp. 799-800.
32. George A. Kelly, *The Catholic Youth's Guide to Life and Love* (New York: Random House, Inc., 1960), p. 137.
33. John A. O'Brien, *Happy Marriage* (New York: Hanover House, 1956), pp. 131-2.
34. Thomas, *The American Catholic Family, loc. cit.* (Ch. 3, n. 28), p. 381.
35. Donald F. Miller, C.S.S.R., *Program for Catholics in a Mixed Marriage* (Liguore, Missouri, 1961), p. 5.
36. Thomas, "The Factor of Religion in the Selection of Marriage Mates," *loc. cit.* (Ch. 4, n. 4), pp. 487-91.
37. Ruby Jo Reeves Kennedy, "Single or Triple Melting Pot? *op. cit.* (Ch. 3, n. 26).
38. From a letter to the author by His Excellency, Eric F. MacKenzie, Auxiliary Bishop of Boston, dated May 3, 1961.
39. Thomas, *The American Catholic Family, op. cit.,* p. 227.
40. *Ibid.,* p. 220.
41. *Ibid.,* pp. 227-8.
42. Landis, "Religiousness, Family Relationships and Family Values," *op. cit.* (Ch. 4, n. 7), p. 345.
43. See editorial in *The Christian Century* (April 10, 1963), p. 453.
44. The Directors of Newman Clubs in certain colleges and universities were asked to express their beliefs on this theme. The priests from whom replies were received serve Newman Clubs in the following schools: University of Chicago, University of North Carolina, Stanford University, San Jose State

College, University of Michigan, University of Nebraska, Ohio State University, Northwestern University, Indiana University, University of Pittsburgh, University of Minnesota, Simmons College, Wheelock College, Suffolk University, State College of Boston, Queens College (New York City), Wesleyan University (Connecticut), Hunter College, Dartmouth College, Mt. Holyoke College, University of Pennsylvania, University of Colorado, Tufts University, Brandeis University, Babson Institute, Trinity College (Hartford, Conn.), Northeastern University, Cornell University, University of Washington, Ohio University, Boston University, Emerson College, Harvard University, Radcliffe College.

CHAPTER 7

1. For some Old Testament attitudes toward intermarriage read: Gen. 11:29, 20:12, 24:15, 28:9, 29:12, 38:2, 41:45, 46:10; Exod. 2:21; Num. 21:1. Read also the book of Ruth and the book of Ezra. See also Louis M. Epstein, *Marriage Laws in the Bible and Talmud* (Cambridge, Mass.: Harvard University Press, 1942).

2. Deut. 7:1-4.

3. Epstein, *op. cit.*, p. 164.

4. Louis Finkelstein, ed., *The Jews* (New York: Harper & Row, Publishers, 1950), Vol. 2, p. 1329.

5. Moses Mielziner, *The Jewish Law of Marriage and Divorce* (Cincinnati, Ohio: The Bloch Publishing Co., 1901), pp. 46-7.

6. Leo Littman, in *American Jewish Year Book*, Vol. 57 (published by American Jewish Committee, New York, 1956), p. 343.

7. *American Jewish Year Book*, 1957, p. 261; see also *American Jewish Year Book*, 1958, pp. 263-4.

8. See Jewish Telegraphic Agency *Bulletin* (July 15, 1963), p. 3.

9. Arthur Ruppin, *Jews in the Modern World* (London: The Macmillan Company, 1934).

10. Bruno Blau, "Die Mischele in Nazireich," *Judaica*, Heft 1.1 (Zurich: April, 1948).

11. Harry Maor, *A Demographic Study of West Germany's Jews* (Mainz University: June, 1961).

12. Uriah Z. Engelman in *The Jews*, ed. Finkelstein, *op. cit.* (n. 4), pp. 1191-2.

13. Israel Cohen, *Contemporary Jewry* (London: Methuen & Co., 1950), p. 262.

14. Cecil Roth, *The History of the Jews of Italy* (Philadelphia: Jewish Publication Society, 1946), p. 505.

15. *Ibid.*, p. 528.

16. *American Jewish Year Book*, 1947, p. 366.

17. Hannah Neustatter, "Demographic and Other Statistical Aspects of Anglo-Jewry," in *A Minority in Britain*, ed. M. Freedman (London: Vallentine Mitchell Co., Ltd., 1955), p. 93.

18. Elliot Slater, quoted in *A Minority in Britain, op. cit.*, pp. 93-4.

19. Reported in *The National Jewish Post and Opinion* (Indianapolis, Ind.: April 6, 1942), p. 14.

20. Rabbi Mika Weiss, formerly Chief Rabbi of Finland, very kindly provided me with this information.

21. *American Jewish Year Book*, 1960, p. 175.

22. Louis Rosenberg, "The Demography of the Jewish Community in Canada," *The Jewish Journal of Sociology*, Vol. 1 (December, 1959), p. 231.

23. Louis Rosenberg, "Two Centuries of Jewish Life in Canada (1760-1960)," in *American Jewish Year Book*, 1961, pp. 42-3.

24. *The Occident*, Vol. 2 (January, 1845), pp. 458-63.

25. Jacob R. Marcus, *Early American Jewry* (Philadelphia: Jewish Publication Society, 1953), Vol. 2, p. 504.

26. Malcom H. Stern, "The Function of Genealogy in American Jewish History," Essays in American Jewish History (Cincinnati, Ohio: published in American Jewish Archives, 1951), pp. 85-6.

27. *Rabbi's Manual*, ed. by Central Conference of American Rabbis (New York: 1961).

28. This convention was held in Minneapolis, Minn., in June, 1962.

29. See interview on "Religion in the American Character," published by the Center for the Study of Democratic Institutions. Dr. Finkelstein was interviewed by Dr. Donald McDonald. A Fund for the Republic, Inc., publication, 1962.

30. Dr. David de Sola Pool, *Essay on Intermarriage*, published by National Jewish Welfare Board, N.Y. 36, N.Y.

31. Mordecai M. Kaplan, *Questions People Ask* (New York: Reconstructionist Press, 1956), p. 225.

32. Excerpts from a letter to the author from Rabbi Roy Rosenberg, Temple Emanu-El, Honolulu, Hawaii, dated June 12, 1961.

33. Rabbi Maurice Pekarsky, late Director, Hillel Foundation at the University of Chicago. Director, Hillel's Department of Leadership Training, in Changing Patterns of Jews. B'nai B'rith, Washington, D.C.

34. Neustatter, *op. cit.* (n. 17), p. 94.

35. Maurice Frischberg, *The Jews* (New York: Charles Scribner's Sons, 1911, p. 181).

36. Stanley K. Bigman, *The Jewish Population of Greater Washington in 1956* (Washington, D.C.: The Jewish Community Council of Greater Washington, May, 1957).

37. Brown University, Brandeis University, University of Pennsylvania, Vassar College, Northwestern University, University of Chicago, University of California (Berkeley), University of Pittsburgh, Duquesne University, Carnegie Institute of Technology, Chatham College, Cornell University, Ohio State University, Adelphi College, Hofstra College, Queens College, Fresno State College, University of Vermont, University of Miami, College of the City of New York, Hunter College, Harvard University, Radcliffe College, Brooklyn College, Washington University, Ohio University, Auburn University, University of Florida.

38. Kurt Lewin, *Resolving Social Conflicts* (New York: Harper & Row, Publishers, 1948), p. 180.

39. Reported in the National Jewish *Post and Opinion*, Indianapolis, Ind., December 15, 1961, p. 1.

40. Handlin, *op. cit.* (Ch. 3, n. 1), p. 117.

41. Benjamin B. Goldman, "The Jewish Population of New Orleans, La., 1953, A Demographic Study" (New York: The Council of Jewish Federations and Welfare Funds), pp. xxiv-xxv.

42. Kennedy, *op. cit.* (Ch. 3, n. 26), pp. 331-39.

43. *Ibid.*

44. The surveys were made by the staff of the American Jewish Committee, New York City.

45. Robert Shosteck, "Small Town Jewry Tell Their Story," B'nai B'rith Vocational Service Bureau, 1948, pp. 45-7.

46. Peter I. Rose, "Small Town Jews and Their Neighbours in the United States," *Jewish Journal of Sociology*, Vol. 3 (1962).

47. Manheim S. Shapiro, *Bayville Survey*, published by the American Jewish Committee, New York, February, 1961.

48. *Ibid.*

49. Sklare and Vosk, "The Riverton Study," *loc. cit.* (Ch. 3, n. 53), p. 32.

50. Manheim S. Shapiro, *Southville Survey*, published by the American Jewish Committee, New York, June, 1959, p. 28.

51. *Ibid.*, p. 72.

52. Henry T. Lipman, *The White Plains Study*, published by the American Jewish Committee, New York, 1958, p. 72.

53. Bigman, *op. cit.* (n. 36), p. 124.

54. Eric Rosenthal, "Jewish Intermarriage" in *American Jewish Year Book, 1963*, Philadelphia, p. 9.

55. Bigman, *op. cit.*, p. 128.

56. *Ibid.*, p. 137.

57. *Ibid.*, p. 138.

58. *Ibid.*

59. *Ibid.*, p. 132.

60. *Ibid.*, p. 139.

61. Fred Massarik, "Report of the Jewish Population of San Francisco, Marin County and the Peninsula, 1959," published by the Jewish Welfare Federation of San Fran-

cisco, Marin County and the Peninsula.
62. *Ibid.*, p. 31.
63. *Ibid.*, p. 29.
64. *Ibid.*, p. 35.
65. *Ibid.*, p. 36.
66. *Ibid.*, p. 38.
67. *Ibid.*, p. 45.
68. *Ibid.*, p. 45.
69. Letter to the author by Rabbi David Max Eichhorn, February 21, 1961.
70. Rabbi Eichhorn in *Jewish Social Studies* (October, 1954), pp. 17-22.
71. Rabbi's Manual, *op. cit.* (n. 27), pp. 153-176.

CHAPTER 8

1. Harry L. Shapiro, "Race Mixture" (pamphlet published by UNESCO, 1953), p. 7.
2. *Ibid.*, p. 9.
3. L. C. Dunn and T. Dobzhansky, *Heredity, Race and Society* (New York: New American Library, 1952), p. 115.
4. The twelve scientists who drafted the UNESCO statement of June 8, 1951, are: R. A. M. Bergman, Royal Tropical Institute, Netherlands Anthropological Society, Amsterdam; G. Dahlberg, Director, State Institute for Human Genetics and Race Biology, University of Upsala; L. C. Dunn, Department of Zoology, Columbia University; I. B. S. Haldane, University College, London; M. F. Ashley Montague, Rutgers University; A. E. Mourant, London; H. Nachsheim, Berlin; E. Schreiber, Paris; Harry L. Shapiro, New York; J. S. Trevor, University of Cambridge, England; H. V. Vallois, Paris; S. Ziecherman, University of Birmingham; T. Dobzhansky, Columbia University. Dr. Julian Huxley assisted in the final wording of the document.
5. Shapiro, *op. cit.* (n. 1), Article 7.
6. Ethel J. Alpenfels, *Sense and Nonsense About Race* (New York: Friendship Books, 1957).
7. States prohibiting Negro-white marriages are: Alabama, Arkansas, Delaware, Florida, North Carolina, Oklahoma, Georgia, Indiana, Kentucky, Louisiana, Maryland, Mississippi, Missouri, South Carolina, Tennessee, Texas, West Virginia, Virginia, Wyoming.
8. Andrew D. Weinberger, "A Reappraisal of the Constitutionality of Miscegenation Statutes, *Journal of the National Medical Association,* Vol. 51 (May, 1959), p. 215.
9. Gunnar Myrdal, *An American Dilemma* (New York: Harper & Row, Publishers, 1944), p. 60.
10. Simpson and Yinger, *Cultural and Racial Minorities, op. cit.* (Ch. 1, n. 2), p. 50.
11. Oregon declares a person of one-fourth or more Negro ancestry to be a Negro, while Indiana, Mississippi, Missouri, Nebraska, North Dakota, and South Carolina refer to one-eighth. Those states that emphasize legislation against Filipino-white marriages are Arizona, California, Georgia, Maryland, Nevada, Oregon, South Carolina, South Dakota, Virginia, and Wyoming.
12. Arizona, Georgia (includes West Indians), North Carolina, Oregon, and South Carolina.
13. Vernon J. Parenton and Roland J. Pellegrin, "The 'Sabines': A Study of Racial Hybrids in a Louisiana Coastal Parish," *Social Forces,* Vol. 29 (December, 1950), pp. 148-54.
14. Grayson Kirk, "The Filipinos," *Annals of the American Academy of Political Science,* Vol. 223 (1942), pp. 45-8.
15. E. S. Bogardus, "Filipino Americans," in F. S. Brown and J. S. Roucek, *Our Racial Minorities* (New York: Prentice-Hall, Inc., 1937), p. 520.
16. Jacobson, *American Marriage and Divorce, loc. cit.* (Ch. 1, n. 1), p. 31.
17. *Ibid.*, p. 32.
18. Shepard Schwartz, "Mate-Selection Among New York City's Chinese Males, 1931-38," *American Journal of Sociology,* Vol. 56 (May, 1951), pp. 562-8.
19. Francis L. K. Hsu, *American and Chinese: Two Ways of Life* (London: Henry Schumann, 1955), p. 345.

20. Rose Hum Lee, *The Chinese in the United States of America* (Hong Kong: Hong Kong Press, 1960), p. 251.
21. Oscar Handlin, *The Newcomers* (Cambridge, Mass.: Harvard University Press, 1959), p. 51.
22. *Ibid.*, p. 49.
23. Constantine Panunzio, "Intermarriage in Los Angeles 1924-33," *American Journal of Sociology*, Vol. 47 (March, 1942), pp. 690-701.
24. Simpson and Yinger, *op. cit.*, p. 507.
25. Romanzo Adams, *Interracial Marriage in Hawaii* (New York: The Macmillan Company, 1937), p. 12.
26. *Ibid.*, p. 48.
27. C. K. Cheng and Douglas S. Yamamura, "Interracial Marriage and Divorce in Hawaii," *Social Forces*, Vol. 36 (October, 1957), pp. 83-4.

CHAPTER 9

1. Langston Hughes, "Cross," in *Selected Poems of Langston Hughes* (New York: Alfred A. Knopf, 1959), p. 158.
2. *World Almanac*, 1962, p. 251.
3. See Melville Herskovits, *The American Negro: A Study in Racial Crossing* (New York: Alfred A. Knopf, Inc., 1928).
4. Maurice R. Davie, *Negroes in American Society* (New York: McGraw-Hill Book Co., Inc., 1949), p. 388.
5. Joseph Golden, "Patterns of Negro-White Intermarriage," *American Sociological Review*, Vol. 19 (April, 1954), p. 154.
6. *Ibid.*, pp. 144-147.
7. *Ibid.*, p. 183.
8. Kennedy, "Single or Triple Melting Pot?" *op. cit.* (Ch. 3, n. 26), p. 331.
9. See W. Lloyd Warner, *American Life: Dream and Reality* (Chicago, Ill.: University of Chicago Press, 1953), p. 68.
10. Allport, *The Nature of Prejudice, loc. cit.* (Ch. 3, n. 46), p. 109.
11. *Ibid.*, p. 376.
12. Charles Edward Smith, "Negro-White Intermarriage in Metropolitan New York," unpublished doctoral thesis at Teacher's College, Columbia University, December, 1960.
13. Milton L. Barron, *When People Marry* (Syracuse: Syracuse University Press, 1946), p. 58.
14. Julius Drachsler, *Democracy and Assimilation* (New York: The Macmillan Company, 1920), p. 129.
15. Joseph Golden, "Facilitating Factors in Negro-White Intermarriage," *Phylon*, Vol. 20 (1959), pp. 273-284.
16. Committee on Church and Race: *A Statement on Interracial Marriage*, June, 1948, p. 6.
17. See the *World Almanac*, 1962, p. 251.
18. This information was provided by Richard L. Plant, President of the National Scholarship Service and Fund for Negro Students (N.Y.), in a letter dated September 6, 1962.
19. See *The Crisis* magazine, published by the NAACP.

CHAPTER 10

1. Brewton Berry, *Race Relations* (Boston: Houghton Mifflin Company, 1951), pp. 75-6.
2. Caroline F. Ware, in *Encyclopedia of the Social Sciences*, Vol. 5 (1930), pp. 607-13.
3. William R. Catton, Jr., "The Functions and Dysfunctions of Ethno-Centrism: A Theory," *Social Problems*, Vol. 8 (Winter, 1960-61).
4. William Graham Sumner, *Folkways* (Boston: Ginn & Co., 1906).
5. Kennedy, "Single or Triple Melting Pot?" *op. cit.* (Ch. 3, n. 26), pp. 56-9.
6. Milton L. Barron, *People Who Intermarry* (Syracuse: Syracuse University Press, 1948), p. 189.
7. Salo Baron, *The Jewish Community* (New York: Jewish Publication Society of America), Philadelphia, 1942. Vol. II, pp. 18-9.
8. Salo Baron, *A Social and Religious History of the Jews* (New York: Columbia University Press, 1937), p. 166.
9. Handlin, *The Uprooted, loc. cit.* (Ch. 3, n. 1), p. 136.

10. *Ibid.*, p. 137.
11. Thomas, *The American Catholic Family*, loc. cit (Ch. 3, n. 28), pp. 117-23.
12. U.S. Bureau of the Census, *General Social and Economic Characteristics of the U.S., 1961* (Washington, D.C., U.S. Government Printing Office), pp. 1-201.
13. Oscar Handlin, "Historical Perspectives on the American Ethnic Group," *Daedalus* (Spring, 1961), p. 220.
14. E. L. Anderson, *We Americans* (Cambridge, Mass.: Harvard University Press, 1937), p. 194.
15. Panunzio, *op. cit.* (Ch. 8, n. 23), pp. 690-700.
16. Ozzie G. Simmons, *Anglo-Americans and Mexican Americans in South Texas,* unpublished thesis, Harvard University, June, 1952.
17. See "Mid-Century Pioneers and Protestants—A Survey Report of the Puerto Rican Migration to the U.S. Mainland" and "A Study of the Protestant Expression Among Puerto Ricans in New York City," Protestant Council of the City of N.Y. (March, 1956, mimeographed), pp. 2-3.

CHAPTER 11

1. Murray H. Leiffer, "Mixed Marriages and Church Loyalties," *The Christian Century* (January 19, 1949), pp. 78-80.
2. Ray E. Baber, "A Study of 325 Mixed Marriages," *American Sociological Review,* Vol. 2 (October, 1937), pp. 705-16.
3. Heinz Hartman, "Ego Psychology and the Problem of Adaptation," *Journal of American Psycho-analytic Association,* Mimeograph Series No. 1 (1958).
4. Landis and Landis, *Building a Successful Marriage, loc. cit.* (Ch. 4, n. 20), pp. 155-59.
5. Everett V. Stonequist, "The Mar-

ginal Character of the Jews," in *Jews in a Gentile World,* ed. I. Graeber and S. H. Britt (New York: The Macmillan Company), p. 297.
6. Lewin, *Resolving Social Conflicts, loc. cit.* (Ch. 7, n. 38), p. 180.
7. Philip M. Rosten, "The Mischling: Child of the Jewish-Gentile Marriage," an honors paper submitted to the Department of Social Relations, Harvard University, April, 1960.
8. *Ibid.*, pp. 123-4.
9. *Ibid.*, p. 60.
10. *Ibid.*, p. 63.
11. John Donne, "Meditation" from "Devotions Upon Emergent Occasions."
12. J. S. Plant, "The Emotions of the Child," University of Iowa Welfare Pamphlets No. 58 (1938).
13. Reported by a Rabbi and incorporated in the files of the Department of Human Relations, Hebrew Union College-Jewish Institute of Religion (Cincinnati, Ohio). The author is indebted to Professor Robert Katz, who made this material available.
14. Zimmerman and Cervantes, *Successful American Families, loc. cit.* (Ch. 3, n. 27), p. 148.
15. Names and places have, of course, been altered.
16. Jacobson, *American Marriage and Divorce, loc. cit.* (Ch. 1, n. 1), pp. 129-30.

CHAPTER 12

1. Lenski, *The Religious Factor, op. cit.* (Ch. 3, n. 50), p. 33.
2. Albert I. Gordon, *Jews in Suburbia* (Boston: Beacon Press, 1959).
3. Israel Zangwill, *The Melting Pot* (New York: The Macmillan Company, 1909), pp. 198-9.
4. Kennedy, "Single or Triple Melting Pot?" *op. cit.* (Ch. 3, n. 26), pp. 331-37.

INDEX

415

National Catholic Family Life Convention, 150

National Council of Churches of Christ, 119

Negroes, 64
in Hawaii, 8
increase in urban U.S. population, 54, 55, 268-269
interviews, 232, 241, 256, 271, 278, 289, 335
mobility of, 268-269
prohibition of intermarriage with, 223
students in colleges and universities, 270
suggested racial origins, 264
and whites, 263-271

Negro-white marriages
attitudes of whites toward, 264
estimate of number in U.S., 263
in Boston, 265, 266
in Chicago, 267
in Connecticut, 267
in New Haven, 265
in New York City, 265-266
in New York State, 266

Newman Clubs and intermarriage, 163-164

New Haven, rates of intermarriage among Jews, 89

Neustatter, Hannah, 180, 195

Northeastern University, student sample, 7

Notre Dame University, survey of religious attitudes, 91

Nuremberg Laws, 179

Occident, The, 183

Panunzio, Constantine, 228

Parents
attitudes of, to intermarriage, 14
problems of intermarried, related to, 310

Pennsylvania Dutch, 299

Plant, J. S., 325

Pluralism, cultural, 299, 301

Pool, David de Sola, 188

Pope Pius XI, encyclical of, 155

Presbyterian, Southern, attitude toward intermarriage, 129

"Promiscuous" person, *see* Jews who intermarry

Propinquity, 56

Proselytes, guide for admission of, to Judaism, 210-211

Protestant clergy, attitudes toward intermarriage, 138-140

Protestant Episcopal Church, 131

Protestants, attitudes toward intermarriage, 71, 90, 119-140; *see also* Intermarriage

Protestant student sample, 9

Psychoanalytical theory and intermarriage, 58, 59

Puerto Ricans in U.S., 300-301

Puerto Ricans, intermarriages with, 227

Questionnaire, used in study, 375-385

Rabbinical Assembly of America, attitude toward intermarriage, 184-185

Rabbis, attitudes toward intermarriage, 189-194

Race, and intermarriage, 221-222

Racial discrimination, 57

"Rebellious" person, *see* Jews who intermarry

Reconstructionism, attitude toward intermarriage stated by M. M. Kaplan, 188

Red Bones, 224

Religion, indifference to, 45, 50, 51

Religious
affiliation, 45-46
affiliation, fathers of student sample, 10
affiliation, mothers of student sample, 11
authority, decline of, 43, 45
devotion and relation to intermarriage
among Catholics, 91
among Jews, 91
discrimination, 57
influence of student sample homes, 13
influence of three major religious groups, compared, 47-48
observances, decline of, 43
pluralism, 50
problems faced by some children of

Made in the USA
Monee, IL
21 August 2023

41398371R00194

ABOUT THE AUTHOR

Michael won a prize at the 2020 Emirates Literature for his debut, Blood Libel, the first Isaac Alvarez mystery. He is originally from London, but currently lives with his family in Dubai.

www.michaellynes.com

ACKNOWLEDGEMENTS

Acknowledgments

Writing is solitary but my experience of writing this book was greatly enriched by a number of people.

Thank you to my Wednesday Critique Group - Sarah Clayton, Gillian Duff, and Katrina Ritters. I've benefited so much from spending time with you over the past year. Your insight and encouragement has been invaluable. Zeenath Khan gave me great feedback on chunks of the manuscript - I hope you finish *Daughters of the Deccan* soon. My editor, Kylie Fitzpatrick, provided high quality comment and guidance. My son, Adam, continues to give expert IT advice.

I might have completed the book without you but it would have been much more of a struggle and nowhere near as good.

Thank you all.